28. GILBERT
    GALILEO
    HARVEY

29. CERVANTES

30. FRANCIS BACON

31. DESCARTES
    SPINOZA

32. MILTON

33. PASCAL

34. NEWTON
    HUYGENS

35. LOCKE
    BERKELEY
    HUME

36. SWIFT
    STERNE

37. FIELDING

38. MONTESQUIEU
    ROUSSEAU

39. ADAM SMITH

40. GIBBON I

42. KANT

43. AMERICAN STATE
    PAPERS
    THE FEDERALIST
    J. S. MILL

44. BOSWELL

45. LAVOISIER
    FOURIER
    FARADAY

46. HEGEL

47. GOETHE

48. MELVILLE

49. DARWIN

50. MARX
    ENGELS

51. TOLSTOY

52. DOSTOEVSKY

53. WILLIAM JAMES

54. FREUD

GREAT BOOKS
OF THE WESTERN WORLD

ROBERT MAYNARD HUTCHINS, *EDITOR IN CHIEF*

34·

NEWTON

HUYGENS

MATHEMATICAL PRINCIPLES OF NATURAL PHILOSOPHY

OPTICS

BY SIR ISAAC NEWTON

TREATISE ON LIGHT

BY CHRISTIAAN HUYGENS

WILLIAM BENTON, *Publisher*

ENCYCLOPÆDIA BRITANNICA, INC.

CHICAGO · LONDON · TORONTO · GENEVA

THE UNIVERSITY OF CHICAGO

*The Great Books
is published with the editorial advice of the faculties
of The University of Chicago*

GENERAL CONTENTS

++++++++++++

++++++++++++

MATHEMATICAL PRINCIPLES
OF NATURAL PHILOSOPHY

BIOGRAPHICAL NOTE

Sir Isaac Newton, 1642–1727

Newton was born at Woolsthorpe, Lincolnshire, on Christmas Day, 1642. His father, a small farmer, died a few months before his birth, and when in 1645 his mother married the rector of North Witham, Newton was left with his maternal grandmother at Woolsthorpe. After having acquired the rudiments of education at small schools close by, Newton was sent at the age of twelve to the grammar school at Grantham, where he lived in the house of an apothecary. By his own account, Newton was at first an indifferent scholar until a successful fight with another boy aroused a spirit of emulation and led to his becoming first in the school. He displayed very early a taste and aptitude for mechanical contrivances; he made windmills, water-clocks, kites, and sun-dials, and he is said to have invented a four-wheel carriage which was to be moved by the rider.

After the death of her second husband in 1656, Newton's mother returned to Woolsthorpe and removed her eldest son from school so that he might prepare himself to manage the farm. But it was soon evident that his interests were not in farming, and upon the advice of his uncle, the rector of Burton Coggles, he was sent to Trinity College, Cambridge, where he matriculated in 1661 as one of the boys who performed menial services in return for their expenses. Although there is no record of his formal progress as a student, Newton is known to have read widely in mathematics and mechanics. His first reading at Cambridge was in the optical works of Kepler. He turned to Euclid because he was bothered by his inability to comprehend certain diagrams in a book on astrology he had bought at a fair; finding its propositions self-evident, he put it aside as "a trifling book," until his teacher, Isaac Barrow, induced him to take up the book again. It appears to have been the study of Descartes' *Geometry* which inspired him to do original mathematical work. In a small commonplace book kept by Newton as an undergraduate, there are several articles on angular sections and the squaring of curves, several calculations about musical notes, geometrical

problems from Vieta and Van Schooten, annotations out of Wallis' *Arithmetic of Infinities*, together with observations on refraction, on the grinding of spherical optic glasses, on the errors of lenses, and on the extraction of all kinds of roots. It was around the time of his taking the Bachelor's degree, in 1665, that Newton discovered the binomial theorem and made the first notes on his discovery of the "method of fluxions."

When the Great Plague spread from London to Cambridge in 1665, college was dismissed, and Newton retired to the farm in Lincolnshire, where he conducted experiments in optics and chemistry and continued his mathematical speculations. From this forced retirement in 1666 he dated his discovery of the gravitational theory: "In the same year I began to think of gravity extending to the orb of the Moon, ... compared the force requisite to keep the Moon in her orb with the force of gravity at the surface of the earth and found them to answer pretty nearly." At about the same time his work on optics led to his explanation of the composition of white light. Of the work he accomplished in these years Newton later remarked: "All this was in the two years of 1665 and 1666, for in those years I was in the prime of my age for invention and minded Mathematics and Philosophy more than at any time since."

On the re-opening of Trinity College in 1667, Newton was elected a fellow, and two years later, a little before his twenty-seventh birthday, he was appointed Lucasian professor of mathematics, succeeding his friend and teacher, Dr. Barrow. Newton had already built a reflecting telescope in 1668; the second telescope of his making he presented to the Royal Society in December, 1671. Two months later, as a fellow of the Society, he communicated his discovery on light and thereby started a controversy which was to run for many years and to involve Hooke, Lucas, Linus, and others. Newton, who always found controversy distasteful, "blamed my own imprudence for parting with so substantial a blessing as my quiet to run after a shadow." His papers on optics, the most important of which were communicated to the Royal Society between 1672 and 1676, were collected in the *Optics* (1704).

It was not until 1684 that Newton began to think of making known his work on gravity. Hooke, Halley, and Sir Christopher Wren had independently come to some notion of the law of gravity but were not having any success in explaining the orbits of the planets. In that year Halley consulted Newton on the problem and was astonished to find that he had already solved it. Newton submitted to him four theorems and seven problems, which proved to be the nucleus of his major work. In some seventeen or eighteen months during 1685 and 1686 he wrote in Latin the *Mathematical Principles of Natural Philosophy*. Newton thought for some time of suppressing the third book, and it was only Halley's insistence that preserved it. Halley also took upon himself the cost of publishing the work in 1687 after the Royal Society proved unable to meet its cost. The book caused great excitement throughout Europe, and in 1689 Huygens, at that time the most famous scientist, came to England to make the personal acquaintance of Newton.

While working upon the *Principles*, Newton had begun to take a more prominent part in university affairs. For his opposition to the attempt of James II to repudiate the oath of allegiance and supremacy at the university, Newton was elected parliamentary member for Cambridge. On his return to the university, he suffered a serious illness which incapacitated him for most of 1692 and 1693 and caused considerable concern to his friends and fellow-workers. After his recovery, he left the university to work for the government. Through his friends Locke, Wren, and Lord Halifax, Newton was made Warden of the Mint in 1695 and four years later, Master of the Mint, a position he held until his death.

For the last thirty years of his life Newton produced little original mathematical work. He kept his interest and his skill in the subject; in 1696 he solved overnight a problem offered by Bernoulli in a competition for which six months had been allowed, and again in 1716 he worked in a few hours a problem which Leibnitz had proposed in order to "feel the pulse of the English analysts." He was much occupied, to his own distress, with two mathematical controversies, one regarding the astronomical observations of the astronomer royal, and the other with Leibnitz regarding the invention of calculus. He also worked on revisions for a second edition of the *Principles*, which appeared in 1713.

Newton's scientific work brought him great fame. He was a popular visitor at the Court and was knighted in 1705. Many honors came to him from the continent; he was in correspondence with all the leading men of science, and visitors became so frequent as to prove a serious discomfort. Despite his fame, Newton maintained his modesty. Shortly before his death, he remarked: "I do not know what I may appear to the world, but to myself I seem to have been only like a boy playing on the seashore, and diverting myself in now and then finding a smoother pebble or a prettier shell than ordinary, whilst the great ocean of truth lay all undiscovered before me."

From an early period of his life Newton had been much interested in theological studies and before 1690 had begun to study the prophecies. In that year he wrote, in the form of a letter to Locke, an *Historical Account of Two Notable Corruptions of the Scriptures*, regarding two passages on the Trinity. He left in manuscript *Observations on the Prophecies of Daniel and the Apocalypse* and other works of exegesis.

After 1725 Newton's health was much impaired, and his duties at the Mint were discharged by a deputy. In February, 1727, he presided for the last time at the Royal Society, of which he had been president since 1703, and died on March 20, 1727, in his eighty-fifth year. He was buried in Westminster Abbey after lying in state in the Jerusalem Chamber.

CONTENTS

xi

PREFACE TO THE FIRST EDITION

SINCE the ancients (as we are told by Pappus) esteemed the science of mechanics of greatest importance in the investigation of natural things, and the moderns, rejecting substantial forms and occult qualities, have endeavored to subject the phenomena of nature to the laws of mathematics, I have in this treatise cultivated mathematics as far as it relates to philosophy. The ancients considered mechanics in a twofold respect; as rational, which proceeds accurately by demonstration, and practical. To practical mechanics all the manual arts belong, from which mechanics took its name. But as artificers do not work with perfect accuracy, it comes to pass that mechanics is so distinguished from geometry that what is perfectly accurate is called geometrical; what is less so, is called mechanical. However, the errors are not in the art, but in the artificers. He that works with less accuracy is an imperfect mechanic; and if any could work with perfect accuracy, he would be the most perfect mechanic of all, for the description of right lines and circles, upon which geometry is founded, belongs to mechanics. Geometry does not teach us to draw these lines, but requires them to be drawn, for it requires that the learner should first be taught to describe these accurately before he enters upon geometry, then it shows how by these operations problems may be solved. To describe right lines and circles are problems, but not geometrical problems. The solution of these problems is required from mechanics, and by geometry the use of them, when so solved, is shown; and it is the glory of geometry that from those few principles, brought from without, it is able to produce so many things. Therefore geometry is founded in mechanical practice, and is nothing but that part of universal mechanics which accurately proposes and demonstrates the art of measuring. But since the manual arts are chiefly employed in the moving of bodies, it happens that geometry is commonly referred to their magnitude, and mechanics to their motion. In this sense rational mechanics will be the science of motions resulting from any forces whatsoever, and of the forces required to produce any motions, accurately proposed and demonstrated. This part of mechanics, as far as it extended to the five powers which relate to manual arts, was cultivated by the ancients, who considered gravity (it not being a manual power) no otherwise than in moving weights by those powers. But I consider philosophy rather than arts and write not concerning manual but natural powers, and consider chiefly those things which relate to gravity, levity, elastic force, the resistance of fluids, and the like forces, whether attractive or impulsive; and therefore I offer this work as the mathematical principles of philosophy, for the whole burden of philosophy seems to consist in this—from the phenomena of motions to investigate the forces of nature, and then from these forces to demonstrate the other phenomena; and to this end the general propositions in the first and second books are directed. In the third book I give an example of this in the explication of the System of the World; for by the propositions mathematically demonstrated in the former books in the third I derive from the celestial phenomena the forces of gravity with which bodies tend to the sun and

1

the several planets. Then from these forces, by other propositions which are also mathematical, I deduce the motions of the planets, the comets, the moon, and the sea. I wish we could derive the rest of the phenomena of Nature by the same kind of reasoning from mechanical principles, for I am induced by many reasons to suspect that they may all depend upon certain forces by which the particles of bodies, by some causes hitherto unknown, are either mutually impelled towards one another, and cohere in regular figures, or are repelled and recede from one another. These forces being unknown, philosophers have hitherto attempted the search of Nature in vain; but I hope the principles here laid down will afford some light either to this or some truer method of philosophy.

In the publication of this work the most acute and universally learned Mr. Edmund Halley not only assisted me in correcting the errors of the press and preparing the geometrical figures, but it was through his solicitations that it came to be published; for when he had obtained of me my demonstrations of the figure of the celestial orbits, he continually pressed me to communicate the same to the Royal Society, who afterwards, by their kind encouragement and entreaties, engaged me to think of publishing them. But after I had begun to consider the inequalities of the lunar motions, and had entered upon some other things relating to the laws and measures of gravity and other forces; and the figures that would be described by bodies attracted according to given laws; and the motion of several bodies moving among themselves; the motion of bodies in resisting mediums; the forces, densities, and motions, of mediums; the orbits of the comets, and such like, I deferred that publication till I had made a search into those matters, and could put forth the whole together. What relates to the lunar motions (being imperfect), I have put all together in the corollaries of Prop. 66, to avoid being obliged to propose and distinctly demonstrate the several things there contained in a method more prolix than the subject deserved and interrupt the series of the other propositions. Some things, found out after the rest, I chose to insert in places less suitable, rather than change the number of the propositions and the citations. I heartily beg that what I have here done may be read with forbearance; and that my labors in a subject so difficult may be examined, not so much with the view to censure, as to remedy their defects.

Is. NEWTON

Cambridge, Trinity College, *May* 8, 1686

PREFACE TO THE SECOND EDITION

IN this second edition of the *Principia* there are many emendations and some additions. In the second section of the first book, the determination of forces, by which bodies may be made to revolve in given orbits, is illustrated and enlarged. In the seventh section of the second book the theory of the resistances of fluids was more accurately investigated, and confirmed by new experiments. In the third book the lunar theory and the precession of the equinoxes were more fully deduced from their principles; and the theory of the comets was confirmed by more examples of the calculation of their orbits, done also with greater accuracy.

Is. NEWTON

London, *March* 28, 1713

PREFACE TO THE THIRD EDITION

IN this third edition, prepared with much care by Henry Pemberton, M.D., a man of the greatest skill in these matters, some things in the second book on the resistance of mediums are somewhat more comprehensively handled than before, and new experiments on the resistance of heavy bodies falling in air are added. In the third book, the argument to prove that the moon is retained in its orbit by the force of gravity is more fully stated; and there are added new observations made by Mr. Pound, concerning the ratio of the diameters of Jupiter to one another. Some observations are also added on the comet which appeared in the year 1680, made in Germany in the month of November by Mr. Kirk; which have lately come to my hands. By the help of these it becomes apparent how nearly parabolic orbits represent the motions of comets. The orbit of that comet is determined somewhat more accurately than before, by the computation of Dr. Halley, in an ellipse. And it is shown that, in this elliptic orbit, the comet took its course through the nine signs of the heavens, with as much accuracy as the planets move in the elliptic orbits given in astronomy. The orbit of the comet which appeared in the year 1723 is also added, computed by Mr. Bradley, Professor of Astronomy at Oxford.

Is. NEWTON

London, *Jan.* 12, 1725–6

DEFINITIONS

DEFINITION I

The quantity of matter is the measure of the same, arising from its density and bulk conjointly.

Thus air of a double density, in a double space, is quadruple in quantity; in a triple space, sextuple in quantity. The same thing is to be understood of snow, and fine dust or powders, that are condensed by compression or lique-faction, and of all bodies that are by any causes whatever differently con-densed. I have no regard in this place to a medium, if any such there is, that freely pervades the interstices between the parts of bodies. It is this quantity that I mean hereafter everywhere under the name of body or mass. And the same is known by the weight of each body, for it is proportional to the weight, as I have found by experiments on pendulums, very accurately made, which shall be shown hereafter.

DEFINITION II

The quantity of motion is the measure of the same, arising from the velocity and quantity of matter conjointly.

The motion of the whole is the sum of the motions of all the parts; and there-fore in a body double in quantity, with equal velocity, the motion is double; with twice the velocity, it is quadruple.

DEFINITION III

The vis insita, *or innate force of matter, is a power of resisting, by which every body, as much as in it lies, continues in its present state, whether it be of rest, or of moving uniformly forwards in a right line.*

This force is always proportional to the body whose force it is and differs nothing from the inactivity of the mass, but in our manner of conceiving it. A body, from the inert nature of matter, is not without difficulty put out of its state of rest or motion. Upon which account, this *vis insita* may, by a most sig-nificant name, be called inertia (*vis inertiæ*) or force of inactivity. But a body only exerts this force when another force, impressed upon it, endeavors to change its condition; and the exercise of this force may be considered as both resistance and impulse; it is resistance so far as the body, for maintaining its present state, opposes the force impressed; it is impulse so far as the body, by not easily giving way to the impressed force of another, endeavors to change the state of that other. Resistance is usually ascribed to bodies at rest, and im-pulse to those in motion; but motion and rest, as commonly conceived, are only relatively distinguished; nor are those bodies always truly at rest, which com-monly are taken to be so.

DEFINITION IV

An impressed force is an action exerted upon a body, in order to change its state, either of rest, or of uniform motion in a right line.

This force consists in the action only, and remains no longer in the body when the action is over. For a body maintains every new state it acquires, by its inertia only. But impressed forces are of different origins, as from percussion, from pressure, from centripetal force.

DEFINITION V

A centripetal force is that by which bodies are drawn or impelled, or any way tend, towards a point as to a centre.

Of this sort is gravity, by which bodies tend to the centre of the earth; magnetism, by which iron tends to the loadstone; and that force, whatever it is, by which the planets are continually drawn aside from the rectilinear motions, which otherwise they would pursue, and made to revolve in curvilinear orbits. A stone, whirled about in a sling, endeavors to recede from the hand that turns it; and by that endeavor, distends the sling, and that with so much the greater force, as it is revolved with the greater velocity, and as soon as it is let go, flies away. That force which opposes itself to this endeavor, and by which the sling continually draws back the stone towards the hand, and retains it in its orbit, because it is directed to the hand as the centre of the orbit, I call the centripetal force. And the same thing is to be understood of all bodies, revolved in any orbits. They all endeavor to recede from the centres of their orbits; and were it not for the opposition of a contrary force which restrains them to, and detains them in their orbits, which I therefore call centripetal, would fly off in right lines, with an uniform motion. A projectile, if it was not for the force of gravity, would not deviate towards the earth, but would go off from it in a right line, and that with an uniform motion, if the resistance of the air was taken away. It is by its gravity that it is drawn aside continually from its rectilinear course, and made to deviate towards the earth, more or less, according to the force of its gravity, and the velocity of its motion. The less its gravity is, or the quantity of its matter, or the greater the velocity with which it is projected, the less will it deviate from a rectilinear course, and the farther it will go. If a leaden ball, projected from the top of a mountain by the force of gunpowder, with a given velocity, and in a direction parallel to the horizon, is carried in a curved line to the distance of two miles before it falls to the ground; the same, if the resistance of the air were taken away, with a double or decuple velocity, would fly twice or ten times as far. And by increasing the velocity, we may at pleasure increase the distance to which it might be projected, and diminish the curvature of the line which it might describe, till at last it should fall at the distance of 10, 30, or 90 degrees, or even might go quite round the whole earth before it falls; or lastly, so that it might never fall to the earth, but go forwards into the celestial spaces, and proceed in its motion *in infinitum.* And after the same manner that a projectile, by the force of gravity, may be made to revolve in an orbit, and go round the whole earth, the moon also, either by the force of gravity, if it is endued with gravity, or by any other force, that impels it towards the earth, may be continually drawn aside towards the earth, out of the rectilinear way which by its innate force it would pursue; and would be made to revolve in the orbit which it now describes; nor could the moon without some such force be retained in its orbit. If this force was too small, it would not sufficiently turn the moon out of a rectilinear course; if it was too great, it would turn it too much, and draw down the moon from its orbit towards the earth. It is necessary that the force be of a just quantity, and it belongs to the mathematicians to find the force that may serve exactly to retain a body in a given orbit with a given velocity; and *vice versa*, to determine the curvilinear way into which a body projected from a given place, with a given velocity, may be made to deviate from its natural rectilinear way, by means of a given force.

The quantity of any centripetal force may be considered as of three kinds: absolute, accelerative, and motive.

DEFINITION VI

The absolute quantity of a centripetal force is the measure of the same, proportional to the efficacy of the cause that propagates it from the centre, through the spaces round about.

Thus the magnetic force is greater in one loadstone and less in another, according to their sizes and strength of intensity.

DEFINITION VII

The accelerative quantity of a centripetal force is the measure of the same, proportional to the velocity which it generates in a given time.

Thus the force of the same loadstone is greater at a less distance, and less at a greater: also the force of gravity is greater in valleys, less on tops of exceeding high mountains; and yet less (as shall hereafter be shown), at greater distances from the body of the earth; but at equal distances, it is the same everywhere; because (taking away, or allowing for, the resistance of the air), it equally accelerates all falling bodies, whether heavy or light, great or small.

DEFINITION VIII

The motive quantity of a centripetal force is the measure of the same, proportional to the motion which it generates in a given time.

Thus the weight is greater in a greater body, less in a less body; and, in the same body, it is greater near to the earth, and less at remoter distances. This sort of quantity is the centripetency, or propension of the whole body towards the centre, or, as I may say, its weight; and it is always known by the quantity of an equal and contrary force just sufficient to hinder the descent of the body.

These quantities of forces, we may, for the sake of brevity, call by the names of motive, accelerative, and absolute forces; and, for the sake of distinction, consider them with respect to the bodies that tend to the centre, to the places of those bodies, and to the centre of force towards which they tend; that is to say, I refer the motive force to the body as an endeavor and propensity of the whole towards a centre, arising from the propensities of the several parts taken together; the accelerative force to the place of the body, as a certain power diffused from the centre to all places around to move the bodies that are in them; and the absolute force to the centre, as endued with some cause, without which those motive forces would not be propagated through the spaces round about; whether that cause be some central body (such as is the magnet in the centre of the magnetic force, or the earth in the centre of the gravitating force), or anything else that does not yet appear. For I here design only to give a mathematical notion of those forces, without considering their physical causes and seats.

Wherefore the accelerative force will stand in the same relation to the motive, as celerity does to motion. For the quantity of motion arises from the celerity multiplied by the quantity of matter; and the motive force arises from the accelerative force multiplied by the same quantity of matter. For the sum of the actions of the accelerative force, upon the several particles of the body, is the motive force of the whole. Hence it is, that near the surface of the earth, where the accelerative gravity, or force productive of gravity, in all bodies is the same, the motive gravity or the weight is as the body; but if we should ascend to higher regions, where the accelerative gravity is less, the weight would be equally diminished, and would always be as the product of the body, by the accelerative gravity. So in those regions, where the accelerative gravity is diminished into one-half, the weight of a body two or three times less, will be four or six times less.

I likewise call attractions and impulses, in the same sense, accelerative, and motive; and use the words attraction, impulse, or propensity of any sort towards a centre, promiscuously, and indifferently, one for another; considering those forces not physically, but mathematically: wherefore the reader is not to imagine that by those words I anywhere take upon me to define the kind, or the manner of any action, the causes or the physical reason thereof, or that I attribute forces, in a true and physical sense, to certain centres (which are only mathematical points); when at any time I happen to speak of centres as attracting, or as endued with attractive powers.

SCHOLIUM

Hitherto I have laid down the definitions of such words as are less known, and explained the sense in which I would have them to be understood in the following discourse. I do not define time, space, place, and motion, as being well known to all. Only I must observe, that the common people conceive those quantities under no other notions but from the relation they bear to sensible objects. And thence arise certain prejudices, for the removing of which it will be convenient to distinguish them into absolute and relative, true and apparent, mathematical and common.

I. Absolute, true, and mathematical time, of itself, and from its own nature, flows equably without relation to anything external, and by another name is called duration: relative, apparent, and common time, is some sensible and external (whether accurate or unequable) measure of duration by the means of motion, which is commonly used instead of true time; such as an hour, a day, a month, a year.

II. Absolute space, in its own nature, without relation to anything external, remains always similar and immovable. Relative space is some movable dimension or measure of the absolute spaces; which our senses determine by its position to bodies; and which is commonly taken for immovable space; such is the dimension of a subterraneous, an aerial, or celestial space, determined by its position in respect of the earth. Absolute and relative space are the same in figure and magnitude; but they do not remain always numerically the same.

For if the earth, for instance, moves, a space of our air, which relatively and in respect of the earth remains always the same, will at one time be one part of the absolute space into which the air passes; at another time it will be another part of the same, and so, absolutely understood, it will be continually changed.

III. Place is a part of space which a body takes up, and is according to the space, either absolute or relative. I say, a part of space; not the situation, nor the external surface of the body. For the places of equal solids are always equal; but their surfaces, by reason of their dissimilar figures, are often unequal. Positions properly have no quantity, nor are they so much the places themselves, as the properties of places. The motion of the whole is the same with the sum of the motions of the parts; that is, the translation of the whole, out of its place, is the same thing with the sum of the translations of the parts out of their places; and therefore the place of the whole is the same as the sum of the places of the parts, and for that reason, it is internal, and in the whole body.

IV. Absolute motion is the translation of a body from one absolute place into another; and relative motion, the translation from one relative place into another. Thus in a ship under sail, the relative place of a body is that part of the ship which the body possesses; or that part of the cavity which the body fills, and which therefore moves together with the ship: and relative rest is the continuance of the body in the same part of the ship, or of its cavity. But real, absolute rest, is the continuance of the body in the same part of that immovable space, in which the ship itself, its cavity, and all that it contains, is moved. Wherefore, if the earth is really at rest, the body, which relatively rests in the ship, will really and absolutely move with the same velocity which the ship has on the earth. But if the earth also moves, the true and absolute motion of the body will arise, partly from the true motion of the earth, in immovable space, partly from the relative motion of the ship on the earth; and if the body moves also relatively in the ship, its true motion will arise, partly from the true motion of the earth, in immovable space, and partly from the relative motions as well of the ship on the earth, as of the body in the ship; and from these relative motions will arise the relative motion of the body on the earth. As if that part of the earth, where the ship is, was truly moved towards the east, with a velocity of 10,010 parts; while the ship itself, with a fresh gale, and full sails, is carried towards the west, with a velocity expressed by 10 of those parts; but a sailor walks in the ship towards the east, with 1 part of the said velocity; then the sailor will be moved truly in immovable space towards the east, with a velocity of 10,001 parts, and relatively on the earth towards the west, with a velocity of 9 of those parts.

Absolute time, in astronomy, is distinguished from relative, by the equation or correction of the apparent time. For the natural days are truly unequal, though they are commonly considered as equal, and used for a measure of time; astronomers correct this inequality that they may measure the celestial motions by a more accurate time. It may be, that there is no such thing as an equable motion, whereby time may be accurately measured. All motions may be accelerated and retarded, but the flowing of absolute time is not liable to any change. The duration of perseverance of the existence of things remains the same, whether the motions are swift or slow, or none at all: and therefore this duration ought to be distinguished from what are only sensible measures thereof; and from which we deduce it, by means of the astronomical equation. The necessity of this equation, for determining the times of a phenomenon, is evinced as well from the experiments of the pendulum clock, as by eclipses of the satellites of Jupiter.

As the order of the parts of time is immutable, so also is the order of the parts of space. Suppose those parts to be moved out of their places, and they will be moved (if the expression may be allowed) out of themselves. For times and spaces are, as it were, the places as well of themselves as of all other things. All things are placed in time as to order of succession; and in space as to order of situation. It is from their essence or nature that they are places; and that the primary places of things should be movable, is absurd. These are therefore the absolute places; and translations out of those places, are the only absolute motions.

But because the parts of space cannot be seen, or distinguished from one another by our senses, therefore in their stead we use sensible measures of them. For from the positions and distances of things from any body considered as immovable, we define all places; and then with respect to such places, we estimate all motions, considering bodies as transferred from some of those places into others. And so, instead of absolute places and motions, we use relative ones; and that without any inconvenience in common affairs; but in philosophical disquisitions, we ought to abstract from our senses, and consider things themselves, distinct from what are only sensible measures of them. For it may be that there is no body really at rest, to which the places and motions of others may be referred.

But we may distinguish rest and motion, absolute and relative, one from the other by their properties, causes, and effects. It is a property of rest, that bodies really at rest do rest in respect to one another. And therefore as it is possible, that in the remote regions of the fixed stars, or perhaps far beyond them, there may be some body absolutely at rest; but impossible to know, from the position of bodies to one another in our regions, whether any of these do keep the same position to that remote body, it follows that absolute rest cannot be determined from the position of bodies in our regions.

It is a property of motion, that the parts, which retain given positions to their wholes, do partake of the motions of those wholes. For all the parts of revolving bodies endeavor to recede from the axis of motion; and the impetus of bodies moving forwards arises from the joint impetus of all the parts. Therefore, if surrounding bodies are moved, those that are relatively at rest within them will partake of their motion. Upon which account, the true and absolute motion of a body cannot be determined by the translation of it from those which only seem to rest; for the external bodies ought not only to appear at rest, but to be really at rest. For otherwise, all included bodies, besides their translation from near the surrounding ones, partake likewise of their true motions; and though that translation were not made, they would not be really at rest, but only seem to be so. For the surrounding bodies stand in the like relation to the surrounded as the exterior part of a whole does to the interior, or as the shell does to the kernel; but if the shell moves, the kernel will also move, as being part of the whole, without any removal from near the shell.

A property, near akin to the preceding, is this, that if a place is moved, whatever is placed therein moves along with it; and therefore a body, which is moved from a place in motion, partakes also of the motion of its place. Upon which account, all motions, from places in motion, are no other than parts of entire and absolute motions; and every entire motion is composed of the motion of the body out of its first place, and the motion of this place out of its place; and so on, until we come to some immovable place, as in the before-mentioned example of the sailor. Wherefore, entire and absolute motions can be no otherwise determined than by immovable places; and for that reason I did before refer those absolute motions to immovable places, but relative ones to movable places. Now no other places are immovable but those that, from infinity to infinity, do all retain the same given position one to another; and upon this account must ever remain unmoved; and do thereby constitute immovable space.

The causes by which true and relative motions are distinguished, one from the other, are the forces impressed upon bodies to generate motion. True motion is neither generated nor altered, but by some force impressed upon the body moved; but relative motion may be generated or altered without any force impressed upon the body. For it is sufficient only to impress some force on other bodies with which the former is compared, that by their giving way, that relation may be changed, in which the relative rest or motion of this other body did consist. Again, true motion suffers always some change from any force impressed upon the moving body; but relative motion does not necessarily undergo any change by such forces. For if the same forces are likewise impressed on those other bodies, with which the comparison is made, that the relative position may be preserved, then that condition will be preserved in which the relative motion consists. And therefore any relative motion may be changed when the true motion remains unaltered, and the relative may be preserved when the true suffers some change. Thus, true motion by no means consists in such relations.

The effects which distinguish absolute from relative motion are, the forces of receding from the axis of circular motion. For there are no such forces in a circular motion purely relative, but in a true and absolute circular motion, they are greater or less, according to the quantity of the motion. If a vessel, hung by a long cord, is so often turned about that the cord is strongly twisted, then filled with water, and held at rest together with the water; thereupon, by the sudden action of another force, it is whirled about the contrary way, and while the cord is untwisting itself, the vessel continues for some time in this motion; the surface of the water will at first be plain, as before the vessel began to move; but after that, the vessel, by gradually communicating its motion to the water, will make it begin sensibly to revolve, and recede by little and little from the middle, and ascend to the sides of the vessel, forming itself into a concave figure (as I have experienced), and the swifter the motion becomes, the higher will the water rise, till at last, performing its revolutions in the same times with the vessel, it becomes relatively at rest in it. This ascent of the water shows its endeavor to recede from the axis of its motion; and the true and absolute circular motion of the water, which is here directly contrary to the relative, becomes known, and may be measured by this endeavor. At first, when the relative motion of the water in the vessel was greatest, it produced no endeavor to recede from the axis; the water showed no tendency to the circumference, nor any ascent towards the sides of the vessel, but remained of a plain surface, and therefore its true circular motion had not yet begun. But afterwards, when the relative motion of the water had decreased, the ascent thereof towards the sides of the vessel proved its endeavor to recede from the axis; and this endeavor showed the real circular motion of the water continually increasing, till it had acquired its greatest quantity, when the water rested relatively in the vessel. And therefore this endeavor does not depend upon any translation of the water in respect of the ambient bodies, nor can true circular motion be defined by such translation. There is only one real circular motion of any one revolving body, corresponding to only one power of endeavoring to recede from its axis of motion, as its proper and adequate effect; but relative motions, in one and the same body, are innumerable, according to the various relations it bears to external bodies, and, like other relations, are altogether destitute of any real effect, any otherwise than they may perhaps partake of that one only true motion. And therefore in their system who suppose that our heavens, revolving below the sphere of the fixed stars, carry the planets along with them; the several parts of those heavens, and the planets, which are indeed relatively at rest in their heavens, do yet really move. For they change their position one to another (which never happens to bodies truly at rest), and being carried together with their heavens, partake of their motions, and as parts of revolving wholes, endeavor to recede from the axis of their motions.

Wherefore relative quantities are not the quantities themselves, whose names they bear, but those sensible measures of them (either accurate or inaccurate), which are commonly used instead of the measured quantities themselves. And if the meaning of words is to be determined by their use, then by the names time, space, place, and motion, their [sensible] measures are properly to be understood; and the expression will be unusual, and purely mathematical, if the measured quantities themselves are meant. On this account, those violate the accuracy of language, which ought to be kept precise, who interpret these words for the measured quantities. Nor do those less defile the purity of mathematical and philosophical truths, who confound real quantities with their relations and sensible measures.

It is indeed a matter of great difficulty to discover, and effectually to distinguish, the true motions of particular bodies from the apparent; because the parts of that immovable space, in which those motions are performed, do by no means come under the observation of our senses. Yet the thing is not altogether desperate; for we have some arguments to guide us, partly from the apparent motions, which are the differences of the true motions; partly from the forces, which are the causes and effects of the true motions. For instance, if two globes, kept at a given distance one from the other by means of a cord that connects them, were revolved about their common centre of gravity, we might, from the tension of the cord, discover the endeavor of the globes to recede from the axis of their motion, and from thence we might compute the quantity of their circular motions. And then if any equal forces should be impressed at once on the alternate faces of the globes to augment or diminish their circular motions, from the increase or decrease of the tension of the cord, we might infer the increment or decrement of their motions; and thence would be found on what faces those forces ought to be impressed, that the motions of the globes might be most augmented; that is, we might discover their hindmost faces, or those which, in the circular motion, do follow. But the faces which follow being known, and consequently the opposite ones that precede, we should likewise know the determination of their motions. And thus we might find both the quantity and the determination of this circular motion, even in an immense vacuum, where there was nothing external or sensible with which the globes could be compared. But now, if in that space some remote bodies were placed that kept always a given position one to another, as the fixed stars do in our regions, we could not indeed determine from the relative translation of the globes among those bodies, whether the motion did belong to the globes or to the bodies. But if we observed the cord, and found that its tension was that very tension which the motions of the globes required, we might conclude the motion to be in the globes, and the bodies to be at rest; and then, lastly, from the translation of the globes among the bodies, we should find the determination of their motions. But how we are to obtain the true motions from their causes, effects, and apparent differences, and the converse, shall be explained more at large in the following treatise. For to this end it was that I composed it.

AXIOMS, OR LAWS OF MOTION

LAW I

Every body continues in its state of rest, or of uniform motion in a right line, unless it is compelled to change that state by forces impressed upon it.

Projectiles continue in their motions, so far as they are not retarded by the resistance of the air, or impelled downwards by the force of gravity. A top, whose parts by their cohesion are continually drawn aside from rectilinear motions, does not cease its rotation, otherwise than as it is retarded by the air. The greater bodies of the planets and comets, meeting with less resistance in freer spaces, preserve their motions both progressive and circular for a much longer time.

LAW II

The change of motion is proportional to the motive force impressed; and is made in the direction of the right line in which that force is impressed.

If any force generates a motion, a double force will generate double the motion, a triple force triple the motion, whether that force be impressed altogether and at once, or gradually and successively. And this motion (being always directed the same way with the generating force), if the body moved before, is added to or subtracted from the former motion, according as they directly conspire with or are directly contrary to each other; or obliquely joined, when they are oblique, so as to produce a new motion compounded from the determination of both.

LAW III

To every action there is always opposed an equal reaction: or, the mutual actions of two bodies upon each other are always equal, and directed to contrary parts.

Whatever draws or presses another is as much drawn or pressed by that other. If you press a stone with your finger, the finger is also pressed by the stone. If a horse draws a stone tied to a rope, the horse (if I may so say) will be equally drawn back towards the stone; for the distended rope, by the same endeavor to relax or unbend itself, will draw the horse as much towards the stone as it does the stone towards the horse, and will obstruct the progress of the one as much as it advances that of the other. If a body impinge upon another, and by its force change the motion of the other, that body also (because of the equality of the mutual pressure) will undergo an equal change, in its own motion, towards the contrary part. The changes made by these actions are equal, not in the velocities but in the motions of bodies; that is to say, if the bodies are not hindered by any other impediments. For, because the motions are equally changed, the changes of the velocities made towards contrary parts are inversely proportional to the bodies. This law takes place also in attractions, as will be proved in the next Scholium.

COROLLARY I

A body, acted on by two forces simultaneously, will describe the diagonal of a parallelogram in the same time as it would describe the sides by those forces separately.

If a body in a given time, by the force M impressed apart in the place A, should with an uniform motion be carried from A to B, and by the force N impressed apart in the same place, should be carried from A to C, let the parallelogram ABCD be completed, and, by both forces acting together, it will in the same time be carried in the diagonal from A to D. For since the force N acts in the direction of the line AC, parallel to BD, this force (by the second Law) will not at all alter the velocity generated by the other force M, by which the body is carried towards the line BD. The body therefore will arrive at the line BD in the same time, whether the force N be impressed or not; and therefore at the end of that time it will be found somewhere in the line BD. By the same argument, at the end of the same time it will be found somewhere in the line CD. Therefore it will be found in the point D, where both lines meet. But it will move in a right line from A to D, by Law i.

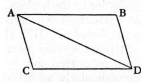

COROLLARY II

And hence is explained the composition of any one direct force AD, out of any two oblique forces AC and CD; and, on the contrary, the resolution of any one direct force AD into two oblique forces AC and CD: which composition and resolution are abundantly confirmed from mechanics.

As if the unequal radii OM and ON drawn from the centre O of any wheel, should sustain the weights A and P by the cords MA and NP; and the forces of those weights to move the wheel were required. Through the centre O draw the right line KOL, meeting the cords perpendicularly in K and L; and from the centre O, with OL the greater of the distances OK and OL, describe a circle, meeting the cord MA in D; and drawing OD, make AC parallel and DC perpendicular thereto. Now, it being indifferent whether the points K, L, D, of the cords be fixed to the plane of the wheel or not, the weights will have the same effect whether they are suspended from the points K and L, or from D and L. Let the whole force of the weight A be represented by the line AD, and let it be resolved into the forces AC and CD, of which the force AC, drawing the radius OD directly from the centre, will have no effect to move the wheel; but the other force DC, drawing the radius DO perpendicularly, will have the same effect as if it drew perpendicularly the radius OL equal to OD; that is, it will have the same effect as the weight P, if

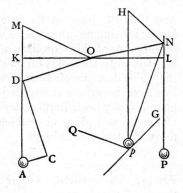

$$P : A = DC : DA,$$
but because the triangles ADC and DOK are similar,
$$DC : DA = OK : OD = OK : OL.$$

Therefore,

$$P : A = radius\ OK : radius\ OL.$$

As these radii lie in the same right line they will be equipollent, and so remain in equilibrium; which is the well-known property of the balance, the lever, and the wheel. If either weight is greater than in this ratio, its force to move the wheel will be so much greater.

If the weight $p = P$, is partly suspended by the cord Np, partly sustained by the oblique plane pG; draw pH, NH, the former perpendicular to the horizon, the latter to the plane pG; and if the force of the weight p tending downwards is represented by the line pH, it may be resolved into the forces pN, HN. If there was any plane pQ, perpendicular to the cord pN, cutting the other plane pG in a line parallel to the horizon, and the weight p was supported only by those planes pQ, pG, it would press those planes perpendicularly with the forces pN, HN; to wit, the plane pQ with the force pN, and the plane pG with the force HN. And therefore if the plane pQ was taken away, so that the weight might stretch the cord, because the cord, now sustaining the weight, supplied the place of the plane that was removed, it would be strained by the same force pN which pressed upon the plane before. Therefore, the

$$\text{tension of } pN : \text{tension of } PN = \text{line } pN : \text{line } pH.$$

Therefore, if p is to A in a ratio which is the product of the inverse ratio of the least distances of their cords pN and AM from the centre of the wheel, and of the ratio pH to pN, then the weights p and A will have the same effect towards moving the wheel, and will, therefore, sustain each other; as anyone may find by experiment.

But the weight p pressing upon those two oblique planes, may be considered as a wedge between the two internal surfaces of a body split by it; and hence the forces of the wedge and the mallet may be determined: because the force with which the weight p presses the plane pQ is to the force with which the same, whether by its own gravity, or by the blow of a mallet, is impelled in the direction of the line pH towards both the planes, as

$$pN : pH;$$

and to the force with which it presses the other plane pG, as

$$pN : NH.$$

And thus the force of the screw may be deduced from a like resolution of forces; it being no other than a wedge impelled with the force of a lever. Therefore the use of this Corollary spreads far and wide, and by that diffusive extent the truth thereof is further confirmed. For on what has been said depends the whole doctrine of mechanics variously demonstrated by different authors. For from hence are easily deduced the forces of machines, which are compounded of wheels, pullies, levers, cords, and weights, ascending directly or obliquely, and other mechanical powers; as also the force of the tendons to move the bones of animals.

COROLLARY III

The quantity of motion, which is obtained by taking the sum of the motions directed towards the same parts, and the difference of those that are directed to contrary parts, suffers no change from the action of bodies among themselves.

For action and its opposite reaction are equal, by Law III, and therefore, by Law II, they produce in the motions equal changes towards opposite parts.

Therefore if the motions are directed towards the same parts, whatever is added to the motion of the preceding body will be subtracted from the motion of that which follows; so that the sum will be the same as before. If the bodies meet, with contrary motions, there will be an equal deduction from the motions of both; and therefore the difference of the motions directed towards opposite parts will remain the same.

Thus, if a spherical body A is 3 times greater than the spherical body B, and has a velocity $=2$, and B follows in the same direction with a velocity $=10$, then the

$$\text{motion of A : motion of B} = 6 : 10.$$

Suppose, then, their motions to be of 6 parts and of 10 parts, and the sum will be 16 parts. Therefore, upon the meeting of the bodies, if A acquire 3, 4, or 5 parts of motion, B will lose as many; and therefore after reflection A will proceed with 9, 10, or 11 parts, and B with 7, 6, or 5 parts; the sum remaining always of 16 parts as before. If the body A acquire 9, 10, 11, or 12 parts of motion, and therefore after meeting proceed with 15, 16, 17, or 18 parts, the body B, losing so many parts as A has got, will either proceed with 1 part, having lost 9, or stop and remain at rest, as having lost its whole progressive motion of 10 parts; or it will go back with 1 part, having not only lost its whole motion, but (if I may so say) one part more; or it will go back with 2 parts, because a progressive motion of 12 parts is taken off. And so the sums of the conspiring motions,

$$15+1 \quad \text{or} \quad 16+0,$$

and the differences of the contrary motions,

$$17-1 \quad \text{and} \quad 18-2,$$

will always be equal to 16 parts, as they were before the meeting and reflection of the bodies. But the motions being known with which the bodies proceed after reflection, the velocity of either will be also known, by taking the velocity after to the velocity before reflection, as the motion after is to the motion before. As in the last case, where the

$$\text{motion of A before reflection (6) : motion of A after (18)}$$
$$= \text{velocity of A before (2) : velocity of A after } (x);$$

that is,

$$6 : 18 = 2 : x, \ x = 6.$$

But if the bodies are either not spherical, or, moving in different right lines, impinge obliquely one upon the other, and their motions after reflection are required, in those cases we are first to determine the position of the plane that touches the bodies in the point of impact, then the motion of each body (by Cor. II) is to be resolved into two, one perpendicular to that plane, and the other parallel to it. This done, because the bodies act upon each other in the direction of a line perpendicular to this plane, the parallel motions are to be retained the same after reflection as before; and to the perpendicular motions we are to assign equal changes towards the contrary parts; in such manner that the sum of the conspiring and the difference of the contrary motions may remain the same as before. From such kind of reflections sometimes arise also the circular motions of bodies about their own centres. But these are cases which I do not consider in what follows; and it would be too tedious to demonstrate every particular case that relates to this subject.

COROLLARY IV

The common centre of gravity of two or more bodies does not alter its state of motion or rest by the actions of the bodies among themselves; and therefore the common centre of gravity of all bodies acting upon each other (excluding external actions and impediments) is either at rest, or moves uniformly in a right line.

For if two points proceed with an uniform motion in right lines, and their distance be divided in a given ratio, the dividing point will be either at rest, or proceed uniformly in a right line. This is demonstrated hereafter in Lem. 23 and Corollary, when the points are moved in the same plane; and by a like way of arguing, it may be demonstrated when the points are not moved in the same plane. Therefore if any number of bodies move uniformly in right lines, the common centre of gravity of any two of them is either at rest, or proceeds uniformly in a right line; because the line which connects the centres of those two bodies so moving is divided at that common centre in a given ratio. In like manner the common centre of those two and that of a third body will be either at rest or moving uniformly in a right line; because at that centre the distance between the common centre of the two bodies, and the centre of this last, is divided in a given ratio. In like manner the common centre of these three, and of a fourth body, is either at rest, or moves uniformly in a right line; because the distance between the common centre of the three bodies, and the centre of the fourth, is there also divided in a given ratio, and so on *in infinitum*. Therefore, in a system of bodies where there is neither any mutual action among themselves, nor any foreign force impressed upon them from without, and which consequently move uniformly in right lines, the common centre of gravity of them all is either at rest or moves uniformly forwards in a right line.

Moreover, in a system of two bodies acting upon each other, since the distances between their centres and the common centre of gravity of both are reciprocally as the bodies, the relative motions of those bodies, whether of approaching to or of receding from that centre, will be equal among themselves. Therefore since the changes which happen to motions are equal and directed to contrary parts, the common centre of those bodies, by their mutual action between themselves, is neither accelerated nor retarded, nor suffers any change as to its state of motion or rest. But in a system of several bodies, because the common centre of gravity of any two acting upon each other suffers no change in its state by that action; and much less the common centre of gravity of the others with which that action does not intervene; but the distance between those two centres is divided by the common centre of gravity of all the bodies into parts inversely proportional to the total sums of those bodies whose centres they are; and therefore while those two centres retain their state of motion or rest, the common centre of all does also retain its state: it is manifest that the common centre of all never suffers any change in the state of its motion or rest from the actions of any two bodies between themselves. But in such a system all the actions of the bodies among themselves either happen between two bodies, or are composed of actions interchanged between some two bodies; and therefore they do never produce any alteration in the common centre of all as to its state of motion or rest. Wherefore since that centre, when the bodies do not act one upon another, either is at rest or moves uniformly forwards in some right line, it will, notwithstanding the mutual actions of the bodies among themselves, always continue in its state, either of rest, or of proceeding uniformly in a right line, unless it is forced out of this state by the action of some power impressed from without upon the whole system. And therefore the same law takes place in a system consisting of many bodies as in one single body, with regard to their persevering in their state of motion or of rest. For the progressive motion, whether of one single body, or of a whole system of bodies, is always to be estimated from the motion of the centre of gravity.

COROLLARY V

The motions of bodies included in a given space are the same among themselves, whether that space is at rest, or moves uniformly forwards in a right line without any circular motion.

For the differences of the motions tending towards the same parts, and the sums of those that tend towards contrary parts, are, at first (by supposition), in both cases the same; and it is from those sums and differences that the collisions and impulses do arise with which the bodies impinge one upon another. Wherefore (by Law 2), the effects of those collisions will be equal in both cases; and therefore the mutual motions of the bodies among themselves in the one case will remain equal to the motions of the bodies among themselves in the other. A clear proof of this we have from the experiment of a ship; where all motions happen after the same manner, whether the ship is at rest, or is carried uniformly forwards in a right line.

COROLLARY VI

If bodies, moved in any manner among themselves, are urged in the direction of parallel lines by equal accelerative forces, they will all continue to move among themselves, after the same manner as if they had not been urged by those forces.

For these forces acting equally (with respect to the quantities of the bodies to be moved), and in the direction of parallel lines, will (by Law 2) move all the bodies equally (as to velocity), and therefore will never produce any change in the positions or motions of the bodies among themselves.

SCHOLIUM

Hitherto I have laid down such principles as have been received by mathematicians, and are confirmed by abundance of experiments. By the first two Laws and the first two Corollaries, Galileo discovered that the descent of bodies varied as the square of the time (*in duplicata ratione temporis*) and that the motion of projectiles was in the curve of a parabola; experience agreeing with both, unless so far as these motions are a little retarded by the resistance of the air. When a body is falling, the uniform force of its gravity acting equally, impresses, in equal intervals of time, equal forces upon that body, and therefore generates equal velocities; and in the whole time impresses a whole force, and generates a whole velocity proportional to the time. And the spaces described in proportional times are as the product of the velocities and the times; that is, as the squares of the times. And when a body is thrown upwards, its uniform gravity impresses forces and reduces velocities proportional to the times; and the times of ascending to the greatest heights are as the velocities to be taken away, and those heights are as the product of the velocities and the times, or as the squares of the velocities. And if a body be projected in any direction, the motion arising from its projection is compounded with the motion arising from its gravity. Thus, if the body A by its motion of projection alone could describe in a given time the right line AB, and with its motion of falling alone could describe in the same time the altitude AC; complete the parallelogram ABCD, and the body by that compounded motion will at the end of the time be found in the place D; and the curved line AED, which that body describes, will be a parabola, to which the right line AB will be a tangent at A; and whose ordinate BD will be as the square of the line AB. On the same Laws and Corollaries depend those things which have been demonstrated concerning the times of the vibration of pendulums, and are confirmed by the daily experiments of pendulum clocks. By the same, together with Law 3, Sir Christopher Wren, Dr. Wallis, and Mr. Huygens, the greatest geometers of our times, did severally determine the rules of the impact and reflection of hard bodies, and about the same time communicated their discoveries to the Royal Society, exactly agreeing among themselves as to those rules. Dr. Wallis, indeed, was somewhat earlier in the publication; then followed Sir Christopher Wren, and, lastly, Mr. Huygens. But Sir Christopher Wren confirmed the truth of the thing before the Royal Society by the experiments on pendulums, which M. Mariotte soon after thought fit to explain in a treatise entirely upon that subject. But to bring this experiment to an accurate agreement with the theory, we are to have due regard as well to the resistance of the air as to the elastic force of the concurring bodies. Let the spherical bodies A, B be sus-

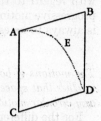

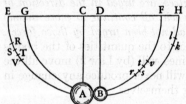

pended by the parallel and equal strings AC, BD, from the centres C, D. About these centres, with those lengths as radii, describe the semicircles EAF, GBH, bisected respectively by the radii CA, DB. Bring the body A to any point R of the arc EAF, and (withdrawing the body B) let it go from thence, and after one oscillation suppose it to return to the point V: then RV will be the retardation arising from the resistance of the air. Of this RV let ST be a fourth part, situated in the middle, namely, so that

$$RS = TV,$$

and

$$RS : ST = 3 : 2,$$

then will ST represent very nearly the retardation during the descent from S to A. Restore the body B to its place: and, supposing the body A to be let fall from the point S, the velocity thereof in the place of reflection A, without sensible error, will be the same as if it had descended *in vacuo* from the point T. Upon which account this velocity may be represented by the chord of the arc TA. For it is a proposition well known to geometers, that the velocity of a pendulous body in the lowest point is as the chord of the arc which it has described in its descent. After reflection, suppose the body A comes to the place *s*, and the body B to the place *k*. Withdraw the body B, and find the place *v*, from which if the body A, being let go, should after one oscillation return to the place *r*, *st* may be a fourth part of *rv*, so placed in the middle thereof as to leave *rs* equal to *tv*, and let the chord of the arc *t*A represent the velocity which the body A had in the place A immediately after reflection. For t will be the true and correct place to which the body A should have ascended, if the resistance of the air had been taken off. In the same way we are to correct the place k to which the body B ascends, by finding the place l to which it should have ascended *in vacuo*. And thus everything may be subjected to experiment, in the same manner as if we were really placed *in vacuo*. These things being done, we are to take the product (if I may so say) of the body A, by the chord of the arc TA (which represents its velocity), that we may have its motion in the place A immediately before reflection; and then by the chord of the arc tA, that we may have its motion in the place A immediately after reflection. And so we are to take the product of the body B by the chord of the arc Bl, that we may have the motion of the same immediately after reflection. And in like manner, when two bodies are let go together from different places, we are to find the motion of each, as well before as after reflection; and then we may compare the motions between themselves, and collect the effects of the reflection. Thus trying the thing with pendulums of 10 feet, in unequal as well as equal bodies, and making the bodies to concur after a descent through large spaces, as of 8, 12, or 16 feet, I found always, without an error of 3 inches, that when the bodies concurred together directly, equal changes towards the contrary parts were produced in their motions, and, of consequence, that the action and reaction were always equal. As if the body A impinged upon the body B at rest with 9 parts of motion, and losing 7, proceeded after reflection with 2, the body B was carried backwards with those 7 parts. If the bodies concurred with contrary motions, A with 12 parts of motion, and B with 6, then if A receded with 2, B receded with 8; namely, with a deduction of 14 parts of motion on each side. For from the motion of A subtracting 12 parts, nothing will remain; but subtracting 2 parts more, a motion will be generated of 2 parts towards the contrary way; and so, from the motion of the body B of 6 parts, subtracting 14 parts, a motion is generated of 8 parts towards the contrary way. But if the bodies were made both to move towards the same way, A, the swifter, with 14 parts of motion, B, the slower, with 5, and after reflection A went on with 5, B likewise went on with 14 parts; 9 parts being transferred from A to B. And so in other cases. By the meeting and collision of bodies, the quantity of motion, obtained from the sum of the motions directed towards the same way, or from the difference of those that were directed towards contrary ways, was never changed. For the error of an inch or two in measures may be easily ascribed to the difficulty of executing everything with accuracy. It was not easy to let go the two pendulums so exactly together that the bodies should impinge one upon the other in the lowermost place AB; nor to mark the places s, and k, to which the bodies ascended after impact. Nay, and some errors, too, might have happened from the unequal density of the parts of the pendulous bodies themselves, and from the irregularity of the texture proceeding from other causes.

But to prevent an objection that may perhaps be alleged against the rule, for the proof of which this experiment was made, as if this rule did suppose that the bodies were either absolutely hard, or at least perfectly elastic (whereas no such bodies are to be found in Nature), I must add, that the experiments we have been describing, by no means depending upon that quality of hardness, do succeed as well in soft as in hard bodies. For if the rule is to be tried in bodies not perfectly hard, we are only to diminish the reflection in such a certain proportion as the quantity of the elastic force requires. By the theory of Wren and Huygens, bodies absolutely hard return one from another with the same velocity with which they meet. But this may be affirmed with more certainty of bodies perfectly elastic. In bodies imperfectly elastic the velocity of the return is to be diminished together with the elastic force; because that force (except when the parts of bodies are bruised by their impact, or suffer some such extension as happens under the strokes of a hammer) is (as far as I can perceive) certain and determined, and makes the bodies to return one from the other with a relative velocity, which is in a given ratio to that relative velocity with which they met. This I tried in balls of wool, made up tightly, and strongly compressed. For, first, by letting go the pendulous bodies, and measuring their reflection, I determined the quantity of their elastic force; and then, according to this force, estimated the reflections that ought to happen in other cases of impact. And with this computation other experiments made afterwards did accordingly agree; the balls always receding one from the other with a relative velocity, which was to the relative velocity with which they met as about 5 to 9. Balls of steel returned with almost the same velocity; those of cork with a a velocity something less; but in balls of glass the proportion was as about 15 to 16. And thus the third Law, so far as it regards percussions and reflections, is proved by a theory exactly agreeing with experience.

In attractions, I briefly demonstrate the thing after this manner. Suppose an obstacle is interposed to hinder the meeting of any two bodies A, B, attracting one the other: then if either body, as A, is more attracted towards the other body B, than that other body B is towards the first body A, the obstacle will be more strongly urged by the pressure of the body A than by the pressure of the body B, and therefore will not remain in equilibrium: but the stronger pressure will prevail, and will make the system of the two bodies, together with the obstacle, to move directly towards the parts on which B lies; and in free spaces, to go forwards *in infinitum* with a motion continually accelerated; which is absurd and contrary to the first Law. For, by the first Law, the system ought to continue in its state of rest, or of moving uniformly forwards in a right line; and therefore the bodies must equally press the obstacle, and be equally attracted one by the other. I made the experiment on the loadstone and iron. If these, placed apart in proper vessels, are made to float by one another in standing water, neither of them will propel the other; but, by being equally attracted, they will sustain each other's pressure, and rest at last in an equilibrium.

So the gravitation between the earth and its parts is mutual. Let the earth FI by cut by any plane EG into two parts EGF and EGI, and their weights one towards the other will be mutually equal. For if by another plane HK, parallel to the former EG, the greater part EGI is cut into two parts EGKH and HKI, whereof HKI is equal to the part EFG, first cut off, it is evident that the middle part EGKH will have no propension by its proper weight towards either side, but will hang as it were, and rest in an equilib- rium between both. But the one extreme part HKI will with its whole weight bear upon and press the middle part towards the other extreme part EGF; and therefore the force with which EGI, the sum of the parts HKI and EGKH, tends towards the

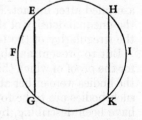

third part EGF, is equal to the weight of the part HKI, that is, to the weight of the third part EGF. And therefore the weights of the two parts EGI and EGF, one towards the other, are equal, as I was to prove. And indeed if those weights were not equal, the whole earth floating in the nonresisting ether would give way to the greater weight, and, retiring from it, would be carried off *in infinitum*.

And as those bodies are equipollent in the impact and reflection, whose velocities are inversely as their innate forces, so in the use of mechanic instruments those agents are equipollent, and mutually sustain each the contrary pressure of the other, whose velocities, estimated according to the determination of the forces, are inversely as the forces.

So those weights are of equal force to move the arms of a balance, which during the play of the balance are inversely as their velocities upwards and downwards; that is, if the ascent or descent is direct, those weights are of equal force, which are inversely as the distances of the points at which they are suspended from the axis of the balance; but if they are turned aside by the interposition of oblique planes, or other obstacles, and made to ascend or descend obliquely, those bodies will be equipollent, which are inversely as the heights of their ascent and descent taken according to the perpendicular; and that on account of the determination of gravity downwards.

And in like manner in the pulley, or in a combination of pulleys, the force of a hand drawing the rope directly, which is to the weight, whether ascending directly or obliquely, as the velocity of the perpendicular ascent of the weight to the velocity of the hand that draws the rope, will sustain the weight.

In clocks and such like instruments, made up from a combination of wheels, the contrary forces that promote and impede the motion of the wheels, if they are inversely as the velocities of the parts of the wheel on which they are impressed, will mutually sustain each other.

The force of the screw to press a body is to the force of the hand that turns the handles by which it is moved as the circular velocity of the handle in that part where it is impelled by the hand is to the progressive velocity of the screw towards the pressed body.

The forces by which the wedge presses or drives the two parts of the wood it cleaves are to the force of the mallet upon the wedge as the progress of the wedge in the direction of the force impressed upon it by the mallet is to the velocity with which the parts of the wood yield to the wedge, in the direction of lines perpendicular to the sides of the wedge. And the like account is to be given of all machines.

The power and use of machines consist only in this, that by diminishing the velocity we may augment the force, and the contrary; from whence, in all sorts of proper machines, we have the solution of this problem: *To move a given weight with a given power,* or with a given force to overcome any other given resistance. For if machines are so contrived that the velocities of the agent and resistant are inversely as their forces, the agent will just sustain the resistant, but with a greater disparity of velocity will overcome it. So that if the disparity of velocities is so great as to overcome all that resistance which commonly arises either from the friction of contiguous bodies as they slide by one another, or from the cohesion of continuous bodies that are to be separated, or from the weights of bodies to be raised, the excess of the force remaining, after all those resistances are overcome, will produce an acceleration of motion proportional thereto, as well in the parts of the machine as in the resisting body. But to treat of mechanics is not my present business. I was aiming only to show by those examples the great extent and certainty of the third Law of Motion. For if we estimate the action of the agent from the product of its force and velocity, and likewise the reaction of the impediment from the product of the velocities of its several parts, and the forces of resistance arising from the friction, cohesion, weight, and acceleration of those parts, the action and reaction in the use of all sorts of machines will be found always equal to one another. And so far as the action is propagated by the intervening instruments, and at last impressed upon the resisting body, the ultimate action will be always contrary to the reaction.

BOOK ONE

THE MOTION OF BODIES

SECTION I

LEMMA 1

Quantities, and the ratios of quantities, which in any finite time converge continually to equality, and before the end of that time approach nearer to each other than by any given difference, become ultimately equal.

If you deny it, suppose them to be ultimately unequal, and let D be their ultimate difference. Therefore they cannot approach nearer to equality than by that difference D; which is contrary to the supposition.

LEMMA 2

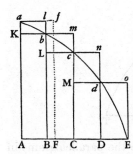

If in any figure AacE, terminated by the right lines Aa, AE, and the curve acE, there be inscribed any number of parallelograms Ab, Bc, Cd, &c., comprehended under equal bases AB, BC, CD, &c., and the sides, Bb, Cc, Dd, &c., parallel to one side Aa of the figure; and the parallelograms aKbl, bLcm, cMdn, &c., are completed: then if the breadth of those parallelograms be supposed to be diminished, and their number to be augmented in infinitum, I say, that the ultimate ratios which the inscribed figure AKbLcMdD, the circumscribed figure AalbmcndoE, and curvilinear figure AabcdE, will have to one another, are ratios of equality.

For the difference of the inscribed and circumscribed figures is the sum of the parallelograms Kl, Lm, Mn, Do, that is (from the equality of all their bases), the rectangle under one of their bases Kb and the sum of their altitudes Aa, that is, the rectangle ABla. But this rectangle, because its breadth AB is supposed diminished *in infinitum*, becomes less than any given space. And therefore (by Lem. 1) the figures inscribed and circumscribed become ultimately equal one to the other; and much more will the intermediate curvilinear figure be ultimately equal to either.   Q.E.D.

LEMMA 3

The same ultimate ratios are also ratios of equality, when the breadths AB, BC, DC, &c., of the parallelograms are unequal, and are all diminished in infinitum.

For suppose AF equal to the greatest breadth, and complete the parallelogram FAaf. This parallelogram will be greater than the difference of the inscribed and circumscribed figures; but, because its breadth AF is diminished *in infinitum,* it will become less than any given rectangle.   Q.E.D.

COR. I. Hence the ultimate sum of those evanescent parallelograms will in all parts coincide with the curvilinear figure.

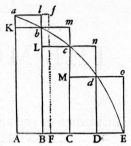

COR. II. Much more will the rectilinear figure comprehended under the chords of the evanescent arcs *ab*, *bc*, *cd*, &c., ultimately coincide with the curvilinear figure.

COR. III. And also the circumscribed rectilinear figure comprehended under the tangents of the same arcs.

COR. IV. And therefore these ultimate figures (as to their perimeters *ac*E) are not rectilinear, but curvilinear limits of rectilinear figures.

LEMMA 4

If in two figures AacE, PprT, *there are inscribed (as before) two series of parallelograms, an equal number in each series, and, their breadths being diminished in* infinitum, *if the ultimate ratios of the parallelograms in one figure to those in the other, each to each respectively, are the same: I say, that those two figures,* AacE, PprT, *are to each other in that same ratio.*

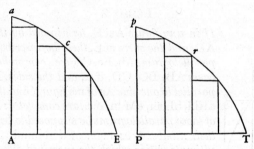

For as the parallelograms in the one are severally to the parallelograms in the other, so (by composition) is the sum of all in the one to the sum of all in the other; and so is the one figure to the other; because (by Lem. 3) the former figure to the former sum, and the latter figure to the latter sum, are both in the ratio of equality.   Q.E.D.

COR. Hence if two quantities of any kind are divided in any manner into an equal number of parts, and those parts, when their number is augmented, and their magnitude diminished *in infinitum,* have a given ratio to each other, the first to the first, the second to the second, and so on in order, all of them taken together will be to each other in that same given ratio. For if, in the figures of this Lemma, the parallelograms are taken to each other in the ratio of the parts, the sum of the parts will always be as the sum of the parallelograms; and therefore supposing the number of the parallelograms and parts to be augmented, and their magnitudes diminished *in infinitum,* those sums will be in the ultimate ratio of the parallelogram in the one figure to the correspondent parallelogram in the other; that is (by the supposition), in the ultimate ratio of any part of the one quantity to the correspondent part of the other.

LEMMA 5

All homologous sides of similar figures, whether curvilinear or rectilinear, are proportional; and the areas are as the squares of the homologous sides.

LEMMA 6

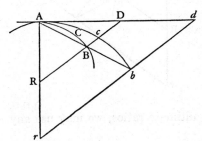

If any arc ACB, given in position, is subtended by its chord AB, and in any point A, in the middle of the continued curvature, is touched by a right line AD, produced both ways; then if the points A and B approach one another and meet, I say, the angle BAD, contained between the chord and the tangent, will be diminished in infinitum, *and ultimately will vanish.*

For if that angle does not vanish, the arc ACB will contain with the tangent AD an angle equal to a rectilinear angle; and therefore the curvature at the point A will not be continued, which is against the supposition.

LEMMA 7

The same things being supposed, I say that the ultimate ratio of the arc, chord, and tangent, any one to any other, is the ratio of equality.

For while the point B approaches towards the point A, consider always AB and AD as produced to the remote points *b* and *d;* and parallel to the secant BD draw *bd;* and let the arc A*cb* be always similar to the arc ACB. Then, supposing the points A and B to coincide, the angle *dAb* will vanish, by the preceding Lemma; and therefore the right lines A*b*, A*d* (which are always finite), and the intermediate arc A*cb*, will coincide, and become equal among themselves. Wherefore, the right lines AB, AD, and the intermediate arc ACB (which are always proportional to the former), will vanish, and ultimately acquire the ratio of equality.   Q.E.D.

Cor. I. Whence if through B we draw BF parallel to the tangent, always cutting any right line AF passing through A in F, this line BF will be ultimately in the ratio of equality with the evanescent arc ACB; because, completing the parallelogram AFBD, it is always in a ratio of equality with AD.

Cor. II. And if through B and A more right lines are drawn, as BE, BD, AF, AG, cutting the tangent AD and its parallel BF; the ultimate ratio of all the abscissas AD, AE, BF, BG, and of the chord and arc AB, any one to any other, will be the ratio of equality.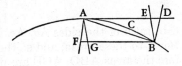

Cor. III. And therefore in all our reasoning about ultimate ratios, we may freely use any one of those lines for any other.

LEMMA 8

If the right lines AR, BR, with the arc ACB, the chord AB, and the tangent AD, constitute three triangles RAB, RACB, RAD, and the points A and B approach and meet: I say, that the ultimate form of these evanescent triangles is that of similitude, and their ultimate ratio that of equality.

For while the point B approaches towards the point A, consider always AB, AD, AR, as produced to the remote points *b*, *d*, and *r*, and *rbd* as drawn parallel to RD, and let the arc A*cb* be always simi-

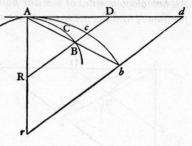

lar to the arc ACB. Then supposing the points A and B to coincide, the angle *bAd* will vanish; and therefore the three triangles *rAb*, *rAcb*, *rAd* (which are always finite), will coincide, and on that account become both similar and equal. And therefore the triangles RAB, RACB, RAD, which are always similar and proportional to these, will ultimately become both similar and equal among themselves.

Q.E.D.

Cor. And hence in all reasonings about ultimate ratios, we may use any one of those triangles for any other.

Lemma 9

If a right line AE, *and a curved line* ABC, *both given by position, cut each other in a given angle,* A; *and to that right line, in another given angle,* BD, CE *are ordinately applied, meeting the curve in* B, C; *and the points* B *and* C *together approach towards and meet in the point* A: *I say, that the areas of the triangles* ABD, ACE, *will ultimately be to each other as the squares of homologous sides.*

For while the points B, C, approach towards the point A, suppose always AD to be produced to the remote points *d* and *e*, so as A*d*, A*e* may be propor-

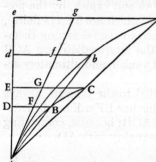

tional to AD, AE; and the ordinates *db*, *ec*, to be drawn parallel to the ordinates DB and EC, and meeting AB and AC produced in *b* and *c*. Let the curve A*bc* be similar to the curve ABC, and draw the right line A*g* so as to touch both curves in A, and cut the ordinates DB, EC, *db*, *ec*, in F, G, *f*, *g*. Then, supposing the length A*e* to remain the same, let the points B and C meet in the point A; and the angle *cAg* vanishing, the curvilinear areas A*bd*, A*ce* will coincide with the rectilinear areas A*fd*, A*ge;* and therefore (by Lem. 5) will be one to the other in the dupli-

cate ratio of the sides A*d*, A*e*. But the areas ABD, ACE are always proportional to these areas; and so the sides AD, AE are to these sides. And therefore the areas ABD, ACE are ultimately to each other as the squares of the sides AD, AE.

Q.E.D.

Lemma 10

The spaces which a body describes by any finite force urging it, whether that force is determined and immutable, or is continually augmented or continually diminished, are in the very beginning of the motion to each other as the squares of the times.

Let the times be represented by the lines AD, AE, and the velocities generated in those times by the ordinates DB, EC. The spaces described with these velocities will be as the areas ABD, ACE, described by those ordinates, that is, at the very beginning of the motion (by Lem. 9), in the duplicate ratio of the times AD, AE.   Q.E.D.

COR. I. And hence one may easily infer, that the errors of bodies describing similar parts of similar figures in proportional times, the errors being generated by any equal forces similarly applied to the bodies, and measured by the distances of the bodies from those places of the similar figures, at which, without the action of those forces, the bodies would have arrived in those proportional times—are nearly as the squares of the times in which they are generated.

COR. II. But the errors that are generated by proportional forces, similarly applied to the bodies at similar parts of the similar figures, are as the product of the forces and the squares of the times.

COR. III. The same thing is to be understood of any spaces whatsoever described by bodies urged with different forces; all which, in the very beginning of the motion, are as the product of the forces and the squares of the times.

COR. IV. And therefore the forces are directly as the spaces described in the very beginning of the motion, and inversely as the squares of the times.

COR. V. And the squares of the times are directly as the spaces described, and inversely as the forces.

SCHOLIUM

If in comparing with each other indeterminate quantities of different sorts, any one is said to be directly or inversely as any other, the meaning is, that the former is augmented or diminished in the same ratio as the latter, or as its reciprocal. And if any one is said to be as any other two or more, directly or inversely, the meaning is, that the first is augmented or diminished in the ratio compounded of the ratios in which the others, or the reciprocals of the others, are augmented or diminished. Thus, if A is said to be as B directly, and C directly, and D inversely, the meaning is, that A is augmented or diminished in the same ratio as $B \cdot C \cdot \frac{1}{D}$, that is to say, that A and $\frac{BC}{D}$ are to each other in a given ratio.

LEMMA 11

The evanescent subtense of the angle of contact, in all curves which at the point of contact have a finite curvature, is ultimately as the square of the subtense of the conterminous arc.

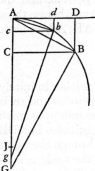

CASE 1. Let AB be that arc, AD its tangent, BD the subtense of the angle of contact perpendicular on the tangent, AB the subtense of the arc. Draw BG perpendicular to the subtense AB, and AG perpendicular to the tangent AD, meeting in G; then let the points D, B, and G approach to the points d, b, and g, and suppose J to be the ultimate intersection of the lines BG, AG, when the points D, B have come to A. It is evident that the distance GJ may be less than any assignable distance. But (from the nature of the circles passing through the points A, B, G, and through A, b, g),

$$AB^2 = AG \cdot BD, \text{ and}$$
$$Ab^2 = Ag \cdot bd.$$

But because GJ may be assumed of less length than any assignable, the ratio of AG to Ag may be such as to differ from unity by less than any assignable difference; and therefore the ratio of AB^2 to Ab^2 may be such as to differ from the ratio of BD to bd by less than any assignable difference. Therefore, by Lem. 1, ultimately,

$$AB^2 : Ab^2 = BD : bd.$$

Q.E.D.

CASE 2. Now let BD be inclined to AD in any given angle, and the ultimate ratio of BD to bd will always be the same as before, and therefore the same with the ratio of AB^2 to Ab^2.

Q.E.D.

CASE 3. And if we suppose the angle D not to be given, but that the right line BD converges to a given point, or is determined by any other condition whatever; nevertheless the angles D, d, being determined by the same law, will always draw nearer to equality, and approach nearer to each other than by any assigned difference, and therefore, by Lem. 1, will at last be equal; and therefore the lines BD, bd are in the same ratio to each other as before. Q.E.D.

COR. I. Therefore since the tangents AD, Ad, the arcs AB, Ab, and their sines, BC, bc, become ultimately equal to the chords AB, Ab, their squares will ultimately become as the subtenses BD, bd.

COR. II. Their squares are also ultimately as the versed sines of the arcs, bisecting the chords, and converging to a given point. For those versed sines are as the subtenses BD, bd.

COR. III. And therefore the versed sine is as the square of the time in which a body will describe the arc with a given velocity.

COR. IV. The ultimate proportion,

$$\triangle ADB : \triangle Adb = AD^3 : Ad^3 = DB^{3/2} : db^{3/2},$$

is derived from

$$\triangle ADB : \triangle Adb = AD \cdot DB : Ad \cdot db$$

and from the ultimate proportion

$$AD^2 : Ad^2 = DB : db.$$

So also is obtained ultimately

$$\triangle ABC : \triangle Abc = BC^3 : bc^3.$$

COR. V. And because DB, db are ultimately parallel and as the squares of the lines AD, Ad, the ultimate curvilinear areas ADB, Adb will be (by the nature of the parabola) two-thirds of the rectilinear triangles ADB, Adb, and the segments, AB, Ab will be one-third of the same triangles. And thence those areas and those segments will be as the cubes of the tangents AD, Ad, and also of the chords and arcs AB, Ab.

SCHOLIUM

But we have all along supposed the angle of contact to be neither infinitely greater nor infinitely less than the angles of contact made by circles and their tangents; that is, that the curvature at the point A is neither infinitely small nor infinitely great, and that the interval AJ is of a finite magnitude. For DB may be taken as AD^3: in which case no circle can be drawn through the point A, between the tangent AD and the curve AB, and therefore the angle of contact will be infinitely less than those of circles. And by a like reasoning, if DB be made successfully as AD^4, AD^5, AD^6, AD^7, &c., we shall have a series of angles of contact, proceeding *in infinitum*, wherein every succeeding term is infinitely less than the preceding. And if DB be made successively as AD^2, $AD^{3/2}$, $AD^{4/3}$, $AD^{5/4}$, $AD^{6/5}$, $AD^{7/6}$, &c., we shall have another infinite series of angles of contact, the first of which is of the same sort with those of circles, the second infinitely greater, and every succeeding one infinitely greater than the preceding. But between any two of these angles another series of intermediate angles of contact may be interposed, proceeding both ways *in infinitum*, wherein every succeeding angle shall be infinitely greater or infinitely less than the preceding. As if between the terms AD^2 and AD^3 there were interposed the series $AD^{13/6}$, $AD^{11/5}$, $AD^{9/4}$, $AD^{7/3}$, $AD^{5/2}$, $AD^{3/3}$, $AD^{11/4}$, $AD^{14/5}$, $AD^{17/6}$, &c. And again, between any two angles of this series, a new series of intermediate angles may be interposed, differing from one another by infinite intervals. Nor is Nature confined to any bounds.

Those things which have been demonstrated of curved lines, and the surfaces which they comprehend, may be easily applied to the curved surfaces and contents of solids. These Lemmas are premised to avoid the tediousness of deducing involved demonstrations *ad absurdum*, according to the method of the ancient geometers. For demonstrations are shorter by the method of indivisibles; but because the hypothesis of indivisibles seems somewhat harsh, and therefore that method is reckoned less geometrical, I chose rather to reduce the demonstrations of the following Propositions to the first and last sums and ratios of nascent and evanescent quantities, that is, to the limits of those sums and ratios, and so to premise, as short as I could, the demonstrations of those limits. For hereby the same thing is performed as by the method of indivisibles; and now those principles being demonstrated, we may use them with greater safety. Therefore if hereafter I should happen to consider quantities as made up of particles, or should use little curved lines for right ones, I would not be understood to mean indivisibles, but evanescent divisible quantities; not the sums and ratios of determinate parts, but always the limits of sums and ratios; and that the force of such demonstrations always depends on the method laid down in the foregoing Lemmas.

Perhaps it may be objected, that there is no ultimate proportion of evanescent quantities; because the proportion, before the quantities have vanished, is not the ultimate, and when they are vanished, is none. But by the same argument it may be alleged that a body arriving at a certain place, and there stopping, has no ultimate velocity; because the velocity, before the body comes to the place, is not its ultimate velocity; when it has arrived, there is none. But the answer is easy; for by the ultimate velocity is meant that with which the body is moved, neither before it arrives at its last place and the motion ceases, nor after, but at the very instant it arrives; that is, that velocity with which the body arrives at its last place, and with which the motion ceases. And in like manner, by the ultimate ratio of evanescent quantities is to be understood the ratio of the quantities not before they vanish, nor afterwards, but with which they vanish. In like manner the first ratio of nascent quantities is that with which they begin to be. And the first or last sum is that with which they begin and cease to be (or to be augmented or diminished). There is a limit which the velocity at the end of the motion may attain, but not exceed. This is the ultimate velocity. And there is the like limit in all quantities and proportions that begin and cease to be. And since such limits are certain and definite, to determine the same is a problem strictly geometrical. But whatever is geometrical we may use in determining and demonstrating any other thing that is also geometrical.

It may also be objected, that if the ultimate ratios of evanescent quantities are given, their ultimate magnitudes will be also given: and so all quantities will consist of indivisibles, which is contrary to what Euclid has demonstrated concerning incommensurables, in the tenth book of his *Elements*. But this objection is founded on a false supposition. For those ultimate ratios with which quantities vanish are not truly the ratios of ultimate quantities, but limits towards which the ratios of quantities decreasing without limit do always converge; and to which they approach nearer than by any given difference, but never go beyond, nor in effect attain to, till the quantities are diminished *in infinitum*. This thing will appear more evident in quantities infinitely great. If two quantities, whose difference is given, be augmented *in infinitum*, the ultimate ratio of these quantities will be given, namely, the ratio of equality; but it does not from thence follow, that the ultimate or greatest quantities themselves, whose ratio that is, will be given. Therefore if in what follows, for the sake of being more easily understood, I should happen to mention quantities as least, or evanescent, or ultimate, you are not to suppose that quantities of any determinate magnitude are meant, but such as are conceived to be always diminished without end.

SECTION II

The determination of centripetal forces

Proposition 1. Theorem 1

The areas which revolving bodies describe by radii drawn to an immovable centre of force do lie in the same immovable planes, and are proportional to the times in which they are described.

For suppose the time to be divided into equal parts, and in the first part of that time let the body by its innate force describe the right line AB. In the second part of that time, the same would (by Law I), if not hindered, proceed directly to *c*, along the line B*c* equal to AB; so that by the radii AS, BS, *c*S, drawn to the centre, the equal areas ASB, BS*c*, would be described. But when the body is arrived at B, suppose that a centripetal force acts at once with a great impulse, and, turning aside the body from the right line B*c*, compels it afterwards to continue its motion along the right line BC. Draw *c*C parallel to BS, meeting BC in C; and at the end of the second part of the time, the body (by Cor. I of the Laws) will be found in C, in the same plane with the triangle ASB. Join SC, and, because SB and C*c* are parallel, the triangle SBC will be equal to the triangle SB*c*, and therefore also to the triangle SAB. By the like argument, if the centripetal force acts successively in C, D, E, &c., and makes the body, in each single particle of time, to describe the right lines CD, DE, EF, &c., they will all lie in the same plane; and the triangle SCD will be equal to the triangle SBC, and SDE to SCD, and SEF to SDE. And therefore, in equal times, equal areas are described in one immovable plane: and, by composition, any sums SADS, SAFS, of those areas, are to each other as the times in which they are described. Now let the number of those triangles be augmented, and their breadth diminished *in infinitum;* and (by Cor. IV, Lem. 3) their ultimate perimeter ADF will be a curved line: and therefore the centripetal force, by which the body is continually drawn back from the tangent of this curve, will act continually; and any described areas SADS, SAFS, which are always proportional to the times of description, will, in this case also, be proportional to those times.

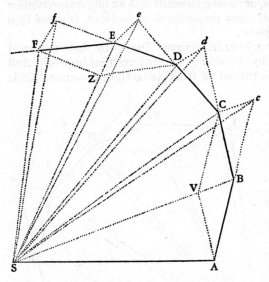

Q.E.D.

COR. I. The velocity of a body attracted towards an immovable centre, in spaces void of resistance, is inversely as the perpendicular let fall from that centre on the right line that touches the orbit. For the velocities in those places A, B, C, D, E, are as the bases AB, BC, CD, DE, EF, of equal triangles; and these bases are inversely as the perpendiculars let fall upon them.

COR. II. If the chords AB, BC of two arcs, successively described in equal times by the same body, in spaces void of resistance, are completed into a parallelogram ABCV, and the diagonal BV of this parallelogram, in the position which it ultimately acquires when those arcs are diminished *in infinitum,* is produced both ways, it will pass through the centre of force.

COR. III. If the chords AB, BC, and DE, EF, of arcs described in equal times, in spaces void of resistance, are completed into the parallelograms ABCV, DEFZ, the forces in B and E are one to the other in the ultimate ratio of the diagonals BV, EZ, when those arcs are diminished *in infinitum.* For the motions BC and EF of the body (by Cor. 1 of the Laws) are compounded of the motions Bc, BV, and Ef, EZ; but BV and EZ, which are equal to Cc and Ff, in the demonstration of this Proposition, were generated by the impulses of the centripetal force in B and E, and are therefore proportional to those impulses.

COR. IV. The forces by which bodies, in spaces void of resistance, are drawn back from rectilinear motions, and turned into curvilinear orbits, are to each other as the versed sines of arcs described in equal times; which versed sines tend to the centre of force, and bisect the chords when those arcs are diminished to infinity. For such versed sines are the halves of the diagonals mentioned in Cor. III.

COR. V. And therefore those forces are to the force of gravity as the said versed sines to the versed sines perpendicular to the horizon of those parabolic arcs which projectiles describe in the same time.

COR. VI. And the same things do all hold good (by Cor. V of the Laws) when the planes in which the bodies are moved, together with the centres of force which are placed in those planes, are not at rest, but move uniformly forwards in right lines.

Proposition 2. Theorem 2

Every body that moves in any curved line described in a plane, and by a radius drawn to a point either immovable, or moving forwards with an uniform rectilinear motion, describes about that point areas proportional to the times, is urged by a centripetal force directed to that point.

Case 1. For every body that moves in a curved line is (by Law I) turned aside from its rectilinear course by the action of some force that impels it. And that force by which the body is turned off from its rectilinear course, and is

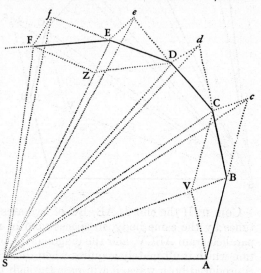

made to describe, in equal times, the equal least triangles SAB, SBC, SCD, &c., about the immovable point S (by Prop. 40, Book 1, *Elements* of Euclid, and Law II), acts in the place B, according to the direction of a line parallel to *c*C, that is, in the direction of the line BS; and in the place C, according to the direction of a line parallel to *d*D, that is, in the direction of the line CS, &c.; and therefore acts always in the direction of lines tending to the immovable point S. Q.E.D.

Case 2. And (by Cor. V of the Laws) it is indifferent whether the surface in which a body describes a curvilinear figure be at rest, or moves together with the body, the figure described, and its point S, uniformly forwards in a right line.

Cor. I. In nonresisting spaces or mediums, if the areas are not proportional to the times, the forces are not directed to the point in which the radii meet, but deviate therefrom towards the part to which the motion is directed, if the description of the areas is accelerated, and away from that part, if retarded.

Cor. II. And even in resisting mediums, if the description of the areas is accelerated, the directions of the forces deviate from the point in which the radii meet, towards the part to which the motion tends.

Scholium

A body may be urged by a centripetal force compounded of several forces; in which case the meaning of the Proposition is, that the force which results out of all tends to the point S. But if any force acts continually in the direction of lines perpendicular to the described surface, this force will make the body to deviate from the plane of its motion; but will neither augment nor diminish the area of the described surface, and is therefore to be neglected in the composition of forces.

PROPOSITION 3. THEOREM 3

Every body, that by a radius drawn to the centre of another body, howsoever moved, describes areas about that centre proportional to the times, is urged by a force compounded of the centripetal force tending to that other body, and of all the accelerative force by which that other body is impelled.

Let L represent the one, and T the other body; and (by Cor. VI of the Laws) if both bodies are urged in the direction of parallel lines, by a new force equal and contrary to that by which the second body T is urged, the first body L will go on to describe about the other body T the same areas as before: but the force by which that other body T was urged will be now destroyed by an equal and contrary force; and therefore (by Law I) that other body T, now left to itself, will either rest, or move uniformly forwards in a right line: and the first body L, impelled by the difference of the forces, that is, by the force remaining, will go on to describe about the other body T areas proportional to the times. And therefore (by Theor. 2) the difference of the forces is directed to the other body T as its centre.   Q.E.D.

COR. I. Hence if the one body L, by a radius drawn to the other body T, describes areas proportional to the times; and from the whole force, by which the first body L is urged (whether that force is simple, or, according to Cor. II of the Laws, compounded out of several forces), we subtract (by the same Cor.) that whole accelerative force by which the other body is urged; the whole remaining force by which the first body is urged will tend to the other body T, as its centre.

COR. II. And, if these areas are proportional to the times nearly, the remaining force will tend to the other body T nearly.

COR. III. And *vice versa*, if the remaining force tends nearly to the other body T, those areas will be nearly proportional to the times.

COR. IV. If the body L, by a radius drawn to the other body T, describes areas, which, compared with the times, are very unequal; and that other body T be either at rest, or moves uniformly forwards in a right line: the action of the centripetal force tending to that other body T is either none at all, or it is mixed and compounded with very powerful actions of other forces: and the whole force compounded of them all, if they are many, is directed to another (immovable or movable) centre. The same thing obtains, when the other body is moved by any motion whatsoever; provided that centripetal force is taken, which remains after subtracting that whole force acting upon that other body T.

SCHOLIUM

Since the equable description of areas indicates that there is a centre to which tends that force by which the body is most affected, and by which it is drawn back from its rectilinear motion, and retained in its orbit, why may we not be allowed, in the following discourse, to use the equable description of areas as an indication of a centre, about which all circular motion is performed in free spaces?

PROPOSITION 4. THEOREM 4

The centripetal forces of bodies, which by equable motions describe different circles, tend to the centres of the same circles; and are to each other as the squares of the arcs described in equal times divided respectively by the radii of the circles.

These forces tend to the centres of the circles (by Prop. 2, and Cor. II, Prop. 1), and are to one another as the versed sines of the least arcs described in equal times (by Cor. IV, Prop. 1); that is, as the squares of the same arcs divided by the diameters of the circles (by Lem. 7); and therefore since those arcs are as arcs described in any equal times, and the diameters are as the radii, the forces will be as the squares of any arcs described in the same time divided by the radii of the circles.   Q.E.D.

Cor. I. Therefore, since those arcs are as the velocities of the bodies, the centripetal forces are as the squares of the velocities divided by the radii.

Cor. II. And since the periodic times are as the radii divided by the velocities, the centripetal forces are as the radii divided by the square of the periodic times.

Cor. III. Whence if the periodic times are equal, and the velocities therefore as the radii, the centripetal forces will be also as the radii; and conversely.

Cor. IV. If the periodic times and the velocities are both as the square roots of the radii, the centripetal forces will be equal among themselves; and conversely.

Cor. V. If the periodic times are as the radii, and therefore the velocities equal, the centripetal forces will be inversely as the radii; and conversely.

Cor. VI. If the periodic times are as the $\frac{3}{2}$th powers of the radii, and therefore the velocities inversely as the square roots of the radii, the centripetal forces will be inversely as the squares of the radii; and conversely.

Cor. VII. And universally, if the periodic time is as any power R^n of the radius R, and therefore the velocity inversely as the power R^{n-1} of the radius, the centripetal force will be inversely as the power R^{2n-1} of the radius; and conversely.

Cor. VIII. The same things hold concerning the times, the velocities, and the forces by which bodies describe the similar parts of any similar figures that have their centres in a similar position with those figures; as appears by applying the demonstration of the preceding cases to those. And the application is easy, by only substituting the equable description of areas in the place of equable motion, and using the distances of the bodies from the centres instead of the radii.

Cor. IX. From the same demonstration it likewise follows, that the arc which a body, uniformly revolving in a circle with a given centripetal force, describes in any time, is a mean proportional between the diameter of the circle, and the space which the same body falling by the same given force would describe in the same given time.

SCHOLIUM

The case of the sixth Corollary obtains in the celestial bodies (as Sir Christopher Wren, Dr. Hooke, and Dr. Halley have severally observed); and therefore in what follows, I intend to treat more at large of those things which relate to centripetal force decreasing as the squares of the distances from the centres.

Moreover, by means of the preceding Proposition and its Corollaries, we may discover the proportion of a centripetal force to any other known force, such as that of gravity. For if a body by means of its gravity revolves in a circle concentric to the earth, this gravity is the centripetal force of that body. But from the descent of heavy bodies, the time of one entire revolution, as well as the arc described in any given time, is given (by Cor. IX of this Prop.). And by such propositions, Mr. Huygens, in his excellent book *De horologio oscillatorio*, has compared the force of gravity with the centrifugal forces of revolving bodies.

The preceding Proposition may be likewise demonstrated after this manner. In any circle suppose a polygon to be inscribed of any number of sides. And if a body, moved with a given velocity along the sides of the polygon, is reflected from the circle at the several angular points, the force, with which at every reflection it strikes the circle, will be as its velocity: and therefore the sum of the forces, in a given time, will be as the product of that velocity and the number of reflections; that is (if the species of the polygon be given), as the length described in that given time, and increased or diminished in the ratio of the same length to the radius of the circle; that is, as the square of that length divided by the radius; and therefore the polygon, by having its sides diminished *in infinitum*, coincides with the circle, as the square of the arc described in a given time divided by the radius. This is the centrifugal force, with which the body impels the circle; and to which the contrary force, wherewith the circle continually repels the body towards the centre, is equal.

PROPOSITION 5. PROBLEM 1

There being given, in any places, the velocity with which a body describes a given figure, by means of forces directed to some common centre: to find that centre.

Let the three right lines PT, TQV, VR touch the figure described in as many points, P, Q, R, and meet in T and V. On the tangents erect the perpendiculars

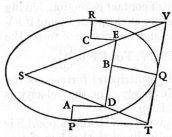

PA, QB, RC, inversely proportional to the velocities of the body in the points P, Q, R, from which the perpendiculars were raised; that is, so that PA may be to QB as the velocity in Q to the velocity in P, and QB to RC as the velocity in R to the velocity in Q. Through the ends A, B, C of the perpendiculars draw AD, DBE, EC, at right angles, meeting in D and E: and the right lines TD, VE produced, will meet in S, the centre required.

For the perpendiculars let fall from the centre S on the tangents PT, QT, are inversely as the velocities of the bodies in the points P and Q (by Cor. I, Prop. 1), and therefore, by construction, directly as the perpendiculars AP, BQ; that is, as the perpendiculars let fall from the point D on the tangents. Whence it is easy to infer that the points S, D, T are in one right line. And by the like argument the points S, E, V are also in one right line; and therefore the centre S is in the point where the right lines TD, VE meet.   Q.E.D.

PROPOSITION 6. THEOREM 5

In a space void of resistance, if a body revolves in any orbit about an immovable centre, and in the least time describes any arc just then nascent; and the versed sine of that arc is supposed to be drawn bisecting the chord, and produced passing through the centre of force: the centripetal force in the middle of the arc will be directly as the versed sine and inversely as the square of the time.

For the versed sine in a given time is as the force (by Cor. IV, Prop. 1); and augmenting the time in any ratio, because the arc will be augmented in the same ratio, the versed sine will be augmented in the square of that ratio (by Cor. II and III, Lem. 11), and therefore is as the force and the square of the time. Divide both sides by the square of the time, and the force will be directly as the versed sine, and inversely as the square of the time.   Q.E.D.

And the same thing may also be easily demonstrated by Cor. IV, Lem. 10.

COR. I. If a body P revolving about the centre S describes a curved line APQ, which a right line ZPR touches in any point P; and from any other point Q of the curve, QR is drawn parallel to the distance SP, meeting the tangent in R; and QT is drawn perpendicular to the distance SP; the centripetal force will be inversely as the solid $\frac{SP^2 \cdot QT^2}{QR}$, if the solid be taken of that magnitude which it ultimately acquires when the points P and Q coincide. For QR is equal to the versed sine of double the arc QP, whose middle is P: and double the triangle SQP, or SP·QT is proportional to the time in which that double arc is described; and therefore may be used to represent the time.

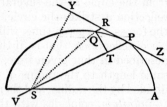

COR. II. By a like reasoning, the centripetal force is inversely as the solid $\frac{SY^2 \cdot QP^2}{QR}$; if SY is a perpendicular from the centre of force on PR, the tangent of the orbit. For the rectangles SY·QP and SP·QT are equal.

COR. III. If the orbit is either a circle, or touches or cuts a circle concentrically, that is, contains with a circle the least angle of contact or section, having the same curvature and the same radius of curvature at the point P; and if PV be a chord of this circle, drawn from the body through the centre of force; the centripetal force will be inversely as the solid $SY^2 \cdot PV$. For PV is $\frac{QP^2}{QR}$.

COR. IV. The same things being supposed, the centripetal force is as the square of the velocity directly, and the chord inversely. For the velocity is reciprocally as the perpendicular SY, by Cor. I, Prop. 1.

COR. V. Hence if any curvilinear figure APQ is given, and therein a point S is also given, to which a centripetal force is continually directed, that law of centripetal force may be found, by which the body P will be continually drawn back from a rectilinear course, and, being detained in the perimeter of that figure, will describe the same by a continual revolution. That is, we are to find, by computation, either the solid $\frac{SP^2 \cdot QT^2}{QR}$ or the solid $SY^2 \cdot PV$, inversely proportional to this force. Examples of this we shall give in the following Problems.

PROPOSITION 7. PROBLEM 2

If a body revolves in the circumference of a circle, it is proposed to find the law of centripetal force directed to any given point.

Let VQPA be the circumference of the circle; S the given point to which as to a centre the force tends; P the body moving in the circumference; Q the next place into which it is to move; and PRZ the tangent of the circle at the preceding place. Through the point S draw the chord PV, and the diameter VA of the circle; join AP, and draw QT perpendicular to SP, which produced, may meet the tangent PR in Z; and lastly, through the point Q, draw LR parallel to SP, meeting the circle in L, and the tangent PZ in R. And, because of the similar triangles ZQR, ZTP, VPA, we shall have

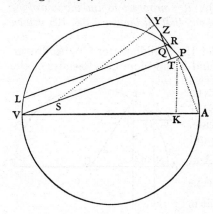

$$RP^2 : QT^2 = AV^2 : PV^2.$$

Since $RP^2 = RL \cdot QR$, $QT^2 = \dfrac{RL \cdot QR \cdot PV^2}{AV^2}$.

Multiply those equals by $\dfrac{SP^2}{QR}$, and the points P and Q coinciding, for RL write PV; then we shall have

$$\frac{SP^2 \cdot PV^3}{AV^2} = \frac{SP^2 \cdot QT^2}{QR}.$$

And therefore (by Cor. I and V, Prop. 6) the centripetal force is inversely as $\dfrac{SP^2 \cdot PV^3}{AV^2}$; that is (because AV^2 is given), inversely as the product of SP^2 and PV^3.

Q.E.I.

The same otherwise.

On the tangent PR produced let fall the perpendicular SY; and (because of the similar triangles SYP, VPA) we shall have AV to PV as SP to SY, and therefore $\dfrac{SP \cdot PV}{AV} = SY$, and $\dfrac{SP^2 \cdot PV^3}{AV^2} = SY^2 \cdot PV$. And therefore (by Cor. III and V, Prop. 6) the centripetal force is inversely as $\dfrac{SP^2 \cdot PV^3}{AV^2}$; that is (because AV is given), inversely as $SP^2 \cdot PV^3$.

Q.E.I.

COR. I. Hence if the given point S, to which the centripetal force always tends, is placed in the circumference of the circle, as at V, the centripetal force will be inversely as the fifth power of the altitude SP.

COR. II. The force by which the body P in the circle APTV revolves about the centre of force S is to the force by which the same body P may revolve in the same circle, and in the same periodic time, about any other centre of force R, as $RP^2 \cdot SP$ to the cube of the right line SG, which from the first centre of force S is drawn parallel to the distance PR of the body from the second centre of force R, meeting the tangent PG of the orbit in G. For by the construction of this Proposition, the former force is to the latter as $RP^2 \cdot PT^3$ to $SP^2 \cdot PV^3$; that

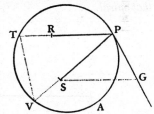

is, as $SP \cdot RP^2$ to $\dfrac{SP^3 \cdot PV^3}{PT^3}$; or (because of the similar triangles PSG, TPV) to SG^3.

COR. III. The force by which the body P in any orbit revolves about the centre of force S, is to the force by which the same body may revolve in the same orbit, and the same periodic time, about any other centre of force R, as the solid $SP \cdot RP^2$, contained under the distance of the body from the first centre of force S, and the square of its distance from the second centre of force R, to the cube of the right line SG, drawn from the first centre of the force S, parallel to the distance RP of the body from the second centre of force R, meeting the tangent PG of the orbit in G. For the force in this orbit at any point P is the same as in a circle of the same curvature.

PROPOSITION 8. PROBLEM 3

If a body moves in the semicircumference PQA; it is proposed to find the law of the centripetal force tending to a point S, so remote, that all the lines PS, RS drawn thereto, may be taken for parallels.

From C, the centre of the semicircle, let the semidiameter CA be drawn, cutting the parallels at right angles in M and N, and join CP. Because of the similar triangles CPM, PZT, and RZQ, we shall have $CP^2 : PM^2 = PR^2 : QT^2$. From the nature of the circle, $PR^2 = QR(RN+QN) = QR \cdot 2PM$, when the points P and Q coincide. Therefore $CP^2 : PM^2 = QR \cdot 2PM : QT^2$; and $\dfrac{QT^2}{QR} = \dfrac{2PM^3}{CP^2}$, and $\dfrac{QT^2 \cdot SP^2}{QR} = \dfrac{2PM^3 \cdot SP^2}{CP^2}$. And therefore (by Cor. I and V, Prop. 6) the centripetal force is inversely as $\dfrac{2PM^3 \cdot SP^2}{CP^2}$; that is

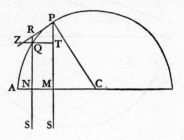

(neglecting the given ratio $\dfrac{2SP^2}{CP^2}$), inversely as PM^3.   Q.E.I.

And the same thing is likewise easily inferred from the preceding Proposition.

SCHOLIUM

And by a like reasoning, a body will be moved in an ellipse, or even in an hyperbola, or parabola, by a centripetal force which is inversely as the cube of the ordinate directed to an infinitely remote centre of force.

PROPOSITION 9. PROBLEM 4

If a body revolves in a spiral PQS, cutting all the radii SP, SQ, &c., in a given angle; it is proposed to find the law of the centripetal force tending to the centre of that spiral.

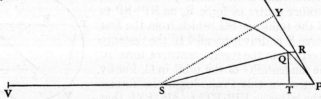

Suppose the indefinitely small angle PSQ to be given; because, then, all the angles are given, the figure SPRQT will be given in kind. Therefore the ratio $\dfrac{QT}{QR}$ is also given, and $\dfrac{QT^2}{QR}$ is as QT, that is (because the figure is given in kind), as SP. But if the angle PSQ is any way changed, the right line QR, subtending the angle of contact QPR (by Lem. 11) will be changed in the ratio of PR^2 or QT^2. Therefore the ratio $\dfrac{QT^2}{QR}$ remains the same as before, that is, as SP. And $\dfrac{QT^2 \cdot SP^2}{QR}$ is as SP^3, and therefore (by Cor. I and V, Prop. 6) the centripetal force is inversely as the cube of the distance SP.   Q.E.I.

The same otherwise.

The perpendicular SY let fall upon the tangent, and the chord PV of the circle concentrically cutting the spiral, are in given ratios to the height SP; and therefore SP³ is as SY²·PV, that is (by Cor. III and V, Prop. 6) inversely as the centripetal force.

LEMMA 12

All parallelograms circumscribed about any conjugate diameters of a given ellipse or hyperbola are equal among themselves.

This is demonstrated by the writers on the conic sections.

PROPOSITION 10. PROBLEM 5

If a body revolves in an ellipse; it is proposed to find the law of the centripetal force tending to the centre of the ellipse.

Suppose CA, CB to be semiaxes of the ellipse; GP, DK, conjugate diameters; PF, QT, perpendiculars to those diameters; Qv, an ordinate to the diam-

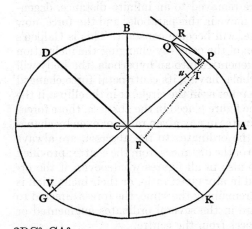

eter GP; and if the parallelogram QvPR be completed, then (by the properties of the conic sections) $Pv \cdot vG : Qv^2 = PC^2 : CD^2$, and, because of the similar triangles QvT, PCF, $Qv^2 : QT^2 = PC^2 : PF^2$; and by eliminating Qv^2, $vG : \dfrac{QT^2}{Pv} = PC^2 : \dfrac{CD^2 \cdot PF^2}{PC^2}$. Since QR = Pv, and (by Lem. 12) BC·CA = CD·PF, and, when the points P and Q coincide, 2PC = vG, we shall have, multiplying the extremes and means together, $\dfrac{QT^2 \cdot PC^2}{QR} =$

$\dfrac{2BC^2 \cdot CA^2}{PC}$. Therefore (by Cor. V, Prop. 6), the centripetal force is inversely as $\dfrac{2BC^2 \cdot CA^2}{PC}$; that is (because 2BC²·CA² is given), inversely as $\dfrac{1}{PC}$; that is, directly as the distance PC.   Q.E.I.

The same otherwise.

In the right line PG on the other side of the point T, take the point u so that Tu may be equal to Tv; then take uV, such that uV : vG = DC² : PC². Since, by the conic sections, $Qv^2 : Pv \cdot vG = DC^2 : PC^2$, we have $Qv^2 = Pv \cdot uV$. Add Pu·Pv to both sides, and the square of the chord of the arc PQ will be equal to the rectangle PV·Pv; and therefore a circle which touches the conic section in P, and passes through the point Q, will pass also through the point V. Now let the points P and Q meet, and the ratio of uV to vG, which is the same with the ratio of DC² to PC², will become the ratio of PV to PG, or PV to 2PC; and therefore PV will be equal to $\dfrac{2DC^2}{PC}$. And therefore the force by which the body P revolves in the ellipse will be inversely as $\dfrac{2DC^2}{PC} \cdot PF^2$ (by Cor. III, Prop. 6); that is (because 2DC²·PF² is given), directly as PC.   Q.E.I.

COR. I. And therefore the force is as the distance of the body from the centre of the ellipse; and, *vice versa*, if the force is as the distance, the body will move in an ellipse whose centre coincides with the centre of force, or perhaps in a circle into which the ellipse may degenerate.

COR. II. And the periodic times of the revolutions made in all ellipses whatsoever about the same centre will be equal. For those times in similar ellipses will be equal (by Cor. III and VIII, Prop. 4); but in ellipses that have their greater axis common, they are to each other as the whole areas of the ellipses directly, and the parts of the areas described in the same time inversely; that is, as the lesser axes directly, and the velocities of the bodies in their principal vertices inversely; that is, as those lesser axes directly, and the ordinates to the same point of the common axes inversely; and therefore (because of the equality of the direct and inverse ratios) in the ratio of equality, 1 : 1.

SCHOLIUM

If the ellipse, by having its centre removed to an infinite distance, degenerates into a parabola, the body will move in this parabola; and the force, now tending to a centre infinitely remote, will become constant. This is Galileo's theorem. And if the parabolic section of the cone (by changing the inclination of the cutting plane to the cone) degenerates into an hyperbola, the body will move in the perimeter of this hyperbola, having its centripetal force changed into a centrifugal force. And in like manner as in the circle, or in the ellipse, if the forces are directed to the centre of the figure placed in the abscissa, those forces by increasing or diminishing the ordinates in any given ratio, or even by changing the angle of the inclination of the ordinates to the abscissa, are always augmented or diminished in the ratio of the distances from the centre; provided the periodic times remain equal; so also in all figures whatsoever, if the ordinates are augmented or diminished in any given ratio, or their inclination is any way changed, the periodic time remaining the same, the forces directed to any centre placed in the abscissa are in the several ordinates augmented or diminished in the ratio of the distances from the centre.

SECTION III

THE MOTION OF BODIES IN ECCENTRIC CONIC SECTIONS

PROPOSITION 11. PROBLEM 6

If a body revolves in an ellipse; it is required to find the law of the centripetal force tending to the focus of the ellipse.

Let S be the focus of the ellipse. Draw SP cutting the diameter DK of the ellipse in E, and the ordinate Qv in x; and complete the parallelogram QxPR. It is evident that EP is equal to the greater semiaxis AC: for drawing HI from the other focus H of the ellipse parallel to EC, because CS, CH are equal, ES, EI will also be equal; so that EP is the half-sum of PS, PI, that is (because of the parallels HI, PR, and the equal angles IPR, HPZ), of PS, PH, which taken together are equal to the whole axis 2AC. Draw QT perpendicular to SP, and putting L for the principal latus rectum of the ellipse (or for $\frac{2BC^2}{AC}$), we shall have

$$L \cdot QR : L \cdot Pv = QR : Pv = PE : PC = AC : PC,$$
also, $L \cdot Pv : Gv \cdot Pv = L : Gv,$ and, $Gv \cdot Pv : Qv^2 = PC^2 : CD^2.$

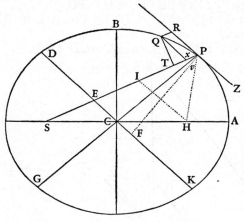

By Cor. II, Lem. 7, when the points P and Q coincide, $Qv^2 = Qx^2$, and Qx^2 or $Qv^2 : QT^2 = EP^2 : PF^2 = CA^2 : PF^2$, and (by Lem. 12) $= CD^2 : CB^2$. Multiplying together corresponding terms of the four proportions, and simplifying, we shall have $L \cdot QR : QT^2 = AC \cdot L \cdot PC^2 \cdot CD^2 : PC \cdot Gv \cdot CD^2 \cdot CB^2 = 2PC : Gv$, since $AC \cdot L = 2BC^2$. But the points Q and P coinciding, 2PC and Gv are equal. And therefore the quantities $L \cdot QR$ and QT^2, proportional to these, will be also equal. Let those equals be multiplied by $\dfrac{SP^2}{QR}$, and $L \cdot SP^2$ will be-

come equal to $\dfrac{SP^2 \cdot QT^2}{QR}$. And therefore (by Cor. I and V, Prop. 6) the centripetal force is inversely as $L \cdot SP^2$, that is, inversely as the square of the distance SP.   Q.E.I.

The same otherwise.

Since the force tending to the centre of the ellipse, by which the body P may revolve in that ellipse, is (by Cor. I, Prop. 10) as the distance CP of the body from the centre C of the ellipse, let CE be drawn parallel to the tangent PR of the ellipse; and the force by which the same body P may revolve about any other point S of the ellipse, if CE and PS intersect in E, will be as $\dfrac{PE^3}{SP^2}$ (by Cor. III, Prop. 7); that is, if the point S is the focus of the ellipse, and therefore PE be given as SP^2 reciprocally.   Q.E.I.

With the same brevity with which we reduced the fifth Problem to the parabola, and hyperbola, we might do the like here; but because of the dignity of the Problem and its use in what follows, I shall confirm the other cases by particular demonstrations.

PROPOSITION 12. PROBLEM 7

Suppose a body to move in an hyperbola; it is required to find the law of the centripetal force tending to the focus of that figure.

Let CA, CB be the semiaxes of the hyperbola; PG, KD other conjugate diameters; PF a perpendicular to the diameter KD; and Qv an ordinate to the diameter GP. Draw SP cutting the diameter DK in E, and the ordinate Qv in x, and complete the parallelogram QRPx. It is evident that EP is equal to the semitransverse axis AC; for drawing HI, from the other focus H of the hyperbola, parallel to EC, because CS, CH are equal, ES, EI will be also equal; so that EP is the half difference of PS, PI; that is (because of the parallels IH, PR, and the equal angles IPR, HPZ), of PS, PH, the difference of which is equal to the whole axis 2AC. Draw QT perpendicular to SP; and putting L for the principal latus rectum of the hyperbola (that is, for $\dfrac{2BC^2}{AC}$), we shall have

$$L \cdot QR : L \cdot Pv = QR : Pv = Px : Pv = PE : PC = AC : PC,$$

also, $L \cdot Pv : Gv \cdot Pv = L : Gv$, and $Gv \cdot Pv : Qv^2 = PC^2 : CD^2$. By Cor. II, Lem. 7, when P and Q coincide, $Qx^2 = Qv^2$, and,

$$Qx^2 \text{ or } Qv^2 : QT^2 = EP^2 : PF^2 = CA^2 : PF^2, \text{ by Lem. 12, } = CD^2 : CB^2.$$

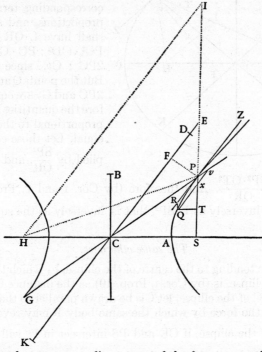

Multiplying together corresponding terms of the four proportions, and simplifying,

$$L \cdot QR : QT^2 = AC \cdot L \cdot PC^2 \cdot CD^2 : PC \cdot Gv \cdot CD^2 \cdot CB^2 = 2PC : Gv,$$

since $AC \cdot L = 2BC^2$. But the points P and Q coinciding, 2PC and Gv are equal. And therefore the quantities $L \cdot QR$ and QT^2, proportional to them, will also be equal. Let those equals be drawn into $\dfrac{SP^2}{QR}$, and we shall have $L \cdot SP^2$ equal to $\dfrac{SP^2 \cdot QT^2}{QR}$. And therefore (by Cor. I and V, Prop. 6) the centripetal force is inversely as $L \cdot SP^2$, that is, inversely as the square of the distance SP. Q.E.I.

The same otherwise.

Find out the force tending from the centre C of the hyperbola. This will be proportional to the distance CP. But from thence (by Cor. III, Prop. 7) the force tending to the focus S will be as $\dfrac{PE^3}{SP^2}$, that is, because PE is given reciprocally as SP^2. Q.E.I.

And the same way may it be demonstrated, that the body having its centripetal changed into a centrifugal force, will move in the conjugate hyperbola.

LEMMA 13

The latus rectum of a parabola belonging to any vertex is four times the distance of that vertex from the focus of the figure.

This is demonstrated by the writers on the conic sections.

LEMMA 14

The perpendicular, let fall from the focus of a parabola on its tangent, is a mean proportional between the distances of the focus from the point of contact, and from the principal vertex of the figure.

For, let AP be the parabola, S its focus, A its principal vertex, P the point of contact, PO an ordinate to the principal diameter, PM the tangent meeting the

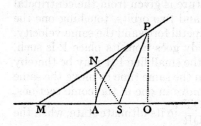

principal diameter in M, and SN the perpendicular from the focus on the tangent: join AN, and because of the equal lines MS and SP, MN and NP, MA and AO, the right lines AN, OP will be parallel; and thence the triangle SAN will be right-angled at A, and similar to the equal triangles SNM, SNP; therefore PS is to SN as SN is to SA.   Q.E.D.

Cor. I. PS² is to SN² as PS is to SA.

Cor. II. And because SA is given, SN² will vary as PS.

Cor. III. And the intersection of any tangent PM, with the right line SN, drawn from the focus perpendicular on the tangent, falls in the right line AN that touches the parabola in the principal vertex.

PROPOSITION 13. PROBLEM 8

If a body moves in the perimeter of a parabola; it is required to find the law of the centripetal force tending to the focus of that figure.

Retaining the construction of the preceding Lemma, let P be the body in the perimeter of the parabola; and from the place Q, into which it is next to succeed, draw QR parallel and QT perpendicular to SP, as also Qv parallel to the tangent, and meeting the diameter PG in v, and the distance SP in x. Now because of the similar triangles Pxv, SPM, and of the equal sides SP, SM of the one, the sides Px or QR and Pv of the other will be also equal. But (by the conic sections) the square of the ordinate Qv is equal to the rectangle under the latus rectum

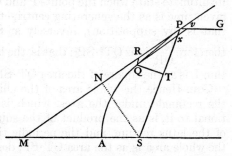

and the segment Pv of the diameter; that is (by Lem. 13), to the rectangle 4PS·Pv, or 4PS·QR; and the points P and Q coinciding, (by Cor. II, Lem. 7), Qx=Qv. And therefore Qx², in this case, becomes equal to the rectangle 4PS·QR. But (because of the similar triangles QxT, SPN),

$$Qx^2 : QT^2 = PS^2 : SN^2 = PS : SA \text{ (by Cor. I, Lem. 14),}$$
$$= 4PS·QR : 4SA·QR.$$

Therefore (by Prop. 9, Book v, *Elements of* Euclid), $QT^2 = 4SA \cdot QR$. Multiply these equals by $\dfrac{SP^2}{QR}$, and $\dfrac{SP^2 \cdot QT^2}{QR}$ will become equal to $SP^2 \cdot 4SA$: and therefore (by Cor. I and v, Prop. 6), the centripetal force is inversely as $SP^2 \cdot 4SA$; that is, because $4SA$ is given, inversely as the square of the distance SP.   Q.E.I.

COR. I. From the three last Propositions it follows, that if any body P goes from the place P with any velocity in the direction of any right line PR, and at the same time is urged by the action of a centripetal force that is inversely proportional to the square of the distance of the places from the centre, the body will move in one of the conic sections, having its focus in the centre of force; and conversely. For the focus, the point of contact, and the position of the tangent, being given, a conic section may be described, which at that point shall have a given curvature. But the curvature is given from the centripetal force and velocity of the body being given; and two orbits, touching one the other, cannot be described by the same centripetal force and the same velocity.

COR. II. If the velocity with which the body goes from its place P is such, that in any infinitely small moment of time the small line PR may be thereby described; and the centripetal force such as in the same time to move the same body through the space QR; the body will move in one of the conic sections, whose principal latus rectum is the quantity $\dfrac{QT^2}{QR}$ in its ultimate state, when the small lines PR, QR are diminished *in infinitum*. In these Corollaries I consider the circle as an ellipse; and I except the case where the body descends to the centre in a right line.

PROPOSITION 14. THEOREM 6

If several bodies revolve about one common centre, and the centripetal force is inversely as the square of the distance of places from the centre: I say, that the principal latera recta of their orbits are as the squares of the areas, which the bodies by radii drawn to the centre describe in the same time.

For (by Cor. II, Prop. 13) the latus rectum L is equal to the quantity $\dfrac{QT^2}{QR}$ in its ultimate state when the points P and Q coincide. But the small line QR in a given time is as the generating centripetal force; that is (by supposition), inversely as SP^2. and therefore $\dfrac{QT^2}{QR}$ is as $QT^2 \cdot SP^2$; that is, the latus rectum L is as the square of the area $QT \cdot SP$.   Q.E.D.

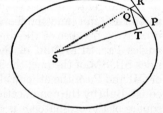

COR. Hence the whole area of the ellipse, and the rectangle under the axes, which is proportional to it, is as the product of the square root of the latus rectum, and the periodic time. For the whole area is as the area $QT \cdot SP$, described in a given time, multiplied by the periodic time.

PROPOSITION 15. THEOREM 7

The same things being supposed, I say, that the periodic times in ellipses are as the ³⁄₂th power (in ratione sesquiplicata) *of their greater axes.*

For the lesser axis is a mean proportional between the greater axis and the latus rectum; and, therefore, the product of the axes is equal to the product of the square root of the latus rectum and the $^3\!/_2$th power of the greater axis. But the product of the axes (by Cor., Prop. 14) varies as the product of the square root of the latus rectum, and the periodic time. Divide both sides by the square root of the latus rectum and it follows that the $^3\!/_2$th power of the greater axis varies as the periodic time.   Q.E.D.

Cor. Therefore the periodic times in ellipses are the same as in circles whose diameters are equal to the greater axes of the ellipses.

PROPOSITION 16. THEOREM 8

The same things being supposed, and right lines being drawn to the bodies that shall touch the orbits, and perpendiculars being let fall on those tangents from the common focus: I say, that the velocities of the bodies vary inversely as the perpendiculars and directly as the square roots of the principal latera recta.

From the focus S draw SY perpendicular to the tangent PR, and the velocity of the body P varies inversely as the square root of the quantity $\dfrac{SY^2}{L}$. For that

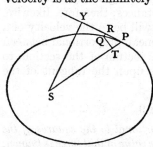

velocity is as the infinitely small arc PQ described in a given moment of time, that is (by Lem. 7), as the tangent PR; that is (because of the proportion, PR : QT = SP : SY), as $\dfrac{SP \cdot QT}{SY}$; or inversely as SY, and directly as SP·QT; but SP·QT is as the area described in the given time, that is (by Prop. 14), as the square root of the latus rectum.   Q.E.D.

Cor. i. The principal latera recta vary as the squares of the perpendiculars and the squares of the velocities.

Cor. ii. The velocities of bodies, in their greatest and least distances from the common focus, are inversely as the distances and directly as the square root of the principal latera recta. For those perpendiculars are now the distances.

Cor. iii. And therefore the velocity in a conic section, at its greatest or least distance from the focus, is to the velocity in a circle, at the same distance from the centre, as the square root of the principal latus rectum is to the square root of double that distance.

Cor. iv. The velocities of the bodies revolving in ellipses, at their mean distances from the common focus, are the same as those of bodies revolving in circles, at the same distances; that is (by Cor. vi, Prop. 4), inversely as the square root of the distances. For the perpendiculars are now the lesser semi-axes, and these are as mean proportionals between the distances and the latera recta. Let the inverse of this ratio [of the minor semiaxes] be multiplied by the square root of the direct ratio of the latera recta, and we shall have the square root of the inverse ratio of the distances.

Cor. v. In the same figure, or even in different figures, whose principal latera recta are equal, the velocity of a body is inversely as the perpendicular let fall from the focus on the tangent.

Cor. vi. In a parabola, the velocity is inversely as the square root of the ratio of the distance of the body from the focus of the figure; it is more variable in the ellipse, and less in the hyperbola, than according to this ratio. For (by Cor. ii, Lem. 14) the perpendicular let fall from the focus on the tangent of a parabola is as the square root of the distance. In the hyperbola the perpendicular is less variable; in the ellipse, more.

COR. VII. In a parabola, the velocity of a body at any distance from the focus is to the velocity of a body revolving in a circle, at the same distance from the centre, as the square root of the ratio of the number 2 to 1; in the ellipse it is less, and in the hyperbola greater, than according to this ratio. For (by Cor. II of this Prop.) the velocity at the vertex of a parabola is in this ratio, and (by Cor. VI of this Prop. and Prop. 4) the same proportion holds in all distances. And hence, also, in a parabola, the velocity is everywhere equal to the velocity of a body revolving in a circle at half the distance; in the ellipse it is less, and in the hyperbola greater.

COR. VIII. The velocity of a body revolving in any conic section is to the velocity of a body revolving in a circle, at the distance of half the principal latus rectum of the section, as that distance to the perpendicular let fall from the focus on the tangent of the section. This appears from Cor. V.

COR. IX. Wherefore, since (by Cor. VI, Prop. 4) the velocity of a body revolving in this circle is to the velocity of another body revolving in any other circle, inversely as the square root of the ratio of the distances; therefore, likewise, the velocity of a body revolving in a conic section will be to the velocity of a body revolving in a circle at the same distance as a mean proportional between that common distance, and half the principal latus rectum of the section, to the perpendicular let fall from the common focus upon the tangent of the section.

PROPOSITION 17. PROBLEM 9

Supposing the centripetal force to be inversely proportional to the squares of the distances of places from the centre, and that the absolute value of that force is known; it is required to determine the line which a body will describe that is let go from a given place with a given velocity in the direction of a given right line.

Let the centripetal force tending to the point S be such as will make the body p revolve in any given orbit pq; and suppose the velocity of this body in the

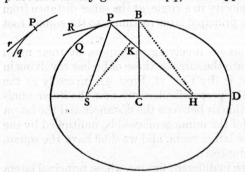

place p is known. Then from the place P suppose the body P to be let go with a given velocity in the direction of the line PR; but by virtue of a centripetal force to be immediately turned aside from that right line into the conic section PQ. This, the right line PR will therefore touch in P. Suppose likewise that the right line pr touches the orbit pq in p; and if from S you suppose perpendiculars let fall on those tangents, the principal latus rectum of the conic section (by Cor. I, Prop. 16) will be to the principal latus rectum of that orbit in a ratio compounded of the squared ratio of the perpendiculars, and the squared ratio of the velocities; and is therefore given. Let this latus rectum be L; the focus S of the conic section is also given. Let the angle RPH be the supplement of the angle RPS, and the line PH, in which the other focus H is placed, is given by position. Let fall SK perpendicular on PH, and erect the conjugate semiaxis BC; this done, we shall have

$$SP^2 - 2PH \cdot PK + PH^2 = SH^2 = 4CH^2 = 4(BH^2 - BC^2) =$$
$$(SP + PH)^2 - L(SP + PH) = SP^2 + 2PS \cdot PH + PH^2 - L(SP + PH).$$

Add on both sides

$$2PK \cdot PH - SP^2 - PH^2 + L(SP + PH),$$

and we shall have

$$L(SP + PH) = 2PS \cdot PH + 2PK \cdot PH, \text{ or}$$
$$(SP + PH) : PH = 2 (SP + KP) : L.$$

Hence PH is given both in length and position. That is, if the velocity of the body in P is such that the latus rectum L is less than 2SP+2KP, PH will lie on the same side of the tangent PR with the line SP; and therefore the figure will be an ellipse, which from the given foci S, H, and the principal axis SP+PH, is given also. But if the velocity of the body is so great, that the latus rectum L becomes equal to 2SP+2KP, the length PH will be infinite; and therefore, the figure will be a parabola, which has its axis SH parallel to the line PK, and is thence given. But if the body goes from its place P with a yet greater velocity, the length PH is to be taken on the other side the tangent; and so the tangent passing between the foci, the figure will be an hyperbola having its principal axis equal to the difference of the lines SP and PH, and thence is given. For if the body, in these cases, revolves in a conic section so found, it is demonstrated in Props. 11, 12, and 13, that the centripetal force will be inversely as the square of the distance of the body from the centre of force S; and therefore we have rightly determined the line PQ, which a body let go from a given place P with a given velocity, and in the direction of the right line PR given by position, would describe with such a force.   Q.E.F.

Cor. i. Hence in every conic section, from the principal vertex D, the latus rectum L, and the focus S given, the other focus H is given, by taking DH to DS as the latus rectum to the difference between the latus rectum and 4DS. For the proportion

$$SP + PH : PH = 2SP + 2KP : L$$

becomes, in the case of this Corollary,

$$DS + DH : DH = 4DS : L,$$
$$\text{and } DS : DH = 4DS - L : L.$$

Cor. ii. Whence if the velocity of a body in the principal vertex D is given, the orbit may be readily found; namely, by taking its latus rectum to twice the distance DS, in the squared ratio of this given velocity to the velocity of a body revolving in a circle at the distance DS (by Cor. iii, Prop. 16), and then taking DH to DS as the latus rectum to the difference between the latus rectum and 4DS.

Cor. iii. Hence also if a body move in any conic section, and if forced out of its orbit by any impulse, you may discover the orbit in which it will afterwards pursue its course. For by compounding the proper motion of the body with that motion, which the impulse alone would generate, you will have the motion with which the body will go off from a given place of impulse in the direction of a right line given in position.

Cor. iv. And if that body is continually disturbed by the action of some foreign force, we may nearly know its course, by collecting the changes which that force introduces in some points, and estimating the continual changes it will undergo in the intermediate places, from the analogy that appears in the progress of the series.

SCHOLIUM

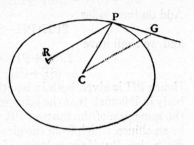

If a body P, by means of a centripetal force tending to any given point R, move in the perimeter of any given conic section whose centre is C; and the law of the centripetal force is required: draw CG parallel to the radius RP, and meeting the tangent PG of the orbit in G; and the force required (by Cor. I and Schol., Prop. 10, and Cor. III, Prop. 7) will be as $\dfrac{CG^3}{RP^2}$.

SECTION IV

THE FINDING OF ELLIPTIC, PARABOLIC, AND HYPERBOLIC ORBITS, FROM THE FOCUS GIVEN

LEMMA 15

If from the two foci S, H, *of any ellipse or hyperbola, we draw to any third point* V *the right lines* SV, HV, *whereof one* HV *is equal to the principal axis of the figure,*

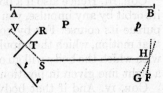

that is, to the axis in which the foci are situated, the other, SV, *is bisected in* T *by the perpendicular* TR *let fall upon it; that perpendicular* TR *will somewhere touch the conic section: and,* vice versa, *if it does touch it,* HV *will be equal to the principal axis of the figure.*

For, let the perpendicular TR cut the right line HV, produced, if need be, in R; and join SR. Because TS, TV are equal, therefore the right lines SR, VR, as well as the angles TRS, TRV, will be also equal. Whence the point R will be in the conic section, and the perpendicular TR will touch the same; and the contrary.　　　　　　　　　　　　　　　　　　　　　　　Q.E.D.

PROPOSITION 18. PROBLEM 10

From a focus and the principal axes given, to describe elliptic and hyperbolic curves which shall pass through given points, and touch right lines given by position.

Let S be the common focus of the figures; AB the length of the principal axis of any conic; P a point through which the conic should pass; and TR a right line which it should touch. About the centre P, with the radius AB−SP, if the orbit is an ellipse, or AB+SP, if the orbit is an hyperbola, describe the circle HG. On the tangent TR let fall the perpendicular ST, and produce the same to V, so that TV may be equal to ST; and about V as a centre with the interval AB describe the circle FH. In this manner, whether two points P, *p*, are given, or two tangents TR, *tr*, or a point P and a tangent TR, we are to describe two circles. Let H be their common intersection, and from the foci S, H, with the given axis describe the conic: I say, the thing is done. For (because PH+SP in the ellipse, and PH−SP in the hyperbola, is equal to the axis) the described conic will pass through the point P, and (by the preceding Lemma) will touch the right line TR. And by the same argument it will either pass through the two points P, p, or touch the two right lines TR, tr.   Q.E.F.

PROPOSITION 19. PROBLEM 11

About a given focus, to describe a parabola which shall pass through given points and touch right lines given by position.

Let S be the focus, P a point, and TR a tangent of the curve to be described. About P as a centre, with the radius PS, describe the circle FG. From the focus let fall ST perpendicular on the tangent, and produce the same to V, so as TV

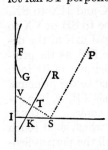

may be equal to ST. After the same manner another circle fg is to be described, if another point p is given; or another point v is to be found, if another tangent tr is given; then draw the right line IF, which shall touch the two circles FG, fg, if two points P, p are given; or pass through the two points V, v, if two tangents TR, tr, are given; or touch the circle FG, and pass through the point V, if the point P and the tangent TR are given. On FI let fall the perpendicular SI, and bisect the same in K; and with the axis SK and principal vertex K describe a parabola: I say, the thing is done. For this parabola (because SK is equal to IK, and SP to FP) will pass through the point P; and (by Cor. III, Lem. 14) because ST is equal to TV, and STR a right angle, it will touch the right line TR.   Q.E.F.

PROPOSITION 20. PROBLEM 12

About a given focus, to describe any given conic which shall pass through given points and touch right lines given by position.

CASE 1. About the focus S it is required to describe a conic ABC, passing through two points B, C. Because the conic is given in kind, the ratio of the principal axis to the distance of the foci will be given. In that ratio take KB to BS, and LC to CS. About the centres B, C, with the intervals BK, CL, describe two circles; and on the right line KL, that touches the same in K and L, let fall the perpendicular SG; which

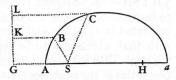

cut in A and a, so that GA may be to AS, and Ga to aS, as KB to BS; and with the axis Aa, and vertices A, a, describe a conic: I say, the thing is done. For let H be the other focus of the described figure, and seeing that GA : AS=Ga : aS, we shall have

Ga−GA : aS−AS=GA : AS, or Aa : SH=GA : AS, and therefore GA and AS are in the ratio which the principal axis of the figure to be described has to the distance of its foci; and therefore the described figure is of the same kind with the figure which was to be described. And since KB to BS, and LC to CS, are in the same ratio, this figure will pass through the points B, C, as is manifest from the conic sections.

CASE 2. About the focus S it is required to describe a conic which shall some-

where touch two right lines TR, *tr*. From the focus on those tangents let fall
the perpendiculars ST, S*t*, which produce to V, *v*, so that TV, *tv* may be equal
to TS, *t*S. Bisect V*v* in O, and erect the indefinite perpendicular OH, and cut
the right line VS infinitely produced in K and *k*,
so that VK be to KS, and V*k* to *k*S, as the principal axis of the conic to be described is to the
distance of its foci. On the diameter K*k* describe
a circle cutting OH in H; and with the foci S, H,
and principal axis equal to VH, describe a
conic: I say, the thing is done. For bisecting K*k*
in X, and joining HX, HS, HV, H*v*, because VK
is to KS as V*k* to *k*S; and by composition, as

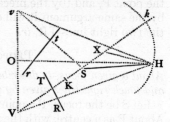

VK+V*k* to KS+*k*S; and by subtraction, as V*k*−VK to *k*S−KS, that is, as
2VX to 2KX, and 2KX to 2SX, and therefore as VX to HX and HX to SX,
the triangles VXH, HXS will be similar; therefore VH will be to SH as VX to
XH; and therefore as VK to KS. Wherefore VH, the principal axis of the described conic, has the same ratio to SH, the distance of the foci, as the principal axis of the conic which was to be described has to the distance of its foci;
and is therefore of the same kind. And seeing VH, *v*H are equal to the principal
axis, and VS, *v*S are perpendicularly bisected by the right lines TR, *tr*, it is evident (by Lem. 15) that those right lines touch the described conic.   Q.E.F.

CASE 3. About the focus S it is required to describe a conic which shall touch
a right line TR in a given point R. On the right line TR let fall the perpendicu-

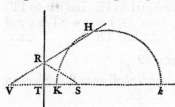

lar ST, which produce to V, so that TV may
be equal to ST; join VR, and cut the right
line VS indefinitely produced in K and *k*, so
that VK may be to SK, and V*k* to S*k*, as the
principal axis of the ellipse to be described to
the distance of its foci; and on the diameter
K*k* describing a circle, cut the right line VR
produced in H; then with the foci S, H, and
principal axis equal to VH, describe a conic: I say, the thing is done. For
VH : SH = VK : SK, and therefore as the principal axis of the conic which was
to be described to the distance of its foci (as appears from what we have demonstrated in Case 2); and therefore the described conic is of the same kind
with that which was to be described; but that the right line TR, by which
the angle VRS is bisected, touches the conic in the point R, is certain from the
properties of the conic sections.   Q.E.F.

CASE 4. About the focus S it is required to describe a conic APB that shall
touch a right line TR, and pass through any given point P without the tangent,
and shall be similar to the figure *apb*, described with the principal axis *ab*, and
foci *s*, *h*. On the tangent TR let fall the perpendicular ST, which produce to V,
so that TV may be equal to ST; and making the angles *hsq*, *shq*, equal to the
angles VSP, SVP, about *q* as a centre, and with a radius which shall be to *ab* as
SP to VS, describe a circle cutting the figure *apb* in *p*. Join *sp*, and draw SH
such that it may be to *sh* as SP is to *sp*, and may make the angle PSH equal to
the angle *psh*, and the angle VSH equal to the angle *psq*. Then with the foci
S, H, and principal axis AB, equal to the distance VH, describe a conic section:
I say, the thing is done; for if *sv* is drawn so that it shall be to *sp* as *sh* is to *sq*,

and shall make the angle *vsp* equal to the angle *hsq*, and the angle *vsh* equal to the angle *psq*, the triangles *svh*, *spq*, will be similar, and therefore *vh* will be to *pq* as *sh* is to *sq*; that is (because of the similar triangles VSP, *hsq*), as VS is to SP, or as *ab* to *pq*. Wherefore *vh* and *ab* are equal. But, because of the similar

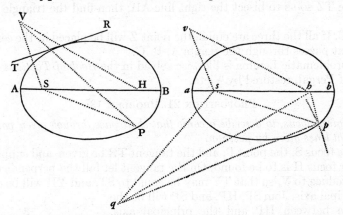

triangles VSH, *vsh*, VH is to SH as *vh* to *sh*; that is, the axis of the conic section now described is to the distance of its foci as the axis *ab* to the distance of the foci *sh*; and therefore the figure now described is similar to the figure *aph*. But, because the triangle PSH is similar to the triangle *psh*, this figure passes through the point P; and because VH is equal to its axis, and VS is perpendicularly bisected by the right line TR, the said figure touches the right line TR. Q.E.F.

LEMMA 16

From three given points to draw to a fourth point that is not given three right lines whose differences either shall be given or are zero.

CASE 1. Let the given points be A, B, C, and Z the fourth point which we are to find; because of the given difference of the lines AZ, BZ, the locus of the point Z will be an hyperbola whose foci are A and B, and whose principal axis

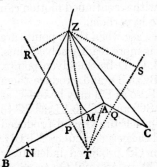

is the given difference. Let that axis be MN. Taking PM to MA as MN to AB, erect PR perpendicular to AB, and let fall ZR perpendicular to PR; then from the nature of the hyperbola, ZR : AZ = MN : AB. And by the like argument, the locus of the point Z will be another hyperbola, whose foci are A, C, and whose principal axis is the difference between AZ and CZ; and QS a perpendicular on AC may be drawn, to which (QS) if from any point Z of this hyperbola a perpendicular ZS is let fall, (this ZS) shall be to AZ as the difference between AZ and CZ is to AC. Wherefore the ratios of ZR and ZS to AZ are given, and consequently the ratio of ZR to ZS one to the other; and therefore if the right lines RP, SQ, meet in T, and TZ and TA are drawn, the figure TRZS will be given in kind, and the right line TZ, in which the point Z is somewhere placed, will be given in position. There will be given also the right line TA, and the angle ATZ; and because the ratios of AZ and TZ to ZS are given, their ratio to each other is given also; and thence will be given likewise the triangle ATZ, whose vertex is the point Z.   Q.E.I.

CASE 2. If two of the three lines, for example AZ and BZ, are equal, draw the right line TZ so as to bisect the right line AB; then find the triangle ATZ as above.   Q.E.I.

CASE 3. If all the three are equal, the point Z will be placed in the centre of a circle that passes through the points A, B, C.   Q.E.I.

This problematic Lemma is likewise solved in the *Book of Tactions* of Apollonius [of Perga], restored by Vieta.

PROPOSITION 21. PROBLEM 13

About a given focus, to describe a conic that shall pass through given points and touch right lines given by position.

Let the focus S, the point P, and the tangent TR be given, and suppose that the other focus H is to be found. On the tangent let fall the perpendicular ST, which produce to Y, so that TY may be equal to ST, and YH will be equal to the principal axis. Join SP, HP, and SP will be the difference between HP and the principal axis. After this manner, if more tangents TR are given, or more points P, we shall always determine as many lines YH, or PH, drawn from the said points Y or P, to the focus H, which either shall be equal to the axes, or differ from the axes by given lengths

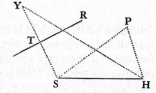

SP; and therefore which shall either be equal among themselves, or shall have given differences; from whence (by the preceding Lemma), that other focus H is given. But having the foci and the length of the axis (which is either YH, or, if the conic be an ellipse, PH+SP; or PH−SP, if it be an hyperbola), the conic is given.   Q.E.I.

SCHOLIUM

When the conic is an hyperbola, I do not include its conjugate hyperbola under the name of this conic. For a body going on with a continued motion can never pass out of one hyperbola into its conjugate hyperbola.

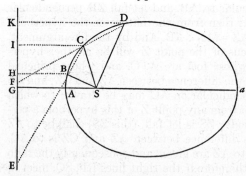

The case when three points are given is more readily solved thus. Let B, C, D be the given points. Join BC, CD, and produce them to E, F, so as EB may be to EC as SB to SC; and FC to FD as SC to SD. On EF drawn and produced let fall the perpendiculars SG, BH, and in GS produced indefinitely take GA to AS, and G*a* to *a*S, as HB is to BS: then A will be the vertex, and A*a* the principal axis of the conic; which, according as GA is greater than, equal to, or less than AS, will be either an ellipse, a parabola, or an hyperbola; the point *a* in the first case falling on the same side of the line GF as the point A; in the second, going off to an infinite distance; in the third, falling on the other side of the line GF. For if on GF the perpendiculars CI, DK are let fall, IC will be to HB as EC to EB; that is, as SC to SB; and by permutation, IC to SC as HB to SB, or as GA to SA. And, by the like argument, we may prove that KD is to SD in the same ratio. Wherefore the points B, C, D lie in a conic section described about the focus S, in such manner that all the right lines drawn from the focus S to the several points of the section, and the perpendiculars let fall from the same points on the right line GF, are in that given ratio.

That excellent geometer M. de la Hire has solved this Problem much after the same way, in his *Conics*, Prop. 25, Book VIII.

SECTION V

HOW THE ORBITS ARE TO BE FOUND WHEN NEITHER FOCUS IS GIVEN

LEMMA 17

If from any point P of a given conic section, to the four produced sides AB, CD, AC, DB of any trapezium ABDC inscribed in that section, as many right lines PQ, PR, PS, PT are drawn in given angles, each line to each side; the rectangle PQ·PR of those on the opposite sides AB, CD, will be to the rectangle PS·PT of those on the other two opposite sides AC, BD, in a given ratio.

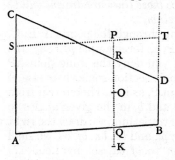

CASE 1. Let us suppose, first, that the lines drawn to one pair of opposite sides are parallel to either of the other sides; as PQ and PR to the side AC, and PS and PT to the side AB. And further, that one pair of the opposite sides, as AC and BD, are parallel between themselves; then the right line which bisects those parallel sides will be one of the diameters of the conic section, and will likewise bisect RQ. Let O be the point in which RQ is bisected, and PO will be an ordinate to that diameter. Produce PO to K, so that OK may be equal to PO, and OK will be an ordinate on the other side of that diameter. Since, therefore, the points A, B, P, and K are placed in the conic section, and PK cuts AB in a given angle, the rectangle PQ·QK (by Props. 17, 19, 21, and 23, Book III, *Conics* of Apollonius) will be to the rectangle AQ·QB in a given ratio. But QK and PR are equal, as being the differences of the equal lines OK, OP, and OQ, OR; whence the rectangles PQ·QK and PQ·PR are equal; and therefore the rectangle PQ·PR is to the rectangle AQ·QB, that is, to the rectangle PS·PT, in a given ratio. Q.E.D.

CASE 2. Let us next suppose that the opposite sides AC and BD of the trapezium are not parallel. Draw B*d* parallel to AC, and meeting as well the right line ST in *t*, as the conic section in *d*. Join C*d* cutting PQ in *r*, and draw DM parallel to PQ, cutting C*d* in M, and AB in N. Then (because of the similar triangles BTt, DBN) Bt or PQ : Tt = DN : NB. And so Rr : AQ or PS = DM : AN. Wherefore, by multiplying the antecedents by the antecedents, and the consequents by the consequents, as the rectangle PQ $\cdot$ Rr is to the rectangle PS $\cdot$ Tt, so will the rectangle DN $\cdot$ DM be to the rectangle NA $\cdot$ NB; and (by Case 1) so is the rectangle PQ $\cdot$ Pr to the rectangle PS $\cdot$ Pt, and, by division, so is the rectangle PQ $\cdot$ PR to the rectangle PS $\cdot$ PT.　　　　Q.E.D.

CASE 3. Let us suppose, lastly, the four lines PQ, PR, PS, PT not to be parallel to the sides AC, AB, but any way in-clined to them. In their place draw Pq, Pr, par-allel to AC; and Ps, Pt parallel to AB; and be-cause the angles of the triangles PQq, PRr, PSs, PTt are given, the ratios of PQ to Pq, PR to Pr, PS to Ps, PT to Pt will be also given; and there-fore the compounded ratios PQ $\cdot$ PR to Pq $\cdot$ Pr, and PS $\cdot$ PT to Ps $\cdot$ Pt are given. But from what we have demonstrated before, the ratio of Pq $\cdot$ Pr to Ps $\cdot$ Pt is given; and therefore also the ratio of PQ $\cdot$ PR to PS $\cdot$ PT.　　　　Q.E.D.

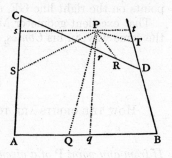

LEMMA 18

The same things supposed, if the rectangle PQ $\cdot$ PR *of the lines drawn to the two opposite sides of the trapezium is to the rectangle* PS $\cdot$ PT *of those drawn to the other two sides in a given ratio, the point* P, *from whence those lines are drawn, will be placed in a conic section described about the trapezium.*

Conceive a conic section to be described passing through the points A, B, C, D, and any one of the infinite number of points P, as for example p: I say, the point P will be always placed in this section. If you deny the thing, join AP

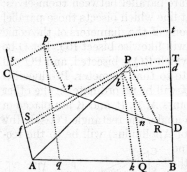

cutting this conic section somewhere else, if possible, than in P, as in b. Therefore if from those points p and b, in the given angles to the sides of the trapezium, we draw the right lines pq, pr, ps, pt, and bk, bn, bf, bd, we shall have, as $bk \cdot bn$ to $bf \cdot bd$, so (by Lem. 17) $pq \cdot pr$ to $ps \cdot pt$; and so (by supposition) PQ $\cdot$ PR to PS $\cdot$ PT. And because of the sim-ilar trapezia bkAf, PQAS, as bk to bf, so PQ to PS. Wherefore by dividing the terms of the preceding proportion by the correspond-ent terms of this, we shall have bn to bd as PR to PT. And therefore the equiangular trapezia Dnbd, DRPT, are similar, and consequently their diagonals Db, DP do coincide. Wherefore b falls in the intersection of the right lines AP, DP, and consequently coincides with the point P. And therefore the point P, wherever it is taken, falls within the assigned conic section.　　　　Q.E.D.

COR. Hence if three right lines PQ, PR, PS are drawn from a common point P, to as many other right lines given in position, AB, CD, AC, each to each, in as many angles respectively given, and the rectangle PQ $\cdot$ PR under any two of the lines drawn be to the square of the third PS in a given ratio; the point P, from which the right lines are drawn, will be placed in a conic section that touches the lines AB, CD in A and C; and the contrary. For the position of the three right lines AB, CD, AC remaining the same, let the line BD approach to and coincide with the line AC; then let the line PT come likewise to coincide with the line PS; and the rectangle PS·PT will become PS², and the right lines AB, CD, which before did cut the curve in the points A and B, C and D, can no longer cut, but only touch, the curve in those coinciding points.

SCHOLIUM

In this Lemma, the name of conic section is to be understood in a large sense, comprehending as well the rectilinear section through the vertex of the cone, as the circular one parallel to the base. For if the point p happens to be in a right line, by which the points A and D, or C and B are joined, the conic section will be changed into two right lines, one of which is that right line upon which the point p falls, and the other is a right line that joins the other two of the four points. If the two opposite angles of the trapezium taken together are equal to two right angles, and if the four lines PQ, PR, PS, PT are drawn to the sides thereof at right angles, or any other equal angles, and the rectangle PQ·PR under two of the lines drawn PQ and PR, is equal to the rectangle PS·PT under the other two PS and PT, the conic section will become a circle. And the same thing will happen if the four lines are drawn in any angles, and the rectangle PQ·PR, under one pair of the lines drawn, is to the rectangle PS·PT under the other pair as the rectangle under the sines of the angles S, T, in which the two last lines PS, PT are drawn, to the rectangle under the sines of the angles Q, R, in which the first two PQ, PR are drawn. In all other cases the locus of the point P will be one of the three figures which pass commonly by the name of the conic sections. But in place of the trapezium ABCD, we may substitute a quadrilateral figure whose two opposite sides cross one another like diagonals. And one or two of the four points A, B, C, D may be supposed to be removed to an infinite distance, by which means the sides of the figure which converge to those points, will become parallel; and in this case the conic section will pass through the other points, and will go the same way as the parallels *in infinitum*.

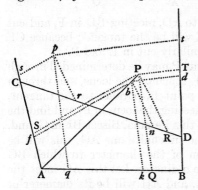

LEMMA 19

To find a point P *from which if four right lines* PQ, PR, PS, PT *are drawn to as many other right lines* AB, CD, AC, BD, *given by position, each to each, at given angles, the rectangle* PQ·PR, *under any two of the lines drawn, shall be to the rectangle* PS·PT, *under the other two, in a given ratio.*

Suppose the lines AB, CD, to which the two right lines PQ, PR, containing one of the rectangles, are drawn to meet two other lines, given by position, in the points A, B, C, D. From one of those, as A, draw any right line AH, in which you would find the point P. Let this cut the opposite lines BD, CD, in H and I; and, because all the angles of the figure are given, the ratio of PQ to PA,

and PA to PS, and therefore of PQ to PS, will be also given. This ratio taken as
a divisor of the given ratio of PQ·PR to PS·PT. gives the ratio of PR to PT;
and multiplying the given ratios of PI to
PR, and PT to PH, the ratio of PI to PH,
and therefore the point P, will be given.
Q.E.I.

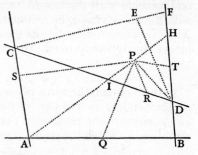

Cor. i. Hence also a tangent may be
drawn to any point D of the locus of all the
points P. For the chord PD, where the
points P and D meet, that is, where AH is
drawn through the point D, becomes a
tangent. In which case the ultimate ratio
of the evanescent lines IP and PH will be
found as above. Therefore draw CF parallel to AD, meeting BD in F, and cut
it in E in the same ultimate ratio, then DE will be the tangent; because CF
and the evanescent IH are parallel, and similarly cut in E and P.

Cor. ii. Hence also the locus of all the points P may be determined. Through
any of the points A, B, C, D, as A, draw AE touching the locus, and through

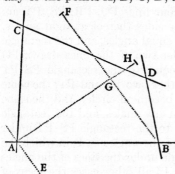

any other point B, parallel to the tangent,
draw BF meeting the locus in F; and find the
point F by this Lemma. Bisect BF in G, and,
drawing the indefinite line AG, this will be
the position of the diameter to which BG
and FG are ordinates. Let this AG meet the
locus in H, and AH will be its diameter or
latus transversum, to which the latus rectum
will be as BG^2 to AG·GH. If AG nowhere
meets the locus, the line AH being infinite,
the locus will be a parabola; and its latus
rectum corresponding to the diameter AG

will be $\frac{BG^2}{AG}$. But if it does meet it anywhere, the locus will be an hyperbola,
when the points A and H are placed on the same side of the point G; and an
ellipse, if the point G falls between the points A and H; unless, perhaps, the
angle AGB is a right angle, and at the same time BG^2 equal to the rectangle
GA·GH, in which case the locus will be a circle.

And so we have given in this Corollary a solution of that famous Problem
of the ancients concerning four lines, begun by Euclid, and carried on by
Apollonius; and this not an analytical calculus but a geometrical composition,
such as the ancients required.

LEMMA 20

*If the two opposite angular points A and P of any parallelogram ASPQ touch any
conic section in the points A and P; and the sides AQ, AS of one of those angles,
indefinitely produced, meet the same conic section in B and C; and from the points
of meeting B and C to any fifth point D of the conic section, two right lines BD,
CD are drawn meeting the two other sides PS, PQ of the parallelogram, indefinitely
produced in T and R; the parts PR and PT, cut off from the sides, will always be
one to the other in a given ratio. And conversely, if those parts cut off are one to the*

other in a given ratio, the locus of the point D *will be a conic section passing through the four points* A, B, C, P.

CASE 1. Join BP, CP, and from the point D draw the two right lines DG, DE, of which the first DG shall be parallel to AB, and meet PB, PQ, CA, in H,

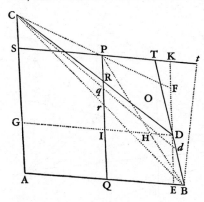

I, G; and the other DE shall be parallel to AC, and meet PC, PS, AB, in F, K, E; and (by Lem. 17) the rectangle DE·DF will be to the rectangle DG·DH in a given ratio. But PQ is to DE (or IQ) as PB to HB, and consequently as PT to DH; and by permutation PQ is to PT as DE to DH. Likewise PR is to DF as RC to DC, and therefore as (IG or) PS to DG; and by permutation PR is to PS as DF to DG; and, by compounding those ratios, the rectangle PQ·PR will be to the rectangle PS·PT as the rectangle DE·DF is to the rectangle DG·DH, and consequently in a given ratio. But PQ and PS are given, and therefore the ratio of PR to PT is given.

Q.E.D.

CASE 2. But if PR and PT are supposed to be in a given ratio one to the other, then by going back again, by a like reasoning, it will follow that the rectangle DE·DF is to the rectangle DG·DH in a given ratio; and so the point D (by Lem. 18) will lie in a conic section passing through the points A, B, C, P, as its locus.

Q.E.D.

COR. I. Hence if we draw BC cutting PQ in r and in PT take P*t* to P*r* in the same ratio which PT has to PR; then B*t* will touch the conic section in the point B. For suppose the point D to coalesce with the point B, so that the chord BD vanishing, BT shall become a tangent; and CD and BT will coincide with CB and B*t*.

COR. II. And, *vice versa*, if B*t* is a tangent, and the lines BD, CD meet in any point D of a conic section, PR will be to PT as P*r* to P*t*. And, on the contrary, if PR is to PT as P*r* to P*t*, then BD and CD will meet in some point D of a conic section.

COR. III. One conic section cannot cut another conic section in more than four points. For, if it is possible, let two conic sections pass through the five points A, B, C, P, O; and let the right line BD cut them in the points D, *d*, and the right line C*d* cut the right line PQ in *q*. Therefore PR is to PT as P*q* to PT: whence PR and P*q* are equal one to the other, against the supposition.

LEMMA 21

If two movable and indefinite right lines BM, CM *drawn through given points* B, C, *as poles, do by their point of meeting* M *describe a third right line* MN *given by position; and other two indefinite right lines* BD, CD *are drawn, making with the former two at those given points* B, C, *given angles,* MBD, MCD: *I say, that those two right lines* BD, CD *will by their point of meeting* D *describe a conic section passing through the points* B, C. *And conversely, if the right lines* BD, CD *do by their point of meeting* D *describe a conic section passing through the given points* B, C, A, *and the angle* DBM *is always equal to the given angle* ABC, *as well as the angle* DCM *always equal to the given angle* ACB, *the point* M *will lie in a right line given by position, as its locus.*

For in the right line MN let a point N be given, and when the movable point M falls on the immovable point N, let the movable point D fall on an immovable point P. Join CN, BN, CP, BP, and from the point P draw the right lines PT, PR meeting BD, CD in T and R, and making the angle BPT equal to the given angle BNM, and the angle CPR equal to the given angle CNM. Wherefore since (by supposition) the angles MBD, NBP are equal, as also the angles MCD, NCP, take away the angles NBD and NCD that are common, and there will remain the angles

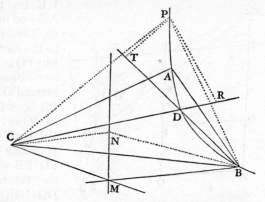

NBM and PBT, NCM and PCR equal; and therefore the triangles NBM, PBT are similar, as also the triangles NCM, PCR. Wherefore PT is to NM as PB to NB; and PR to NM as PC to NC. But the points B, C, N, P are immovable: wherefore PT and PR have a given ratio to NM, and consequently a given ratio between themselves; and therefore, (by Lem. 20) the point D wherein the movable right lines BT and CR continually concur, will be placed in a conic section passing through the points B, C, P.   Q.E.D.

And conversely, if the movable point D lies in a conic section passing through the given points B, C, A; and the angle DBM is always equal to the given

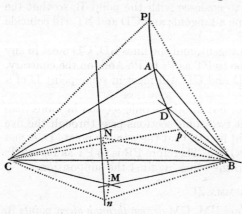

angle ABC, and the angle DCM always equal to the given angle ACB, and when the point D falls successively on any two immovable points *p*, P, of the conic section, the movable point M falls successively on two immovable points *n*, N. Through these points *n*, N, draw the right line *n*N: this line *n*N will be the continual locus of that movable point M. For, if possible, let the point M be placed in any curved line. Therefore the point D will be placed in a conic section passing through the five points B, C, A, *p*, P, when the point M is continually placed in a curved line. But from what was demonstrated before, the point D will be also placed in a conic section passing through the same five points B, C, A, *p*, P, when the point M is continually placed in a right line. Wherefore the two conic sections will both pass through the same five points, against Cor. III, Lem. 20. It is therefore absurd to suppose that the point M is placed in a curved line.   Q.E.D.

PROPOSITION 22. PROBLEM 14

To describe a conic that shall pass through five given points.

Let the five given points be A, B, C, P, D. From any one of them, as A, to
any other two as B, C, which may be called the poles, draw the right lines AB,

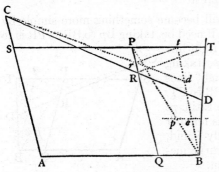

AC, and parallel to those the lines
TPS, PRQ through the fourth point P.
Then from the two poles B, C, draw
through the fifth point D two indefinite lines BDT, CRD, meeting with
the last drawn lines TPS, PRQ (the
former with the former, and the latter
with the latter) in T and R. And then
draw the right line *tr* parallel to TR,
cutting off from the right lines PT,
PR, any segments P*t*,P*r*, proportional
to PT, PR; and if through their ex-
tremities *t*, *r*, and the poles B, C, the right lines B*t*, C*r* are drawn, meeting in
d, that point *d* will be placed in the conic required. For (by Lem. 20) that
point *d* is placed in a conic section passing through the four points A, B, C, P;
and the lines R*r*, T*t* vanishing, the point *d* comes to coincide with the point D.
Wherefore the conic section passes through the five points A, B, C, P, D.

Q.E.D.

The same otherwise.

Of the given points join any three, as A, B, C; and about two of them B, C,
as poles, making the angles ABC, ACB of a given magnitude to revolve, apply

the legs BA, CA, first to the
point D, then to the point P, and
mark the points M, N, in which
the other legs BL, CL intersect
each other in both cases. Draw
the indefinite right line MN, and
let those movable angles revolve
about their poles B, C, in such
manner that the intersection,
which is now supposed to be *m*,
of the legs BL, CL, or BM, CM,
may always fall in that indefinite
right line MN; and the intersection, which is now supposed to
be *d*, of the legs BA, CA, or BD,
CD, will describe the conic required, PAD*d*B. For (by Lem.

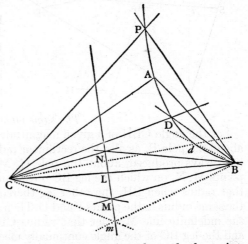

21) the point *d* will be placed in a conic section passing through the points
B, C; and when the point *m* comes to coincide with the points L, M, N, the
point *d* will (by construction) come to coincide with the points A, D, P.
Wherefore a conic section will be described that shall pass through the five
points A, B, C, P, D.   Q.E.F.

COR. I. Hence a right line may be readily drawn which shall be a tangent to the conic in any given point B. Let the point d come to coincide with the point B, and the right line Bd will become the tangent required.

Cor. ii. Hence also may be found the centres, diameters, and latera recta of the conics, as in Cor. ii, Lem. 19.

Scholium

The former of these constructions will become something more simple by joining B, P, and in that line, produced, if need be, taking Bp to BP as PR is to PT; and through p draw the indefinite right line pe parallel to SPT, and in that line pe taking always pe equal to Pr; and draw the right lines Be, Cr to meet in d. For since Pr to Pt, PR to PT, pB to PB, pe to Pt, are all in the same ratio, pe and Pr will be always equal. After this manner the points of the conic are most readily found, unless you would rather describe the curve mechanically, as in the second construction.

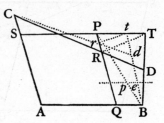

Proposition 23. Problem 15

To describe a conic that shall pass through four given points, and touch a given right line.

Case 1. Suppose that HB is the given tangent, B the point of contact, and C, D, P, the three other given points. Join BC, and draw PS parallel to BH,

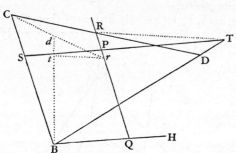

and PQ parallel to BC; complete the parallelogram BSPQ. Draw BD cutting SP in T, and CD cutting PQ in R. Lastly, draw any line tr parallel to TR, cutting off from PQ, PS, the segments Pr, Pt proportional to PR, PT respectively, and draw Cr, Bt; their point of intersection d will (by Lem. 20) always fall on the conic to be described.

The same otherwise.

Let the angle CBH of a given magnitude revolve about the pole B, as also the rectilinear radius DC, both ways produced, about the pole C. Mark the points M, N, on which the leg BC of the angle cuts that radius when BH, the other leg thereof, meets the same radius in the points P and D. Then drawing the indefinite line MN, let that radius CP or CD and the leg BC of the angle continually meet in this line; and the point of meeting of the other leg BH with the radius will delineate the conic required.

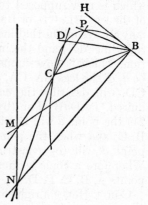

For if in the constructions of the preceding Problem the point A comes to a coincidence with the point B, the lines CA and CB will coincide, and the line AB, in its last situation, will become the tangent BH; and therefore the constructions there set down will become the same with the constructions here described. Wherefore the intersection of the leg BH with the radius will describe a conic section passing through the points C, D, P, and touching the line BH in the point B.   Q.E.F.

Case 2. Suppose the four points B, C, D, P, given, being situated without the tangent HI. Join each two by the lines BD, CP meeting in G, and cutting the tangent in H and I. Cut the tangent in A in such manner that HA may be

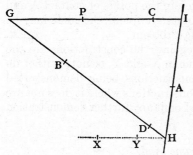

to IA as the product of the mean proportional between CG and GP, and the mean proportional between BH and HD is to the product of the mean proportional between GD and GB, and the mean proportional between PI and IC, and A will be the point of contact. For if HX, a parallel to the right line PI, cuts the conic in any points X and Y, the point A (by the properties of the conic sections) will come to be so placed, that HA² will become to AI² in a ratio that is compounded out of the ratio of the rectangle HX·HY to the rectangle BH·HD, or of the rectangle CG·GP to the rectangle DG·GB; and the ratio of the rectangle BH·HD to the rectangle PI·IC. But after the point of contact A is found, the conic will be described as in the first Case. Q.E.F. But the point A may be taken either between or without the points H and I, upon which account a two-fold conic may be described.

Proposition 24. Problem 16

To describe a conic that shall pass through three given points, and touch two given right lines.

Suppose HI, KL to be the given tangents and B, C, D the given points. Through any two of those points, as B, D, draw the indefinite right line BD meeting the tangents in the points H, K. Then likewise through any other two of these points, as C, D, draw the indefinite right line CD meeting the tangents in the points I, L. Cut the lines drawn in R and S, so that HR may be to KR as the mean proportional between BH and HD is to the mean proportional between BK and KD, and IS to LS as the mean proportional between CI and ID is to the mean proportional between CL and LD. But you may cut, at pleasure, either within or between the points K and H, I and L, or without them. Then draw RS cutting the tangents in A and P, and A and P will be the points of contact. For if A and P are supposed to be the points of contact, situated anywhere else in the tangents, and through any of the points H, I, K, L, as I, situated in either tangent HI, a right line IY is drawn parallel to the other tangent KL, and meeting the curve in X and Y, and in that right line there be taken IZ equal to a mean proportional between IX and IY, the rectangle XI·IY or IZ² will (by the properties of the

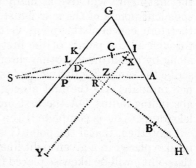

conic sections) be to LP² as the rectangle CI·ID is to the rectangle CL·LD; that is (by the construction), as SI is to SL², and therefore IZ : LP=SI : SL. Wherefore the points S, P, Z are in one right line. Moreover, since the tangents meet in G, the rectangle XI·IY or IZ² will (by the properties of the conic sections) be to IA² as GP² is to GA², and consequently IZ : IA=GP : GA. Wherefore the points P, Z, A lie in one right line, and therefore the points S, P, and A are in one right line. And the same argument will prove that the points R, P, and A are in one right line. Wherefore the points of contact A and P lie in the right line RS. But after these points are found, the conic may be described, as in the first Case of the preceding Problem. Q.E.F.

In this Proposition, and Case 2 of the foregoing, the constructions are the same, whether the right line XY cuts the conic in X and Y, or not; neither do they depend upon that section. But the constructions being demonstrated where that right line does cut the conic, the constructions where it does not are also known; and therefore, for brevity's sake, I omit any further demonstration of them.

LEMMA 22

To transform figures into other figures of the same kind.

Suppose that any figure HGI is to be transformed. Draw, at pleasure, two parallel lines AO, BL, cutting any given third line AB in A and B, and from any point G of the figure, draw out any right line GD, parallel to OA, till it meets the right line AB. Then from any given point O in the line OA, draw to the point D the right line OD, meeting BL in *d*; and from the point of intersection raise the right line *dg* containing any given angle with the right line BL, and having such ratio to O*d* as DG has to OD; and *g* will be the point in the new figure *hgi*, corresponding to the point G. And in like manner the several points of the first figure will give as many correspondent points of the new figure. If we 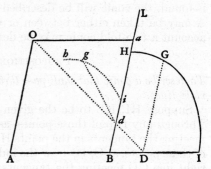 therefore conceive the point G to be carried along by a continual motion through all the points of the first figure, the point *g* will be likewise carried along by a continual motion through all the points of the new figure, and describe the same. For distinction's sake, let us call DG the first ordinate, *dg* the new ordinate, AD the first abscissa, *ad* the new abscissa, O the pole, OD the abscinding radius, OA the first ordinate radius, and O*a* (by which the parallelogram OAB*a* is completed) the new ordinate radius.

I say, then, that if the point G is placed in a given right line, the point *g* will be also placed in a given right line. If the point G is placed in a conic section, the point *g* will be likewise placed in a conic section. And here I understand the circle as one of the conic sections. But further, if the point G is placed in a line of the third analytical order, the point *g* will also be placed in a line of the third order, and so on in curved lines of higher orders. The two lines in which the points G, *g* are placed, will be always of the same analytical order. For as

$$ad : OA = Od : OD = dg : DG = AB : AD;$$ and therefore AD is equal to $\dfrac{OA \cdot AB}{ad}$,

and DG equal to $\dfrac{OA \cdot dg}{ad}$. Now if the point G is placed in a right line, and there-fore, in any equation by which the relation between the abscissa AD and the ordinate GD is expressed, those indetermined lines AD and DG rise no higher than to one dimension, by writing this equation $\dfrac{OA \cdot AB}{ad}$ in place of AD, and $\dfrac{OA \cdot dg}{ad}$ in place of DG, a new equation will be produced, in which the new abscissa ad and new ordinate dg rise only to one dimension; and which therefore must denote a right line. But if AD and DG (or either of them) had risen to two dimensions in the first equation, ad and dg would likewise have risen to two dimensions in the second equation. And so on in three or more dimensions. The indetermined lines, ad, dg in the second equation, and AD, DG in the first, will always rise to the same number of dimensions; and therefore the lines in which the points G, g are placed are of the same analytical order.

I say, further, that if any right line touches the curved line in the first figure, the same right line transferred the same way with the curve into the new figure will touch that curved line in the new figure, and conversely. For if any two points of the curve in the first figure are supposed to approach one the other till they come to coincide, the same points transferred will approach one the other till they come to coincide in the new figure; and therefore the right lines with which those points are joined will become together tangents of the curves in both figures. I might have given demonstrations of these assertions in a more geometrical form; but I study to be brief.

Wherefore if one rectilinear figure is to be transformed into another, we need only transfer the intersections of the right lines of which the first figure consists, and through the transferred intersections to draw right lines in the new figure. But if a curvilinear figure is to be transformed, we must transfer the points, the tangents, and other right lines, by means of which the curved line is defined. This Lemma is of use in the solution of the more difficult Problems; for thereby we may transform the proposed figures, if they are intricate, into others that are more simple. Thus any right lines converging to a point are transformed into parallels, by taking for the first ordinate radius any right line that passes through the point of intersection of the converging lines, and that because their point of intersection is by this means made to go off *in infinitum;* and parallel lines are such as tend to a point infinitely remote. And after the problem is solved in the new figure, if by the inverse operations we transform the new into the first figure, we shall have the solution required.

This Lemma is also of use in the solution of solid problems. For as often as two conic sections occur, by the intersection of which a problem may be solved, any one of them may be transformed, if it is an hyperbola or a parabola, into an ellipse, and then this ellipse may be easily changed into a circle. So also a right line and a conic section, in the construction of plane problems, may be transformed into a right line and a circle.

PROPOSITION 25. PROBLEM 17

To describe a conic that shall pass through two given points, and touch three given right lines.

Through the intersection of any two of the tangents one with the other, and the intersection of the third tangent with the right line which passes through the two given points, draw an indefinite right line; and, taking this line for the first ordinate radius, transform the figure by the preceding Lemma into a new figure. In this figure those two tangents will be-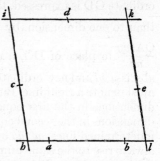come parallel to each other, and the third tangent will be parallel to the right line that passes through the two given points. Suppose *hi, kl* to be those two parallel tangents, *ik* the third tangent, and *hl* a right line parallel thereto, passing through those points *a*, *b*, through which the conic section ought to pass in this new figure; and completing the parallelogram *hikl*, let the right lines *hi, ik, kl* be so cut in *c, d, e*, that *hc* may be to the square root of the rectangle *ahb, ic* to *id*, and *ke* to *kd*, as the sum of the right lines *hi* and *kl* is to the sum of the three lines, the first whereof is the right line *ik*, and the other two are the square roots of the rectangles *ahb* and *alb;* and *c, d, e* will be the points of contact. For by the properties of the conic sections,

$$hc^2 : ah \cdot hb = ic^2 : id^2 = ke^2 : kd^2 = el^2 : al \cdot lb.$$

Therefore,

$$hc : \sqrt{(ah \cdot hb)} = ic : id = ke : kd = el : \sqrt{(al \cdot lb)}$$
$$= hc + ic + ke + el : \sqrt{(ah \cdot hb)} + id + kd + \sqrt{al \cdot lb}$$
$$= hi + kl : \sqrt{(ah \cdot hb)} + ik + \sqrt{(al \cdot lb)}.$$

Wherefore from that given ratio we have the points of contact *c, d, e*, in the new figure. By the inverted operations of the last Lemma, let those points be transferred into the first figure, and the conic will be there described by Prob. 14. Q.E.F. But according as the points *a, b*, fall between the points *h, l*, or without them, the points *c, d, e* must be taken either between the points *h, i, k, l*, or without them. If one of the points *a, b* falls between the points *h, i*, and the other without the points *h, l*, the Problem is impossible.

PROPOSITION 26. PROBLEM 18

To describe a conic that shall pass through a given point, and touch four given right lines.

From the common intersections of any two of the tangents to the common intersection of the other two, draw an indefinite right line; and taking this line

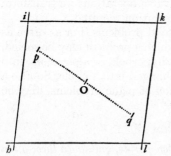

for the first ordinate radius, transform the figure (by Lem. 22) into a new figure, and the two pairs of tangents, each of which before concurred in the first ordinate radius, will now become parallel. Let *hi* and *kl, ik* and *hl*, be those pairs of parallels completing the parallelogram *hikl*. And let *p* be the point in this new figure corresponding to the given point in the first figure. Through O the centre of the figure draw *pq*: and O*q* being equal to O*p*, *q* will be the other point through which the conic section must pass in this new figure. Let this point be transferred, by the inverse operation of Lem. 22, into the first figure, and there we shall have the two points through which the conic is to be described. But through those points that conic may be described by Prop. 17.

LEMMA 23

If two given right lines, as AC, BD, *terminating in given points* A, B, *are in a given ratio one to the other, and the right line* CD, *by which the indetermined points* C, D *are joined is cut in* K *in a given ratio: I say, that the point* K *will be placed in a given right line.*

For let the right lines AC, BD meet in E, and in BE take BG to AE as BD is to AC, and let FD be always equal to the given line EG; and, by construc-

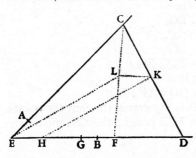

tion, EC will be to GD, that is, to EF, as AC to BD, and therefore in a given ratio; and therefore the triangle EFC will be given in kind. Let CF be cut in L so as CL may be to CF in the ratio of CK to CD; and because that is a given ratio, the triangle EFL will be given in kind, and therefore the point L will be placed in the given right line EL. Join LK, and the triangles CLK, CFD will be similar; and because FD is a given line, and LK is to FD in a given ratio, LK will be also given. To this let EH be taken equal, and ELKH will be always a parallelogram. And therefore the point K is always placed in the given side HK of that parallelogram. Q.E.D.

COR. Because the figure EFLC is given in kind, the three right lines EF, EL, and EC, that is, GD, HK, and EC, will have given ratios to each other.

LEMMA 24

If three right lines, two whereof are parallel, and given in position, touch any conic section: I say, that the semidiameter of the section which is parallel to those two is a mean proportional between the segments of those two that are intercepted between the points of contact and the third tangent.

Let AF, GB be the two parallels touching the conic section ADB in A and B; EF the third right line touching the conic section in I, and meeting the two former tangents in F and G, and let CD be the semidiameter of the figure parallel to those tangents: I say, that AF, CD, BG are continually proportional. For if the conjugate diameters AB, DM meet the tangent FG in E and H, and cut one the other in C, and the parallelogram IKCL be completed; from the nature of the conic sections,

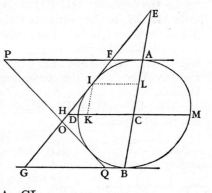

$$EC : CA = CA : CL;$$

thence, $$EC - CA : CA - CL = EC : CA$$

or $$EA : AL = EC : CA;$$

thence, $$EA : EA + AL = EC : EC + CA$$

or $$EA : EL = EC : EB.$$

Therefore, because of the similitude of the triangles EAF, ELI, ECH, EBG,

$$AF : LI = CH : BG.$$

Likewise, from the nature of the conic sections,

$$LI \text{ or } CK : CD = CD : CH.$$

Taking the products of corresponding terms in the last two proportions and simplifying,

$$AF : CD = CD : BG.\qquad \text{Q.E.D.}$$

Cor. I. Hence if two tangents FG, PQ meet two parallel tangents AF, BG in F and G, P and Q, and cut one the other in O; then by the Lemma applied to EG and PQ,

$$AF : CD = CD : BG,$$
$$BQ : CD = CD : AP.$$

Therefore, $\qquad AF : AP = BQ : BG$

and $\qquad AP - AF : AP = BG - BQ : BG$

or $\qquad PF : AP = GQ : BG,$

and $\qquad AP : BG = PF : GQ = FO : GO = AF : BQ.$

Cor. II. Whence also the two right lines PG, FQ drawn through the points P and G, F and Q, will meet in the right line ACB passing through the centre of the figure and the points of contact A, B.

Lemma 25

If four sides of a parallelogram indefinitely produced touch any conic section, and are cut by a fifth tangent: I say, that, taking those segments of any two conterminous sides that terminate in opposite angles of the parallelogram, either segment is to the side from which it is cut off as that part of the other conterminous side which is intercepted between the point of contact and the third side is to the other segment.

Let the four sides ML, IK, KL, MI of the parallelogram MLIK touch the conic section in A, B, C, D; and let the fifth tangent FQ cut those sides in F, Q, H, and E; and taking the segments ME, KQ of the sides MI, KI, or the segments KH, MF of the sides KL, ML: I say, that

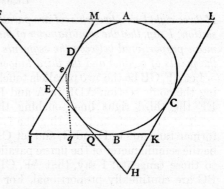

$$ME : MI = BK : KQ,$$

and $\quad KH : KL = AM : MF.$

For, by Cor. I of the preceding Lemma,

$$ME : EI = AM \text{ or } BK : BQ,$$

and by addition,

$$ME : MI = BK : KQ.\qquad \text{Q.E.D.}$$

Also, $\qquad KH : HL = BK \text{ or } AM : AF,$

and by subtraction,

$$KH : KL = AM : MF.\qquad \text{Q.E.D.}$$

Cor. I. Hence if a parallelogram IKLM described about a given conic section is given, the rectangle $KQ \cdot ME$, as also the rectangle $KH \cdot MF$ equal thereto, will be given. For, by reason of the similar triangles KQH, MFE, those rectangles are equal.

Cor. II. And if a sixth tangent *eq* is drawn meeting the tangents KI, MI in *q*

and e, the rectangle KQ·ME will be equal to the rectangle Kq·Me, and
$$KQ : Me = Kq : ME,$$
and by subtraction
$$KQ : Me = Qq : Ee.$$

COR. III. Hence, also, if Eq, eQ are joined and bisected, and a right line is drawn through the points of bisection, this right line will pass through the centre of the conic section. For since Qq : Ee = KQ : Me, the same right line will pass through the middle of all the lines Eq, eQ, MK (by Lem. 23), and the middle point of the right line MK is the centre of the section.

PROPOSITION 27. PROBLEM 19

To describe a conic that may touch five right lines given in position.

Supposing ABG, BCF, GCD, FDE, EA to be the tangents given in position. Bisect in M and N, AF, BE, the diagonals of the quadrilateral figure ABFE contained under any four of them; and (by Cor. III, Lem. 25) the right line MN

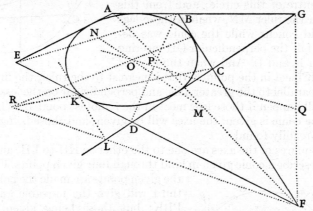

drawn through the points of bisection will pass through the centre of the conic. Again, bisect in P and Q the diagonals (if I may so call them) BD, GF of the quadrilateral figure BGDF contained under any other four tangents, and the right line PQ drawn through the points of bisection will pass through the centre of the conic; and therefore the centre will be given in the intersection of the bisecting lines. Suppose it to be O. Parallel to any tangent BC draw KL at such distance that the centre O may be placed in the middle between the parallels; this KL will touch the conic to be described. Let this cut any other two tangents GCD, FDE, in L and K. Through the points C and K, F and L, where the tangents not parallel, CL, FK, meet the parallel tangents CF, KL, draw CK, FL meeting in R; and the right line OR, drawn and produced, will cut the parallel tangents CF, KL, in the points of contact. This appears from Cor. II, Lem. 24. And by the same method the other points of contact may be found, and then the conic may be described by Prob. 14.   Q.E.F.

SCHOLIUM

Under the preceding Propositions are comprehended those Problems wherein either the centres or asymptotes of the conics are given. For when points and tangents and the centre are given, as many other points and as many other tangents are given at an equal distance on the other side of the centre. And an asymptote is to be considered as a tangent, and its infinitely remote extremity (if we may say so) is a point of contact. Conceive the point of contact of any tangent removed *in infinitum*, and the tangent will degenerate into an asymptote, and the constructions of the preceding Problems will be changed into the constructions of those Problems wherein the asymptote is given.

After the conic is described, we may find its axes and foci in this manner. In the construction and figure of Lem. 21, let those legs BP, CP, of the movable

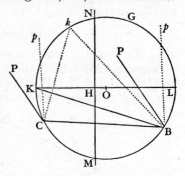

angles PBN, PCN, by the intersection of which the conic was described, be made parallel one to the other; and retaining that position, let them revolve about their poles B, C, in that figure. In the meanwhile let the other legs CN, BN, of those angles, by their intersection K or k, describe the circle BKGC. Let O be the centre of this circle; and from this centre upon the ruler MN, wherein those legs CN, BN did concur while the conic was described, let fall the perpendicular OH meeting the circle in K and L. And when those other legs CK, BK meet in the point K that is nearest to the ruler, the first legs CP, BP will be parallel to the greater axis, and perpendicular on the lesser; and the contrary will happen if those legs meet in the remotest point L. Whence if the centre of the conic is given, the axes will be given; and those being given, the foci will be readily found.

But the squares of the axes are one to the other as KH to LH, and thence it is easy to describe a conic given in kind through four given points. For if two of

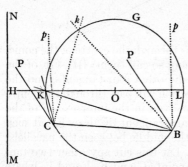

the given points are made the poles C, B, the third will give the movable angles PCK, PBK; but those being given, the circle BGKC may be described. Then, because the conic is given in kind, the ratio of OH to OK, and therefore OH itself, will be given. About the centre O, with the interval OH, describe another circle, and the right line that touches this circle, and passes through the intersection of the legs CK, BK, when the first legs CP, BP meet in the fourth given point, will be the ruler MN, by means of which the conic may be described. Whence also on the other hand a trapezium given in kind (excepting a few cases that are impossible) may be inscribed in a given conic section.

There are also other Lemmas, by the help of which conics given in kind may be described through given points, and touching given lines. Of such a sort is this, that if a right line is drawn through any point given in position, that may cut a given conic section in two points, and the distance of the intersections is bisected, the point of bisection will touch another conic section of the same kind with the former, and having its axes parallel to the axes of the former. But I hasten to things of greater use.

LEMMA 26

To place the three angles of a triangle, given both in kind and in magnitude, in respect to as many right lines given in position, provided they are not all parallel among themselves, in such manner that the several angles may touch the several lines.

Three indefinite right lines AB, AC, BC are given in position, and it is required so to place the triangle DEF that its angle D may touch the line AB, its

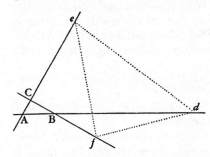

angle E the line AC, and its angle F the line BC. Upon DE, DF, and EF describe three segments of circles DRE, DGF, EMF, capable of angles equal to the angles BAC, ABC, ACB respectively. But those segments are to be described towards such sides of the lines DE, DF, EF, that the letters DRED may turn round about in the same order with the letters BACB; the letters DGFD in the same order with the letters ABCA; and the letters EMFE in the same order with the letters ACBA; then, completing those segments into entire circles, let the two former circles cut each other in G, and suppose P and Q to be their centres. Then joining GP, PQ, take

$$Ga : AB = GP : PQ;$$

and about the centre G, with the interval G*a*, describe a circle that may cut the first circle DGE in *a*. Join *a*D cutting the second circle DFG in *b*, as well as *a*E cutting the third circle EMF in *c*. Complete the figure ABC*def* similar and equal to the figure *abc*DEF: I say, the thing is done.

For drawing F*c* meeting *a*D in *n*, and joining *a*G, *b*G, QG, QD, PD, by construction the angle E*a*D is equal to the angle CAB, and the angle *ac*F equal to the angle ACB; and therefore the triangle *anc* equiangular to the triangle ABC. Wherefore the angle *anc* or F*n*D is equal to the angle ABC, and consequently to the angle F*b*D; and therefore the point *n* falls on the point *b*. Moreover the angle GPQ, which is half the angle GPD at the centre, is equal to the angle G*a*D at the circumference; and the angle GQP, which is half the angle GQD at the centre, is equal to the supplement of the angle G*b*D at the circumference, and therefore equal to the angle G*ba*. Upon which account the triangles GPQ, G*ab* are similar, and

$$Ga : ab = GP : PQ$$

and, by construction,

$$GP : PQ = Ga : AB.$$

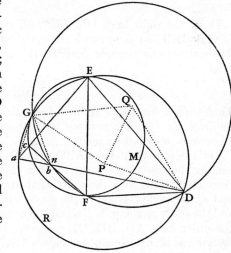

Wherefore *ab* and AB are equal; and consequently the triangles *abc*, ABC, which we have now proved to be similar, are also equal. And therefore since the angles D, E, F of the triangle DEF do respectively touch the sides *ab*, *ac*, *bc* of the triangle *abc*, the figure ABC*def* may be completed similar and equal to the figure *abc*DEF, and by completing it the Problem will be solved.   Q.E.F.

COR. Hence a right line may be drawn whose parts given in length may be intercepted between three right lines given in position. Suppose the triangle DEF, by the approach of its point D to the side EF, and by having the sides DE, DF placed into the same straight line, to be itself changed into a right line whose given part DE is to be placed between the right lines AB, AC given in position; and its given part DF is to be placed between the right lines AB, BC given in position; then, by applying the preceding construction to this case, the Problem will be solved.

PROPOSITION 28. PROBLEM 20

To describe a conic given both in kind and in magnitude, given parts of which shall be placed between three right lines given in position.

Suppose a conic is to be described that may be similar and equal to the curved line DEF, and may be cut by three right lines AB, AC, BC, given in position, into parts DE and EF, similar and equal to the given parts of this curved line.

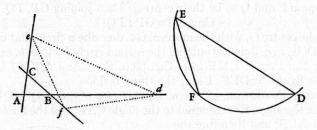

Draw the right lines DE, EF, DF; and place the angles D, E, F, of this triangle DEF, so as to touch those right lines given in position (by Lem. 26). Then about the triangle describe the conic, similar and equal to the curve DEF.   Q.E.F.

LEMMA 27

To describe a trapezium given in kind, the angles whereof may respectively touch four right lines given in position, that are neither all parallel among themselves, nor converge to one common point.

Let the four right lines ABC, AD, BD, CE be given in position; the first cutting the second in A, the third in B, and the fourth in C; and suppose a trapezium *fghi* is to be described that may be similar to the trapezium FGHI, and whose angle *f*, equal to the given angle F, may touch the right line ABC; and the other angles *g*, *h*, *i*, equal to the other given angles G, H, I, may touch the other lines AD, BD, CE respectively. Join FH, and upon FG, FH, FI describe as many segments of circles FSG, FTH, FVI, the first of which FSG may be capable of an angle equal to the angle BAD; the second FTH capable of an angle equal to the angle CBD; and the third FVI of an angle equal to the angle ACE. But the segments are to be described towards those sides of the lines FG, FH, FI, that the circular order of the letters FSGF may be the same as of the letters BADB, and that the letters FTHF may turn about in the same order as the letters CBDC, and the letters FVIF in the same order as the letters ACEA. Complete the segments into entire circles, and let P be the centre

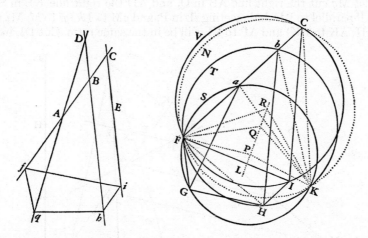

of the first circle FSG, Q the centre of the second FTH. Join and produce both ways the line PQ, and in it take QR so that QR : PQ = BC : AB. But QR is to be taken towards that side of the point Q, that the order of the letters P, Q, R may be the same as of the letters A, B, C; and about the centre R with the radius RF describe a fourth circle FNc cutting the third circle FVI in c. Join Fc cutting the first circle in a, and the second in b. Draw aG, bH, cI, and let the figure ABCfghi be made similar to the figure abcFGHI; and the trapezium fghi will be that which was required to be described.

For let the two first circles FSG, FTH cut one the other in K; join PK, QK, RK, aK, bK, cK, and produce QP to L. The angles FaK, FbK, FcK at the circumferences are the halves of the angles FPK, FQK, FRK at the centres, and therefore equal to LPK, LQK, LRK, the halves of those angles. Therefore the figure PQRK is equiangular and similar to the figure abcK, and consequently ab is to bc as PQ to QR, that is, as AB to BC. But by construction the angles fAg, fBh, fCi are equal to the angles FaG, FbH, FcI. And therefore the figure ABCfghi may be completed similar to the figure abcFGHI. This done, a trapezium fghi will be constructed similar to the trapezium FGHI, and by its angles f, g, h, i will touch the right lines ABC, AD, BD, CE. Q.E.F.

COR. Hence a right line may be drawn whose parts intercepted in a given order, between four right lines given by position, shall have a given proportion among themselves. Let the angles FGH, GHI be so far increased that the right lines FG, GH, HI may lie in the same line; and by constructing the Problem in this case, a right line fghi will be drawn, whose parts fg, gh, hi, intercepted between the four right lines given in position, AB and AD, AD and BD, BD and CE, will be to each other as the lines FG, GH, HI, and will observe the same order among themselves. But the same thing may be more readily done in this manner:

Produce AB to K and BD to L, so as BK may be to AB as HI to GH; and DL to BD as GI to FG; and join KL meeting the right line CE in *i*. Produce *i*L to M, so as LM may be to *i*L as GH to HI; then draw MQ parallel to LB, and meeting the right line AD in *g*, and join *gi* cutting AB, BD in *f*, *h*: I say, the thing is done.

For let M*g* cut the right line AB in Q, and AD the right line KL in S, and draw AP parallel to BD and meeting *i*L in P, and *g*M to L*h* (*gi* to *hi*, M*i* to L*i*, GI to HI, AK to BK) and AP to BL will be in the same ratio. Cut DL in R, so

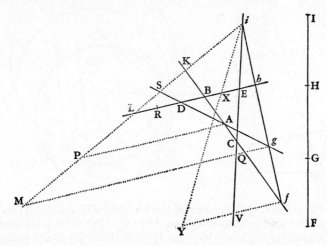

as DL to RL may be in that same ratio; and because *g*S to *g*M, AS to AP, and DS to DL are proportional; therefore, as *g*S to L*h*, so will AS be to BL, and DS to RL; and mixtly, BL−RL to L*h*−BL, as AS−DS to *g*S−AS. That is, BR is to B*h* as AD is to A*g*, and therefore as BD to *g*Q. And alternately BR is to BD as B*h* to *g*Q, or as *fh* to *fg*. But by construction the line BL was cut in D and R in the same ratio as the line FI in G and H; and therefore BR is to BD as FH to FG. Therefore *fh* is to *fg* as FH to FG. Since, therefore, *gi* to *hi* likewise is as M*i* to L*i*, that is, as GI to HI, it is manifest that the lines FI, *fi* are similarly cut in G and H, *g* and *h*.   Q.E.F.

In the construction of this Corollary, after the line LK is drawn cutting CE in *i*, we may produce *i*E to V, so as EV may be to E*i* as FH to HI, and then draw V*f* parallel to BD. It will come to the same, if about the centre *i* with an interval IH, we describe a circle cutting BD in X, and produce *i*X to Y so as *i*Y may be equal to IF, and then draw Y*f* parallel to BD.

Sir Christopher Wren and Dr. Wallis have long ago given other solutions of this Problem.

PROPOSITION 29. PROBLEM 21

To describe a conic given in kind, that may be cut by four right lines given in position, into parts given in order, kind, and proportion.

Suppose a conic is to be described that may be similar to the curved line FGHI, and whose parts, similar and proportional to the parts FG, GH, HI of the other, may be intercepted between the right lines AB and AD, AD and BD, BD and CE given in position, viz., the first between the first pair of those lines, the second between the second, and the third between the third. Draw the right lines FG, GH, HI, FI; and (by Lem. 27) describe a trapezium *fghi* that may be similar to the trapezium FGHI, and whose angles *f*, *g*, *h*, *i* may touch the right lines given in position AB, AD, BD, CE, severally according to their order. And then about this trapezium describe a conic, that conic will be similar to the curved line FGHI.

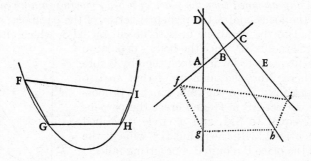

SCHOLIUM

This problem may be likewise constructed in the following manner. Joining FG, GH, HI, FI, produce GF to V, and join FH, IG, and make the angles CAK, DAL equal to the angles FGH, VFH. Let AK, AL meet the right line BD in K and L, and thence draw KM, LN, of which let KM make the angle AKM equal to the angle GHI, and be itself to AK as HI is to GH; and let LN make the angle ALN equal to the angle FHI, and be itself to AL as HI to FH. But AK, KM, AL, LN are to be drawn towards those sides of the lines AD,

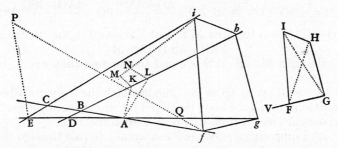

AK, AL, that the letters CAKMC, ALKA, DALND may be carried round in the same order as the letters FGHIF; and draw MN meeting the right line CE in *i*. Make the angle *i*EP equal to the angle IGF, and let PE be to E*i* as FG to GI; and through P draw PQ*f* that may with the right line ADE contain an angle PQE equal to the angle FIG, and may meet the right line AB in *f*, and join *fi*. But PE and PQ are to be drawn towards those sides of the lines CE, PE that the circular order of the letters PE*i*P and PEQP may be the same as of the letters FGHIF; and if upon the line *fi*, in the same order of letters, and similar to the trapezium FGHI, a trapezium *fghi* is constructed, and a conic given in kind is circumscribed about it, the Problem will be solved.

So far concerning the finding of the orbits. It remains that we determine the motions of bodies in the orbits so found.

SECTION VI

HOW THE MOTIONS ARE TO BE FOUND IN GIVEN ORBITS

PROPOSITION 30. PROBLEM 22

To find at any assigned time the place of a body moving in a given parabola.

Let S be the focus, and A the principal vertex of the parabola; and suppose $4AS \cdot M$ equal to the parabolic area to be cut off APS, which either was described by the radius SP, since the body's departure from the vertex, or is to be described thereby before its arrival there. Now the quantity of that area to be cut off is known from the time which is proportional to it. Bisect AS in G, and erect the perpendicular GH equal to 3M, and a circle described about the centre H, with the radius HS, will cut the parabola in the place P required. For letting fall PO perpendicular on the axis, and drawing PH, there will be

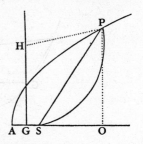

$$AG^2 + GH^2 (= HP^2 = (AO - AG)^2 + (PO - GH)^2)$$
$$= AO^2 + PO^2 - 2AO \cdot AG - 2GH \cdot PO + AG^2 + GH^2.$$

Whence

$$2GH \cdot PO (= AO^2 + PO^2 - 2AO \cdot AG) = AO^2 + \tfrac{3}{4}PO^2. \text{ For } AO^2$$

write $AO \cdot \dfrac{PO^2}{4AS}$; then dividing all the terms by 3PO, and multiplying them by 2AS, we shall have

$$\tfrac{4}{3}GH \cdot AS (= \tfrac{1}{6}AO \cdot PO + \tfrac{1}{2}AS \cdot PO = \frac{AO + 3AS}{6} \cdot PO = \frac{4AO - 3SO}{6} \cdot PO = \text{to the}$$

area, $APO - SPO$) = to the area APS. But GH was 3M, and therefore
$$\tfrac{4}{3}GH \cdot AS \text{ is } 4AS \cdot M.$$
Therefore the area cut off APS is equal to the area that was to be cut off $4AS \cdot M$.   Q.E.D.

COR. I. Hence GH is to AS as the time in which the body described the arc AP to the time in which the body described the arc between the vertex A and the perpendicular erected from the focus S upon the axis.

COR. II. And supposing a circle ASP continually to pass through the moving body P, the velocity of the point H is to the velocity which the body had in the vertex A as 3 to 8; and therefore in the same ratio is the line GH to the right line which the body, in the time of its moving from A to P, would describe with that velocity which it had in the vertex A.

COR. III. Hence, also, on the other hand, the time may be found in which the body has described any assigned arc AP. Join AP, and on its middle point erect a perpendicular meeting the right line GH in H.

LEMMA 28

There is no oval figure whose area, cut off by right lines at pleasure, can be universally found by means of equations of any number of finite terms and dimensions.

Suppose that within the oval any point is given, about which as a pole a right line is continually revolving with an uniform motion, while in that right line a movable point going out from the pole moves always forwards with a velocity proportional to the square of that right line within the oval. By this motion that point will describe a spiral with infinite circumgyrations. Now if a portion of the area of the oval cut off by that right line could be found by a finite equation, the distance of the point from the pole, which is proportional to this area, might be found by the same equation, and therefore all the points of the spiral might be found by a finite equation also; and therefore the intersection of a right line given in position with the spiral might also be found by a finite equation. But every right line infinitely produced cuts a spiral in an infinite number of points; and the equation by which any one intersection of two lines is found at the same time exhibits all their intersections by as many roots, and therefore rises to as many dimensions as there are intersections. Because two circles cut one another in two points, one of those intersections is not to be found but by an equation of two dimensions, by which the other intersection may be also found. Because there may be four intersections of two conic sections, any one of them is not to be found universally, but by an equation of four dimensions, by which they may be all found together. For if those intersections are severally sought, because the law and condition of all is the same, the calculus will be the same in every case, and therefore the conclusion always the same, which must therefore comprehend all those intersections at once within itself, and exhibit them all indifferently. Hence it is that the intersections of the conic sections with the curves of the third order, because they may amount to six, come out together by equations of six dimensions; and the intersections of two curves of the third order, because they may amount to nine, come out together by equations of nine dimensions. If this did not necessarily happen, we might reduce all solid to plane Problems, and those higher than solid to solid Problems. But here I speak of curves irreducible in power. For if the equation by which the curve is defined may be reduced to a lower power, the curve will not be one single curve, but composed of two, or more, whose intersections may be severally found by different calculi. After the same manner the two intersections of right lines with the conic sections come out always by equations of two dimensions; the three intersections of right lines with the irreducible curves of the third order, by equations of three dimensions; the four intersections of right lines with the irreducible curves of the fourth order, by equations of four dimensions; and so on *in infinitum*. Wherefore the innumerable intersections of a right line with a spiral, since this is but one simple curve, and not reducible to more curves, require equations infinite in number of dimensions and roots, by which they may be all exhibited together. For the law and calculus of all is the same. For if a perpendicular is let fall from the pole upon that intersecting right line, and that perpendicular together with the intersecting line revolves about the pole, the intersections of the spiral will mutually pass the one into the other; and that which was first or nearest, after one revolution, will be the second; after two, the third; and so on: nor will the equation in the meantime be changed but as the magnitudes of those quantities are changed, by which the position of the intersecting line is determined. Therefore since those quantities after every revolution return to their first magnitudes, the equation will return to its first form; and consequently one and the same equation will exhibit all the intersections, and will therefore have an infinite number of roots, by which they may be all exhibited. Therefore the intersection of a right line with a spiral cannot be universally found by any finite equation; and hence there is no oval figure whose area, cut off by right lines at pleasure, can be universally exhibited by any such equation.

By the same argument, if the interval of the pole and point by which the spiral is described is taken proportional to that part of the perimeter of the oval which is cut off, it may be proved that the length of the perimeter cannot be universally exhibited by any finite equation. But here I speak of ovals that are not touched by conjugate figures running out *in infinitum*.

Cor. Hence the area of an ellipse, described by a radius drawn from the focus to the moving body, is not to be found from the time given by a finite equation; and therefore cannot be determined by the description of curves geometrically rational. Those curves I call geometrically rational, all the points whereof may be determined by lengths that are definable by equations; that is, by the complicated ratios of lengths. Other curves (such as spirals, quadratrixes, and cycloids) I call geometrically irrational. For the lengths which are or are not as number to number (according to Book x, *Elements* of Euclid) are arithmetically rational or irrational. And therefore I cut off an area of an ellipse proportional to the time in which it is described by a curve geometrically irrational, in the following manner:

PROPOSITION 31. PROBLEM 23

To find the place of a body moving in a given ellipse at any assigned time.

Suppose A to be the principal vertex, S the focus, and O the centre of the ellipse APB; and let P be the place of the body to be found. Produce OA to G so that OG : OA = OA : OS. Erect the perpendicular GH; and about the centre

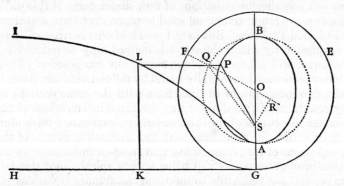

O, with the radius OG, describe the circle GEF; and on the ruler GH, as a base, suppose the wheel GEF to move forwards, revolving about its axis, and in the meantime by its point A describing the cycloid ALI. This done, take GK to the perimeter GEFG of the wheel, in the ratio of the time in which the body proceeding from A described the arc AP, to the time of a whole revolution in the ellipse. Erect the perpendicular KL meeting the cycloid in L; then LP drawn parallel to KG will meet the ellipse in P, the required place of the body.

For about the centre O with the radius OA describe the semicircle AQB, and let LP, produced, if need be, meet the arc AQ in Q, and join SQ, OQ. Let OQ meet the arc EFG in F, and upon OQ let fall the perpendicular SR. The area APS varies as the area AQS, that is, as the difference between the sector OQA and the triangle OQS, or as the difference of the rectangles ½OQ·AQ, and

½OQ·SR, that is, because ½OQ is given, as the difference between the arc AQ and the right line SR; and therefore (because of the equality of the given ratios SR to the sine of the arc AQ, OS to OA, OA to OG, AQ to GF; and by division, AQ−SR to GF−sine of the arc AQ) as GK, the difference between the arc GF and the sine of the arc AQ.   Q.E.D.

SCHOLIUM

But since the description of this curve is difficult, a solution by approximation will be preferable. First, then, let there be found a certain angle B which may be to an angle of 57.29578 degrees, which an arc equal to the radius subtends, as SH, the distance of the foci, to AB, the diameter of the ellipse.

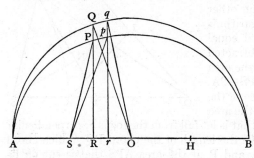

Secondly, a certain length L, which may be to the radius in the same ratio inversely. And these being found, the Problem may be solved by the following analysis. By any construction (or even by conjecture), suppose we know P the place of the body near its true place p. Then letting fall on the axis of the ellipse the ordinate PR from the proportion of the diameters of the ellipse, the ordinate RQ of the circumscribed circle AQB will be given; which ordinate is the sine of the angle AOQ, supposing AO to be the radius, and also cuts the ellipse in P. It will be sufficient if that angle is found by a rude calculus in numbers near the truth. Suppose we also know the angle proportional to the time, that is, which is to four right angles as the time in which the body described the arc Ap to the time of one revolution in the ellipse. Let this angle be N. Then take an angle D, which may be to the angle B as the sine of the angle AOQ to the radius; and an angle E which may be to the angle N−AOQ+D as the length L to the same length L diminished by the cosine of the angle AOQ, when that angle is less than a right angle, or increased thereby when greater. In the next place, take an angle F that may be to the angle B as the sine of the angle AOQ+E to the radius, and an angle G, that may be to the angle N −AOQ−E+F as the length L to the same length L diminished by the cosine of the angle AOQ+E, when that angle is less than a right angle, or increased thereby when greater. For the third time take an angle H, that may be to the angle B as the sine of the angle AOQ+E+G to the radius; and an angle I to the angle N−AOQ−E−G+H, as the length L is to the same length L diminished by the cosine of the angle AOQ+E+G, when that angle is less than a right angle, or increased thereby when greater. And so we may proceed *in infinitum*. Lastly, take the angle AOq equal to the angle AOQ+E+G+I+, &c., and from its cosine Or and the ordinate pr, which is to its sine qr as the lesser axis of the ellipse to the greater, we shall have p the correct place of the body. When the angle N− AOQ+D happens to be negative, the sign + of the angle E must be everywhere changed into −, and the sign − into +. And the same thing is to be understood of the signs of the angles G and I, when the angles N−AOQ−E+F, and N−AOQ−E−G+H come out negative. But the infinite series AOQ+

E+G+I+, &c., converges so very fast, that it will be scarcely ever needful to proceed beyond the second term E. And the calculus is founded upon this Theorem, that the area APS varies as the difference between the arc AQ and the right line let fall from the focus S perpendicularly upon the radius OQ.

And by a calculus not unlike, the Problem is solved in the hyperbola. Let its centre be O, its vertex A, its focus S, and asymptote OK; and suppose the amount of the area to be cut off is known, as being proportional to the time. Let that be A, and by conjecture suppose we know the position of a right line SP, that cuts off an area APS near the truth. Join OP, and from A and P to the asymptote draw AI, PK, parallel to the other asymptote; and by the table of logarithms the area AIKP will be given, and equal thereto the area OPA, which, subtracted from the triangle OPS, will leave the area cut off APS. And by applying 2APS−2A, or 2A−2APS, the double difference of the area A that was to be cut off, and the area

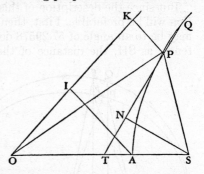

APS that is cut off, to the line SN that is let fall from the focus S, perpendicular upon the tangent TP, we shall have the length of the chord PQ. Which chord PQ is to be inscribed between A and P, if the area APS that is cut off be greater than the area A that was to be cut off, but towards the contrary side of the point P, if otherwise: and the point Q will be the place of the body more accurately. And by repeating the computation the place may be found continually to greater and greater accuracy.

And by such computations we have a general analytical resolution of the Problem. But the particular calculus that follows is better fitted for astronomical purposes. Supposing AO, OB, OD to be the semiaxes of the ellipse, and L its latus rectum, and D the difference between the lesser semiaxis OD, and

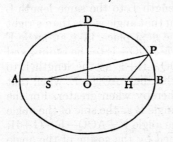

½L the half of the latus rectum: let an angle Y be found, whose sine may be to the radius as the rectangle under that difference D, and AO+OD the half sum of the axes, to the square of the greater axis AB. Find also an angle Z, whose sine may be to the radius as the double rectangle under the distance of the foci SH and that difference D, to triple the square of half the greater semiaxis AO. Those angles being once found, the place of the body may be thus determined.

Take the angle T proportional to the time in which the arc BP was described, or equal to what is called the mean motion; and take an angle V, the first equation of the mean motion, to the angle Y, the greatest first equation, as the sine of double the angle T is to the radius; and take an angle X, the second equation, to the angle Z, the second greatest equation, as the cube of the sine of the angle T is to the cube of the radius. Then take the angle BHP, the mean equated motion either equal to T+X+V, the sum of the angles T, V, X, if the angle T is less than a right angle, or equal to T+X−V, the difference of the same, if that angle T is greater than one and less than two right angles; and if HP meets the ellipse in P, draw SP, and it will cut off the area BSP, nearly proportional to the time.

This practice seems to be expeditious enough, because the angles V and X, taken in fractions of seconds, if you please, being very small, it will be sufficient to find two or three of their first figures. But it is likewise sufficiently accurate to answer to the theory of the planets' motions. For even in the orbit of Mars, where the greatest equation of the centre amounts to ten degrees, the error will scarcely exceed one second. But when the angle of the mean motion equated BHP is found, the angle of the true motion BSP, and the distance SP, are readily had by the known methods.

And so far concerning the motion of bodies in curved lines. But it may also come to pass that a moving body shall ascend or descend in a right line; and I shall now go on to explain what belongs to such kind of motions.

SECTION VII

THE RECTILINEAR ASCENT AND DESCENT OF BODIES

PROPOSITION 32. PROBLEM 24

Supposing that the centripetal force is inversely proportional to the square of the distance of the places from the centre; it is required to define the spaces which a body, falling directly, describes in given times.

CASE 1. If the body does not fall perpendicularly, it will (by Cor. I, Prop. 13) describe some conic section whose focus is placed in the centre of force. Sup-

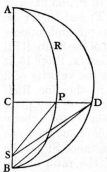

pose that conic section to be ARPB and its focus S. And, first, if the figure be an ellipse, upon the greater axis thereof AB describe the semicircle ADB, and let the right line DPC pass through the falling body, making right angles with the axis; and drawing DS, PS, the area ASD will be proportional to the area ASP, and therefore also to the time. The axis AB still remaining the same, let the breadth of the ellipse be continually diminished, and the area ASD will always remain proportional to the time. Suppose that breadth to be diminished *in infinitum;* and the orbit APB in that case coinciding with the axis AB, and the focus S with the extreme point of the axis B, the body will descend in the right line AC, and the area ABD will become proportional to the time. Therefore the space AC will be given which the body describes in a given time by its perpendicular fall from the place A, if the area ABD is taken proportional to the time, and from the point D the right line DC is let fall perpendicularly on the right line AB. Q.E.I.

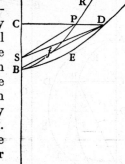

CASE 2. If the figure RPB is an hyperbola, on the same principal diameter AB describe the rectangular hyperbola BED; and because there exist between the several areas and the heights CP and CD relations, A

CSP : CSD = CB*f*P : CBED = SP*f*B : SDEB = CP : CD, and since the area SP*f*B varies as the time in which the body P will move through the arc P*f*B, the area SDEB will also vary as that time. Let the latus rectum of the hyperbola RPB be diminished *in infinitum*, the transverse axis remaining the same; and the arc PB will come to coincide with the right line CB, and the focus S with the vertex B, and the right line SD with the right line BD. And therefore the area BDEB will vary as the time in which the body C, by its perpendicular descent, describes the line CB.   Q.E.I.

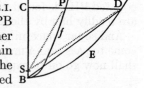

CASE 3. And by the like argument, if the figure RPB is a parabola, and to the same principal vertex B another parabola BED is described, that may always remain given while the former parabola in whose perimeter the body P moves, by having its latus rectum diminished and reduced to nothing, comes to coincide with the line CB, the parabolic segment BDEB will vary as the time in which that body P or C will descend to the centre S or B.   Q.E.I.

PROPOSITION 33. THEOREM 9

The things above found being supposed, I say, that the velocity of a falling body in any place C is to the velocity of a body, describing a circle about the centre B at the distance BC, as the square root of the ratio of AC, the distance of the body from the remoter vertex A of the circle or rectangular hyperbola, to ½AB, the principal semidiameter of the figure.

Let AB, the common diameter of both figures RPB, DEB, be bisected in O; and draw the right line PT that may touch the figure RPB in P, and likewise cut that common diameter AB (produced, if need be) in T; and let SY be perpendicular to this line, and BQ perpendicular to this diameter, and suppose

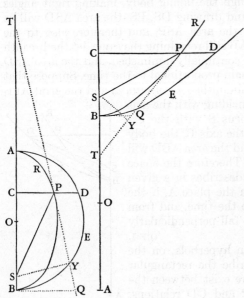

the latus rectum of the figure RPB to be L. From Cor. IX, Prop. 16, it is manifest that the velocity of a body, moving in the line RPB about the centre S, in any place P, is to the velocity of a body describing a circle about the same centre, at the distance SP, as the square root of the ratio of the rectangle ½L·SP to SY². For by the properties of the conic sections AC·CB is to CP² as 2AO to L, and therefore $\dfrac{2CP^2 \cdot AO}{AC \cdot CB}$ is equal to L. Therefore those velocities are to each other as the square root of the ratio of $\dfrac{CP^2 \cdot AO \cdot SP}{AC \cdot CB}$ to SY². Moreover, by the properties of the conic sections,

$$CO : BO = BO : TO,$$

thence,
$$CO + BO : BO = BO + TO : TO,$$

and
$$CO : BO = CB : BT.$$

From this,
$$BO - CO : BO = BT - CB : BT$$

and
$$AC : AO = TC : BT = CP : BQ;$$

and, since
$$CP = \frac{BQ \cdot AC}{AO},$$

one obtains $\dfrac{CP^2 \cdot AO \cdot SP}{AC \cdot CB}$ equal to $\dfrac{BQ^2 \cdot AC \cdot SP}{AO \cdot BC}$.

Now suppose CP, the breadth of the figure RPB, to be diminished *in infinitum*, so that the point P may come to coincide with the point C, and the point S with the point B, and the line SP with the line BC, and the line SY with the line BQ; and the velocity of the body now descending perpendicularly in the line CB will be to the velocity of a body describing a circle about the centre B, at the distance BC, as the square root of the ratio of $\dfrac{BQ^2 \cdot AC \cdot SP}{AO \cdot BC}$ to SY^2, that is (neglecting the ratios of equality of SP to BC, and BQ^2 to SY^2), as the square root of the ratio of AC to AO, or ½AB.   Q.E.D.

COR. I. When the points B and S come to coincide, TC will become to TS as AC to AO.

COR. II. A body revolving in any circle at a given distance from the centre, by its motion converted upwards, will ascend to double its distance from the centre.

PROPOSITION 34. THEOREM 10

If the figure BED is a parabola, I say, that the velocity of a falling body in any place C is equal to the velocity by which a body may uniformly describe a circle about the centre B at half the interval BC.

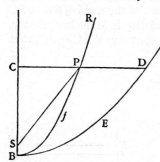

For (by Cor. VII, Prop. 16) the velocity of a body describing a parabola RPB about the centre S, in any place P, is equal to the velocity of a body uniformly describing a circle about the same centre S at half the interval SP. Let the breadth CP of the parabola be diminished *in infinitum*, so that the parabolic arc PfB may come to coincide with the right line CB, the centre S with the vertex B, and the interval SP with the interval BC, and the Proposition will be manifest.   Q.E.D.

PROPOSITION 35. THEOREM 11

The same things supposed, I say, that the area of the figure DES, described by the indefinite radius SD, is equal to the area which a body with a radius equal to half the latus rectum of the figure DES describes in the same time, by uniformly revolving about the centre S.

For suppose a body C in the smallest moment of time describes in falling the infinitely little line Cc, while another body K, uniformly revolving about the centre S in the circle OKk, describes the arc Kk. Erect the perpendiculars CD, cd, meeting the figure DES in D, d. Join SD, Sd, SK, Sk, and draw Dd meeting the axis AS in T, and thereon let fall the perpendicular SY.

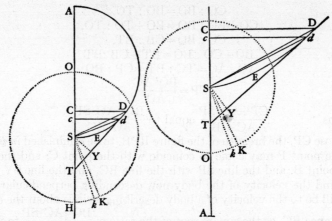

CASE 1. If the figure DES is a circle, or a rectangular hyperbola, bisect its transverse diameter AS in O, and SO will be half the latus rectum. And because

$$TC : TD = Cc : Dd,$$
and
$$TD : TS = CD : Sy,$$
there follows
$$TC : TS = CD \cdot Cc : SY \cdot Dd.$$
But (by Cor. I, Prop. 33)　　$TC : TS = AC : AO,$
namely, if in the coalescence of the points D, d the ultimate ratios of the lines are taken. Therefore,

$$AC : AO \text{ or } SK = CD \cdot Cc : SY \cdot Dd.$$

Further, the velocity of the descending body in C is to the velocity of a body describing a circle about the centre S, at the interval SC, as the square root of the ratio of AC to AO or SK (by Prop. 33); and this velocity is to the velocity of a body describing the circle OKk as the square root of the ratio of SK to SC (by Cor. VI, Prop. 4); and, consequently, the first velocity is to the last, that is, the little line Cc to the arc Kk, as the square root of the ratio of AC to SC, that is, in the ratio of AC to CD. Therefore,

$$CD \cdot Cc = AC \cdot Kk,$$
hence,　　　　　　　　　$AC : SK = AC \cdot Kk : SY \cdot Dd,$
and　　　　　　　　　　$SK \cdot Kk = SY \cdot Dd,$
and　　　　　　　　　　$\tfrac{1}{2}SK \cdot Kk = \tfrac{1}{2}SY \cdot Dd,$

that is, the area KSk is equal to the area SDd. Therefore in every moment of time two equal particles, KSk and SDd, of areas are generated, which, if their magnitude is diminished, and their number increased *in infinitum*, obtain the ratio of equality, and consequently (by Cor., Lem. IV) the whole areas together generated are always equal.　Q.E.D.

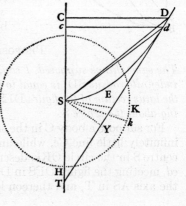

CASE 2. But if the figure DES is a parabola, we shall find, as above,

$$CD \cdot Cc : SY \cdot Dd = TC : TS,$$
that is, $= 2 : 1$; therefore,

$$\tfrac{1}{4}CD \cdot Cc = \tfrac{1}{2} SY \cdot Dd.$$

But the velocity of the falling body in C is

equal to the velocity with which a circle may be uniformly described at the interval ½SC (by Prop. 34). And this velocity to the velocity with which a circle may be described with the radius SK, that is, the little line Cc to the arc Kk, is (by Cor. VI, Prop. 4) as the square root of the ratio of SK to ½SC; that is, in the ratio of SK to ½CD. Therefore ½SK·Kk is equal to ¼CD·Cc, and therefore equal to ½SY·Dd; that is, the area KSk is equal to the area SDd, as above.   Q.E.D.

PROPOSITION 36. PROBLEM 25

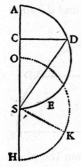

To determine the times of the descent of a body falling from a given place A.

Upon the diameter AS, the distance of the body from the centre at the beginning, describe the semicircle ADS, as likewise the semicircle OKH equal thereto, about the centre S. From any place C of the body erect the ordinate CD. Join SD, and make the sector OSK equal to the area ASD. It is evident (by Prop. 35) that the body in falling will describe the space AC in the same time in which another body, uniformly revolving about the centre S, may describe the arc OK.   Q.E.F.

PROPOSITION 37. PROBLEM 26

To define the times of the ascent or descent of a body projected upwards or downwards from a given place.

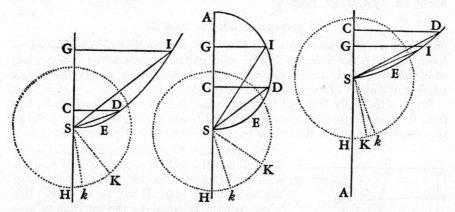

Suppose the body to go off from the given place G, in the direction of the line GS, with any velocity. Take GA to ½AS as the square of the ratio of this velocity to the uniform velocity in a circle, with which the body may revolve about the centre S at the given interval SG. If that ratio is the same as of the number 2 to 1, the point A is infinitely remote; in which case a parabola is to be described with any latus rectum to the vertex S, and axis SG; as appears by Prop. 34. But if that ratio is less or greater then the ratio of 2 to 1, in the former case a circle, in the latter a rectangular hyperbola, is to be described on the diameter SA; as appears by Prop. 33. Then about the centre S, with a radius equal to half the latus rectum, describe the circle HkK; and at the place G of the ascending or descending body, and at any other place C, erect the perpendiculars GI, CD, meeting the conic section or circle in I and D. Then joining SI, SD, let the sectors HSK, HS*k* be made equal to the segments SEIS,SEDS, and (by Prop. 35) the body G will describe the space GC in the same time in which the body K may describe the arc K*k*. Q.E.F.

PROPOSITION 38. THEOREM 12

Supposing that the centripetal force is proportional to the altitude or distance of places from the centre, I say, that the times and velocities of falling bodies, and the spaces which they describe, are respectively proportional to the arcs, and the sines and versed sines of the arcs.

Suppose the body to fall from any place A in the right line AS; and about the centre of force S, with the radius AS, describe the quadrant of a circle AE; and let CD be the sine of any arc AD; and the body A will in the time AD in falling describe the space AC, and in the place C will acquire the velocity CD.

This is demonstrated the same way from Prop. 10, as Prop. 32 was demonstrated from Prop. 11.

COR. I. Hence the times are equal in which one body falling from the place A arrives at the centre S, and another body revolving describes the quadrantal arc ADE.

COR. II. Therefore all the times are equal in which bodies falling from whatsoever places arrive at the centre. For all the periodic times of revolving bodies are equal (by Cor. III, Prop. 4).

PROPOSITION 39. PROBLEM 27

Supposing a centripetal force of any kind, and granting the quadratures of curvilinear figures; it is required to find the velocity of a body, ascending or descending in a right line, in the several places through which it passes, as also the time in which it will arrive at any place; and conversely.

Suppose the body E to fall from any place A in the right line ADEC; and from its place E imagine a perpendicular EG always erected proportional to the centripetal force in that place tending to the centre C; and let BFG be a curved line, the locus of the point G. And in the beginning of the motion suppose EG to coincide with the perpendicular AB; and the velocity of the body in any place E will be as a right line whose square is equal to the curvilinear area ABGE. Q.E.I.

In EG take EM inversely proportional to a right line whose square is equal to the area ABGE, and let VLM be a curved line wherein the point M is always placed, and to which the right line AB produced is an asymptote; and the time in which the body in falling describes the line AE, will be as the curvilinear area ABTVME. Q.E.I.

For in the right line AE let there be taken the very small line DE of a given length, and let

DLF be the place of the line EMG, when the body was in D; and if the centripetal force be such, that a right line, whose square is equal to the area ABGE, is as the velocity of the descending body, the area itself will be as the square of that velocity; that is, if for the velocities in D and E we write V and V+I, the area ABFD will be as VV, and the area ABGE as VV+2VI+II; and by subtraction, the area DFGE as 2VI+II, and therefore $\frac{DFGE}{DE}$ will be as $\frac{2VI+II}{DE}$; that is, if we take the first ratios of those quantities when just nascent, the length DF is as the quantity $\frac{2VI}{DE}$, and therefore also as half that quantity $\frac{I \cdot V}{DE}$. But the time in which the body in falling describes the very small line DE, is directly as that line and inversely as the velocity V; and the force will be directly as the increment I of the velocity and inversely as the time; and therefore if we take the first ratios when those quantities are just nascent, as $\frac{I \cdot V}{DE}$, that is, as the length DF. Therefore a force proportional to DF or EG will cause the body to descend with a velocity that is as the right line whose square is equal to the area ABGE.   Q.E.D.

Moreover, since the time in which a very small line DE of a given length may be described is inversely as the velocity and therefore also inversely as a right line whose square is equal to the area ABFD; and since the line DL, and by consequence the nascent area DLME, will be inversely as the same right line, the time will be as the area DLME, and the sum of all the times will be as the sum of all the areas; that is (by Cor., Lem. 4), the whole time in which the line AE is described will be as the whole area ATVME.   Q.E.D.

Cor. i. Let P be the place from whence a body ought to fall, so as that, when urged by any known uniform centripetal force (such as gravity is commonly supposed to be), it may acquire in the place D a velocity equal to the velocity which another body, falling by any force whatever, hath acquired in that place D. In the perpendicular DF let there be taken DR, which may be to DF as that uniform force to the other force in the place D. Complete the rectangle PDRQ, and cut off the area ABFD equal to that rectangle. Then A will be the place from whence the other body fell. For completing the rectangle DRSE, since the area ABFD is to the area DFGE as VV to 2VI, and therefore as ½V to I, that is, as half the whole velocity to the increment of the velocity of the body falling by the variable force; and in like manner the area PQRD to the area DRSE as half the whole velocity to the increment of the velocity of the body falling by the uniform force; and since those increments (by reason of the equality of the nascent times) are as the generating forces, that is, as the ordinates DF, DR, and consequently as the nascent areas DFGE, DRSE; therefore, the whole areas ABFD, PQRD will be to each other as the halves of the whole velocities; and therefore, because the velocities are equal, they become equal also.

Cor. ii. Whence if any body be projected either upwards or downwards with a given velocity from any place D, and there be given the law of centripetal force acting on it, its velocity will be found in any other place, as e, by erecting the ordinate eg, and taking that velocity to the velocity in the place D as a right line whose square is equal to the rectangle PQRD, either increased by the curvilinear area DF*ge*, if the place *e* is below the place D, or diminished by the same area DF*ge*, if it be higher, is to the right line whose square is equal to the rectangle PQRD alone.

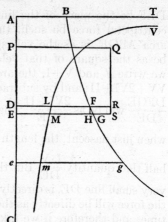

Cor. III. The time is also known by erecting the ordinate *em* inversely proportional to the square root of PQRD+or−DF*ge*, and taking the time in which the body has described the line D*e* to the time in which another body has fallen with an uniform force from P, and in falling arrived at D in the proportion of the curvilinear area DL*me* to the rectangle 2PD·DL. For the time in which a body falling with an uniform force hath described the line PD is to the time in which the same body hath described the line PE as the square root of the ratio of PD to PE; that is (the very small line DE being just nascent), in the ratio of PD to PD+½DE or 2PD to 2PD+DE, and, by subtraction, to the time in which the body hath described the small line DE, as 2PD to DE, and therefore as the rectangle 2PD·DL to the area DLME; and the time in which both the bodies described the very small line DE is to the time in which the body with the variable motion described the line D*e* as the area DLME to the area DL*me*; and therefore the first mentioned of these times is to the last as the rectangle 2PD·DL to the area DL*me*.

SECTION VIII

The determination of orbits in which bodies will revolve, being acted upon by any sort of centripetal force

Proposition 40. Theorem 13

If a body, acted upon by any centripetal force, is moved in any manner, and another body ascends or descends in a right line, and their velocities are equal in any one case of equal altitudes, their velocities will be also equal at all equal altitudes.

Let a body descend from A through D and E, to the centre C; and let another body move from V in the curved line VIK*k*. From the centre C, with any distances, describe the concentric circles DI, EK, meeting the right line AC in D and E, and the curve VIK in I and K. Draw IC meeting KE in N, and on IK let fall the perpendicular NT; and let the interval DE or IN between the circumferences of the circles be very small; and imagine the bodies in D and I to have equal velocities. Then because the distances CD and CI are equal, the centripetal forces in D and I will be also equal. Let those forces be expressed by the equal short lines DE and IN; and let the force IN (by Cor. II of the Laws of Motion) be resolved into two others, NT and IT. Then the force NT acting in the direction of the line NT perpendicular to the path ITK of the body will not at all affect or change the velocity of the body in that path, but only draw it aside from a rectilinear course, and make it deflect continually from the tangent of the orbit, and proceed in the curvilinear path ITK*k*. That

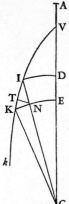

whole force, therefore, will be spent in producing this effect; but the other force IT, acting in the direction of the course of the body, will be all employed in accelerating it, and in the least given time will produce an acceleration proportional to itself. Therefore the accelerations of the bodies in D and I, produced in equal times, are as the lines DE, IT (if we take the first ratios of the nascent lines DE, IN, IK, IT, NT); and in unequal times as the product of those lines and the times. But the times in which DE and IK are described, are, by reason of the equal velocities (in D and I), as the spaces described DE and IK, and therefore the accelerations in the course of the bodies through the lines DE and IK are as DE and IT, and DE and IK conjointly; that is, as the square of DE to the rectangle IT·IK. But the rectangle IT·IK is equal to the square of IN, that is, equal to the square of DE; and therefore the accelerations generated in the passage of the bodies from D and I to E and K are equal. Therefore the velocities of the bodies in E and K are also equal: and by the same reasoning they will always be found equal in any subsequent equal distances. Q.E.D.

By the same reasoning, bodies of equal velocities and equal distances from the centre will be equally retarded in their ascent to equal distances. Q.E.D.

COR. I. Therefore if a body either oscillates by hanging to a string, or by any polished and perfectly smooth impediment is forced to move in a curved line; and another body ascends or descends in a right line, and their velocities be equal at any one equal altitude, their velocities will be also equal at all other equal altitudes. For by the string of the pendulous body, or by the impediment of a vessel perfectly smooth, the same thing will be effected as by the transverse force NT. The body is neither accelerated nor retarded by it, but only is obliged to leave its rectilinear course.

COR. II. Suppose the quantity P to be the greatest distance from the centre to which a body can ascend, whether it be oscillating, or revolving in a curve, and so the same projected upwards from any point of a curve with the velocity it has in that point. Let the quantity A be the distance of the body from the centre in any other point of the orbit; and let the centripetal force be always as the power A^{n-1}, of the quantity A, the index of which power $n-1$ is any number n diminished by unity. Then the velocity in every altitude A will be as $\sqrt{(P^n - A^n)}$, and therefore will be given. For by Prop. 39, the velocity of a body ascending and descending in a right line is in that very ratio.

PROPOSITION 41. PROBLEM 28

Supposing a centripetal force of any kind, and granting the quadratures of curvilinear figures; it is required to find as well the curves in which bodies will move, as the times of their motions in the curves found.

Let any centripetal force tend to the centre C, and let it be required to find the curve VIKk. Let there be given the circle VR, described from the centre C with any radius CV; and from the same centre describe any other circles ID, KE, cutting the curve in I and K, and the right line CV in D and E. Then draw the right line CNIX cutting the circles KE, VR in N and X, and the right line CKY meeting the circle VR in Y. Let the points I and K be indefinitely near; and let the body go on from V through I and K to k; and let the point A

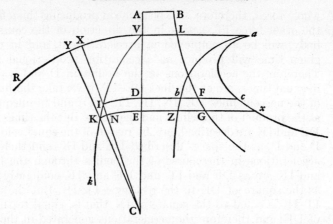

be the place from which another body is to fall, so as in the place D to acquire a velocity equal to the velocity of the first body in I. And things remaining as in Prop. 39, the short line IK, described in the least given time, will be as the velocity, and therefore as the right line whose square is equal to the area ABFD, and the triangle ICK proportional to the time will be given, and therefore KN will be inversely as the altitude IC; that is (if there be given any quantity Q, and the altitude IC be called A), as $\frac{Q}{A}$. This quantity $\frac{Q}{A}$ call Z, and suppose the magnitude of Q to be such that in some one case

$$\sqrt{ABFD} : Z = IK : KN,$$

and then in all cases

$$\sqrt{ABFD} : Z = IK : KN,$$

and

$$ABFD : ZZ = IK^2 : KN^2,$$

and by subtraction,

$$ABFD - ZZ : ZZ = IN^2 : KN^2,$$

and therefore

$$\sqrt{(ABFD - ZZ)} : Z \text{ or } \frac{Q}{A} = IN : KN,$$

and

$$A \cdot KN = \frac{Q \cdot IN}{\sqrt{(ABFD - ZZ)}}.$$

Since

$$YX \cdot XC : A \cdot KN = CX^2 : AA,$$

it follows that

$$YX \cdot XC = \frac{Q \cdot IN \cdot CX^2}{AA\sqrt{(ABFD - ZZ)}}.$$

Therefore in the perpendicular DF let there be taken continually Db, Dc equal to $\dfrac{Q}{2\sqrt{(ABFD - ZZ)}}$, $\dfrac{Q \cdot CX^2}{2AA\sqrt{(ABFD - ZZ)}}$ respectively, and let the curved lines ab, ac, the foci of the points b and c, be described; and from the point V let the perpendicular Va be erected to the line AC, cutting off the curvilinear areas VDba, VDca, and let the ordinates Ez, Ex, be erected also. Then because the rectangle D$b \cdot$ IN or DbzE is equal to half the rectangle A $\cdot$ KN, or to the triangle ICK; and the rectangle D$c \cdot$ IN or DcxE is equal to half the rectangle YX $\cdot$ XC, or to the triangle XCY; that is, because the nascent particles DbzE, ICK of the areas VDba, VIC are always equal; and the nascent particles DcxE,

XCY of the areas VD*ca*, VCX are always equal: therefore the generated area VD*ba* will be equal to the generated area VIC, and therefore proportional to the time; and the generated area VD*ca* is equal to the generated sector VCX. If, therefore, any time be given during which the body has been moving from V, there will be also given the area proportional to it VD*ba*; and thence will be given the altitude of the body CD or CI; and the area VD*ca*, and the sector VCX equal thereto, together with its angle VCI. But the angle VCI, and the altitude CI being given, there is also given the place I, in which the body will be found at the end of that time.   Q.E.I.

COR. I. Hence the greatest and least altitudes of the bodies, that is, the apsides of the curves, may be found very readily. For the apsides are those points in which a right line IC drawn through the centre falls perpendicularly upon the curves VIK; which comes to pass when the right lines IK and NK become equal; that is, when the area ABFD is equal to ZZ.

COR. II. So also the angle KIN, in which the curve at any place cuts the line IC, may be readily found by the given altitude IC of the body; namely, by making the sine of that angle to the radius as KN to IK, that is, as Z to the square root of the area ABFD.

COR. III. If to the centre C, and the principal vertex V, there be described a conic section VRS; and from any point thereof, as R, there be drawn the tangent RT meeting the axis CV indefinitely produced in the point T; and then

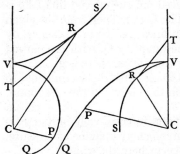

joining CR there be drawn the right line CP, equal to the abscissa CT, making an angle VCP proportional to the sector VCR; and if a centripetal force inversely proportional to the cubes of the distances of the places from the centre, tends to the centre C; and from the place V there sets out a body with a just velocity in the direction of a line perpendicular to the right line CV; that body will proceed in a curve VPQ, which the point P will always touch; and therefore if the conic section VRS be an hyperbola, the body will descend to the centre; but if it be an ellipse, it will ascend continually, and go farther and farther off *in infinitum*. And, on the contrary, if a body endued with any velocity goes off from the place V, and according as it begins either to descend obliquely to the centre, or to ascend obliquely from it, the figure VRS be either an hyperbola or an ellipse, the curve may be found by increasing or diminishing the angle VCP in a given ratio. And the centripetal force becoming centrifugal, the body will ascend obliquely in the curve VPQ, which is found by taking the angle VCP proportional to the elliptic sector VRC, and the length CP equal to the length CT, as before. All these things follow from the foregoing Proposition, by the quadrature of a certain curve, the invention of which, as being easy enough, for brevity's sake I omit.

PROPOSITION 42. PROBLEM 29

The law of centripetal force being given, it is required to find the motion of a body setting out from a given place, with a given velocity, in the direction of a given right line.

Suppose the same things as in the three preceding Propositions; and let the body go off from the place I in the direction of the little line IK, with the same velocity as another body, by falling with an uniform centripetal force from the place P, may acquire in D; and let this uniform force be to the force with which the body is at first urged in I, as DR to DF. Let the body go on towards k; and

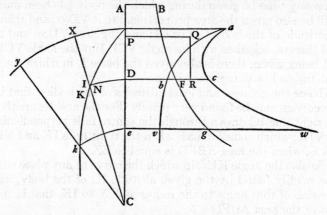

about the centre C, with the radius Ck, describe the circle ke, meeting the right line PD in e, and let there be erected the lines eg, ev, ew, ordinately applied to the curves BFg, abv, acw. From the given rectangle PDRQ and the given law of centripetal force, by which the first body is acted on, the curved line BFg is also given, by the construction of Prop. 27, and its Cor. I. Then from the given angle CIK is given the proportion of the nascent lines IK, KN; and thence, by the construction of Prob. 28, there is given the quantity Q, with the curved lines abv, acw; and therefore, at the end of any time Dbve, there is given both the altitude of the body Ce or Ck, and the area Dcwe, with the sector equal to it XCy, the angle ICk, and the place k, in which the body will then be found.

Q.E.I.

We suppose in these Propositions the centripetal force to vary in its recess from the centre according to some law, which anyone may imagine at pleasure, but at equal distances from the centre to be everywhere the same.

I have hitherto considered the motions of bodies in immovable orbits. It remains now to add something concerning their motions in orbits which revolve round the centres of force.

SECTION IX

The motion of bodies in movable orbits; and the motion of the apsides

Proposition 43. Problem 30

It is required to make a body move in a curve that revolves about the centre of force in the same manner as another body in the same curve at rest.

In the fixed orbit VPK, let the body P revolve, proceeding from V towards K. From the centre C let there be continually drawn Cp, equal to CP, making the angle VCp proportional to the angle VCP; and the area which the line Cp describes will be to the area VCP, which the line CP describes at the same time, as the velocity of the describing line Cp to the velocity of the describing line

CP; that is, as the angle VCp to the angle VCP, therefore in a given ratio, and therefore proportional to the time. Since, then, the area described by the line Cp in a fixed plane is proportional to the time, it is manifest that a body, being

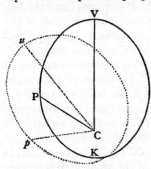

acted upon by a suitable centripetal force, may revolve with the point p in the curved line which the same point p, by the method just now explained, may be made to describe in a fixed plane. Make the angle VCu equal to the angle PCp, and the line Cu equal to CV, and the figure uCp equal to the figure VCP, and the body being always in the point p, will move in the perimeter of the revolving figure uCp, and will describe its (revolving) arc up in the same time that the other body P describes the similar and equal arc VP in the fixed figure VPK. Find, then, by Cor. v, Prop. 6, the centripetal force by which the body may be made to revolve in the curved line which the point p describes in a fixed plane, and the Problem will be solved.   Q.E.F.

PROPOSITION 44. THEOREM 14

The difference of the forces, by which two bodies may be made to move equally, one in a fixed, the other in the same orbit revolving, varies inversely as the cube of their common altitudes.

Let the parts of the fixed orbit VP, PK be similar and equal to the parts of the revolving orbit up, pk; and let the distance of the points P and K be supposed of the utmost smallness. Let fall a perpendicular kr from the point k to the right line pC, and produce it to m, so that mr may be to kr as the angle VCp to the angle VCP. Because the altitudes of the bodies PC and pC, KC and kC, are always equal, it is manifest that the increments or decrements of the lines PC and pC are always equal; and therefore if each of the several motions of the bodies in the places P and p be resolved into two (by Cor. II of the Laws of Motion), one of which is directed towards the centre, or according to the lines PC, pC, and the other, transverse to the former, hath a direction perpendicular to the lines PC and pC; the motions towards the centre will be equal, and the transverse motion of the body p will be to the trans-

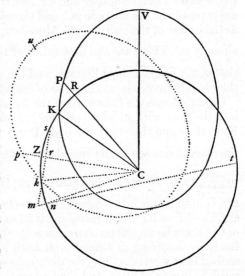

verse motion of the body P as the angular motion of the line pC to the angular motion of the line PC; that is, as the angle VCp to the angle VCP. Therefore, at the same time that the body P, by both its motions, comes to the point K, the body p, having an equal motion towards the centre, will be equally moved from p towards C; and therefore that time being expired, it will be found some-where in the line mkr, which, passing through the point k, is perpendicular to the line pC; and by its transverse motion will acquire a distance from the line pC, that will be to the distance which the other body P acquires from the line PC as the transverse motion of the body p to the transverse motion of the other body P. Therefore since kr is equal to the distance which the body P ac-quires from the line PC, and mr is to kr as the angle VCp to the angle VCP, that is, as the transverse motion of the body p to the transverse motion of the body P, it is manifest that the body p, at the expiration of that time, will be found in the place m. These things will be so, if the bodies p and P are equally moved in the directions of the lines pC and PC, and are therefore urged with equal forces in those directions. But if we take an angle pCn that is to the angle pCk as the angle VCp to the angle VCP, and nC be equal to kC, in that case the body p at the expiration of the time will really be in n; and is therefore urged with a greater force than the body P, if the angle nCp is greater than the angle kCp, that is, *if* the orbit upk moves either progressively, or in a retrograde direction, with a velocity greater than the double of that with which the line CP is carried forwards; and with a less force if the retrograde motion of the orbit is slower. And the difference of the forces will be as the interval mn of the places through which the body would be carried by the action of that difference in that given space of time. About the centre C with the interval Cn or Ck suppose a circle described cutting the lines mr, mn produced in s and t, and the rectangle $mn \cdot mt$ will be equal to the rectangle $mk \cdot ms$, and therefore mn will be equal to $\dfrac{mk \cdot ms}{mt}$. But since the triangles pCk, pCn, in a given time, are of a given magnitude, kr and mr, and their difference mk, and their sum ms, are inversely as the altitude pC, and therefore the rectangle $mk \cdot ms$ is inversely as the square of the altitude pC. Moreover, mt is directly as $\frac{1}{2}mt$, that is, as the altitude pC. These are the first ratios of the nascent lines; and hence $\dfrac{mk \cdot ms}{mt}$, that is, the nascent short line mn, and the difference of the forces proportional thereto, are inversely as the cube of the altitude pC. Q.E.D.

Cor. I. Hence the difference of the forces in the places P and p, or K and k, is to the force with which a body may revolve with a circular motion from R to K, in the same time that the body P in a fixed orbit describes the arc PK, as the nascent line mn to the versed sine of the nascent arc RK, that is, as $\dfrac{mk \cdot ms}{mt}$ to $\dfrac{rk^2}{2k\text{C}}$, or as $mk \cdot ms$ to the square of rk; that is, if we take given quantities F and G in the same ratio to each other as the angle VCP bears to the angle VCp, as GG $-$ FF to FF. And, therefore, if from the centre C, with any distance CP or Cp, there be described a circular sector equal to the whole area VPC, which the body revolving in a fixed orbit hath by a radius drawn to the centre de-scribed in any certain time, the difference of the forces, with which the body P revolves in a fixed orbit, and the body p in a movable orbit, will be to the cen-tripetal force, with which another body by a radius drawn to the centre can uniformly describe that sector in the same time as the area VPC is described, as GG $-$ FF to FF. For that sector and the area pCk are to each other as the times in which they are described.

COR. II. If the orbit VPK be an ellipse, having its focus C, and its highest apse V, and we suppose the ellipse upk similar and equal to it, so that pC may be always equal to PC, and the angle VCp be to the angle VCP in the given ratio of G to F; and for the altitude PC or pC we put A, and 2R for the latus

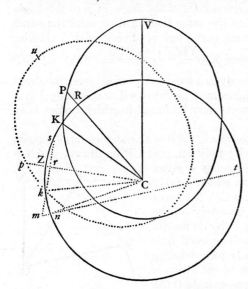

rectum of the ellipse, the force with which a body may be made to revolve in a movable ellipse will be as $\dfrac{FF}{AA} + \dfrac{RGG - RFF}{A^3}$, and conversely.

Let the force with which a body may revolve in a fixed ellipse be expressed by the quantity $\dfrac{FF}{AA}$, and the force in V will be $\dfrac{FF}{CV^2}$. But the force with which a body may revolve in a circle at the distance CV, with the same velocity as a body revolving in an ellipse has in V, is to the force with which a body revolving in an ellipse is acted upon in the apse V, as half the latus rectum of the ellipse to the semidiameter CV of the circle, and there-

fore is as $\dfrac{RFF}{CV^3}$; and the force which is to this as GG−FF to FF, is as $\dfrac{RGG - RFF}{CV^3}$; and this force (by Cor. I of this Prop.) is the difference of the forces in V, with which the body P revolves in the fixed ellipse VPK, and the body p in the movable ellipse upk. Then since by this Proposition that difference at any other altitude A is to itself at the altitude CV as $\dfrac{1}{A^3}$ to $\dfrac{1}{CV^2}$, the same difference in every altitude A will be as $\dfrac{RGG - RFF}{A^3}$. Therefore to the force $\dfrac{FF}{AA}$, by which the body may revolve in a fixed ellipse VPK, add the excess $\dfrac{RGG - RFF}{A^3}$, and the sum will be the whole force $\dfrac{FF}{AA} + \dfrac{RGG - RFF}{A^3}$ by which a body may revolve in the same time in the movable ellipse upk.

COR. III. In the same manner it will be found, that, if the fixed orbit VPK be an ellipse having its centre in the centre of the forces C, and there be supposed a movable ellipse upk, similar, equal, and concentric to it; and 2R be the principal latus rectum of that ellipse, and 2T the latus transversum, or greater axis; and the angle VCp be continually to the angle VCP as G to F; the forces with which bodies may revolve in the fixed and movable ellipse, in equal times, will be as $\dfrac{FFA}{T^3}$ and $\dfrac{FFA}{T^3} + \dfrac{RGG - RFF}{A^3}$ respectively.

COR. IV. And universally, if the greatest altitude CV of the body be called T, and the radius of the curvature which the orbit VPK has in V, that is, the radius of a circle equally curved, be called R, and the centripetal force with which a body may revolve in any fixed curve VPK at the place V be called $\frac{VFF}{TT}$, and in other places P be indefinitely styled X; and the altitude CP be called A, and G be taken to F in the given ratio of the angle VCp to the angle VCP; the centripetal force with which the same body will perform the same motions in the same time, in the same curve upk revolving with a circular motion, will be as the sum of the forces $X + \frac{VRGG - VRFF}{A^3}$.

COR. V. Therefore the motion of a body in a fixed orbit being given, its angular motion round the centre of the forces may be increased or diminished in a given ratio; and thence new fixed orbits may be found in which bodies may revolve with new centripetal forces.

COR. VI. Therefore if there be erected the line VP of an indeterminate length, perpendicular to the line CV given by position, and CP be drawn, and Cp equal to it, making the angle VCp having a given ratio to the angle VCP, the force with which a body may revolve in the curved line Vpk, which the point p is continually describing, will be inversely as the cube of the altitude Cp. For the body P, by its inertia alone, no other force impelling it, will proceed uniformly in the right line VP. Add, then, a force tending to the centre C inversely as the cube of the altitude CP or Cp, and (by what was just demonstrated) the

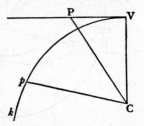

body will deflect from the rectilinear motion into the curved line Vpk. But this curve Vpk is the same with the curve VPQ found in Cor. III, Prop. 41, in which, I said, bodies attracted with such forces would ascend obliquely.

PROPOSITION 45. PROBLEM 31

To find the motion of the apsides in orbits approaching very near to circles.

This problem is solved arithmetically by reducing the orbit, which a body revolving in a movable ellipse (as in Cor. II and III of the above Prop.) describes in a fixed plane, to the figure of the orbit whose apsides are required; and then seeking the apsides of the orbit which that body describes in a fixed plane. But orbits acquire the same figure, if the centripetal forces with which they are described, compared between themselves, are made proportional at equal altitudes. Let the point V be the highest apse, and write T for the greatest altitude CV, A for any other altitude CP or Cp, and X for the difference of the altitudes CV−CP; and the force with which a body moves in an ellipse revolving about its focus C (as in Cor. II), and which in Cor. II was as $\frac{FF}{AA} + \frac{RGG - RFF}{A^3}$, that is, as $\frac{FFA + RGG - RFF}{A^3}$, by substituting T−X for A, will become as $\frac{RGG - RFF + TFF - FFX}{A^3}$. In like manner any other centripetal force is to be reduced to a fraction whose denominator is A^3, and the numerators are to be made analogous by collating together the homologous terms. This will be made plainer by Examples.

EXAM. I. Let us suppose the centripetal force to be uniform, and therefore as

$\frac{A^3}{A^3}$, or, writing $T-X$ for A in the numerator, as $\frac{T^3-3TTX+3TXX-X^3}{A^3}$. Then collating together the correspondent terms of the numerators, that is, those that consist of given quantities with those of given quantities, and those of quantities not given with those of quantities not given, it will become

$$RGG-RFF+TFF : T^3 = -FFX : -3TTX+3TXX-X^3$$
$$= -FF : -3TT+3TX-XX.$$

Now since the orbit is supposed extremely near to a circle, let it coincide with a circle; and because in that case R and T become equal, and X is infinitely diminished, the last ratios will be

$$GG : T^2 = -FF : -3TT,$$

and again, $\qquad GG : FF = TT : 3TT = 1 : 3;$

and therefore G is to F, that is, the angle VCp to the angle VCP, as 1 to $\sqrt{3}$. Therefore since the body, in a fixed ellipse, in descending from the upper to the lower apse, describes an angle, if I may so speak, of 180°, the other body in a movable ellipse, and therefore in the fixed plane we are treating of, will in its descent from the upper to the lower apse, describe an angle VCp of $\frac{180°}{\sqrt{3}}$. And this comes to pass by reason of the likeness of this orbit which a body acted upon by an uniform centripetal force describes, and of that orbit which a body performing its circuits in a revolving ellipse will describe in a fixed plane. By this collation of the terms, these orbits are made similar; not universally, indeed, but then only when they approach very near to a circular figure. A body, therefore, revolving with an uniform centripetal force in an orbit nearly circular, will always describe an angle of $\frac{180°}{\sqrt{3}}$, or 103° 55′ 23″ at the centre; moving from the upper apse to the lower apse when it has once described that angle, and thence returning to the upper apse when it has described that angle again; and so on *in infinitum*.

EXAM. 2. Suppose the centripetal force to be as any power of the altitude A, as, for example, A^{n-3}, or $\frac{A^n}{A^3}$; where $n-3$ and n signify any indices of powers whatever, whether integers or fractions, rational or surd, affirmative or negative. That numerator A^n or $(T-X)^n$ being reduced to an indeterminate series by my method of converging series, will become

$$T^n - nXT^{n-1} + \frac{nn-n}{2}XXT^{n-2}, \&c.$$

And comparing these terms with the terms of the other numerator,

$$RGG - RFF + TFF - FFX,$$

it becomes

$$RGG - RFF + TFF : T^n = -FF : -nT^{n-1} + \frac{nn-n}{2}XT^{n-2}, \&c.$$

And taking the last ratios where the orbits approach to circles, it becomes

$$RGG : T^n = -FF : -nT^{n-1},$$

or, $\qquad GG : T^{n-1} = FF : nT^{n-1},$

and again, $\qquad GG : FF = T^{n-1} : nT^{n-1} = 1 : n;$

and therefore G is to F, that is, the angle VCp to the angle VCP, as 1 to $\sqrt{n}$. Therefore since the angle VCP, described in the descent of the body from the upper apse to the lower apse in an ellipse, is of 180°, the angle VCp, described in the descent of the body from the upper apse to the lower apse in an orbit nearly circular which a body describes with a centripetal force proportional to the power A^{n-3}, will be equal to an angle of $\dfrac{180°}{\sqrt{n}}$, and this angle being repeated, the body will return from the lower to the upper apse, and so on *in infinitum*. As if the centripetal force be as the distance of the body from the centre, that is, as A, or $\dfrac{A^4}{A^3}$, n will be equal to 4, and $\sqrt{n}$ equal to 2; and therefore the angle between the upper and the lower apse will be equal to $\dfrac{180°}{2}$, or 90°. Therefore the body having performed a fourth part of one revolution, will arrive at the lower apse, and having performed another fourth part, will arrive at the upper apse, and so on *in infinitum*. This appears also from Prop. x. For a body acted on by this centripetal force will revolve in a fixed ellipse, whose centre is the centre of force. If the centripetal force is inversely as the distance, that is, directly as $\dfrac{1}{A}$ or $\dfrac{A^2}{A^3}$, n will be equal to 2; and therefore the angle between the upper and the lower apse will be $\dfrac{180°}{\sqrt{2}}$, or 127° 16′ 45″; and hence a body revolving with such a force will, by a continual repetition of this angle, move alternately from the upper to the lower and from the lower to the upper apse forever. So, also, if the centripetal force be inversely as the fourth root of the eleventh power of the altitude, that is, inversely as $A^{\frac{11}{4}}$, and therefore directly as $\dfrac{1}{A^{\frac{11}{4}}}$, or as $\dfrac{A^{\frac{1}{4}}}{A^3}$, n will be equal to ¼, and $\dfrac{180°}{\sqrt{n}}$ will be equal to 360°; and therefore the body parting from the upper apse, and from thence continually descending, will arrive at the lower apse when it has completed one entire revolution; and thence ascending continually, when it has completed another entire revolution, it will arrive again at the upper apse; and so alternately forever.

Exam. 3. Taking m and n for any indices of the powers of the altitude, and b and c for any given numbers, suppose the centripetal force to be as $(bA^m + cA^n) \div A^3$, that is, as $[b(T-X)^m \div c(T-X)^n] \div A^3$, or (by the method of converging series above mentioned) as

$$[bT^m + cT^n - mbXT^{m-1} - ncXT^{n-1} + \frac{mm-m}{2}\,bXXT^{m-2} + \frac{nn-n}{2}$$
$$- cXXT^{n-2}, \&c.] \div A^3;$$

and comparing the terms of the numerators, there will arise,

$$RGG - RFF + TFF : bT^m + cT^n = -FF : -mbT^{m-1} - ncT^{n-1} +$$
$$\frac{mm-m}{2}\,bXT^{m-2} + \frac{nn-n}{2}\,cXT^{n-2}, \&c.$$

And taking the last ratios that arise when the orbits come to a circular form, there will come forth

$$GG : bT^{m-1} + cT^{n-1} = FF : mbT^{m-1} + ncT^{n-1};$$

and again, $GG : FF = bT^{m-1} + cT^{n-1} : mbT^{m-1} + ncT^{n-1}$.

This proportion, by expressing the greatest altitude CV or T arithmetically by unity, becomes, $GG : FF = b + c : mb + nc = 1 : \dfrac{mb+nc}{b+c}$. Whence G becomes to F, that is, the angle VCp to the angle VCP, as 1 to $\sqrt{\dfrac{mb+nc}{b+c}}$. And therefore, since the angle VCP between the upper and the lower apse, in a fixed ellipse, is of 180°, the angle VCp between the same apsides in an orbit which a body describes with a centripetal force, that is, as $\dfrac{bA^m + cA^n}{A^3}$, will be equal to an angle of 180° $\sqrt{\dfrac{b+c}{mb+nc}}$. And by the same reasoning, if the centripetal force be as $\dfrac{bA^m - cA^n}{A^3}$, the angle between the apsides will be found equal to

$$180° \sqrt{\frac{b-c}{mb-nc}}.$$

After the same manner the Problem is solved in more difficult cases. The quantity to which the centripetal force is proportional must always be resolved into a converging series whose denominator is A^3. Then the given part of the numerator arising from that operation is to be supposed in the same ratio to that part of it which is not given, as the given part of this numerator RGG − RFF + TFF − FFX is to that part of the same numerator which is not given. And taking away the superfluous quantities, and writing unity for T, the proportion of G to F is obtained.

COR. I. Hence if the centripetal force be as any power of the altitude, that power may be found from the motion of the apsides; and conversely. That is, if the whole angular motion, with which the body returns to the same apse, be to the angular motion of one revolution, or 360°, as any number as m to another as n, and the altitude be called A; the force will be as the power $A^{\frac{nn}{mm}-3}$ of the altitude A; the index of which power is $\dfrac{nn}{mm} - 3$. This appears by the second Example. Hence it is plain that the force in its recess from the centre cannot decrease in a greater than a cubed ratio of the altitude. A body revolving with such a force, and parting from the apse, if it once begins to descend, can never arrive at the lower apse or least altitude, but will descend to the centre, describing the curved line treated of in Cor. III, Prop. 41. But if it should, at its parting from the lower apse, begin to ascend ever so little, it will ascend *in infinitum*, and never come to the upper apse; but will describe the curved line spoken of in the same Cor., and Cor. VI, Prop. 45. So that where the force in its recess from the centre decreases in a greater than a cubed ratio of the altitude, the body at its parting from the apse, will either descend to the centre, or ascend *in infinitum*, according as it descends or ascends at the beginning of its motion. But if the force in its recess from the centre either decreases in a less than a cubed ratio of the altitude, or increases in any ratio of the altitude whatsoever, the body will never descend to the centre, but will at some time arrive at the lower apse; and, on the contrary, if the body alternately ascending and descending from one apse to another never comes to the centre, then either the force increases in the recess from the centre, or it decreases in a less than a cubed ratio of the altitude; and the sooner the body returns from one apse to another, the farther is the ratio of the forces from the cubed ratio. As if the body should return to and from the upper apse by an alternate descent and ascent in 8 revolutions, or in 4, or 2, or 1½; that is, if m should be to n as 8, or 4, or 2, or 1½ to 1, and therefore $\dfrac{nn}{mm} - 3$, be $\frac{1}{64} - 3$, or $\frac{1}{16} - 3$, or $\frac{1}{4} - 3$, or $\frac{4}{9} - 3$; then the force will be as $A^{\frac{1}{64}-3}$, or $A^{\frac{1}{16}-3}$, or $A^{\frac{1}{4}-3}$, or $A^{\frac{4}{9}-3}$; that is, it will be inversely as $A^{3-\frac{1}{64}}$, or $A^{3-\frac{1}{16}}$, or $A^{3-\frac{1}{4}}$, or $A^{3-\frac{4}{9}}$. If the body after each revolution returns to the same apse, and the apse remains unmoved, then m will be to n as 1 to 1, and therefore $A^{\frac{nn}{mm}-3}$ will be equal to A^{-2}, or $\dfrac{1}{AA}$; and therefore the decrease of the forces will be in a squared ratio of the altitude; as was demonstrated above. If the body in three fourth parts, or two thirds, or one third, or one fourth part of an entire revolution, return to the same apse; m will be to n as ¾ or ⅔ or ⅓ or ¼ to 1, and therefore $A^{\frac{nn}{mm}-3}$ is equal to $A^{\frac{16}{9}-3}$, or $A^{\frac{9}{4}-3}$, or A^{9-3}, or A^{16-3}; and therefore the force is either inversely as $A^{\frac{11}{9}}$ or $A^{\frac{3}{4}}$, or directly as A^6 or A^{13}. Lastly if the body in its progress from the upper apse to the same upper apse again, goes over one entire revolution and three degrees more, and therefore that apse in each revolution of the body moves forward three degrees, then m will be to n as 363° to 360°, or as 121 to 120, and therefore $A^{\frac{nn}{mm}-3}$ will be equal to $A^{-\frac{29523}{14641}}$, and therefore the centripetal force will be inversely as $A^{\frac{29523}{14641}}$, or inversely as $A^{2\frac{4}{243}}$ very nearly. Therefore the centripetal force decreases in a ratio something greater than the squared ratio; but approaching 59¾ times nearer to the squared than the cubed.

Cor. ii. Hence also if a body, urged by a centripetal force which is inversely as the square of the altitude, revolves in an ellipse whose focus is in the centre of the forces; and a new and foreign force should be added to or subtracted from this centripetal force, the motion of the apsides arising from that foreign force may (by the third Example) be known; and conversely: If the force with which the body revolves in the ellipse be as $\dfrac{1}{AA}$; and the foreign force as cA, and therefore the remaining force as $\dfrac{A-cA^4}{A^3}$; then (by the third Example) b will be equal to 1, m equal to 1, and n equal to 4; and therefore the angle of revolution between the apsides is equal to $180°\sqrt{\dfrac{1-c}{1-4c}}$. Suppose that foreign force to be 357.45 times less than the other force with which the body revolves in the ellipse; that is, c to be $\frac{100}{35745}$, A or T being equal to 1; and then $180°$ $\sqrt{\dfrac{1-c}{1-4c}}$ will be $180°$ $\sqrt{\frac{35645}{35345}}$ or $180°\cdot7623$, that is, $180°\ 45'\ 44''$. Therefore the body, parting from the upper apse, will arrive at the lower apse with an angular motion of $180°\ 45'\ 44''$, and this angular motion being repeated, will return to the upper apse; and therefore the upper apse in each revolution will go forward $1°\ 31'\ 28''$. The apse of the moon is about twice as swift.

So much for the motion of bodies in orbits whose planes pass through the centre of force. It now remains to determine those motions in eccentric planes. For those authors who treat of the motion of heavy bodies used to consider the ascent and descent of such bodies, not only in a perpendicular direction, but at all degrees of obliquity upon any given planes; and for the same reason we are to consider in this place the motions of bodies tending to centres by means of any forces whatsoever, when those bodies move in eccentric planes. These planes are supposed to be perfectly smooth and polished, so as not to retard the motion of the bodies in the least. Moreover, in these demonstrations, instead of the planes upon which those bodies roll or slide, and which are therefore tangent planes to the bodies, I shall use planes parallel to them, in which the centres of the bodies move, and by that motion describe orbits. And by the same method I afterwards determine the motions of bodies performed in curved surfaces.

SECTION X

THE MOTION OF BODIES IN GIVEN SURFACES; AND THE OSCILLATING PENDULOUS MOTION OF BODIES

PROPOSITION 46. PROBLEM 32

Any kind of centripetal force being supposed, and the centre of force, and any plane whatsoever in which the body revolves, being given, and the quadratures of curvilinear figures being allowed; it is required to determine the motion of a body going off from a given plane with a given velocity, in the direction of a given right line in that plane.

Let S be the centre of force, SC the least distance of that centre from the given plane, P a body issuing from the place P in the direction of the right line PZ, Q the same body revolving in its curve, and PQR the curve itself which is required to be found, described in that given plane. Join CQ, QS, and if in QS

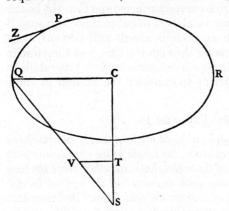

we take SV proportional to the centripetal force with which the body is attracted towards the centre S, and draw VT parallel to CQ, and meeting SC in T; then will the force SV be resolved into two (by Cor. II of the Laws of Motion), the force ST, and the force TV; of which ST attracting the body in the direction of a line perpendicular to that plane, does not at all change its motion in that plane. But the action of the other force TV, coinciding with the position of the plane itself, attracts the body directly towards the given point C in that plane; and therefore causes the body to move in the plane in the same manner as if the force ST were taken away, and the body were to revolve in free space about the centre C by means of the force TV alone. But there being given the centripetal force TV with which the body Q revolves in free space about the given centre C, there is given (by Prop. 42) the curve PQR which the body describes; the place Q, in which the body will be found at any given time; and, lastly, the velocity of the body in that place Q. And conversely.   Q.E.I.

PROPOSITION 47. THEOREM 15

Supposing the centripetal force to be proportional to the distance of the body from the centre; all bodies revolving in any planes whatsoever will describe ellipses, and complete their revolutions in equal times; and those which move in right lines, running backwards and forwards alternately, will complete their several periods of going and returning in the same times.

For letting all things stand as in the foregoing Proposition, the force SV, with which the body Q revolving in any plane PQR is attracted towards the centre S, is as the distance SQ; and therefore because SV and SQ, TV and CQ are proportional, the force TV with which the body is attracted towards the given point C in the plane of the orbit, is as the distance CQ. Therefore the forces with which bodies found in the plane PQR are attracted towards the point C, are in proportion to the distances equal to the forces with which the same bodies are attracted every way towards the centre S; and therefore the bodies will move in the same times, and in the same figures, in any plane PQR about the point C, as they would do in free spaces about the centre S; and therefore (by Cor. ɪɪ, Prop. 10, and Cor. ɪɪ, Prop. 38) they will in equal times either describe ellipses in that plane about the centre C, or move to and fro in right lines passing through the centre C in that plane; completing the same periods of time in all cases.   Q.E.D.

SCHOLIUM

The ascent and descent of bodies in curved surfaces has a near relation to these motions we have been speaking of. Imagine curved lines to be described on any plane, and to revolve about any given axes passing through the centre of force, and by that revolution to describe curved surfaces; and that the bodies move in such sort that their centres may be always found in those surfaces. If those bodies oscillate to and fro with an oblique ascent and descent, their motions will be performed in planes passing through the axis, and therefore in the curved lines, by whose revolution those curved surfaces were generated. In those cases, therefore, it will be sufficient to consider the motion in those curved lines.

PROPOSITION 48. THEOREM 16

If a wheel stands upon the outside of a globe at right angles thereto, and revolving about its own axis goes forwards in a great circle, the length of the curvilinear path which any point, given in the perimeter of the wheel, hath described since the time that it touched the globe (which curvilinear path we may call the cycloid or epicycloid), will be to double the versed sine of half the arc which since that time hath touched the globe in passing over it, as the sum of the diameters of the globe and the wheel to the semidiameter of the globe.

PROPOSITION 49. THEOREM 17

If a wheel stands upon the inside of a concave globe at right angles thereto, and revolving about its own axis goes forwards in one of the great circles of the globe, the length of the curvilinear path which any point, given in the perimeter of the wheel, hath described since it touched the globe, will be to the double of the versed sine of half the arc which in all that time hath touched the globe in passing over it, as the difference of the diameters of the globe and the wheel to the semidiameter of the globe.

Let ABL be the globe, C its centre, BPV the wheel resting on it, E the centre of the wheel, B the point of contact, and P the given point in the perimeter of the wheel. Imagine this wheel to proceed in the great circle ABL from A through B towards L, and in its progress to revolve in such a manner that the arcs AB, PB may be always equal one to the other, and the given point P in the perimeter of the wheel may describe in the meantime the curvilinear path AP. Let AP be the whole curvilinear path described since the wheel touched the globe in A, and the length of this path AP will be to twice the versed sine of the arc ½PB as 2CE to CB. For let the right line CE (produced if need be) meet the wheel in V, and join CP, BP, EP, VP; produce CP, and let fall thereon the perpendicular VF. Let PH, VH, meeting in H, touch the circle in P and V, and let PH cut VF in G, and to VP let fall the perpendiculars GI, HK. From

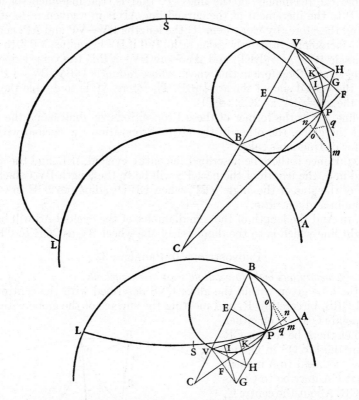

the centre C with any radius let there be described the circle *nom*, cutting the right line CP in *n*, the perimeter of the wheel BP in *o*, and the curvilinear path AP in *m*; and from the centre V with the radius V*o* let there be described a circle cutting VP produced in *q*.

Because the wheel in its progress always revolves about the point of contact B, it is manifest that the right line BP is perpendicular to that curved line AP which the point P of the wheel describes, and therefore that the right line VP will touch this curve in the point P. Let the radius of the circle *nom* be gradually increased or diminished so that at last it becomes equal to the distance CP; and by reason of the similitude of the evanescent figure P*nomq*, and the figure PFGVI, the ultimate ratio of the evanescent short lines P*m*, P*n*, P*o*, P*q*, that is, the ratio of the momentary increments of the curve AP, the right line CP, the circular arc BP, and the right line VP, will be the same as of the lines

PV, PF, PG, PI, respectively. But since VF is perpendicular to CF, and VH to CV, and therefore the angles HVG, VCF equal; and the angle VHG (because the angles of the quadrilateral HVEP are right in V and P) is equal to the angle CEP, the triangles VHG, CEP will be similar; and thence it will come to pass that $$EP : CE = HG : HV \text{ or } HP = KI : PK,$$ and by addition or subtraction,

$$CB : CE = PI : PK,$$

and $$CB : 2CE = PI : PV = Pq : Pm.$$

Therefore the decrement of the line VP, that is, the increment of the line BV−VP to the increment of the curved line AP is in a given ratio of CB to 2CE, and therefore (by Cor., Lem. 4) the lengths BV−VP and AP, generated by those increments, are in the same ratio. But if BV be radius, VP is the cosine of the angle BVP or ½BEP, and therefore BV−VP is the versed sine of the same angle, and therefore in this wheel, whose radius is ½BV, BV−VP will be double the versed sine of the arc ½BP. Therefore AP is to double the versed sine of the arc ½BP as 2CE to CB.   Q.E.D.

The line AP in the former of these Propositions we shall name the cycloid without the globe, the other in the latter Proposition the cycloid within the globe, for distinction's sake.

Cor. I. Hence if there be described the entire cycloid ASL, and the same be bisected in S, the length of the part PS will be to the length PV (which is the double of the sine of the angle VBP, when EB is radius) as 2CE to CB, and therefore in a given ratio.

Cor. II. And the length of the semidiameter of the cycloid AS will be equal to a right line which is to the diameter of the wheel BV as 2CE to CB.

Proposition 50. Problem 33

To cause a pendulous body to oscillate in a given cycloid.

Let there be given within the globe QVS described with the centre C, the cycloid QRS, bisected in R, and meeting the surface of the globe with its extreme points Q and S on either hand. Let there be drawn CR bisecting the arc QS in O, and let it be produced to A in such sort that CA may be to CO as CO to CR. About the centre C, with the radius CA, let there be described an exterior globe DAF; and within this globe, by a wheel whose diameter is AO, let there be described two semicycloids AQ, AS, touching the interior globe in Q and S, and meeting the exterior globe in A. From that point A, with a thread APT in length equal to the line AR, let the body T be suspended and oscillated in such manner between the two

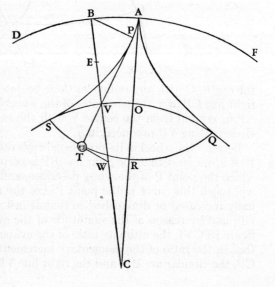

semicycloids AQ, AS, that, as often as the pendulum parts from the perpendicular AR, the upper part of the thread AP may be applied to that semicycloid APS towards which the motion tends, and fold itself round that curved line, as if it were some solid obstacle, the remaining part of the same thread PT which has not yet touched the semicycloid continuing straight. Then will the weight T oscillate in the given cycloid QRS.   Q.E.F.

For let the thread PT meet the cycloid QRS in T, and the circle QOS in V, and let CV be drawn; and to the rectilinear part of the thread PT from the extreme points P and T let there be erected the perpendiculars BP, TW, meeting the right line CV in B and W. It is evident, from the construction and generation of the similar figures AS, SR, that those perpendiculars PB, TW, cut off from CV the lengths VB, VW, equal the diameters of the wheels OA, OR. Therefore TP is to VP (which is double the sine of the angle VBP when ½BV is radius) as BW to BV, or AO+OR to AO, that is (since CA and CO, CO and CR, and by division AO and OR are proportional), as CA+CO to CA, or, if BV be bisected in E, as 2CE to CB. Therefore (by Cor. I, Prop. 49), the length of the rectilinear part of the thread PT is always equal to the arc of the cycloid PS, and the whole thread APT is always equal to half the cycloid APS, that is (by Cor. II, Prop. 49), to the length AR. And conversely, if the string is always equal to the length AR, the point T will always move in the given cycloid QRS.
                    Q.E.D.

Cor. The string AR is equal to the semicycloid AS, and therefore has the same ratio to AC, the semidiameter of the exterior globe, as the like semicycloid SR has to CO, the semidiameter of the interior globe.

Proposition 51. Theorem 18

If a centripetal force tending on all sides to the centre C of a globe, be in all places as the distance of the place from the centre; and, by this force alone acting upon it, the body T oscillate (in the manner above described) in the perimeter of the cycloid QRS: I say, that all the oscillations, howsoever unequal in themselves, will be performed in equal times.

For upon the tangent TW indefinitely produced let fall the perpendicular CX, and join CT. Because the centripetal force with which the body T is impelled towards C is as the distance CT, let this (by Cor. II of the Laws) be resolved into the parts CX, TX, of which CX impelling the body directly from P stretches the thread PT, and by the resistance the thread makes to it is totally employed, producing no other effect; but the other part TX, impelling the body transversely or towards X, directly accelerates the motion in the cycloid. Then it is plain that the acceleration of the body, proportional to this accelerating force, will be every moment as the length TX, that is (because CV, WV, and TX, TW proportional to them are given), as the length TW, that is (by Cor. 1, Prop. 39), as the length of the arc of the cycloid TR. If therefore two pendulums APT, A*pt*, be unequally drawn aside from the perpendicular AR, and let fall together, their accelerations will be always as the arcs to be described TR, *t*R. But the parts described at the beginning of the motion are as the accelerations, that is, as the whole spaces that are to be described at the beginning, and therefore the parts which remain to be described, and the subsequent accelerations proportional to those parts, are also as the whole, and so on. Therefore the accelerations, and consequently the velocities generated, and the parts described with those velocities, and the parts to be described, are always as the whole; and therefore the parts to be described preserving a given ratio to each other will vanish together, that is, the two bodies oscillating will arrive together at the perpendicular AR. And since on the other hand the ascent of the pendulums from the lowest place R through the same cycloidal arcs with a retrograde motion, is retarded in the several places they pass through by the same forces by which their descent was accelerated, it is plain that the velocities of their ascent and descent through the same arcs are equal, and consequently performed in equal times; and, therefore, since the two parts of the cycloid RS and RQ lying on either side of the perpendicular are similar and equal, the two pendulums will perform as well the whole as the half of their oscillations in the same times.   Q.E.D.

Cor. The force with which the body T is accelerated or retarded in any place T of the cycloid, is to the whole weight of the same body in the highest place S or Q as the arc of the cycloid TR is to the arc SR or QR.

PROPOSITION 52. PROBLEM 34

To define the velocities of pendulums in the several places, and the times in which both the entire oscillations and their several parts are performed.

About any centre G, with the radius GH equal to the arc of the cycloid RS, describe a semicircle HKM bisected by the semidiameter GK. And if a centripetal force proportional to the distance of the places from the centre tend to the centre G, and it be in the perimeter HIK equal to the centripetal force in the perimeter of the globe QOS tending towards its centre, and at the same time that the pendulum T is let fall from the highest place S, a body, as L, is let fall from H to G; then because the forces which act upon the bodies are equal at the beginning, and always proportional to the spaces to be described TR, LG, and therefore if TR and LG are equal, are also equal in the places T and L, it is plain that those bodies describe at the beginning equal spaces ST, HL, and therefore are still acted upon equally, and continue to describe equal spaces. Therefore by Prop. 38, the time in which the body describes the arc ST is to the time of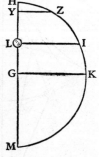
one oscillation, as the arc HI the time in which the body H arrives at L, to the semiperiphery HKM, the time in which the body H will come to M. And the velocity of the pendulous body in the place T is to its velocity in the lowest place R, that is, the velocity of the body H in the place L to its velocity in the place G, or the momentary increment of the line HL to the momentary increment of the line HG (the arcs HI, HK increasing with an uniform velocity)

as the ordinate LI to the radius GK, or as $\sqrt{(SR^2 - TR^2)}$ to SR. Hence, since in unequal oscillations there are described in equal times arcs proportional to the entire arcs of the oscillations, there are obtained, from the times given, both the velocities and the arcs described in all the oscillations universally. Which was first required.

Let now any pendulous bodies oscillate in different cycloids described within different globes, whose absolute forces are also different; and if the absolute force of any globe QOS be called V, the accelerative force with which the pendulum is acted on in the circumference of this globe, when it begins to move directly towards its centre, will be as the distance of the pendulous body from that centre and the absolute force of the globe conjointly, that is, as CO · V. Therefore the short line HY, which is as 'this accelerated force CO · V, will be described in a given time; and if there be erected the perpendicular YZ meeting the circumference in Z, the nascent arc HZ will denote that given time. But that nascent arc HZ varies as the square root of the rectangle GH · HY, and therefore as $\sqrt{(GH \cdot CO \cdot V)}$. Whence the time of an entire oscillation in the cycloid QRS (it being as the semiperiphery HKM, which denotes that entire oscillation, directly; and as the arc HZ, which in like manner denotes a given time, inversely) will be as GH directly and $\sqrt{(GH \cdot CO \cdot V)}$ inversely; that is, because GH and SR are equal, as $\sqrt{\dfrac{SR}{CO \cdot V}}$, or (by Cor., Prop. 50), as $\sqrt{\dfrac{AR}{AC \cdot V}}$. Therefore the oscillations in all globes and cycloids, performed with any absolute forces whatever, vary directly as the square root of the length of the string, and inversely as the square root of the distance between the point of suspension and the centre of the globe, and also inversely as the square root of the absolute force of the globe.   Q.E.I.

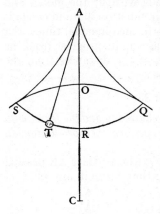

COR. I. Hence also the times of oscillating, falling, and revolving bodies may be compared among themselves. For if the diameter of the wheel with which the cycloid is described within the globe is supposed equal to the semidiameter of the globe, the cycloid will become a right line passing through the centre of the globe, and the oscillation will be changed into a descent and subsequent ascent in that right line. Hence there is given both the time of the descent from any place to the centre, and the time equal to it in which the body revolving uniformly about the centre of the globe at any distance describes an arc of a quadrant. For this time (by Case 2) is to the time of half the oscillation in any cycloid QRS as 1 to $\sqrt{\dfrac{AR}{AC}}$.

COR. II. Hence also follow what Sir Christopher Wren and Mr. Huygens have discovered concerning the common cycloid. For if the diameter of the globe be infinitely increased, its spherical surface will be changed into a plane, and the centripetal force will act uniformly in the direction of lines perpendicular to that plane, and our cycloid will become the same with the common cycloid. But in that case the length of the arc of the cycloid between that plane and the describing point will become equal to four times the versed sine of half the arc of the wheel between the same plane and the describing point, as was discovered by Sir Christopher Wren. And a pendulum between two such cycloids will oscillate in a similar and equal cycloid in equal times, as Mr. Huygens demonstrated. The descent of heavy bodies also in the time of one oscillation will be the same as Mr. Huygens exhibited.

The Propositions here demonstrated are adapted to the true constitution of the earth, so far as wheels moving in any of its great circles will describe, by the motions of nails fixed in their perimeters, cycloids without the globe; and pendulums, in mines and deep caverns of the earth, must oscillate in cycloids within the globe, that those oscillations may be performed in equal times. For gravity (as will be shown in the third book) decreases in its progress from the surface of the earth; upwards as the square root of the distances from the centre of the earth; downwards as these distances.

PROPOSITION 53. PROBLEM 35

Granting the quadratures of curvilinear figures, it is required to find the forces with which bodies moving in given curved lines may always perform their oscillations in equal times.

Let the body T oscillate in any curved line STRQ, whose axis is AR passing through the centre of force C. Draw TX touching that curve in any place of the body T, and in that tangent TX take TY equal to the arc TR. The length of that arc is known from the common methods used for the quadratures of figures. From the point Y draw the right line YZ perpendicular to the tangent. Draw CT meeting YZ in Z, and the centripetal force will be proportional to the right line TZ.

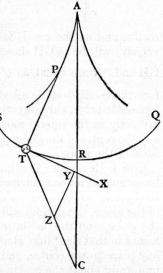

Q.E.I.

For if the force with which the body is attracted from T towards C be expressed by the right line TZ taken proportional to it, that force will be resolved into two forces TY, YZ, of which YZ, drawing the body in the direction of the length of the thread PT, does not at all change its motion; whereas the other force TY directly accelerates or retards its motion in the curve STRQ. Therefore since that force is as the space to be described TR, the accelerations or retardations of the body in describing two proportional parts (a greater and a less) of two oscillations, will be always as those parts, and therefore will cause those parts to be described together. But bodies which continually describe in the same time parts proportional to the whole, will describe the whole in the same time.   Q.E.D.

COR. I. Hence if the body T, hanging by a rectilinear thread AT from the centre A, describe the circular arc STRQ, and in the meantime be acted on by any force tending downwards with parallel directions, which is to the uniform force of gravity as the arc TR to its sine TN, the times of the several oscillations will be equal. For because TZ, AR are parallel, the triangles ATN, ZTY

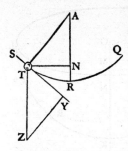

are similar; and therefore TZ will be to AT as TY to TN; that is, if the uniform force of gravity be expressed by the given length AT, the force TZ, by which the oscillations become isochronous, will be to the force of gravity AT, as the arc TR equal to TY is to TN the sine of that arc.

COR. II. And therefore in clocks, if forces are impressed by some machine upon the pendulum which continues the motion, and so compounded with the force of gravity that the whole force tending downwards will be always as a line which is obtained by dividing the product of the arc TR and the radius AR, by the sine TN, then all the oscillations will become isochronous.

PROPOSITION 54. PROBLEM 36

Granting the quadratures of curvilinear figures, it is required to find the times in which bodies by means of any centripetal force will descend or ascend in any curved lines in a plane passing through the centre of force.

Let the body descend from any place S, and move in any curve ST*t*R given in a plane passing through the centre of force C. Join CS, and let it be divided into innumerable equal parts, and let D*d* be one of those parts. From the centre C, with the radii CD, C*d*, let the circles DT, *dt* be described, meeting the curved line ST*t*R in T and *t*. And because the law of centripetal force is given, and also the altitude CS from which the body at first fell, there will be given the velocity of the body in any other altitude CT (by Prop. 39). But the time in which the body describes the short line T*t* is as the length of that short line, that is, directly as the secant of the angle *t*TC and inversely as the velocity. Let the ordinate DN, proportional to this time, be made perpendicular to the right line CS at the point D, and because D*d* is given, the rectangle D*d*·DN, that is, the area DN*nd*, will be proportional to the same time. Therefore if PN*n* be a

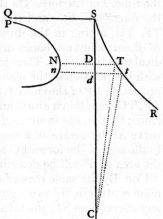

curved line which the point N continually touches, and its asymptote be the right line SQ standing upon the line CS at right angles, the area SQPND will be proportional to the time in which the body in its descent hath described the line ST; and therefore that area being found, the time is also given.   Q.E.I.

PROPOSITION 55. THEOREM 19

If a body move in any curved surface, whose axis passes through the centre of force, and from the body a perpendicular be let fall upon the axis; and a line parallel and equal thereto be drawn from any given point of the axis: I say, that this parallel line will describe an area proportional to the time.

Let BKL be a curved surface, T a body revolving in it, STR a curve which the body describes in the same, S the beginning of the curve, OMK the axis of the curved surface, TN a right line let fall perpendicularly from the body to the axis; OP a line parallel and equal thereto drawn from the given point O in the

axis; AP the path described by the point
P in the plane AOP in which the revolving line OP is found; A the beginning of that path answering to the
point S; TC a right line drawn from the
body to the centre; TG a part thereof
proportional to the centripetal force with
which the body tends towards the centre
C; TM a right line perpendicular to the
curved surface; TI a part thereof proportional to the force of pressure with
which the body urges the surface, and
therefore with which it is again repelled
by the surface towards M; PTF a right
line parallel to the axis and passing
through the body, and GF, IH right
lines let fall perpendicularly from the

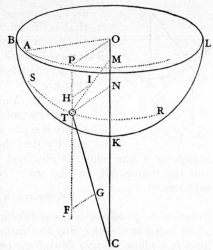

points G and I upon that parallel PHTF. I say, now, that the area AOP, described by the radius OP from the beginning of the motion, is proportional to
the time. For the force TG (by Cor. II of the Laws of Motion) is resolved into
the forces TF, FG; and the force TI into the forces TH, HI; but the forces
TF, TH, acting in the direction of the line PF perpendicular to the plane
AOP, introduce no change in the motion of the body but in a direction perpendicular to that plane. Therefore its motion, so far as it hath the same direction
with the position of the plane, that is, the motion of the point P, by which the
projection AP of the curve is described in that plane, is the same as if the forces
TF, TH were taken away, and the body were acted on by the forces FG, HI
alone; that is, the same as if the body were to describe in the plane AOP the
curve AP by means of a centripetal force tending to the centre O, and equal
to the sum of the forces FG and HI. But with such a force as that (by Prop.1)
the area AOP will be described proportional to the time.   Q.E.D.

Cor. By the same reasoning, if a body, acted on by forces tending to two or
more centres in the same given right line CO, should describe in a free space
any curved line ST, the area AOP would be always proportional to the time.

PROPOSITION 56. PROBLEM 37

*Granting the quadratures of curvilinear figures, and supposing that there are given
both the law of centripetal force tending to a given centre, and the curved surface
whose axis passes through that centre; it is required to find the curve which a body
will describe in that surface, when going off from a given place with a given velocity,
and in a given direction in that surface.*

The last construction remaining, let the body T go from the given place S,
in the direction of a line given by position, and turn into the curve sought STR,
whose orthographic projection in the plane BDO is AP. And from the given
velocity of the body in the altitude SC, its velocity in any other altitude TC
will be also given. With that velocity, in a given moment of time, let the body
describe the segment T*t* of its curve and let P*p* be the projection of that segment described in the plane AOP. Join O*p*, and a little circle being described
upon the curved surface about the centre T with the radius T*t*, let the pro-

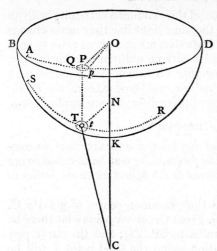

jection of that little circle in the plane AOP be the ellipse pQ. And because the magnitude of that little circle Tt, and TN or PO its distance from the axis CO is also given, the ellipse pQ will be given both in kind and magnitude, as also its position to the right line PO. And since the area POp is proportional to the time, and therefore given because the time is given, the angle POp will be given. And thence will be given p the common intersection of the ellipse and the right line Op, together with the angle OPp, in which the projection APp of the curve cuts the line OP. But from thence (by comparing Prop. 41, with its Cor. II) the manner of determining the curve APp easily appears. Then from the several points P of that projection erecting to the plane AOP, the perpendiculars PT meeting the curved surface in T, there will be given the several points T of the curve.   Q.E.I.

SECTION XI

The motions of bodies tending to each other with centripetal forces

I have hitherto been treating of the attractions of bodies towards an immovable centre; though very probably there is no such thing existent in nature. For attractions are made towards bodies, and the actions of the bodies attracted and attracting are always reciprocal and equal, by Law III; so that if there are two bodies, neither the attracted nor the attracting body is truly at rest, but both (by Cor. IV of the Laws of Motion), being as it were mutually attracted, revolve about a common centre of gravity. And if there be more bodies, which either are attracted by one body, which is attracted by them again, or which all attract each other mutually, these bodies will be so moved among themselves, that their common centre of gravity will either be at rest, or move uniformly forwards in a right line. I shall therefore at present go on to treat of the motion of bodies attracting each other; considering the centripetal forces as attractions; though perhaps in a physical strictness they may more truly be called impulses. But these Propositions are to be considered as purely mathematical; and therefore, laying aside all physical considerations, I make use of a familiar way of speaking, to make myself the more easily understood by a mathematical reader.

Proposition 57. Theorem 20

Two bodies attracting each other mutually describe similar figures about their common centre of gravity, and about each other mutually.

For the distances of the bodies from their common centre of gravity are inversely as the bodies; and therefore in a given ratio to each other; and thence, by composition of ratios, in a given ratio to the whole distance between the bodies. Now these distances are carried round their common extremity with an uniform angular motion, because lying in the same right line they never change their inclination to each other. But right lines that are in a given ratio to each other, and are carried round their extremities with an uniform angular motion, describe upon planes, which either rest together with them, or are moved with any motion not angular, figures entirely similar round those extremities. Therefore the figures described by the revolution of these distances are similar. Q.E.D.

PROPOSITION 58. THEOREM 21

If two bodies attract each other with forces of any kind, and revolve about the common centre of gravity: I say, that, by the same forces, there may be described round either body unmoved a figure similar and equal to the figures which the bodies so moving describe round each other.

Let the bodies S and P revolve about their common centre of gravity C, proceeding from S to T, and from P to Q. From the given point *s* let there be continually drawn *sp*, *sq*, equal and parallel to SP, TQ; and the curve *pqv*, which the point *p* describes in its revolution round the fixed point *s*, will be

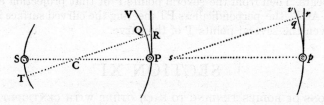

similar and equal to the curves which the bodies S and P describe about each other; and therefore, by Theor. 20, similar to the curves ST and PQV which the same bodies describe about their common centre of gravity C; and that because the proportions of the lines SC, CP, and SP or *sp*, to each other, are given.

CASE 1. The common centre of gravity C (by Cor. IV of the Laws of Motion) is either at rest, or moves uniformly in a right line. Let us first suppose it at rest, and in *s* and *p* let there be placed two bodies, one immovable in *s*, the other movable in *p*, similar and equal to the bodies S and P. Then let the right lines PR and *pr* touch the curves PQ and *pq* in P and *p*, and produce CQ and *sq* to R and *r*. And because the figures CPRQ, *sprq* are similar, RQ will be to *rq* as CP to *sp*, and therefore in a given ratio. Hence if the force with which the body P is attracted towards the body S, and by consequence towards the intermediate centre C, were to the force with which the body *p* is attracted towards the centre *s*, in the same given ratio, these forces would in equal times attract the bodies from the tangents PR, *pr* to the arcs PQ, *pq*, through the intervals proportional to them RQ, *rq*; and therefore this last force (tending to *s*) would make the body *p* revolve in the curve *pqv*, which would become similar to the curve PQV, in which the first force obliges the body P to revolve; and their revolutions would be completed in the same times. But because those forces are not to each other in the ratio of CP to *sp*, but (by reason of the similarity and equality of the bodies S and *s*, P and *p*, and the equality of the distances SP, *sp*) mutually equal, the bodies in equal times will be equally drawn from the tangents; and therefore that the body *p* may be attracted through the greater interval *rq*, there is required a greater time, which will vary as the square root of the intervals; because, by Lem. 10, the spaces described at the beginning of the motion are as the square of the times. Suppose, then, the velocity of the body p to be to the velocity of the body P as the square root of the ratio of the distance sp to the distance CP, so that the arcs pq, PQ, which are in a simple proportion to each other, may be described in times that are as the square root of the distances; and the bodies P, p, always attracted by equal forces, will describe round the fixed centres C and s similar figures PQV, pqv, the latter of which pqv is similar and equal to the figure which the body P describes round the movable body S.   Q.E.D.

CASE 2. Suppose now that the common centre of gravity, together with the space in which the bodies are moved among themselves, proceeds uniformly in a right line; and (by Cor. VI of the Laws of Motion) all the motions in this space will be performed in the same manner as before; and therefore the bodies will describe about each other the same figures as before, which will be therefore similar and equal to the figure pqv.   Q.E.D.

COR I. Hence two bodies attracting each other with forces proportional to their distance, describe (by Prop. 10), both round their common centre of gravity, and round each other, concentric ellipses; and, conversely, if such figures are described, the forces are proportional to the distances.

COR. II. And two bodies, whose forces are inversely proportional to the square of their distance, describe (by Props. 11, 12, 13), both round their common centre of gravity, and round each other, conic sections having their focus in the centre about which the figures are described. And, conversely, if such figures are described, the centripetal forces are inversely proportional to the square of the distance.

COR. III. Any two bodies revolving round their common centre of gravity describe areas proportional to the times, by radii drawn both to that centre and to each other.

PROPOSITION 59. THEOREM 22

The periodic time of two bodies S *and* P *revolving round their common centre of gravity* C, *is to the periodic time of one of the bodies* P *revolving round the other* S *remaining fixed, and describing a figure similar and equal to those which the bodies describe about each other, as* $\sqrt{S}$ *is to* $\sqrt{(S+P)}$.

For, by the demonstration of the last Proposition, the times in which any similar arcs PQ and pq are described are as $\sqrt{CP}$ is to $\sqrt{SP}$, or $\sqrt{sp}$, that is, as $\sqrt{S}$ is to $\sqrt{(S+P)}$. And by composition of ratios, the sums of the times in which all the similar arcs PQ and pq are described, that is, the whole times in which the whole similar figures are described, are in the same ratio, $\sqrt{S}$ to $\sqrt{(S+P)}$.   Q.E.D.

PROPOSITION 60. THEOREM 23

If two bodies S *and* P, *attracting each other with forces inversely proportional to the square of their distance, revolve about their common centre of gravity: I say, that the principal axis of the ellipse which either of the bodies, as* P, *describes by this motion about the other* S, *will be to the principal axis of the ellipse, which the same body* P *may describe in the same periodic time about the other body* S *fixed, as the sum of the two bodies* S+P *to the first of two mean proportionals between that sum and the other body* S.

For if the ellipses described were equal to each other, their periodic times by the last Theorem would be as the square root of the ratio of the body S to the sum of the bodies $S+P$. Let the periodic time in the latter ellipse be diminished in that ratio, and the periodic times will become equal; but, by Prop. 15, the principal axis of the ellipse will be diminished in a ratio which is the $\frac{3}{2}$th power of the former ratio; that is, in a ratio to which the ratio of S to $S+P$ is the cube, and therefore that axis will be to the principal axis of the other ellipse as the first of two mean proportionals between $S+P$ and S to $S+P$. And inversely the principal axis of the ellipse described about the movable body will be to the principal axis of that described round the immovable as $S+P$ to the first of two mean proportionals between $S+P$ and S.   Q.E.D.

PROPOSITION 61. THEOREM 24

If two bodies attracting each other with any kind of forces, and not otherwise agitated or obstructed, are moved in any manner whatsoever, those motions will be the same as if they did not at all attract each other, but were both attracted with the same forces by a third body placed in their common centre of gravity; and the law of the attracting forces will be the same in respect of the distance of the bodies from the common centre, as in respect of the distance between the two bodies.

For those forces with which the bodies attract each other, by tending to the bodies, tend also to the common centre of gravity lying directly between them; and therefore are the same as if they proceeded from an intermediate body.
                                                                      Q.E.D.

And because there is given the ratio of the distance of either body from that common centre to the distance between the two bodies, there is given, of course, the ratio of any power of one distance to the same power of the other distance; and also the ratio of any quantity derived in any manner from one of the distances compounded in any manner with given quantities, to another quantity derived in like manner from the other distance, and as many given quantities having that given ratio of the distances to the first. Therefore if the force with which one body is attracted by another be directly or inversely as the distance of the bodies from each other, or as any power of that distance; or, lastly, as any quantity derived after any manner from that distance compounded with given quantities; then will the same force with which the same body is attracted to the common centre of gravity be in like manner directly or inversely as the distance of the attracted body from the common centre, or as any power of that distance; or, lastly, as a quantity derived in like sort from that distance compounded with analogous given quantities. That is, the law of attracting force will be the same with respect to both distances.   Q.E.D.

PROPOSITION 62. PROBLEM 38

To determine the motions of two bodies which attract each other with forces inversely proportional to the squares of the distance between them, and are let fall from given places.

The bodies, by the last Theorem, will be moved in the same manner as if they were attracted by a third placed in the common centre of their gravity; and by the hypothesis that centre will be fixed at the beginning of their motion, and therefore (by Cor. IV of the Laws of Motion) will be always fixed. The motions of the bodies are therefore to be determined (by Prob. 25) in the same manner as if they were impelled by forces tending to that centre; and then we shall have the motions of the bodies attracting each other.   Q.E.I.

PROPOSITION 63. PROBLEM 39

To determine the motions of two bodies attracting each other with forces inversely proportional to the squares of their distance, and going off from given places in given directions with given velocities.

The motions of the bodies at the beginning being given, there is given also the uniform motion of the common centre of gravity, and the motion of the space which moves along with this centre uniformly in a right line, and also the very first, or beginning motions of the bodies in respect of this space. Then (by Cor. v of the Laws, and the last Theorem) the subsequent motions will be performed in the same manner in that space, as if that space together with the common centre of gravity were at rest, and as if the bodies did not attract each other, but were attracted by a third body placed in that centre. The motion therefore in this movable space of each body going off from a given place, in a given direction, with a given velocity, and acted upon by a centripetal force tending to that centre, is to be determined by Probs. 9 and 26, and at the same time will be obtained the motion of the other round the same centre. With this motion compound the uniform progressive motion of the entire system of the space and the bodies revolving in it, and there will be obtained the absolute motion of the bodies in immovable space. Q.E.I.

PROPOSITION 64. PROBLEM 40

Supposing forces with which bodies attract each other to increase in a simple ratio of their distances from the centres; it is required to find the motions of several bodies among themselves.

Suppose the first two bodies T and L to have their common centre of gravity in D. These, by Cor. I, Theor. 21, will describe ellipses having their centres in D, the magnitudes of which ellipses are known by Prob. 5.

Let now a third body S attract the two former T and L with the accelerative forces ST, SL, and let it be attracted again by them. The force ST (by Cor. II of the Laws of Motion) is resolved into the forces SD, DT; and the force SL into the forces SD and DL. Now the forces DT, DL, which are as their sum

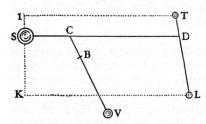

TL, and therefore as the accelerative forces with which the bodies T and L attract each other, added to the forces of the bodies T and L, the first to the first, and the last to the last, compose forces proportional to the distances DT and DL as before, but only greater than those former forces; and therefore (by Cor. I, Prop. 10, and Cor. I and VIII, Prop. 4) they will cause those bodies to describe ellipses as before, but with a swifter motion. The remaining accelerative forces SD and DL, by the motive forces SD·T and SD·L, which are as the bodies attracting those bodies equally and in the direction of the lines TI, LK parallel to DS, do not at all change their situations with respect to one another, but cause them equally to approach to the line IK; which must be imagined drawn through the middle of the body S, and perpendicular to the line DS. But that approach to the line IK will be hindered by causing the system of the bodies T and L on one side, and the body S on the other, with proper velocities, to revolve round the common centre of gravity C. With such a motion the body S, because the sum of the motive forces SD·T and SD·L is proportional to the distance CS, tends to the centre C, and will describe an ellipse round that centre; and the point D, because the lines CS and CD are proportional, will describe a like ellipse over against it. But the bodies T and L, attracted by the motive forces SD·T and SD·L, the first by the first, and the last by the last, equally and in the direction of the parallel lines TI and LK, as was said before, will (by Cor. v and vi of the Laws of Motion) continue to describe their ellipses round the movable centre D, as before.   Q.E.I.

Let there be added a fourth body V, and, by the like reasoning, it will be demonstrated that this body and the point C will describe ellipses about the common centre of gravity B; the motions of the bodies T, L, and S round the centres D and C remaining the same as before, but accelerated. And by the same method one may add yet more bodies at pleasure.   Q.E.I.

This would be the case, though the bodies T and L should attract each other with accelerative forces greater or less than those with which they attract the other bodies in proportion to their distance. Let all the accelerative attractions be to each other as the distances multiplied into the attracting bodies; and from what has gone before it will easily be concluded that all the bodies will describe different ellipses with equal periodic times about their common centre of gravity B, in an immovable plane.   Q.E.I.

PROPOSITION 65. THEOREM 25

Bodies, whose forces decrease as the square of their distances from their centres, may move among themselves in ellipses; and by radii drawn to the foci may describe areas very nearly proportional to the times.

In the last Proposition we demonstrated that case in which the motions will be performed exactly in ellipses. The more distant the law of the forces is from the law in that case, the more will the bodies disturb each other's motions; neither is it possible that bodies attracting each other according to the law supposed in this Proposition should move exactly in ellipses, unless by keeping a certain proportion of distances from each other. However, in the following cases the orbits will not much differ from ellipses.

CASE 1. Imagine several lesser bodies to revolve about some very great one at different distances from it, and suppose absolute forces tending to every one of the bodies proportional to each. And because (by Cor. IV of the Laws) the common centre of gravity of them all is either at rest, or moves uniformly forwards in a right line, suppose the lesser bodies so small that the great body may be never at a sensible distance from that centre; and then the great body will, without any sensible error, be either at rest, or move uniformly forwards in a right line; and the lesser will revolve about that great one in ellipses, and by radii drawn thereto will describe areas proportional to the times; if we except the errors that may be introduced by the receding of the great body from the common centre of gravity, or by the actions of the lesser bodies upon each other. But the lesser bodies may be so far diminished, as that this recess and the actions of the bodies on each other may become less than any assignable; and therefore so as that the orbits may become ellipses, and the areas answer to the times, without any error that is not less than any assignable.   Q.E.O.

CASE 2. Let us imagine a system of lesser bodies revolving about a very great one in the manner just described, or any other system of two bodies revolving about each other, to be moving uniformly forwards in a right line, and in the meantime to be impelled sideways by the force of another vastly greater body situate at a great distance. And because the equal accelerative forces with which the bodies are impelled in parallel directions do not change the situation of the bodies with respect to each other, but only oblige the whole system to change its place while the parts still retain their motions among themselves, it is manifest that no change in those motions of the attracted bodies can arise from their attractions towards the greater, unless by the inequality of the accelerative attractions, or by the inclinations of the lines towards each other, in whose directions the attractions are made. Suppose, therefore, all the accelerative attractions made towards the great body to be among themselves inversely as the squares of the distances; and then, by increasing the distance of the great body till the differences of the right lines drawn from that to the others in respect of their length, and the inclinations of those lines to each other, be less than any given, the motions of the parts of the system will continue without errors that are not less than any given. And because, by the small distance of those parts from each other, the whole system is attracted as if it were but one body, it will therefore be moved by this attraction as if it were one body; that is, its centre of gravity will describe about the great body one of the conic sections (that is, a parabola or hyperbola when the attraction is but languid and an ellipse when it is more vigorous); and by radii drawn thereto, it will describe areas proportional to the times, without any errors but those which arise from the distances of the parts, and these are by the supposition exceedingly small, and may be diminished at pleasure. Q.E.O.

By a like reasoning one may proceed to more complicated cases *in infinitum*.

COR. I. In the second Case, the nearer the very great body approaches to the system of two or more revolving bodies, the greater will the perturbation be of the motions of the parts of the system among themselves; because the inclinations of the lines drawn from that great body to those parts become greater; and the inequality of the proportion is also greater.

COR. II. But the perturbation will be greatest of all, if we suppose the accelerative attractions of the parts of the system towards the greatest body of all are not to each other inversely as the squares of the distances from that great body; especially if the inequality of this proportion be greater than the inequality of the proportion of the distances from the great body. For if the accelerative force, acting in parallel directions and equally, causes no perturbation in the motions of the parts of the system, it must of course, when it acts unequally, cause a perturbation somewhere, which will be greater or less as the inequality is greater or less. The excess of the greater impulses acting upon some bodies, and not acting upon others, must necessarily change their situation among themselves. And this perturbation, added to the perturbation arising from the inequality and inclination of the lines, makes the whole perturbation greater.

COR. III. Hence if the parts of this system move in ellipses or circles without any remarkable perturbation, it is manifest that, if they are at all impelled by accelerative forces tending to any other bodies, the impulse is very weak, or else is impressed very near equally and in parallel directions upon all of them.

PROPOSITION 66. THEOREM 26

If three bodies, whose forces decrease as the square of the distances, attract each other; and the accelerative attractions of any two towards the third be between themselves inversely as the squares of the distances; and the two least revolve about the greatest: I say, that the interior of the two revolving bodies will, by radii drawn to the innermost and greatest, describe round that body areas more proportional to the times, and a figure more approaching to that of an ellipse having its focus in the point of intersection of the radii, if that great body be agitated by those attractions, than it would do if that great body were not attracted at all by the lesser, but remained at rest; or than it would do if that great body were very much more or very much less attracted, or very much more or very much less agitated, by the attractions.

This appears plainly enough from the demonstration of the second Corollary of the foregoing Proposition; but it may be made out after this manner by a way of reasoning more distinct and more universally convincing.

CASE 1. Let the lesser bodies P and S revolve in the same plane about the greatest body T, the body P describing the interior orbit PAB, and S the exterior orbit ESE. Let SK be the mean distance of the bodies P and S; and let the accelerative attraction of the body P towards S, at that mean distance, be expressed by that line SK. Make SL to SK as the square of SK to the square of SP, and SL will be the accelerative attraction of the body P towards S at any distance SP. Join PT, and draw LM parallel to it meeting ST in M; and

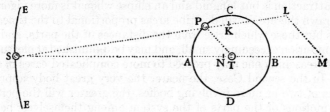

the attraction SL will be resolved (by Cor. II of the Laws of Motion) into the attractions SM, LM. And so the body P will be urged with a threefold accelerative force. One of these forces tends towards T, and arises from the mutual attraction of the bodies T and P. By this force alone the body P would describe round the body T, by the radius PT, areas proportional to the times, and an ellipse whose focus is in the centre of the body T; and this it would do whether the body T remained unmoved, or whether it were agitated by that attraction. This appears from Prop. 11, and Cor. II and III of Theor. 21. The other force is that of the attraction LM, which, because it tends from P to T, will be superadded to and coincide with the former force; and cause the areas to be still proportional to the times, by Cor. III, Theor. 21. But because it is not inversely proportional to the square of the distance PT, it will compose, when added to the former, a force varying from that proportion; this variation will be the greater by as much as the proportion of this force to the former is greater, other things remaining the same. Therefore, since by Prop. 11, and by Cor. II, Theor. 21, the force with which the ellipse is described about the focus T ought to be directed to that focus, and to be inversely proportional to the square of the distance PT, that compounded force varying from that proportion will make the orbit PAB vary from the figure of an ellipse that has its focus in the point T; and so much the more by as much as the variation from that proportion is greater; and in consequence by as much as the proportion of the second force LM to the first force is greater, other things remaining the same. But now the third force SM, attracting the body P in a direction parallel to ST, composes with the other forces a new force which is no longer directed from P to T; and this varies so much more from this direction by as much as the proportion of the third force to the other forces is greater, other things remaining the same; and therefore causes the body P to describe, by the radius TP, areas no longer proportional to the times; and therefore makes the variation from that proportionality so much greater by as much as the proportion of this force to the others is greater. But this third force will increase the variation of the orbit PAB from the elliptical figure before mentioned upon two accounts: first, because that force is not directed from P to T; and, secondly, because it is not inversely proportional to the square of the distance PT. These things being premised, it is manifest that the areas are then most nearly proportional to the times, when that third force is the least possible, the rest preserving their former quantity; and that the orbit PAB does then approach nearest to the elliptical figure above mentioned, when both the second and third, but especially the third force, is the least possible; the first force remaining in its former quantity.

Let the accelerative attraction of the body T towards S be expressed by the line SN; then if the accelerative attractions SM and SN were equal, these, attracting the bodies T and P equally and in parallel directions, would not at all change their situation with respect to each other. The motions of the bodies between themselves would be the same in that case as if those attractions did not act at all, by Cor. VI of the Laws of Motion. And, by a like reasoning, if the attraction SN is less than the attraction SM, it will take away out of the attraction SM the part SN, so that there will remain only the part (of the attraction) MN to disturb the proportionality of the areas and times, and the elliptical figure of the orbit. And in like manner if the attraction SN be greater than the attraction SM, the perturbation of the orbit and proportion will be produced by the difference MN alone. After this manner the attraction SN reduces always the attraction SM to the attraction MN, the first and second attractions remaining perfectly unchanged; and therefore the areas and times come then nearest to proportionality, and the orbit PAB to the above-mentioned elliptical figure, when the attraction MN is either none, or the least that is possible; that is, when the accelerative attractions of the bodies P and T approach as near as possible to equality; that is, when the attraction SN is neither none at all, nor less than the least of all the attractions SM, but is, as it were, a mean between the greatest and least of all those attractions SM, that is, not much greater nor much less than the attraction SK.   Q.E.D.

CASE 2. Let now the lesser bodies P, S revolve about a greater T in different planes; and the force LM, acting in the direction of the line PT situated in the plane of the orbit PAB, will have the same effect as before; neither will it draw the body P from the plane of its orbit. But the other force NM, acting in the direction of a line parallel to ST (and therefore, when the body S is without the line of the nodes, inclined to the plane of the orbit PAB), besides the perturbation of the motion just now spoken of as to longitude, introduces another perturbation also as to latitude, attracting the body P out of the plane of its orbit. And this perturbation, in any given situation of the bodies P and T to each other, will be as the generating force MN; and therefore becomes least when the force MN is least, that is (as was just now shown), where the attraction SN is not much greater nor much less than the attraction SK.   Q.E.D.

Cor. I. Hence it may be easily inferred, that if several less bodies P, S, R, &c., revolve about a very great body T, the motion of the innermost revolving body P will be least disturbed by the attractions of the others, when the great body is as well attracted and agitated by the rest (according to the ratio of the accelerative forces) as the rest are by each other.

Cor. II. In a system of three bodies T, P, S, if the accelerative attractions of any two of them towards a third be to each other inversely as the squares of the distances, the body P, by the radius PT, will describe its area about the body T swifter near the conjunction A and the opposition B than it will near the quadratures C and D. For every force with which the body P is acted on and the body T is not, and which does not act in the direction of the line PT, does either accelerate or retard the description of the area, according as its direction is the same as, or contrary to that of the motion of the body. Such is the force NM. This force in the passage of the body P from C to A tends in the direction in which the body is moving, and therefore accelerates it; then as far as D, it tends in the opposite direction, and retards the motion; then in the direction of the body, as far as B; and lastly in a contrary direction, as it moves from B to C.

Cor. III. And from the same reasoning it appears that the body P, other things remaining the same, moves more swiftly in the conjunction and opposition than in the quadratures.

Cor. IV. The orbit of the body P, other things remaining the same, is more curved at the quadratures than at the conjunction and opposition. For the swifter bodies move, the less they deflect from a rectilinear path. And besides, the force KL, or NM, at the conjunction and opposition, is contrary to the force with which the body T attracts the body P, and therefore diminishes that force; but the body P will deflect the less from a rectilinear path the less it is impelled towards the body T.

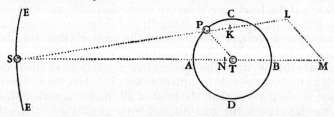

Cor. V. Hence the body P, other things remaining the same, goes farther from the body T at the quadratures than at the conjunction and opposition. This is said, however, when no account is taken of the variable eccentricity. For if the orbit of the body P be eccentric, its eccentricity (as will be shown presently by Cor. IX) will be greatest when the apsides are in the syzygies; and thence it may sometimes come to pass that the body P, in its near approach to the farther apse, may go farther from the body T at the syzygies than at the quadratures.

Cor. VI. Because the centripetal force of the central body T, by which the body P is retained in its orbit, is increased at the quadratures by the addition caused by the force LM, and diminished at the syzygies by the subtraction of the force KL, and, because the force KL is greater than LM, it is more diminished than increased; and, moreover, since that centripetal force (by Cor. II, Prop. 4) varies directly as the radius TP, and inversely as the square of the periodical time, it is plain that the resulting ratio is diminished by the action of the force KL; and therefore that the periodical time, supposing the radius of the orbit PT to remain the same, will be increased, and that as the square root of that ratio in which the centripetal force is diminished; and, therefore, supposing this radius increased or diminished, the periodical time will be increased more or diminished less than in the $\frac{3}{2}$th power of this radius, by Cor. VI, Prop. 4. If that force of the central body should gradually decay, the body P being less and less attracted would go farther and farther from the centre T; and, on the contrary, if it were increased, it would draw nearer to it. Therefore if the action of the distant body S, by which that force is diminished, were to increase and decrease by turns, the radius TP would be also increased and diminished by turns; and the periodical time would be increased and diminished in a ratio compounded of the $\frac{3}{2}$th power of the ratio of the radius, and of the square root of that ratio in which the centripetal force of the central body T was diminished or increased, by the increase or decrease of the action of the distant body S.

COR. VII. It also follows, from what was before laid down, that the axis of the ellipse described by the body P, or the line of the apsides, does as to its angular motion go forwards and backwards by turns, but more forwards than backwards, and by the excess of its direct motion is on the whole carried for-

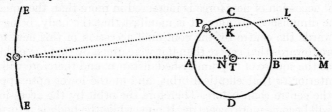

wards. For the force with which the body P is urged to the body T at the quadratures, where the force MN vanishes, is compounded of the force LM and the centripetal force with which the body T attracts the body P. The first force LM, if the distance PT be increased, is increased in nearly the same proportion with that distance, and the other force decreases as the square of the ratio of the distance; and therefore the sum of these two forces decreases in less than the square of the ratio of the distance PT; and therefore, by Cor. I, Prop. 45, will make the line of the apsides, or, which is the same thing, the upper apse, to go backwards. But at the conjunction and opposition the force with which the body P is urged towards the body T is the difference of the force KL, and of the force with which the body T attracts the body P; and that difference, because the force KL is very nearly increased in the ratio of the distance PT, decreases in more than the square of the ratio of the distance PT; and therefore, by Cor. I, Prop. 45, causes the line of the apsides to go forwards. In the places between the syzygies and the quadratures, the motion of the line of the apsides depends upon both of these causes conjointly, so that it either goes forwards or backwards in proportion to the excess of one of these causes above the other. Therefore since the force KL in the syzygies is almost twice as great as the force LM in the quadratures, the excess will be on the side of the force KL, and by consequence the line of the apsides will be carried forwards. The truth of this and the foregoing Corollary will be more easily understood by conceiving the system of the two bodies T and P to be surrounded on every side by several bodies S, S, S, &c., disposed about the orbit ESE. For by the actions of these bodies the action of the body T will be diminished on every side, and decrease in more than the square of the ratio of the distance.

COR. VIII. But since the direct or retrograde motion of the apsides depends upon the decrease of the centripetal force, that is, upon its being in a greater or less ratio than the square of the ratio of the distance TP, in the passage of the body from the lower apse to the upper; and upon a like increase in its return to the lower apse again; and therefore becomes greatest where the proportion of the force at the upper apse to the force at the lower apse recedes farthest from the inverse square of the ratio of the distances; it is plain that, when the apsides are in the syzygies, they will, by reason of the subtracted force KL or NM−LM, go forwards more swiftly; and in the quadratures by the additional force LM go backwards more slowly. Because the velocity of the progression or the slowness of the retrogression is continued for a long time, this inequality becomes exceedingly great.

COR. IX. If a body is obliged, by a force inversely proportional to the square of its distance from any centre, to revolve in an ellipse round that centre; and afterwards in its descent from the upper apse to the lower apse, that force by a continual accession of new force is increased in more than the square of the ratio of the diminished distance; it is manifest that the body, being impelled always towards the centre by the continual accession of this new force, will incline more towards that centre than if it were urged by that force alone which decreases as the square of the diminished distance, and therefore will describe an orbit interior to that elliptical orbit, and at the lower apse approaching nearer to the centre than before. Therefore the orbit by the accession of this new force will become more eccentric. If now, while the body is returning from the lower to the upper apse, it should decrease by the same degrees by which it increased before, the body would return to its first distance; and therefore if the force decreases in a yet greater ratio, the body, being now less attracted than before, will ascend to a still greater distance, and so, the eccentricity of the orbit will be increased still more. Therefore if the ratio of the increase and decrease of the centripetal force be augmented with each revolution, the eccentricity will be augmented also; and, on the contrary, if that ratio decrease, it will be diminished.

Now, therefore, in the system of the bodies T, P, S, when the apsides of the orbit PAB are in the quadratures, the ratio of that increase and decrease is least of all, and becomes greatest when the apsides are in the syzygies. If the apsides are placed in the quadratures, the ratio near the apsides is less, and near the syzygies greater, than the square of the ratio of the distances; and from that greater ratio arises a direct motion of the line of the apsides, as was just now said. But if we consider the ratio of the whole increase or decrease in the progress between the apsides, this is less than the square of the ratio of the distances. The force in the lower is to that in the upper apse in less than the square of the ratio of the distance of the upper apse from the focus of the ellipse to the distance of the lower apse from the same focus; and conversely, when the apsides are placed in the syzygies, the force in the lower apse is to the force in the upper apse in a greater than the square of the ratio of the distances. For the forces LM in the quadratures added to the forces of the body T, compose forces in a less ratio; and the forces KL in the syzygies subtracted from the forces of the body T, leave the forces in a greater ratio. Therefore the ratio of the whole increase and decrease in the passage between the apsides is least at the quadratures and greatest at the syzygies; and therefore in the passage of the apsides from the quadratures to the syzygies it is continually augmented, and increases the eccentricity of the ellipse; and in the passage from the syzygies to the quadratures it is continually decreasing, and diminishes the eccentricity.

COR. X. That we may give an account of the errors of latitude, let us suppose the plane of the orbit EST to remain immovable; and from the cause of the errors above explained, it is manifest that, of the two forces NM, ML, which are the only and entire cause of them, the force ML acting always in the plane of the orbit PAB never disturbs the motions as to latitude; and that the force NM, when the nodes are in the syzygies, acting also in the same plane of the orbit, does not at that time affect those motions. But when the nodes are in the quadratures, it disturbs them very much, and, attracting the body P continually out of the plane of its orbit, it diminishes the inclination of the plane in the passage of the body from the quadratures to the syzygies, and again increases the same in the passage from the syzygies to the quadratures. Hence it comes to pass that when the body is in the syzygies, the inclination is then least of all, and returns to the first magnitude nearly, when the body arrives

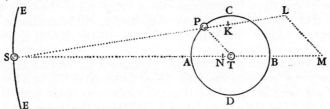

at the next node. But if the nodes are situated at the octants after the quadratures, that is, between C and A, D and B, it will appear, from what was just now shown, that in the passage of the body P from either node to the ninetieth degree from thence, the inclination of the plane is continually diminished; then, in the passage through the next 45 degrees to the next quadrature, the inclination is increased; and afterwards, again, in its passage through another 45 degrees to the next node, it is diminished. Therefore the inclination is more diminished than increased, and is therefore always less in the subsequent node than in the preceding one. And, by a like reasoning, the inclination is more increased than diminished when the nodes are in the other octants between A and D, B and C. The inclination, therefore, is the greatest of all when the nodes are in the syzygies. In their passage from the syzygies to the quadratures the inclination is diminished at each appulse of the body to the nodes; and becomes least of all when the nodes are in the quadratures, and the body in the syzygies; then it increases by the same degrees by which it decreased before; and, when the nodes come to the next syzygies, returns to its former magnitude.

Cor. xi. Because when the nodes are in the quadratures the body P is continually attracted from the plane of its orbit; and because this attraction is made towards S in its passage from the node C through the conjunction A to the node D; and in the opposite direction in its passage from the node D through the opposition B to the node C; it is manifest that, in its motion from the node C, the body recedes continually from the former plane CD of its orbit till it comes to the next node; and therefore at that node, being now at its greatest distance from the first plane CD, it will pass through the plane of the orbit EST not in D, the other node of that plane, but in a point that lies nearer to the body S, which therefore becomes a new place of the node behind its former place. And, by a like reasoning, the nodes will continue to recede in their passage from this node to the next. The nodes, therefore, when situated in the quadratures, recede continually; and at the syzygies, where no perturbation can be produced in the motion as to latitude, are quiescent; in the intermediate places they partake of both conditions, and recede more slowly; and, therefore, being always either retrograde or stationary, they will be carried backwards, or made to recede in each revolution.

Cor. xii. All the errors described in these Corollaries are a little greater at the conjunction of the bodies P, S than at their opposition; because the generating forces NM and ML are greater.

Cor. xiii. And since the causes and proportions of the errors and variations mentioned in these Corollaries do not depend upon the magnitude of the body S, it follows that all things before demonstrated will happen, if the magnitude of the body S be imagined so great that the system of the two bodies P and T may revolve about it. And from this increase of the body S, and the consequent increase of its centripetal force, from which the errors of the body P arise, it will follow that all these errors, at equal distances, will be greater in this case, than in the other where the body S revolves about the system of the bodies P and T.

Cor. xiv. But since the forces NM, ML, when the body S is exceedingly distant, are very nearly as the force SK and the ratio PT to ST conjointly; that is, if both the distance PT and the absolute force of the body S be given, inversely as ST^3; and since those forces NM, ML are the causes of all the errors and effects treated of in the foregoing Corollaries; it is manifest that all those effects, if the system of bodies T and P continue as before, and only the distance ST and the absolute force of the body S be changed, will be very nearly in a ratio compounded of the direct ratio of the absolute force of the body S, and the cubed inverse ratio of the distance ST. Hence if the system of bodies T and P revolve about a distant body S, those forces NM, ML, and their effects, will be (by Cor. ii and vi, Prop. 4) inversely as the square of the periodical time. And thence, also, if the magnitude of the body S be proportional to its absolute force, those forces NM, ML, and their effects, will be directly as the cube of the apparent diameter of the distant body S viewed from T; and conversely. For these ratios are the same as the compounded ratio above mentioned.

Cor. xv. If the orbits ESE and PAB, retaining their figure, proportions, and inclination to each other, should alter their magnitude, and if the forces of the bodies S and T should either remain unaltered or be changed in any given ratio, then these forces (that is, the force of the body T, which obliges the body

P to deflect from a rectilinear course into the orbit PAB, and the force of the body S, which causes the body P to deviate from that orbit) will act always in the same manner, and in the same proportion. Consequently it follows, that all the effects will be similar and proportional, and the times of those effects will be proportional also; that is, that all the linear errors will be as the diameters of the orbits, the angular errors the same as before; and the times of similar linear errors, or equal angular errors, are as the periodical times of the orbits.

COR. XVI. Therefore if the figures of the orbits and their inclination to each other be given, and the magnitudes, forces, and distances of the bodies be changed in any manner, we may, from the errors and times of those errors in one case, obtain very nearly the errors and times of the errors in any other case. But this may be done more expeditiously by the following method. The forces NM, ML, other things remaining unaltered, are as the radius TP; and their periodical effects (by Cor. II, Lem. 10) are as the forces and the square of the periodical time of the body P jointly. These are the linear errors of the body P; and hence the angular errors as they appear from the centre T (that is, the motion of the apsides and of the nodes, and all the apparent errors of longitude and latitude) are in each revolution of the body P as the square of the time of the revolution, very nearly. Let these ratios be compounded with

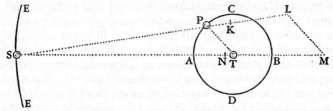

the ratios in Cor. XIV, and in any system of bodies T, P, S, where P revolves about T very near to it, and T revolves about S at a great distance, the angular errors of the body P, observed from the centre T, will be in each revolution of the body P directly as the square of the periodical time of the body P, and inversely as the square of the periodical time of the body T. And therefore the mean motion of the line of the apsides will be in a given ratio to the mean motion of the nodes; and both those motions will be directly as the periodical time of the body P, and inversely as the square of the periodical time of the body T. The increase or diminution of the eccentricity and inclination of the orbit PAB makes no sensible variation in the motions of the apsides and nodes, unless that increase or diminution be very great indeed.

COR. XVII. Since the line LM becomes sometimes greater and sometimes less than the radius PT, let the mean quantity of the force LM be expressed by that radius PT; and then that mean force will be to the mean force SK or SN (which may be also expressed by ST) as the length PT to the length ST. But the mean force SN or ST, by which the body T is retained in the orbit it describes about S, is to the force with which the body P is retained in its orbit about T in a ratio compounded of the ratio of the radius ST to the radius PT, and the squared ratio of the periodical time of the body P about T to the periodical time of the body T about S. And, consequently, the mean force LM is to the force by which the body P is retained in its orbit about T (or by which the same body P might revolve at the distance PT in the same periodical time about any immovable point T) in the same squared ratio of the periodical times. The periodical times therefore being given, together with the distance PT, the mean force' LM is also given; and that force being given, there is given also the force MN, very nearly, by the analogy of the lines PT and MN.

Cor. xviii. By the same laws by which the body P revolves about the body T, let us suppose many fluid bodies to move round T at equal distances from it; and to be so numerous, that they may all become contiguous to each other, so as to form a fluid annulus, or ring, of a round figure, and concentric to the body T; and the several parts of this ring, performing their motions by the same law as the body P, will draw nearer to the body T, and move swifter in the conjunction and opposition of themselves and the body S, than in the quadratures. And the nodes of this ring or its intersections with the plane of the orbit of the body S or T, will rest at the syzygies; but out of the syzygies they will be carried backwards, or in a retrograde direction, with the greatest swiftness in the quadratures, and more slowly in other places. The inclination of this ring also will vary, and its axis will oscillate in each revolution, and when the revolution is completed will return to its former situation, except only that it will be carried round a little by the precession of the nodes.

Cor. xix. Suppose now the spherical body T, consisting of some matter not fluid, to be enlarged, and to extend itself on every side as far as that ring, and that a channel were cut all round its circumference containing water; and that this sphere revolves uniformly about its own axis in the same periodical time. This water being accelerated and retarded by turns (as in the last Corollary), will be swifter at the syzygies, and slower at the quadratures, than the surface of the globe, and so will ebb and flow in its channel after the manner of the sea. If the attraction of the body S were taken away, the water would acquire no motion of flux and reflux by revolving round the quiescent centre of the globe. The case is the same of a globe moving uniformly forwards in a right line, and in the meantime revolving about its centre (by Cor. v of the Laws of Motion), and of a globe uniformly attracted from its rectilinear course (by Cor. vi of the same Laws). But let the body S come to act upon it, and by its varying attraction the water will receive this new motion; for there will be a stronger attraction upon that part of the water that is nearest to the body, and a weaker upon that part which is more remote. And the force LM will attract the water downwards at the quadratures, and depress it as far as the syzygies; and the force KL will attract it upwards in the syzygies, and withhold its descent, and make it rise as far as the quadratures; except only so far as the motion of flux and reflux may be directed by the channel, and be a little retarded by friction.

Cor. xx. If, now, the ring becomes hard, and the globe is diminished, the motion of flux and reflux will cease; but the oscillating motion of the inclination and the precession of the nodes will remain. Let the globe have the same axis with the ring, and perform its revolutions in the same times, and at its surface touch the ring within, and adhere to it; then the globe partaking of the motion of the ring, this whole body will oscillate, and the nodes will go backwards for the globe, as we shall show presently, is perfectly indifferent to the receiving of all impressions. The greatest angle of the inclination of the ring alone is when the nodes are in the syzygies. Thence in the progress of the nodes to the quadratures, it endeavors to diminish its inclination, and by that endeavor impresses a motion upon the whole globe. The globe retains this motion impressed, till the ring by a contrary endeavor destroys that motion, and impresses a new motion in a contrary direction. And by this means the greatest motion of the decreasing inclination happens when the nodes are in the quadratures, and the least angle of inclination in the octants after the quadratures; and, again, the greatest motion of the reclination happens when the nodes are in the syzygies; and the greatest angle of inclination in the octants following. And the case is the same of a globe without this ring, if it be a little higher or a little denser in the equatorial than in the polar regions; for the excess of that matter in the regions near the equator supplies the place of the ring. And al-

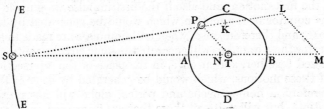

though we should suppose the centripetal force of this globe to be increased in any manner, so that all its parts tend downwards, as the parts of our earth gravitate to the centre, yet the phenomena of this and the preceding Corollary would scarce be altered; except that the places of the greatest and least height of the water will be different; for the water is now no longer sustained and kept in its orbit by its centrifugal force, but by the channel in which it flows. And, besides, the force LM attracts the water downwards most in the quadratures, and the force KL or NM−LM attracts it upwards most in the syzygies. And these forces conjoined cease to attract the water downwards, and begin to attract it upwards in the octants before the syzygies; and cease to attract the water upwards, and begin to attract the water downwards in the octants after the syzygies. And thence the greatest height of the water may happen about the octants after the syzygies; and the least height about the octants after the quadratures; excepting only so far as the motion of ascent or descent impressed by these forces may by the inertia of the water continue a little longer, or be stopped a little sooner by impediments in its channel.

Cor. xxi. For the same reason that redundant matter in the equatorial regions of a globe causes the nodes to go backwards, and therefore by the increase of that matter that retrograde motion is increased, by the diminution is diminished, and by the removal quite ceases; it follows, that, if more than that redundant matter be taken away, that is, if the globe be either more depressed, or of a rarer consistence near the equator than near the poles, there will arise a direct motion of the nodes.

Cor. xxii. And thence from the motion of the nodes is known the constitution of the globe. That is, if the globe retains unalterably the same poles, and the motion (of the nodes) is retrograde, there is a redundance of the matter near the equator; but if that motion is direct, a deficiency. Suppose a uniform and exactly spherical globe to be first at rest in a free space; then by some impulse made obliquely upon its surface to be driven from its place, and to receive a motion partly circular and partly straight forward. Since this globe is perfectly indifferent to all the axes that pass through its centre, nor has a greater propensity to one axis or to one situation of the axis than to any other, it is manifest that by its own force it will never change its axis, or the inclination of its axis. Let now this globe be impelled obliquely by a new impulse in the same part of its surface as before; and since the effect of an impulse is not at all changed by its coming sooner or later, it is manifest that these two impulses, successively impressed, will produce the same motion, as if they had been impressed at the same time; that is, the same motion, as if the globe had been impelled by a simple force compounded of them both (by Cor. II of the Laws), that is, a simple motion about an axis of a given inclination. And the case is the same if the second impulse were made upon any other place of the equator of the first motion; and also if the first impulse were made upon any place in the equator of the motion which would be generated by the second impulse alone; and therefore, also, when both impulses are made in any places whatsoever; for these impulses will generate the same circular motion as if they were impressed together, and at once, in the place of the intersections of the equators of those motions, which would be generated by each of them separately. Therefore, a homogeneous and perfect globe will not retain several motions distinct, but will unite all those that are impressed on it, and reduce them into one; revolving, as far as in it lies, always with a simple and uniform motion about one single given axis, with an inclination always invariable. And the inclination of the axis, or the velocity of the rotation, will not be changed by centripetal force. For if the globe be supposed to be divided into two hemispheres, by any plane whatsoever passing through its own centre, and the centre to which the force is directed, that force will always urge each hemisphere equally; and therefore will not incline the globe to any side with respect to its motion round its own axis. But let there be added anywhere between the pole and the equator a heap of new matter like a mountain, and this, by its continual endeavor to recede from the centre of its motion, will disturb the motion of the globe, and cause its poles to wander about its surface describing circles about themselves and the points opposite to them. Neither can this enormous deviation of the poles be corrected otherwise than by placing that mountain either in one of the poles, in which case, by Cor. XXI, the nodes of the equator will go forwards; or in the equatorial regions, in which case, by Cor. XX, the nodes will go backwards; or, lastly, by adding on the other side of the axis a new quantity of matter, by which the mountain may be balanced in its motion; and then the nodes will either go forwards or backwards, as the mountain and this newly added matter happen to be nearer to the pole or to the equator.

PROPOSITION 67. THEOREM 27

The same laws of attraction being supposed, I say, that the exterior body S *does, by radii drawn to the point* O, *the common centre of gravity of the interior bodies* P *and* T, *describe round that centre areas more proportional to the times, and an orbit more approaching to the form of an ellipse having its focus in that centre, than it can describe round the innermost and greatest body* T *by radii drawn to that body.*

For the attractions of the body S towards T and P compose its absolute attraction, which is more directed towards O, the common centre of gravity of the bodies T and P, than it is to the greatest body T; and which approaches nearer to the inverse proportion of the square of the distance SO, than of the square of the distance ST; as will easily appear by a little consideration.

PROPOSITION 68. THEOREM 28

The same laws of attraction supposed, I say, that the exterior body S will, by radii drawn to O, the common centre of gravity of the interior bodies P and T, describe round that centre areas more proportional to the times, and an orbit more approaching to the form of an ellipse having its focus in that centre, if the innermost and greatest body be agitated by these attractions as well as the rest, than it would do if that body either were at rest and not attracted at all, or were much more or much less attracted, or were much more or much less agitated.

This may be demonstrated after the same manner as Prop. 66, but by a more prolix reasoning, which I therefore pass over. It will be sufficient to consider it after this manner. From the demonstration of the last Proposition it is plain, that the centre, towards which the body S is urged by the two forces conjointly, is very near to the common centre of gravity of those two other bodies. If this centre were to coincide with that common centre, and moreover the common centre of gravity of all the three bodies were at rest, the body S on

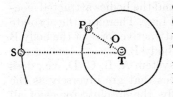

one side, and the common centre of gravity of the other two bodies on the other side, would describe true ellipses about that quiescent common centre. This appears from Cor. II, Prop. 58, compared with what was demonstrated in Props. 64 and 65. Now this accurate elliptical motion will be disturbed a little by the distance of the centre of the two bodies from the centre towards which the third body S is attracted. Let there be added, moreover, a motion to the common centre of the three, and the perturbation will be increased yet more. Therefore the perturbation is least when the common centre of the three bodies is at rest; that is, when the innermost and greatest body T is attracted according to the same law as the rest are; and is always greatest when the common centre of the three, by the diminution of the motion of the body T, begins to be moved, and is more and more agitated.

COR. And hence if several smaller bodies revolve about the great one, it may easily be inferred that the orbits described will approach nearer to ellipses; and the descriptions of areas will be more nearly uniform, if all the bodies attract and agitate each other with accelerative forces that are directly as their absolute forces, and inversely as the squares of the distances, and if the focus of each orbit be placed in the common centre of gravity of all the interior bodies (that is, if the focus of the first and innermost orbit be placed in the centre of gravity of the greatest and innermost body; the focus of the second orbit in the common centre of gravity of the two innermost bodies; the focus of the third orbit in the common centre of gravity of the three innermost; and so on), than if the innermost body were at rest, and was made the common focus of all the orbits.

PROPOSITION 69. THEOREM 29

In a system of several bodies A, B, C, D, *&c., if any one of those bodies, as* A, *attract all the rest,* B, C, D, *&c., with accelerative forces that are inversely as the squares of the distances from the attracting body; and another body, as* B, *attracts also the rest,* A, C, D, *&c., with forces that are inversely as the squares of the distances from the attracting body; the absolute forces of the attracting bodies* A *and* B *will be to each other as those very bodies* A *and* B *to which those forces belong.*

For the accelerative attractions of all the bodies B, C, D, towards A, are by the supposition equal to each other at equal distances; and in like manner the accelerative attractions of all the bodies towards B are also equal to each other at equal distances. But the absolute attractive force of the body A is to the absolute attractive force of the body B as the accelerative attraction of all the bodies towards A is to the accelerative attraction of all the bodies towards B at equal distances; and so is also the accelerative attraction of the body B towards A to the accelerative attraction of the body A towards B. But the accelerative attraction of the body B towards A is to the accelerative attraction of the body A towards B as the mass of the body A is to the mass of the body B; because the motive forces which (by the second, seventh and eighth Definitions) are as the accelerative forces and the bodies attracted conjointly are here equal to one another by the third Law. Therefore the absolute attractive force of the body A is to the absolute attractive force of the body B as the mass of the body A is to the mass of the body B.   Q.E.D.

COR. I. Therefore if each of the bodies of the system A, B, C, D, &c., does singly attract all the rest with accelerative forces that are inversely as the squares of the distances from the attracting body, the absolute forces of all those bodies will be to each other as the bodies themselves.

COR. II. By a like reasoning, if each of the bodies of the system A, B, C, D, &c., does singly attract all the rest with accelerative forces, which are either inversely or directly in the ratio of any power whatever of the distances from the attracting body; or which are defined by the distances from each of the attracting bodies according to any common law; it is plain that the absolute forces of those bodies are as the bodies themselves.

COR. III. In a system of bodies whose forces decrease as the square of the distances, if the lesser revolve about one very great one in ellipses, having their common focus in the centre of that great body, and of a figure exceedingly accurate; and moreover by radii drawn to that great body describe areas proportional to the times exactly; the absolute forces of those bodies to each other will be either accurately or very nearly in the ratio of the bodies. And so conversely. This appears from Cor. of Prop. 68, compared with the first Corollary of this Proposition.

SCHOLIUM

These Propositions naturally lead us to the analogy there is between centripetal forces and the central bodies to which those forces are usually directed; for it is reasonable to suppose that forces which are directed to bodies should depend upon the nature and quantity of those bodies, as we see they do in magnetical experiments. And when such cases occur, we are to compute the attractions of the bodies by assigning to each of their particles its proper force, and then finding the sum of them all. I here use the word *attraction* in general

for any endeavor whatever, made by bodies to approach to each other, whether
that endeavor arise from the action of the bodies themselves, as tending to
each other or agitating each other by spirits emitted; or whether it arises from
the action of the ether or of the air, or of any medium whatever, whether corporeal or incorporeal, in any manner impelling bodies placed therein towards
each other. In the same general sense I use the word *impulse,* not defining in
this treatise the species or physical qualities of forces, but investigating the
quantities and mathematical proportions of them; as I observed before in the
Definitions. In mathematics we are to investigate the quantities of forces with
their proportions consequent upon any conditions supposed; then, when we
enter upon physics, we compare those proportions with the phenomena of
Nature, that we may know what conditions of those forces answer to the several kinds of attractive bodies. And this preparation being made, we argue
more safely concerning the physical species, causes, and proportions of the
forces. Let us see, then, with what forces spherical bodies consisting of particles
endued with attractive powers in the manner above spoken of must act upon
one another; and what kind of motions will follow from them.

SECTION XII

THE ATTRACTIVE FORCES OF SPHERICAL BODIES

PROPOSITION 70. THEOREM 30

*If to every point of a spherical surface there tend equal centripetal forces decreasing
as the square of the distances from those points, I say, that a corpuscle placed
within that surface will not be attracted by those forces any way.*

Let HIKL be that spherical surface, and P a corpuscle placed within.
Through P let there be drawn to this surface two lines HK, IL, intercepting
very small arcs HI, KL; and because (by Cor. III, Lem. 7) the triangles HPI,

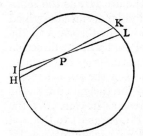

LPK are alike, those arcs will be proportional to the
distances HP, LP; and any particles at HI and KL of
the spherical surface, terminated by right lines passing
through P, will be as the square of those distances.
Therefore the forces of these particles exerted upon the
body P are equal between themselves. For the forces
are directly as the particles, and inversely as the square
of the distances. And these two ratios compose the
ratio of equality, 1 : 1. The attractions therefore,
being equal, but exerted in opposite directions, de-
stroy each other. And by a like reasoning all the attractions through the whole
spherical surface are destroyed by contrary attractions. Therefore the body
P will not be any way impelled by those attractions.   Q.E.D.

PROPOSITION 71. THEOREM 31

*The same things supposed as above, I say, that a corpuscle placed without the
spherical surface is attracted towards the centre of the sphere with a force inversely
proportional to the square of its distance from that centre.*

Let AHKB, *ahkb* be two equal spherical surfaces described about the centres
S, *s;* their diameters AB, *ab;* and let P and *p* be two corpuscles situate without

the spheres in those diameters produced. Let there be drawn from the corpuscles the lines PHK, PIL, *phk*, *pil*, cutting off from the great circles AHB, *ahb*, the equal arcs HK, *hk*, IL, *il*; and to those lines let fall the perpendiculars SD, *sd*, SE, *se*, IR, *ir*; of which let SD, *sd*, cut PL, *pl*, in F and *f*. Let fall also

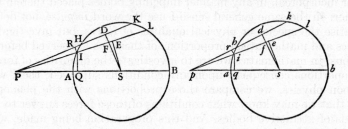

to the diameters the perpendiculars IQ, *iq*. Let now the angles DPE, *dpe* vanish; and because DS and *ds*, ES and *es* are equal, the lines PE, PF, and *pe*, *pf*, and the short lines DF, *df* may be taken for equal; because their last ratio, when the angles DPE, *dpe* vanish together, is the ratio of equality. These things being thus determined, it follows that

$$\text{PI} : \text{PF} = \text{RI} : \text{DF}$$

and $\qquad\qquad\qquad pf : pi = df \text{ or } \text{DF} : ri.$

Multiplying corresponding terms,

$$\text{PI} \cdot pf : \text{PF} \cdot pi = \text{RI} : ri = \text{arc IH} : \text{arc } ih \text{ (by Cor. III, Lem. VII)}.$$

Again, $\qquad\qquad\qquad \text{PI} : \text{PS} = \text{IQ} : \text{SE}$

and $\qquad\qquad\qquad ps : pi = se \text{ or } \text{SE} : iq.$

Hence, $\qquad\qquad\qquad \text{PI} \cdot ps : \text{PS} \cdot pi = \text{IQ} : iq.$

Multiplying together corresponding terms of this and the similarly derived preceding proportion,

$$\text{PI}^2 \cdot pf \cdot ps : pi^2 \cdot \text{PF} \cdot \text{PS} = \text{HI} \cdot \text{IQ} : ih \cdot iq,$$

that is, as the circular surface which is described by the arc IH, as the semicircle AKB revolves about the diameter AB, is to the circular surface described by the arc *ih* as the semicircle *akb* revolves about the diameter *ab*. And the forces with which these surfaces attract the corpuscles P and *p* in the direction of lines tending to those surfaces are directly, by the hypothesis, as the surfaces themselves, and inversely as the squares of the distances of the surfaces from those corpuscles; that is, as *pf* · *ps* to PF · PS. And these forces again are to the oblique parts of them which (by the resolution of forces as in Cor. II of the Laws) tend to the centres in the directions of the lines PS, *ps*, as PI to PQ, and *pi* to *pq*; that is (because of the like triangles PIQ and PSF, *piq* and *psf*), as PS to PF and *ps* to *pf*. Thence, the attraction of the corpuscle P towards S is to the attraction of the corpuscle *p* towards *s* as $\dfrac{\text{PF} \cdot pf \cdot ps}{\text{PS}}$ is to $\dfrac{pf \cdot \text{PF} \cdot \text{PS}}{ps}$, that is, as ps^2 to PS^2. And, by a like reasoning, the forces with which the surfaces described by the revolution of the arcs KL, *kl* attract those corpuscles, will be as ps^2 to PS^2. And in the same ratio will be the forces of all the circular surfaces into which each of the spherical surfaces may be divided by taking *sd* always equal to SD, and *se* equal to SE. And therefore, by composition, the forces of the entire spherical surfaces exerted upon those corpuscles will be in the same ratio.   Q.E.D.

PROPOSITION 72. THEOREM 32

If to the several points of a sphere there tend equal centripetal forces decreasing as the square of the distances from those points; and there be given both the density of the sphere and the ratio of the diameter of the sphere to the distance of the corpuscle from its centre: I say, that the force with which the corpuscle is attracted is proportional to the semidiameter of the sphere.

For conceive two corpuscles to be severally attracted by two spheres, one by one, the other by the other, and their distances from the centres of the spheres to be proportional to the diameters of the spheres respectively; and the spheres to be resolved into like particles, disposed in a like situation to the corpuscles. Then the attractions of one corpuscle towards the several particles of one sphere will be to the attractions of the other towards as many analogous particles of the other sphere in a ratio compounded of the ratio of the particles directly, and the square of the distances inversely. But the particles are as the spheres, that is, as the cubes of the diameters, and the distances are as the diameters; and the first ratio directly with the last ratio taken twice inversely, becomes the ratio of diameter to diameter. Q.E.D.

COR. I. Hence if corpuscles revolve in circles about spheres composed of matter equally attracting, and the distances from the centres of the spheres be proportional to their diameters, the periodic times will be equal.

COR. II. And, *vice versa*, if the periodic times are equal, the distances will be proportional to the diameters. These two Corollaries appear from Cor. III, Prop. 4.

COR. III. If to the several points of any two solids whatever, of like figure and equal density, there tend equal centripetal forces decreasing as the square of the distances from those points, the forces, with which corpuscles placed in a like situation to those two solids will be attracted by them, will be to each other as the diameters of the solids.

PROPOSITION 73. THEOREM 33

If to the several points of a given sphere there tend equal centripetal forces decreasing as the square of the distances from the points, I say, that a corpuscle placed within the sphere is attracted by a force proportional to its distance from the centre.

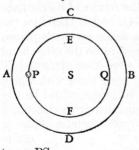

In the sphere ACBD, described about the centre S, let there be placed the corpuscle P; and about the same centre S, with the interval SP, conceive described an interior sphere PEQF. It is plain (by Prop. 70) that the concentric spherical surfaces of which the difference AEBF of the spheres is composed, have no effect at all upon the body P, their attractions being destroyed by contrary attractions. There remains, therefore, only the attraction of the interior sphere PEQF. And (by Prop. 72) this is as the distance PS. Q.E.D.

SCHOLIUM

By the surfaces of which I here imagine the solids composed, I do not mean surfaces purely mathematical, but orbs so extremely thin, that their thickness is as nothing; that is, the evanescent orbs of which the sphere will at last con-

sist, when the number of the orbs is increased, and their thickness diminished
without end. In like manner, by the points of which lines, surfaces, and solids
are said to be composed, are to be understood equal particles, whose magnitude
is perfectly inconsiderable.

Proposition 74. Theorem 34

*The same things supposed, I say, that a corpuscle situated without the sphere is
attracted with a force inversely proportional to the square of its distance from the
centre.*

For suppose the sphere to be divided into innumerable concentric spherical
surfaces, and the attractions of the corpuscle arising from the several surfaces
will be inversely proportional to the square of the distance of the corpuscle
from the centre of the sphere (by Prop. 71). And, by composition, the sum of
those attractions, that is, the attraction of the corpuscle towards the entire
sphere, will be in the same ratio.   q.e.d.

Cor. i. Hence the attractions of homogeneous spheres at equal distances
from the centres will be as the spheres themselves. For (by Prop. 72) if the
distances be proportional to the diameters of the spheres, the forces will be as
the diameters. Let the greater distance be diminished in that ratio; and the
distances now being equal, the attraction will be increased as the square of
that ratio; and therefore will be to the other attraction as the cube of that
ratio; that is, in the ratio of the spheres.

Cor. ii. At any distances whatever the attractions are as the spheres applied
to the squares of the distances.

Cor. iii. If a corpuscle placed without an homogeneous sphere is attracted
by a force inversely proportional to the square of its distance from the centre,
and the sphere consists of attractive particles, the force of every particle will
decrease as the square of the distance from each particle.

Proposition 75. Theorem 35

*If to the several points of a given sphere there tend equal centripetal forces decreas-
ing as the square of the distances from the point, I say, that another similar sphere
will be attracted by it with a force inversely proportional to the square of the distance
of the centres.*

For the attraction of every particle is inversely as the square of its distance
from the centre of the attracting sphere (by Prop. 74), and is therefore the
same as if that whole attracting force issued from one single corpuscle placed
in the centre of this sphere. But this attraction is as great as on the other hand
the attraction of the same corpuscle would be, if that were itself attracted by
the several particles of the attracted sphere with the same force with which
they are attracted by it. But that attraction of the corpuscle would be (by
Prop. 74) inversely proportional to the square of its distance from the centre
of the sphere; therefore the attraction of the sphere, equal thereto, is also in
the same ratio.   q.e.d.

Cor. i. The attractions of spheres towards other homogeneous spheres are
as the attracting spheres applied to the squares of the distances of their centres
from the centres of those which they attract.

Cor. ii. The case is the same when the attracted sphere does also attract.
For the several points of the one attract the several points of the other with

the same force with which they themselves are attracted by the others again; and therefore since in all attractions (by Law III) the attracted and attracting point are both equally acted on, the force will be doubled by their mutual attractions, the proportions remaining.

COR. III. Those several truths demonstrated above concerning the motion of bodies about the focus of the conic sections will take place when an attracting sphere is placed in the focus, and the bodies move without the sphere.

COR. IV. Those things which were demonstrated before of the motion of bodies about the centre of the conic sections take place when the motions are performed within the sphere.

PROPOSITION 76. THEOREM 36

If spheres be however dissimilar (as to density of matter and attractive force) in the same ratio onwards from the centre to the circumference; but everywhere similar, at every given distance from the centre, on all sides round about; and the attractive force of every point decreases as the square of the distance of the body attracted: I say, that the whole force with which one of these spheres attracts the other will be inversely proportional to the square of the distance of the centres.

Imagine several concentric similar spheres AB, CD, EF, &c., the innermost of which added to the outermost may compose a matter more dense towards the centre, or subtracted from them may leave the same more lax and rare.

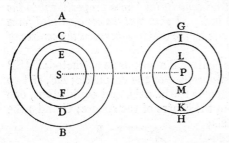

Then, by Prop. 75, these spheres will attract other similar concentric spheres GH, IK, LM, &c., each the other, with forces inversely proportional to the square of the distance SP. And, by addition or subtraction, the sum of all those forces, or the excess of any of them above the others; that is, the entire force with which the whole sphere AB (composed of any concentric spheres or of their differences) will attract the whole sphere GH (composed of any concentric spheres or their differences) in the same ratio. Let the number of the concentric spheres be increased *in infinitum*, so that the density of the matter together with the attractive force may, in the progress from the circumference to the centre, increase or decrease according to any given law; and by the addition of matter not attractive, let the deficient density be supplied, that so the spheres may acquire any form desired; and the force with which one of these attracts the other will be still, by the former reasoning, in the same inverse ratio of the square of the distance.   Q.E.D.

COR. I. Hence if many spheres of this kind, similar in all respects, attract each other, the accelerative attractions of each to each, at any equal distances of the centres, will be as the attracting spheres.

COR. II. And at any unequal distances, as the attracting spheres divided by the squares of the distances between the centres.

COR. III. The motive attractions, or the weights of the spheres towards one another, will be at equal distances of the centres conjointly as the attracting and attracted spheres; that is, as the products arising from multiplying the spheres into each other.

Cor. IV. And at unequal distances directly as those products and inversely as the squares of the distances between the centres.

Cor. V. These proportions hold true also when the attraction arises from the attractive power of both spheres exerted upon each other. For the attraction is only doubled by the conjunction of the forces, the proportions remaining as before.

Cor. VI. If spheres of this kind revolve about others at rest, each about each, and the distances between the centres of the quiescent and revolving bodies are proportional to the diameters of the quiescent bodies, the periodic times will be equal.

Cor. VII. And, again, if the periodic times are equal, the distances will be proportional to the diameters.

Cor. VIII. All those truths above demonstrated, relating to the motions of bodies about the foci of conic sections, will take place when an attracting sphere, of any form and condition like that above described, is placed in the focus.

Cor. IX. And also when the revolving bodies are also attracting spheres of any condition like that above described.

PROPOSITION 77. THEOREM 37

If to the several points of spheres there tend centripetal forces proportional to the distances of the points from the attracted bodies, I say, that the compounded force with which two spheres attract each other is as the distance between the centres of the spheres.

Case 1. Let AEBF be a sphere; S its centre; P a corpuscle attracted; PASB the axis of the sphere passing through the centre of the corpuscle; EF, *ef* two planes cutting the sphere, and perpendicular to the axis, and equidistant, one on one side, the other on the other, from the centre of the sphere; G and *g* the

intersections of the planes and the axis; and H any point in the plane EF. The centripetal force of the point H upon the corpuscle P, exerted in the direction of the line PH, is as the distance PH; and (by Cor. II of the Laws) the same exerted in the direction of the line PG, or towards the centre S, is as the length PG. Therefore the force of all the points in the plane EF

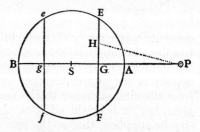

(that is, of that whole plane) by which the corpuscle P is attracted towards the centre S is as the distance PG multiplied by the number of those points, that is, as the solid contained under that plane EF and the distance PG. And in like manner the force of the plane *ef*, by which the corpuscle P is attracted towards the centre S, is as that plane multiplied by its distance P*g*, or as the equal plane EF multiplied by that distance P*g*; and the sum of the forces of both planes as the plane EF multiplied by the sum of the distances PG+P*g*, that is, as that plane multiplied by twice the distance PS of the centre and the corpuscle; that is, as twice the plane EF multiplied by the distance PS, or as the sum of the equal planes EF+*ef* multiplied by the same distance. And, by a like reasoning, the forces of all the planes in the whole sphere, equidistant on each side from the centre of the sphere, are as the sum of those planes multiplied by the distance PS, that is, as the whole sphere and the distance PS conjointly.   Q.E.D.

Case 2. Let now the corpuscle P attract the sphere AEBF. And, by the same reasoning, it will appear that the force with which the sphere is attracted is as the distance PS.   Q.E.D.

Case 3. Imagine another sphere composed of innumerable corpuscles P; and because the force with which every corpuscle is attracted is as the distance of the corpuscle from the centre of the first sphere, and as the same sphere conjointly, and is therefore the same as if it all proceeded from a single corpuscle situated in the centre of the sphere, the entire force with which all the corpuscles in the second sphere are attracted, that is, with which that whole sphere is attracted, will be the same as if that sphere were attracted by a force issuing from a single corpuscle in the centre of the first sphere; and is therefore proportional to the distance between the centres of the spheres.   Q.E.D.

Case 4. Let the spheres attract each other, and the force will be doubled, but the proportion will remain.   Q.E.D.

Case 5. Let the corpuscle p be placed within the sphere AEBF; and because the force of the plane ef upon the corpuscle is as the solid contained under that plane and the distance pg; and the contrary force of the plane EF as the solid

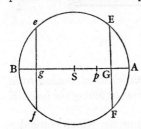

contained under that plane and the distance pG; the force compounded of both will be as the difference of the solids, that is, as the sum of the equal planes multiplied by half the difference of the distances; that is, as that sum multiplied by pS, the distance of the corpuscle from the centre of the sphere. And, by a like reasoning, the attraction of all the planes EF, ef, throughout the whole sphere, that is, the attraction of the whole sphere, is conjointly as the sum of all the planes, or as the whole sphere, and as pS, the distance of the corpuscle from the centre of the sphere.   Q.E.D.

Case 6. And if there be composed a new sphere out of innumerable corpuscles such as p, situated within the first sphere AEBF, it may be proved, as before, that the attraction, whether single of one sphere towards the other, or mutual of both towards each other, will be as the distance pS of the centres.
                                                                                Q.E.D.

Proposition 78. Theorem 38

If spheres in the progress from the centre to the circumference be however dissimilar and unequable, but similar on every side round about at all given distances from the centre; and the attractive force of every point be as the distance of the attracted body: I say, that the entire force with which two spheres of this kind attract each other mutually is proportional to the distance between the centres of the spheres.

This is demonstrated from the foregoing Proposition, in the same manner as Prop. 76 was demonstrated from Prop. 75.

Cor. Those things that were above demonstrated in Props. 10 and 64, of the motion of bodies round the centres of conic sections, take place when all the attractions are made by the force of spherical bodies of the condition above described, and the attracted bodies are spheres of the same kind.

I have now explained the two principal cases of attractions; to wit, when the centripetal forces decrease as the square of the ratio of the distances, or increase in a simple ratio of the distances, causing the bodies in both cases to revolve in conic sections, and composing spherical bodies whose centripetal forces observe the same law of increase or decrease in the recess from the centre as the forces of the particles themselves do; which is very remarkable. It would be tedious to run over the other cases, whose conclusions are less elegant and important, so particularly as I have done these. I choose rather to comprehend and determine them all by one general method as follows.

Lemma 29

If about the centre S *there be described any circle as* AEB, *and about the centre* P *there be also described two circles* EF, ef, *cutting the first in* E *and* e, *and the line* PS *in* F *and* f; *and there be let fall to* PS *the perpendiculars* ED, ed: *I say, that if*

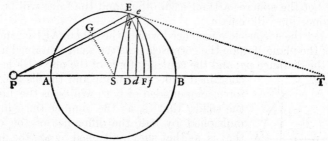

the distance of the arcs EF, ef *be supposed to be infinitely diminished, the last ratio of the evanescent line* Dd *to the evanescent line* Ff *is the same as that of the line* PE *to the line* PS.

For if the line Pe cut the arc EF in q; and the right line Ee, which coincides with the evanescent arc Ee, be produced, and meet the right line PS in T; and there be let fall from S to PE the perpendicular SG; then, because of the like triangles DTE, dTe, DES,

$$Dd : Ee = DT : TE = DE : ES;$$

and because the triangles, Eeq, ESG (by Lem. 8, and Cor. III, Lem. 7) are similar,   Ee : eq or Ff = Es : SG.

Multiplying together corresponding terms of the two proportions,

$$Dd : Ff = DE : SG = PE : PS$$

(because of the similar triangles PDE, PGS).   q.e.d.

Proposition 79. Theorem 39

Suppose a surface as EFfe *to have its breadth infinitely diminished, and to be just vanishing; and that the same surface by its revolution round the axis* PS *describes a spherical concavoconvex solid, to the several equal particles of which there tend equal centripetal forces: I say, that the force with which that solid attracts a corpuscle situated in* P *is in a ratio compounded of the ratio of the solid* DE$^2 \cdot$ Ff *and the ratio of the force with which the given particle in the place* Ff *would attract the same corpuscle.*

For if we consider, first, the force of the spherical surface FE which is generated by the revolution of the arc FE, and is cut anywhere, as in r, by the line *de*, the annular part of the surface generated by the revolution of the arc *r*E will be as the short line D*d*, the radius of the sphere PE remaining the same; as Archimedes has demonstrated in his *Book on the Sphere and Cylinder*. And the force of this surface exerted in the direction of the lines PE or P*r* situated

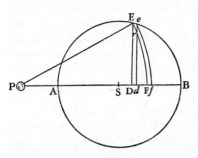

all round in the conical surface, will be as this annular surface itself; that is, as the short line D*d*, or, which is the same, as the rectangle under the given radius PE of the sphere and the short line D*d*; but that force, exerted in the direction of the line PS tending to the centre S, will be less in the ratio PD to PE, and therefore will be as PD·D*d*. Suppose now the line DF to be divided into innumerable little equal particles, each of which call D*d*, and then the surface FE will be divided into so many equal annuli, whose forces will be as the sum of all the rectangles PD·D*d*, that is, as $\frac{1}{2}$PF^2 − $\frac{1}{2}$PD^2, and therefore as DE^2. Let now the surface FE be multiplied by the altitude F*f*; and the force of the solid EF*fe* exerted upon the corpuscle P will be as DE^2·F*f*; that is, if the force be given which any given particle as F*f* exerts upon the corpuscle P at the distance PF. But if that force be not given, the force of the solid EF*fe* will be conjointly as the solid DE^2·F*f* and that force not given.   Q.E.D.

PROPOSITION 80. THEOREM 40

If to the several equal parts of a sphere ABE *described about the centre* S *there tend equal centripetal forces; and from the several points* D *in the axis of the sphere* AB *in which a corpuscle, as* P, *is placed, there be erected the perpendiculars* DE *meeting the sphere in* E, *and if in those perpendiculars the lengths* DN *be taken as the quantity* $\frac{\mathrm{DE}^2 \cdot \mathrm{PS}}{\mathrm{PE}}$, *and as the force which a particle of the sphere situated in the axis exerts at the distance* PE *upon the corpuscle* P *conjointly: I say, that the whole force with which the corpuscle* P *is attracted towards the sphere is as the area* ANB, *comprehended under the axis of the sphere* AB, *and the curved line* ANB, *the locus of the point* N.

For supposing the construction in the last Lemma and Theorem to stand, conceive the axis of the sphere AB to be divided into innumerable equal particles D*d*, and the whole sphere to be divided into so many spheri-

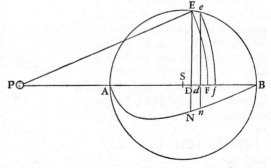

cal concavoconvex laminæ EF*fe*; and erect the perpendicular *dn*. By the last Theorem, the force with which the laminæ EF*fe* attract the corpuscle P is as DE^2·F*f* and the force of one particle exerted at the distance PE or PF, conjointly. But (by the last Lemma) D*d* is to F*f* as PE to PS, and therefore F*f* is equal to $\dfrac{\text{PS} \cdot \text{D}d}{\text{PE}}$; and $\text{DE}^2 \cdot \text{F}f$ is equal to $\text{D}d \cdot \dfrac{\text{DE}^2 \cdot \text{PS}}{\text{PE}}$; and therefore the force

of the lamina $\text{EF}fe$ is as $\text{D}d \cdot \dfrac{\text{DE}^2 \cdot \text{PS}}{\text{PE}}$ and the force of a particle exerted at

the distance PF conjointly; that is, by the supposition, as $\text{DN} \cdot \text{D}d$, or as the evanescent area $\text{DN}nd$. Therefore the forces of all the laminæ exerted upon the corpuscle P are as all the areas $\text{DN}nd$, that is, the whole force of the sphere will be as the whole area ANB.　　　　　　　　　　　　　　　　　　　　　　　Q.E.D.

Cor. i. Hence if the centripetal force tending to the several particles remain

always the same at all distances, and DN be made as $\dfrac{\text{DE}^2 \cdot \text{PS}}{\text{PE}}$, the whole force

with which the corpuscle is attracted by the sphere is as the area ANB.

Cor. ii. If the centripetal force of the particles be inversely as the distance

of the corpuscle attracted by it, and DN be made as $\dfrac{\text{DE}^2 \cdot \text{PS}}{\text{PE}^2}$, the force with

which the corpuscle P is attracted by the whole sphere will be as the area ANB.

Cor. iii. If the centripetal force of the particles be inversely as the cube of

the distance of the corpuscle attracted by it, and DN be made as $\dfrac{\text{DE}^2 \cdot \text{PS}}{\text{PE}^4}$, the

force with which the corpuscle is attracted by the whole sphere will be as the area ANB.

Cor. iv. And universally if the centripetal force tending to the several particles of the sphere be supposed to be inversely as the quantity V; and DN be

made as $\dfrac{\text{DE}^2 \cdot \text{PS}}{\text{PE} \cdot \text{V}}$; the force with which a corpuscle is attracted by the whole

sphere will be as the area ANB.

Proposition 81. Problem 41

The things remaining as above, it is required to measure the area ANB.

From the point P let there be drawn the right line PH touching the sphere in H; and to the axis PAB, letting fall the perpendicular HI, bisect PI in L; and (by Prop. 12, Book ii, *Elements* of Euclid) PE^2 is equal to $\text{PS}^2 + \text{SE}^2 + 2\text{PS} \cdot \text{SD}$.

But because the triangles SPH, SHI are alike, SE^2 or SH^2 is equal to the rectangle $\text{PS} \cdot \text{IS}$. Therefore PE^2 is equal to the rectangle contained under PS and $\text{PS} + \text{SI} + 2\text{SD}$; that is, under PS and $2\text{LS} + 2\text{SD}$; that is, under PS and 2LD. Moreover DE^2 is equal to $\text{SE}^2 - \text{SD}^2$, or

$\quad \text{SE}^2 - \text{LS}^2 + 2\text{LS} \cdot \text{LD} - \text{LD}^2,$

that is,

$$2\text{LS} \cdot \text{LD} - \text{LD}^2 - \text{LA} \cdot \text{LB}.$$

For $\text{LS}^2 - \text{SE}^2$ or $\text{LS}^2 - \text{SA}^2$ (by Prop. 6, Book ii, *Elements* of Euclid) is equal to the rectangle $\text{LA} \cdot \text{LB}$. Therefore if instead of DE^2 we write

$$2\text{LS} \cdot \text{LD} - \text{LD}^2 - \text{LA} \cdot \text{LB},$$

the quantity $\dfrac{DE^2 \cdot PS}{PE \cdot V}$,which (by Cor. IV of the foregoing Prop.) is as the length

of the ordinate DN, will now resolve itself into three parts

$$\frac{2SLD \cdot PS}{PE \cdot V} - \frac{LD^2 \cdot PS}{PE \cdot V} - \frac{ALB \cdot PS}{PE \cdot V} ;$$

where if instead of V we write the inverse ratio of the centripetal force, and instead of PE the mean proportional between PS and 2LD, those three parts will become ordinates to so many curved lines, whose areas are discovered by the common methods.   Q.E.D.

EXAM. 1. If the centripetal force tending to the several particles of the sphere be inversely as the distance; instead of V write PE the distance, then $2PS \cdot LD$

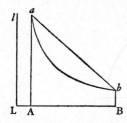

for PE²; and DN will become as $SL - \frac{1}{2}LD - \dfrac{LA \cdot LB}{2LD}$.

Suppose DN equal to its double $2SL - LD - \dfrac{LA \cdot LB}{LD}$;

and 2SL the given part of the ordinate drawn into the length AB will describe the rectangular area $2SL \cdot AB$; and the indefinite part LD, drawn perpendicularly into the same length with a continued motion, in such sort as in its motion one way or another it may either by increasing or decreasing remain always equal to the length LD, will describe

the area $\dfrac{LB^2 - LA^2}{2}$, that is, the area $SL \cdot AB$; which taken from the former area

$2SL \cdot AB$, leaves the area $SL \cdot AB$. But the third part $\dfrac{LA \cdot LB}{LD}$, drawn after the

same manner with a continued motion perpendicularly into the same length, will describe the area of an hyperbola, which subtracted from the area $SL \cdot AB$ will leave ANB the area sought. Whence arises this construction of the Problem. At the points L, A, B, erect the perpendiculars L*l*, A*a*, B*b*; making A*a* equal to LB, and B*b* equal to LA. Making L*l* and LB asymptotes, describe through the points *a*, *b* the hyperbolic curve *ab*. And the chord *ba* being drawn, will inclose the area *aba* equal to the area sought ANB.

EXAM. 2. If the centripetal force tending to the several particles of the sphere be inversely as the cube of the distance, or (which is the same thing) as that

cube applied to any given plane; write $\dfrac{PE^3}{2AS^2}$ for V,

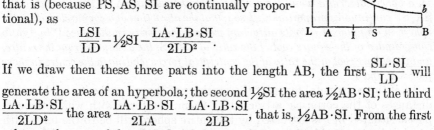

and $2PS \cdot LD$ for PE²; and DN will become as

$$\frac{SL \cdot AS^2}{PS \cdot LD} - \frac{AS^2}{2PS} - \frac{LA \cdot LB \cdot AS^2}{2PS \cdot LD^2} ,$$

that is (because PS, AS, SI are continually proportional), as

$$\frac{LSI}{LD} - \frac{1}{2}SI - \frac{LA \cdot LB \cdot SI}{2LD^2} .$$

If we draw then these three parts into the length AB, the first $\dfrac{SL \cdot SI}{LD}$ will

generate the area of an hyperbola; the second $\frac{1}{2}$SI the area $\frac{1}{2}AB \cdot SI$; the third

$\dfrac{LA \cdot LB \cdot SI}{2LD^2}$ the area $\dfrac{LA \cdot LB \cdot SI}{2LA} - \dfrac{LA \cdot LB \cdot SI}{2LB}$, that is, $\frac{1}{2}AB \cdot SI$. From the first

subtract the sum of the second and third, and there will remain ANB the area sought. Whence arises this construction of the Problem. At the points L, A, S, B, erect the perpendiculars Ll, Aa, Ss, Bb, of which suppose Ss equal to SI; and through the point s, to the asymptotes Ll, LB, describe the hyperbola asb meeting the perpendiculars Aa, Bb in a and b; and the rectangle 2SA·SI subtracted from the hyperbolic area AasbB, will leave ANB the area sought.

EXAM. 3. If the centripetal force tending to the several particles of the spheres decrease as the fourth power of the distance from the particles; write $\frac{PE^4}{2AS^3}$ for V, then $\sqrt{(2PS+LD)}$ for PE, and DN will become as

$$\frac{SI^2 \cdot SL}{\sqrt{2SI}} \cdot \frac{1}{\sqrt{LD^3}} - \frac{SI^2}{2\sqrt{2SI}} \cdot \frac{1}{\sqrt{LD}} - \frac{SI^2 \cdot LA \cdot LB}{2\sqrt{2SI}} \cdot \frac{1}{\sqrt{LD^5}}.$$

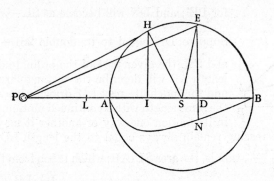

These three parts drawn into the length AB, produce so many areas, viz., $\frac{2SI^2 \cdot SL}{\sqrt{2SI}}$ into $\left(\frac{1}{\sqrt{LA}} - \frac{1}{\sqrt{LB}}\right)$; $\frac{SI^2}{\sqrt{2SI}}$ into $\sqrt{(LB - \sqrt{LA})}$; and $\frac{SI^2 \cdot LA \cdot LB}{3\sqrt{2SI}}$ into $\left(\frac{1}{\sqrt{LA^3}} - \frac{1}{\sqrt{LB^3}}\right)$. And these after due reduction come forth $\frac{2SI^2 \cdot SL}{LI}$, SI^2, and $SI^2 + \frac{2SI^3}{3LI}$. And these by subtracting the last from the first, become $\frac{4SI^3}{3LI}$. Therefore the entire force with which the corpuscle P is attracted towards the centre of the sphere is as $\frac{SI^3}{PI}$, that is, inversely as $PS^3 \cdot PI$. Q.E.I.

By the same method one may determine the attraction of a corpuscle situated within the sphere, but more expeditiously by the following Theorem.

PROPOSITION 82. THEOREM 41

In a sphere described about the centre S with the radius SA, if there be taken SI, SA, SP continually proportional: I say, that the attraction of a corpuscle within the sphere in any place I is to its attraction without the sphere in the place P in a ratio compounded of the square root of the ratio of IS, PS, the distances from the centre, and the square root of the ratio of the centripetal forces tending to the centre in those places P and I.

As, if the centripetal forces of the particles of the sphere be inversely as the distances of the corpuscle attracted by them, the force with which the corpuscle situated in I is attracted by the entire sphere will be to the force with which it is attracted in P in a ratio compounded of the square root of the ratio of the distance SI to the distance SP, and the square root of the ratio of the centripetal force in the place I arising from any particle in the centre to the centripetal force in the place P arising from the same particle in the centre; that is, inversely as the square root of the ratio of the distances SI, SP to each

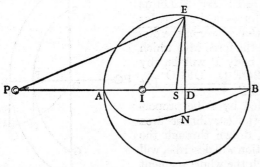

other. These two square roots of ratios compose the ratio of equality, and therefore the attractions in I and P produced by the whole sphere are equal. By the like calculation, if the forces of the particles of the sphere are inversely as the square of the ratio of the distances, it will be found that the attraction in I is to the attraction in P as the distance SP to the semidiameter SA of the sphere. If those forces are inversely as the cube of the ratio of the distances, the attractions in I and P will be to each other as SP^2 to SA^2; if as the fourth power of the ratio, as SP^3 to SA^3. Therefore since the attraction in P was found in this last case to be inversely as $PS^3 \cdot PI$, the attraction in I will be inversely as $SA^3 \cdot PI$, that is, because SA^3 is given, inversely as PI. And the progression is the same *in infinitum*. The demonstration of this Theorem is as follows:

The things remaining as above constructed, and a corpuscle being in any place P, the ordinate DN was found to be as $\dfrac{DE^2 \cdot PS}{PE \cdot V}$. Therefore if IE be drawn, that ordinate for any other place of the corpuscle, as I, will become (other things being equal) as $\dfrac{DE^2 \cdot IS}{IE \cdot V}$. Suppose the centripetal forces flowing from any point of the sphere, as E, to be to each other at the distances IE and PE as PE^n to IE^n (where the number n denotes the index of the powers of PE and IE), and those ordinates will become as $\dfrac{DE^2 \cdot PS}{PE \cdot PE^n}$ and $\dfrac{DE^2 \cdot IS}{IE \cdot IE^n}$, whose ratio to each other is as $PS \cdot IE \cdot IE^n$ to $IS \cdot PE \cdot PE^n$. Because SI, SE, SP are in continued proportion, the triangles SPE, SEI are alike; and thence IE is to PE as IS to SE or SA. For the ratio of IE to PE write the ratio of IS to SA; and the ratio of the ordinates becomes that of $PS \cdot IE^n$ to $SA \cdot PE^n$. But the ratio of PS to SA is the square root of that of the distances PS, SI; and the ratio of IE^n to PE^n (because IE is to PE as IS to SA) is the square root of that of the forces at the distances PS, IS. Therefore the ordinates, and consequently the areas which the ordinates describe, and the attractions proportional to them, are in a ratio compounded of the square root of those ratios. Q.E.D.

PROPOSITION 83. PROBLEM 42

To find the force with which a corpuscle placed in the centre of a sphere is attracted towards any segment of that sphere whatsoever.

Let P be a body in the centre of that sphere, and RBSD a segment thereof contained under the plane RDS and the spherical surface RBS. Let DB be cut in F by a spherical surface EFG described from the centre P, and let the segment be divided into the parts BREFGS, FEDG. Let us suppose that segment to be not a purely mathematical but a physical surface, having some, but a perfectly inconsiderable thickness. Let that thickness be called O, and (by what Archimedes hath demonstrated) that surface will be as PF·DF·O. Let us suppose, besides, the attractive forces of the particles of the sphere to be inversely as that power of the distances, of which n is index; and the force with which the surface EFG attracts the body P will be (by Prop. 79) as $\dfrac{DE^2 \cdot O}{PF^n}$, that is, as $\dfrac{2DF \cdot O}{PF^{n-1}} - \dfrac{DF^2 \cdot O}{PF^n}$. Let the perpendicular FN multiplied by O be proportional to this quantity; and the curvilinear area BDI, which the ordinate FN, drawn through the length DB with a continued motion will describe, will be as the whole force with which the whole segment RBSD attracts the body P. Q.E.I.

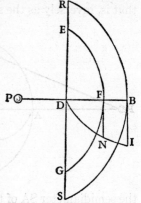

PROPOSITION 84. PROBLEM 43

To find the force with which a corpuscle, placed without the centre of a sphere in the axis of any segment, is attracted by that segment.

Let the body P placed in the axis ADB of the segment EBK be attracted by that segment. About the centre P, with the radius PE, let the spherical surface EFK be described; and let it divide the segment into two parts EBKFE and EFKDE. Find the force of the first of those parts by Prop. 81, and the force of the latter part by Prop. 83, and the sum of the forces will be the force of the whole segment EBKDE. Q.E.I.

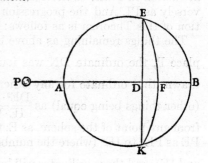

SCHOLIUM

The attractions of spherical bodies being now explained, it comes next in order to treat of the laws of attraction in other bodies consisting in like manner of attractive particles; but to treat of them particularly is not necessary to my design. It will be sufficient to add some general Propositions relating to the forces of such bodies, and the motions thence arising, because the knowledge of these will be of some little use in philosophical inquiries.

SECTION XIII

THE ATTRACTIVE FORCES OF BODIES WHICH ARE NOT SPHERICAL

PROPOSITION 85. THEOREM 42

If a body be attracted by another, and its attraction be vastly stronger when it is contiguous to the attracting body than when they are separated from each other by a very small interval; the forces of the particles of the attracting body decrease, in the recess of the body attracted, in more than the squared ratio of the distance of the particles.

For if the forces decrease as the square of the distances from the particles, the attraction towards a spherical body being (by Prop. 74) inversely as the square of the distance of the attracted body from the centre of the sphere, will not be sensibly increased by the contact, and it will be still less increased by it, if the attraction, in the recess of the body attracted, decreases in a still less proportion. The Proposition, therefore, is evident concerning attractive spheres. And the case is the same of concave spherical orbs attracting external bodies. And much more does it appear in orbs that attract bodies placed within them, because there the attractions diffused through the cavities of those orbs are (by Prop. 70) destroyed by contrary attractions, and therefore have no effect even in the place of contact. Now if from these spheres and spherical orbs we take away any parts remote from the place of contact, and add new parts anywhere at pleasure, we may change the figures of the attractive bodies at pleasure; but the parts added or taken away, being remote from the place of contact, will cause no remarkable excess of the attraction arising from the contact of the two bodies. Therefore the Proposition holds good in bodies of all figures. Q.E.D.

PROPOSITION 86. THEOREM 43

If the forces of the particles of which an attractive body is composed decrease, in the recession of the attractive body, as the third or more than the third power of the distance from the particles, the attraction will be vastly stronger in the point of contact than when the attracting and attracted bodies are separated from each other, though by ever so small an interval.

For that the attraction is infinitely increased when the attracted corpuscle comes to touch an attracting sphere of this kind, appears, by the solution of Problem 41, exhibited in the second and third Examples. The same will also appear (by comparing those Examples and Theor. 41 together) of attractions of bodies made towards concavoconvex orbs, whether the attracted bodies be placed without the orbs, or in the cavities within them. And by adding to or taking from those spheres and orbs any attractive matter anywhere without the place of contact, so that the attractive bodies may receive any assigned figure, the Proposition will hold good of all bodies universally.   Q.E.D.

PROPOSITION 87. THEOREM 44

If two bodies similar to each other, and consisting of matter equally attractive, attract separately two corpuscles proportional to those bodies, and in a like situation to them, the accelerative attractions of the corpuscles towards the entire bodies will be as the accelerative attractions of the corpuscles towards particles of the bodies proportional to the wholes, and similarly situated in them.

For if the bodies are divided into particles proportional to the wholes, and alike situated in them, it will be, as the attraction towards any particle of one of the bodies to the attraction towards the correspondent particle in the other body, so are the attractions towards the several particles of the first body, to the attractions towards the several correspondent particles of the other body; and, by composition, so is the attraction towards the first whole body to the attraction towards the second whole body.   Q.E.D.

COR. I. Therefore if, as the distances of the corpuscles attracted increase, the attractive forces of the particles decrease in the ratio of any power of the distances, the accelerative attractions towards the whole bodies will be directly as the bodies, and inversely as those powers of the distances. As if the forces of the particles decrease as the square of the distances from the corpuscles attracted, and the bodies are as A^3 and B^3, and therefore both the cubic sides of the bodies, and the distance of the attracted corpuscles from the bodies, are as A and B; the accelerative attractions towards the bodies will be as $\dfrac{A^3}{A^2}$ and $\dfrac{B^3}{B^2}$, that is, as A and B the cubic sides of those bodies. If the forces of the particles decrease as the cube of the distances from the attracted corpuscles, the accelerative attractions towards the whole bodies will be as $\dfrac{A^3}{A^3}$ and $\dfrac{B^3}{B^3}$, that is, equal. If the forces decrease as the fourth power, the attractions towards the bodies will be as $\dfrac{A^3}{A^4}$ and $\dfrac{B^3}{B^4}$, that is, inversely as the cubic sides A and B. And so in other cases.

COR. II. Hence, on the other hand, from the forces with which like bodies attract corpuscles similarly situated, may be obtained the ratio of the decrease of the attractive forces of the particles as the attracted corpuscle recedes from them; if only that decrease is directly or inversely in any ratio of the distances.

PROPOSITION 88. THEOREM 45

If the attractive forces of the equal particles of any body be as the distance of the places from the particles, the force of the whole body will tend to its centre of gravity; and will be the same with the force of a globe, consisting of similar and equal matter, and having its centre in the centre of gravity.

Let the particles A, B of the body RSTV attract any corpuscle Z with forces which, supposing the particles to be equal between themselves, are as the distances AZ, BZ; but, if they are supposed unequal, are as those particles and their distances AZ, BZ conjointly, or (if I may so speak) as those particles multiplied by their distances AZ, BZ respectively. And let those forces be expressed by the contents under A·AZ, and B·BZ. Join AB, and let it be cut in G, so that AG may be to BG as the particle B to the particle A; and G will be the common centre of gravity of the particles A and B. The force A·AZ will (by Cor. II of the Laws) be resolved into the forces A·GZ and A·AG; and the force B·BZ into the forces B·GZ and B·BG. Now

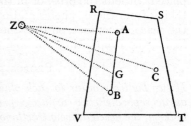

the forces A·AG and B·BG, because A is proportional to B, and BG to AG, are equal, and therefore having contrary directions destroy one another. There remain then the forces A·GZ and B·GZ. These tend from Z towards the centre G, and compose the force $(A+B)\cdot GZ$; that is, the same force as if the attractive particles A and B were placed in their common centre of gravity G, composing there a little globe.

By the same reasoning, if there be added a third particle C, and the force of it be compounded with the force $(A+B)\cdot GZ$ tending to the centre G, the force thence arising will tend to the common centre of gravity of that globe in G and of the particle C; that is, to the common centre of gravity of the three particles A, B, C; and will be the same as if that globe and the particle C were placed in that common centre composing a greater globe there; and so we may go on *in infinitum*. Therefore the whole force of all the particles of any body whatever RSTV is the same as if that body, without removing its centre of gravity, were to put on the form of a globe.   Q.E.D.

COR. Hence the motion of the attracted body Z will be the same as if the attracting body RSTV were spherical; and therefore if that attracting body be either at rest, or proceed uniformly in a right line, the body attracted will move in an ellipse having its centre in the centre of gravity of the attracting body.

PROPOSITION 89. THEOREM 46

If there be several bodies consisting of equal particles whose forces are as the distances of the places from each, the force compounded of all the forces by which any corpuscle is attracted will tend to the common centre of gravity of the attracting bodies; and will be the same as if those attracting bodies, preserving their common centre of gravity, should unite there, and be formed into a globe.

This is demonstrated after the same manner as the foregoing Proposition.

COR. Therefore the motion of the attracted body will be the same as if the attracting bodies, preserving their common centre of gravity, should unite there, and be formed into a globe. And, therefore, if the common centre of gravity of the attracting bodies be either at rest, or proceed uniformly in a right line, the attracted body will move in an ellipse having its centre in the common centre of gravity of the attracting bodies.

PROPOSITION 90. PROBLEM 44

If to the several points of any circle there tend equal centripetal forces, increasing or decreasing in any ratio of the distances; it is required to find the force with which a corpuscle is attracted, that is, situated anywhere in a right line which stands at right angles to the plane of the circle at its centre.

Suppose a circle to be described about the centre A with any radius AD in a plane to which the right line AP is perpendicular; and let it be required to find

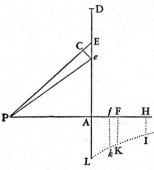

the force with which a corpuscle P is attracted towards the same. From any point E of the circle, to the attracted corpuscle P, let there be drawn the right line PE. In the right line PA take PF equal to PE, and make a perpendicular FK, erected at F, to be as the force with which the point E attracts the corpuscle P. And let the curved line IKL be the locus of the point K. Let that curve meet the plane of the circle in L. In PA take PH equal to PD, and erect the perpendicular HI meeting that curve in I; and the attraction of the corpuscle P towards the circle will be as the area AHIL multiplied by the altitude AP.   Q.E.I.

For let there be taken in AE a very small line E*e*. Join P*e*, and in PE, PA take PC, P*f*, both equal to P*e*. And because the force, with which any point E of the ring described about the centre A with the radius AE in the aforesaid plane attracts to itself the body P, is supposed to be as FK; and, therefore, the force with which that point attracts the body P towards A is as $\dfrac{\text{AP} \cdot \text{FK}}{\text{PE}}$; and the force with which the whole ring attracts the body P towards A is as the ring and $\dfrac{\text{AP} \cdot \text{FK}}{\text{PE}}$ conjointly; and that ring also is as the rectangle under the radius AE and the breadth Ee, and this rectangle (because PE and AE, Ee and CE are proportional) is equal to the rectangle PE·CE or PE·Ff; the force with which that ring attracts the body P towards A will be as PE·Ff and $\dfrac{\text{AP} \cdot \text{FK}}{\text{PE}}$ conjointly; that is, as the content under Ff·FK·AP, or as the area FKkf multiplied by AP. And therefore the sum of the forces with which all the rings, in the circle described about the centre A with the radius AD, attract the body P towards A, is as the whole area AHIKL multiplied by AP.   Q.E.D.

Cor. i. Hence if the forces of the points decrease as the square of the distances, that is, if FK be as $\dfrac{1}{\text{PF}^2}$, and therefore the area AHIKL as $\dfrac{1}{\text{PA}} - \dfrac{1}{\text{PH}}$; the attraction of the corpuscle P towards the circle will be as
$$1 - \frac{\text{PA}}{\text{PH}}; \text{ that is, as } \frac{\text{AH}}{\text{PH}}.$$

Cor. ii. And universally if the forces of the points at the distances D be inversely as any power D^n of the distances; that is, if FK be as $\dfrac{1}{D^n}$, and therefore the area AHIKL as $\dfrac{1}{\text{PA}^{n-1}} - \dfrac{1}{\text{PH}^{n-1}}$; the attraction of the corpuscle P towards the circle will be as $\dfrac{1}{\text{PA}^{n-2}} - \dfrac{\text{PA}}{\text{PH}^{n-1}}$.

Cor. iii. And if the diameter of the circle be increased *in infinitum*, and the number n be greater than unity; the attraction of the corpuscle P towards the whole infinite plane will be inversely as PA^{n-2}, because the other term $\dfrac{\text{PA}}{\text{PH}^{n-1}}$ vanishes.

Proposition 91. Problem 45

To find the attraction of a corpuscle situated in the axis of a round solid, to whose several points there tend equal centripetal forces decreasing in any ratio of the distances whatsoever.

Let the corpuscle P, situated in the axis AB of the solid DECG, be attracted towards that solid. Let the solid be cut by any circle as RFS, perpendicular to the axis; and in its semidiameter FS, in any plane PALKB passing through the axis, let there be taken (by Prop. 90) the length FK proportional to the force with which the corpuscle P is attracted towards that circle. Let the locus of the point K be the curved line LKI, meeting the planes of the outermost circles AL and BI in L and I; and the attraction of the corpuscle P towards the solid will be as the area LABI.   Q.E.I.

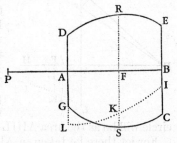

COR. I. Hence if the solid be a cylinder described by the parallelogram ADEB revolved about the axis AB, and the centripetal forces tending to the several points be inversely as the squares of the distances from the points; the attraction of the corpuscle P towards this cylinder will be as $AB-PE+PD$. For the ordinate FK (by Cor. I, Prop. 90) will be as $1-\dfrac{PF}{PR}$. The part 1 of this quantity, multiplied by the length AB, describes the area $1\cdot AB$; and the other part $\dfrac{PF}{PR}$, multiplied by the length PB, describes the area $1\cdot(PE-AD)$ (as may be easily shown from the quadrature of the curve LKI); and, in like manner, the same part multiplied by the length PA describes the area $1\cdot(PD-AD)$, and multiplied by AB, the difference of PB and PA, describes $1\cdot(PE-PD)$, the difference of the areas. From the first content $1\cdot AB$ take away the last content $1\cdot(PE-PD)$, and there will remain the area LABI equal to $1\cdot(AB-PE+PD)$. Therefore the force, being proportional to this area, is as $AB-PE+PD$.

COR. II. Hence also is known the force by which a spheroid AGBC attracts any body P situate externally in its axis AB. Let NKRM be a conic section whose ordinate ER perpendicular to PE may be always equal to the length of the line PD, continually drawn to the point D in which that ordinate cuts the spheroid. From the vertices A, B of the spheroid, let there be erected to its axis AB the perpendiculars AK, BM, respectively equal to AP, BP, and therefore meeting the conic section in K and M; and join KM cutting off from it the segment KMRK. Let S be the centre of the spheroid, and SC its greatest semidiameter; and the force with which the spheroid attracts the body P will be to the force with which a sphere described with the diameter AB attracts the same body as $\dfrac{AS\cdot CS^2-PS\cdot KMRK}{PS^2+CS^2-AS^2}$ is to $\dfrac{AS^3}{3PS^2}$. And by a calculation founded on the same principles may be found the forces of the segments of the spheroid.

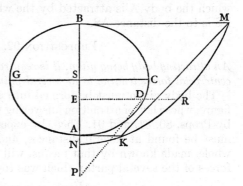

COR. III. If the corpuscle be placed within the spheroid and in its axis, the attraction will be as its distance from the centre. This may be easily inferred from the following reasoning, whether the particle be in the axis or in any other given diameter. Let AGOF be an attracting spheroid, S its centre, and P the body attracted. Through the body P let there be drawn the semidiameter SPA, and two right lines DE, FG meeting the spheroid in D and E, F and G; and let PCM, HLN be the surfaces of two interior spheroids similar and concentric to the exterior, the first of which passes through the body P, and cuts the right lines DE, FG in B and C; the latter cuts the same right lines in H and I, K and

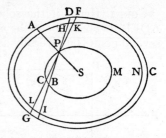

L. Let the spheroids have all one common axis, and the parts of the right lines intercepted on both sides DP and BE, FP and CG, DH and IE, FK and LG, will be mutually equal; because the right lines DE, PB, and HI are bisected in the same point, as are also the right lines FG, PC, and KL. Conceive now DPF, EPG to represent opposite cones described with the infinitely small vertical angles DPF, EPG, and the lines DH, EI to be infinitely small also. Then the particles of the cones DHKF, GLIE, cut off by the spheroidal surfaces, by reason of the equality of the lines DH and EI, will be to one another as the squares of the distances from the body P, and will therefore attract that corpuscle equally. And by a like reasoning if the spaces DPF, EGCB be divided into particles by the surfaces of innumerable similar spheroids concentric to the former and having one common axis, all these particles will equally attract on both sides the body P towards contrary parts. Therefore the forces of the cone DPF, and of the conic segment EGCB, are equal, and by their opposed actions destroy each other. And the case is the same of the forces of all the matter that lies without the interior spheroid PCBM. Therefore the body P is attracted by the interior spheroid PCBM alone, and therefore (by Cor. III, Prop. 72) its attraction is to the force with which the body A is attracted by the whole spheroid AGOD as the distance PS is to the distance AS.   Q.E.D.

PROPOSITION 92. PROBLEM 46

An attracting body being given, it is required to find the ratio of the decrease of the centripetal forces tending to its several points.

The body given must be formed into a sphere, a cylinder, or some regular figure, whose law of attraction answering to any ratio of decrease may be found by Props. 80, 81, and 91. Then, by experiments, the force of the attractions must be found at several distances, and the law of attraction towards the whole, made known by that means, will give the ratio of the decrease of the forces of the several parts; which was to be found.

PROPOSITION 93. THEOREM 47

If a solid be plane on one side, and infinitely extended on all other sides, and consist of equal particles equally attractive, whose forces decrease, in receding from the solid, in the ratio of any power greater than the square of the distances; and a corpuscle placed towards either part of the plane is attracted by the force of the whole solid: I say, that the attractive force of the whole solid, in receding from its plane surface will decrease in the ratio of a power whose side is the distance of the corpuscle from the plane, and its index less by 3 than the index of the power of the distances.

CASE 1. Let LG*l* be the plane by which the solid is terminated. Let the solid lie on that side of the plane that is towards I, and let it be resolved into innumerable planes *m*HM, *n*IN, *o*KO, &c., parallel to GL. And first let the attracted body C be placed without the solid. Let there be drawn CGHI perpendicular to those innumerable planes, and let the attractive forces of the points of the solid decrease in the ratio of a power of the distances whose index is the number *n*

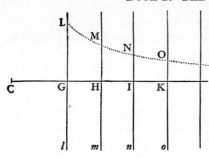

not less than 3. Therefore (by Cor. III, Prop. 90) the force with which any plane mHM attracts the point C is inversely as CH^{n-2}. In the plane mHM take the length HM inversely proportional to CH^{n-2}, and that force will be as HM. In like manner in the several planes lGL, nIN, oKO, &c., take the lengths GL, IN, KO, &c., inversely proportional to CG^{n-2}, CI^{n-2}, CK^{n-2}, &c., and the forces of those planes will be as the lengths so taken, and therefore the sum of the forces as the sum of the lengths, that is, the force of the whole solid as the area GLOK produced infinitely towards OK. But that area (by the known methods of quadratures) is inversely as CG^{n-3}, and therefore the force of the whole solid is inversely as CG^{n-3}.   Q.E.D.

CASE 2. Let the corpuscle C be now placed on that side of the plane lGL that is within the solid, and take the distance CK equal to the distance CG. And the part of the solid LGloKO terminated by the parallel planes lGL, oKO, will attract the corpuscle C, situated in the middle, neither one way nor another, the contrary actions of the opposite points destroying one another by reason of their equality. Therefore the corpuscle C is attracted by the force only of the solid situated beyond the plane OK. But this force (by Case 1) is inversely as CK^{n-3}, that is (because CG, CK are equal), inversely as CG^{n-3}.   Q.E.D.

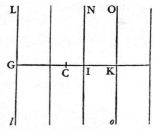

COR. I. Hence if the solid LGIN be terminated on each side by two infinite parallel planes LG, IN, its attractive force is known, subtracting from the attractive force of the whole infinite solid LGKO the attractive force of the more distant part NIKO infinitely produced towards KO.

COR. II. If the more distant part of this solid be rejected, because its attraction compared with the attraction of the nearer part is inconsiderable, the attraction of that nearer part will, as the distance increases, decrease nearly in the ratio of the power CG^{n-3}.

COR. III. And hence if any finite body, plane on one side, attract a corpuscle situated over against the middle of that plane, and the distance between the corpuscle and the plane compared with the dimensions of the attracting body be extremely small; and the attracting body consist of homogeneous particles, whose attractive forces decrease in the ratio of any power of the distances greater than the fourth; the attractive force of the whole body will decrease very nearly in the ratio of a power whose side is that very small distance, and the index less by 3 than the index of the former power. This assertion does not hold good, however, of a body consisting of particles whose attractive forces decrease in the ratio of the third power of the distances; because, in that case, the attraction of the remoter part of the infinite body in the second Corollary is always infinitely greater than the attraction of the nearer part.

SCHOLIUM

If a body is attracted perpendicularly towards a given plane, and from the law of attraction given, the motion of the body be required; the Problem will be solved by seeking (by Prop. 39) the motion of the body descending in a right line towards that plane, and (by Cor. II of the Laws) compounding that motion with an uniform motion performed in the direction of lines parallel to that plane. And, on the contrary, if there be required the law of the attraction tending towards the plane in perpendicular directions, by which the body may be caused to move in any given curved line, the Problem will be solved by working after the manner of the third Problem.

But the operations may be contracted by resolving the ordinates into converging series. As if to a base A the length B be ordinately applied in any given angle, and that length be as any power of the base $A^{\frac{m}{n}}$; and there be sought the force with which a body, either attracted towards the base or driven from it in the direction of that ordinate, may be caused to move in the curved line which that ordinate always describes with its superior extremity; I suppose the base to be increased by a very small part O, and I resolve the ordinate $(A+O)^{\frac{m}{n}}$ into an infinite series

$$A^{\frac{m}{n}}+\frac{m}{n}OA^{\frac{m-n}{n}}+\frac{mm-mn}{2nn}OOA^{\frac{m-2n}{n}} \&c.,$$

and I suppose the force proportional to the term of this series in which O is of two dimensions, that is, to the term $\frac{mm-mn}{2nn}OOA^{\frac{m-2n}{n}}.$ Therefore the force sought is as $\frac{mm-mn}{nn}A^{\frac{m-2n}{n}}$, or, which is the same thing, as $\frac{mm-mn}{nn}B^{\frac{m-2n}{n}}.$ As if the ordinate describe a parabola, m being $=2$, and $n=1$, the force will be as the given quantity $2B^\circ$, and therefore is given. Therefore with a given force the body will move in a parabola, as Galileo hath demonstrated. If the ordinate describe an hyperbola, m being $=0-1$, and $n=1$, the force will be as $2A^{-3}$ or $2B^3$; and therefore a force which is as the cube of the ordinate will cause the body to move in an hyperbola. But leaving Propositions of this kind, I shall go on to some others relating to motion which I have not yet touched upon.

SECTION XIV

THE MOTION OF VERY SMALL BODIES WHEN AGITATED BY CENTRIPETAL FORCES TENDING TO THE SEVERAL PARTS OF ANY VERY GREAT BODY

PROPOSITION 94. THEOREM 48

If two similar mediums be separated from each other by a space terminated on both sides by parallel planes, and a body in its passage through that space be attracted or impelled perpendicularly towards either of those mediums, and not agitated or hindered by any other force; and the attraction be everywhere the same at equal distances from either plane, taken towards the same side of the plane: I say, that the sine of incidence upon either plane will be to the sine of emergence from the other plane in a given ratio.

CASE 1. Let A*a* and B*b* be two parallel planes, and let the body light upon the first plane A*a* in the direction of the line GH, and in its whole passage through

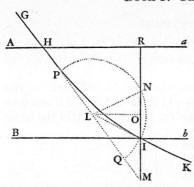

the intermediate space let it be attracted or impelled towards the medium of incidence, and by that action let it be made to describe a curved line HI, and let, it emerge in the direction of the line IK. Let there be erected IM perpendicular to Bb the plane of emergence, and meeting the line of incidence GH prolonged in M, and the plane of incidence Aa in R; and let the line of emergence KI be produced and meet HM in L. About the centre L, with the radius LI, let a circle be described cutting both HM in P and Q, and MI produced in N; and, first, if the attraction or impulse be supposed uniform, the curve HI (by what Galileo hath demonstrated) will be a parabola, whose property is that of a rectangle under its given latus rectum, and the line IM equal to the square of HM; and moreover the line HM will be bisected in L. Hence if to MI there be let fall the perpendicular LO, then MO, OR will be equal; and adding the equal lines ON, OI, the wholes MN, IR will be equal also. Therefore since IR is given, MN is also given, and the rectangle MI·MN is to the rectangle under the latus rectum and IM, that is, to HM² in a given ratio. But the rectangle MI·MN is equal to the rectangle MP·MQ, that is, to the difference of the squares ML², and PL² or LI²; and HM² hath a given ratio to its fourth part ML²; therefore the ratio of ML²−LI² to ML² is given, and by conversion the ratio of LI² to ML², and its square root, the ratio of LI to ML. But in every triangle, as LMI, the sines of the angles are proportional to the opposite sides. Therefore the ratio of the sine of the angle of incidence LMR to the sine of the angle of emergence LIR is given.   Q.E.D.

CASE 2. Let now the body pass successively through several spaces terminated with parallel planes AabB, BbcC, &c., and let it be acted on by a force which is uniform in each of them separately, but different in the different

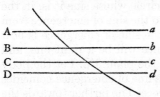

spaces; and by what was just demonstrated, the sine of the angle of incidence on the first plane Aa is to the sine of emergence from the second plane Bb in a given ratio; and this sine of incidence upon the second plane Bb will be to the sine of emergence from the third plane Cc in a given ratio; and this sine to the sine of emergence from the fourth plane Dd in a given ratio; and so on *in infinitum;* and, by multiplication of equals, the sine of incidence on the first plane is to the sine of emergence from the last plane in a given ratio. Let now the intervals of the planes be diminished, and their number be infinitely increased, so that the action of attraction or impulse, exerted according to any assigned law, may become continual, and the ratio of the sine of incidence on the first plane to the sine of emergence from the last plane being all along given, will be given then also.   Q.E.D.

PROPOSITION 95. THEOREM 49

The same things being supposed, I say, that the velocity of the body before its incidence is to its velocity after emergence as the sine of emergence to the sine of incidence.

Make AH and I*d* equal, and erect the perpendiculars AG, *d*K meeting the lines of incidence and emergence GH, IK in G and K. In GH take TH equal to IK, and to the plane A*a* let fall a perpendicular T*v*. And (by Cor. II of the Laws of Motion) let the motion of the body be resolved into two, one perpendicular to the planes A*a*, B*b*, C*c*, &c., and another parallel to them. The force of attraction or impulse, acting in directions perpendicular to those planes, does not at all alter the motion in parallel directions; and therefore the body pro-
ceeding with this motion will in equal times go through those equal parallel intervals that lie between the line AG and the point H, and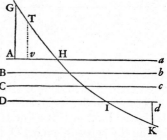
between the point I and the line *d*K; that is, they will describe the lines GH, IK in equal times. Therefore the velocity before incidence is to the velocity after emergence as GH to IK or TH, that is, as AH or I*d* to *v*H, that is (supposing TH or IK radius), as the sine of emergence to the sine of incidence.   Q.E.D.

PROPOSITION 96. THEOREM 50

The same things being supposed, and that the motion before incidence is swifter than afterwards: I say, that if the line of incidence be inclined continually, the body will be at last reflected, and the angle of reflection will be equal to the angle of incidence.

For conceive the body passing between the parallel planes A*a*, B*b*, C*c*, &c., to describe parabolic arcs as above; and let those arcs be HP, PQ, QR, &c. And let the obliquity of the line of incidence GH to the first plane A*a* be such that the sine of incidence may be to the radius of the circle whose sine it is, in the same ratio which the same sine of incidence hath to the sine of emergence from the plane D*d* into the space D*de*E; and because the sine of emergence is now become equal to the radius, the angle of emergence will be a right one, and therefore the line of emergence will coincide with the plane D*d*. Let the body come to this plane in the point R; and because the line of emergence coincides with that plane, it is manifest that the body can proceed no farther towards the plane E*e*. But neither can it proceed in the line of emergence R*d*; because it is perpetually attracted or impelled to-

wards the medium of incidence. It will return, therefore, between the planes C*c*, D*d*, describing an arc of a parabola QR*q*, whose principal vertex (by what Galileo hath demonstrated) is in R, cutting the plane C*c* in the same angle at *q*, that it did before at Q; then going on in the parabolic arcs *qp*, *ph*, &c., similar and equal to the former arcs QP, PH, &c., it will cut the rest of the planes in the same angles at *p*, *h*, &c., as it

did before in P, H, &c., and will emerge at last with the same obliquity at h with which it first impinged on that plane at H. Conceive now the intervals of the planes Aa, Bb, Cc, Dd, Ee, &c., to be infinitely diminished, and the number infinitely increased, so that the action of attraction or impulse, exerted according to any assigned law, may become continual; and, the angle of emergence remaining all along equal to the angle of incidence, will be equal to the same also at last.   Q.E.D.

SCHOLIUM

These attractions bear a great resemblance to the reflections and refractions of light made in a given ratio of the secants, as was discovered by Snell; and

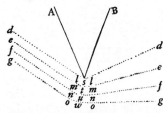

consequently in a given ratio of the sines, as was exhibited by Descartes. For it is now certain from the phenomena of Jupiter's satellites, confirmed by the observations of different astronomers, that light is propagated in succession, and requires about seven or eight minutes to travel from the sun to the earth. Moreover, the rays of light that are in our air (as lately was discovered by Grimaldi, by the admission of light into a dark room through a small hole, which I have also tried) in their passage near the angles of bodies, whether transparent or opaque (such as the circular and rectangular edges of gold, silver, and brass coins, or of knives, or broken pieces of stone or glass), are bent or inflected round those bodies as if they were attracted to them; and those rays which in their passage come nearest to the bodies are the most inflected, as if they were most attracted; which thing I myself have also carefully observed. And those which pass at greater distances are less inflected; and those at still greater distances are a little inflected the contrary way, and form three fringes of colors. In the figure s represents the edge of a knife, or any kind of wedge AsB; and *gowog, fnunf, emtme, dlsld* are rays inflected towards the knife in the arcs *owo, nun, mtm, lsl*; which inflection is greater or less according to their distance from the knife. Now since this inflection of the rays is performed in the air without the knife, it follows that the rays which fall upon the knife are first inflected in the air before they touch the knife. And the case is the same of the rays falling upon glass. The refraction, therefore, is made not in the point of incidence, but gradually, by a continual inflection of the rays; which is done partly in the air before they touch the glass, partly (if I mistake not) within the glass, after they have entered it; as is represented in the rays *ckzc, biyb, ahxa,* falling upon r, q, p, and inflected between k and z, i and y, h and x. Therefore because of the analogy there is between the propagation of the rays of light and the motion of bodies, I thought it not amiss to add the following Propositions for optical uses; not at all considering the nature of the rays of light, or inquiring whether they are bodies or not; but only determining the curves of bodies which are extremely like the curves of the rays.

Proposition 97. Problem 47

Supposing the sine of incidence upon any surface to be in a given ratio to the sine of emergence; and that the inflection of the paths of those bodies near that surface is performed in a very short space, which may be considered as a point; it is required to determine such a surface as may cause all the corpuscles issuing from any one given place to converge to another given place.

Let A be the place from whence the corpuscles diverge; B the place to which they should converge; CDE the curved line which by its revolution round the axis AB describes the surface sought; D, E any two points of that curve; and EF, EG perpendiculars let fall on the paths of the bodies AD, DB. Let the point D approach to and coalesce with the point E; and the ultimate ratio of the line DF by which AD is increased, to the line DG by which DB is dimin-

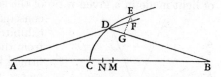

ished, will be the same as that of the sine of incidence to the sine of emergence. Therefore the ratio of the increment of the line AD to the decrement of the line DB is given; and therefore if in the axis AB there be taken anywhere the point C through which the curve CDE must pass, and CM the increment of AC be taken in that given ratio to CN the decrement of BC, and from the centres A, B, with the radii AM, BN, there be described two circles cutting each other in D; that point D will touch the curve sought CDE, and, by touching it anywhere at pleasure, will determine that curve.   q.e.i.

Cor. i. By causing the point A or B to go off sometimes *in infinitum*, and sometimes to move towards other parts of the point C, will be obtained all those figures which Descartes has exhibited in his *Optics* and *Geometry* relating to refractions. The invention of which Descartes having thought fit to conceal is here laid open in this Proposition.

Cor. ii. If a body lighting on any surface CD in the direction of a right line AD, drawn according to any law, should emerge in the direction of another right line DK; and from the point C there be drawn curved lines CP, CQ, always perpendicular to AD, DK; the increments of the lines PD, QD, and there-

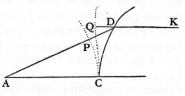

fore the lines themselves PD, QD, generated by those increments, will be as the sines of incidence and emergence to each other, and conversely.

Proposition 98. Problem 48

The same things supposed; if round the axis AB any attractive surface be described, as CD, regular or irregular, through which the bodies issuing from the given place A must pass; it is required to find a second attractive surface EF, which may make those bodies converge to a given place B.

Let a line joining AB cut the first surface in C and the second in E, the point D being taken in any manner at pleasure. And supposing the sine of incidence on the first surface to the sine of emergence from the same, and the sine of emergence from the second surface to the sine of incidence on the same, to be as any given quantity M to another given quantity N; then produce AB to G, so that BG may be to CE as M−N to N; and AD to H, so that AH may be equal to AG; and DF to K, so that DK may be to DH as N to M. Join KB, and about the centre D with the radius DH describe a circle meeting KB produced in L,

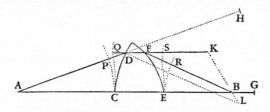

and draw BF parallel to DL; and the point F will touch the line EF, which, being turned round the axis AB, will describe the surface sought.   Q.E.F.

For conceive the lines CP, CQ to be everywhere perpendicular to AD, DF, and the lines ER, ES to FB, FD respectively, and therefore QS to be always equal to CE; and (by Cor. II, Prop. 97) PD will be to QD as M to N, and therefore as DL to DK, or FB to FK; and by subtraction, as DL−FB or PH−PD− FB to FD or FQ−QD; and by addition as PH−FB to FQ, that is (because PH and CG, QS and CE, are equal), as CE+BG−FR to CE−FS. But (because BG is to CE as M−N to N) it comes to pass also that CE+BG is to CE as M to N; and therefore, by subtraction, FR is to FS as M to N; and therefore (by Cor. II, Prop. 97) the surface EF compels a body, falling upon it in the direction DF, to go on in the line FR to the place B.   Q.E.D.

SCHOLIUM

In the same manner one may go on to three or more surfaces. But of all figures the spherical is the most proper for optical uses. If the object glasses of telescopes were made of two glasses of a spherical figure, containing water between them, it is not unlikely that the errors of the refractions made in the extreme parts of the surfaces of the glasses may be accurately enough corrected by the refractions of the water. Such object glasses are to be preferred before elliptic and hyperbolic glasses, not only because they may be formed with more ease and accuracy, but because the pencils of rays situated without the axis of the glass would be more accurately refracted by them. But the different refrangibility of different rays is the real obstacle that hinders optics from being made perfect by spherical or any other figures. Unless the errors thence arising can be corrected, all the labor spent in correcting the others is quite thrown away.

BOOK TWO

THE MOTION OF BODIES
IN RESISTING MEDIUMS

SECTION I

The motion of bodies that are resisted in the ratio of the velocity

Proposition 1. Theorem 1

If a body is resisted in the ratio of its velocity, the motion lost by resistance is as the space gone over in its motion.

For since the motion lost in each equal interval of time is as the velocity, that is, as the small increment of space gone over, then, by composition, the motion lost in the whole time will be as the whole space gone over.   q.e.d.

Cor. Therefore if the body, destitute of all gravity, move by its innate force only in free spaces, and there be given both its whole motion at the beginning, and also the motion remaining after some part of the way is gone over, there will be given also the whole space which the body can describe in an infinite time. For that space will be to the space now described as the whole motion at the beginning is to the part lost of that motion.

Lemma 1

Quantities proportional to their differences are continually proportional.

Let $\qquad$ $A : A - B = B : B - C = C : C - D = \&c.;$
then, by subtraction,

$$A : B = B : C = C : D = \&c. \qquad\qquad \text{q.e.d.}$$

Proposition 2. Theorem 2

If a body is resisted in the ratio of its velocity, and moves, by its inertia only, through an homogeneous medium, and the times be taken equal, the velocities in the beginning of each of the times are in a geometrical progression, and the spaces described in each of the times are as the velocities.

Case 1. Let the time be divided into equal intervals; and if at the very beginning of each interval we suppose the resistance to act with one single impulse which is as the velocity, the decrement of the velocity in each of the intervals of time will be as the same velocity. Therefore the velocities are proportional to their differences, and therefore (by Lem. 1, Book ii) continually proportional. Therefore if out of an equal number of intervals there be compounded any equal portions of time, the velocities at the beginning of those times will be as terms in a continued progression, which are taken by jumps, omitting everywhere an equal number of intermediate terms. But the ratios of these terms are

159

compounded of the equal ratios of the intermediate terms equally repeated, and therefore are equal. Therefore the velocities, being proportional to those terms, are in geometrical progression. Let those equal intervals of time be diminished, and their number increased *in infinitum*, so that the impulse of resistance may become continual; and the velocities at the beginnings of equal times, always continually proportional, will be also in this case continually proportional.   Q.E.D.

CASE 2. And, by division, the differences of the velocities, that is, the parts of the velocities lost in each of the times, are as the wholes; but the spaces described in each of the times are as the lost parts of the velocities (by Prop. 1, Book I), and therefore are also as the wholes.   Q.E.D.

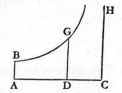

COR. Hence if to the rectangular asymptotes AC, CH, the hyperbola BG is described, and AB, DG be drawn perpendicular to the asymptote AC, and both the velocity of the body, and the resistance of the medium, at the very beginning of the motion, be expressed by any given line AC, and, after some time is elapsed, by the indefinite line DC; the time may be expressed by the area ABGD, and the space described in that time by the line AD. For if that area, by the motion of the point D, be uniformly increased in the same manner as the time, the right line DC will decrease in a geometrical ratio in the same manner as the velocity; and the parts of the right line AC, described in equal times, will decrease in the same ratio.

PROPOSITION 3. PROBLEM 1

To define the motion of a body which, in an homogeneous medium, ascends or descends in a right line, and is resisted in the ratio of its velocity, and acted upon by an uniform force of gravity.

The body ascending, let the gravity be represented by any given rectangle BACH; and the resistance of the medium, at the beginning of the ascent, by

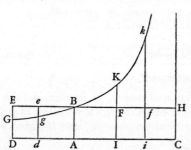

the rectangle BADE, taken on the contrary side of the right line AB. Through the point B, with the rectangular asymptotes AC, CH, describe an hyperbola, cutting the perpendiculars DE, *de* in G, *g*; and the body ascending will in the time DG*gd* describe the space EG*ge*; in the time DGBA, the space of the whole ascent EGB; in the time ABKI, the space of descent BFK; and in the time IK*ki* the space of descent KF*fk*; and the velocities of the bodies (proportional to the resistance of the medium) in these periods of time will be ABED, AB*ed*, o, ABFI, AB*fi* respectively; and the greatest velocity which the body can acquire by descending will be BACH.

For let the rectangle BACH be resolved into innumerable rectangles A*k*, K*l*, L*m*, M*n*, &c., which shall be as the increments of the velocities produced in so many equal times; then will o, A*k*, A*l*, A*m*, A*n*, &c., be as the whole velocities, and therefore (by supposition) as the resistances of the medium in the beginning of each of the equal times. Make AC to AK, or ABHC to AB*k*K, as the force of gravity to the resistance in the beginning of the second time; then from the force of gravity subtract the resistances, and ABHC, KkHC, LlHC, Mm-HC, &c., will be as the absolute forces with which the body is acted upon in the beginning of each of the times, and therefore (by Law I) as the increments of the velocities, that is, as the rectangles Ak, Kl, Lm, Mn, &c., and therefore (by Lem. 1, Book II) in a geometrical progression. Therefore, if the right lines Kk, Ll, Mm, Nn, &c., are produced so as to meet the hyperbola in q, r, s, t, &c., the areas ABqK, KqrL, LrsM, MstN, &c., will be equal, and therefore analogous to

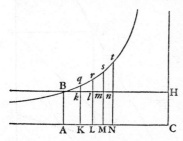

the equal times and equal gravitating forces. But the area ABqK (by Cor. III, Lems. 7 and 8, Book I) is to the area Bkq as Kq to ½kq, or AC to ½AK, that is, as the force of gravity to the resistance in the middle of the first time. And by the like reasoning, the areas qKLr, rLMs, sMNt, &c., are to the areas $qklr$, $rlms$, $smnt$, &c., as the gravitating forces to the resistances in the middle of the second, third, fourth time, and so on. Therefore since the equal areas BAKq, qKLr, rLMs, sMNt, &c., are analogous to the gravitating forces, the areas Bkq, $qklr$, $rlms$, $smnt$, &c., will be analogous to the resistances in the middle of each of the times, that is (by supposition), to the velocities, and so to the spaces described. Take the sums of the analogous quantities, and the areas Bkq, Blr, Bms, Bnt, &c., will be analogous to the whole spaces described; and also the areas ABqK, ABrL, ABsM, ABtN, &c., to the times. Therefore the body, in descending, will in any time ABrL describe the space Blr, and in the time LrtN the space $rlnt$. Q.E.D. And the like demonstration holds in ascending motion.

COR. I. Therefore the greatest velocity that the body can acquire by falling is to the velocity acquired in any given time as the given force of gravity which continually acts upon it to the resisting force which opposes it at the end of that time.

COR. II. But the time being augmented in an arithmetical progression, the sum of that greatest velocity and the velocity in the ascent, and also their difference in the descent, decreases in a geometrical progression.

COR. III. Also the differences of the spaces, which are described in equal differences of the times, decrease in the same geometrical progression.

COR. IV. The space described by the body is the difference of two spaces, whereof one is as the time taken from the beginning of the descent, and the other as the velocity; which [spaces] also at the beginning of the descent are equal among themselves.

PROPOSITION 4. PROBLEM 2

Supposing the force of gravity in any homogeneous medium to be uniform, and to tend perpendicularly to the plane of the horizon: to define the motion of a projectile therein, which suffers resistance proportional to its velocity.

Let the projectile go from any place D in the direction of any right line DP, and let its velocity at the beginning of the motion be represented by the length DP. From the point P let fall the perpendicular PC on the horizontal line DC, and cut DC in A, so that DA may be to AC as the vertical component of the resistance of the medium arising from the motion upwards at the beginning, to the force of gravity; or (which comes to the same) so that the rectangle under DA and DP may be to that under AC and CP as the whole resistance at the beginning of the motion, to the force of gravity. With the asymptotes DC, CP describe any hyperbola GTBS cutting the perpendiculars DG, AB in G and B; complete the parallelogram DGKC, and let its side GK cut AB in Q. Take a line N in the same ratio to QB as DC is in to CP; and from any point R of the right line DC erect RT perpendicular to it, meeting the hyperbola in T, and the right lines EH, GK, DP in I, *t*, and V; in that perpendicular take V*r* equal to $\frac{tGT}{N}$, or, which is the same thing, take R*r* equal to $\frac{GTIE}{N}$; and the projectile in the time DRTG will arrive at the point *r*, describing the curved line D*ra*F, the locus of

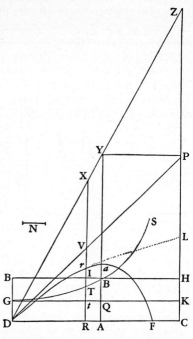

the point *r*; thence it will come to its greatest height *a* in the perpendicular AB; and afterwards ever approach to the asymptote PC. And its velocity in any point *r* will be as the tangent *r*L to the curve.   Q.E.I.

For   N : QB = DC : CP = DR : RV,

and therefore RV is equal to $\frac{DR \cdot QB}{N}$, and R*r*

$\left(\text{that is, RV} - V r, \text{ or } \frac{DR \cdot QB - tGT}{N}\right)$ is equal to $\frac{DR \cdot AB - RDGT}{N}$. Now let

the time be represented by the area RDGT, and (by Laws, Cor. II) distinguish the motion of the body into two others, one of ascent, the other lateral. And since the resistance is as the motion, let that also be distinguished into two parts proportional and contrary to the parts of the motion: and therefore the length described by the lateral motion will be (by Prop. 2, Book II) as the line DR, and the height (by Prop. 3, Book II) as the area DR · AB − RDGT, that is, as the line R*r*. But in the very beginning of the motion the area RDGT is equal to the rectangle DR · AQ, and therefore that line R*r* $\left(\text{or } \frac{DR \cdot AB - DR \cdot AQ}{N}\right)$ will then be to DR as AB − AQ or QB to N, that is, as CP to DC; and therefore as the motion upwards to the motion lengthwise at the beginning. Since, therefore, R*r* is always as the height, and DR always as the length, and R*r* is to DR at the beginning as the height to the length, it follows, that R*r* is always to DR as the height to the length; and therefore that the body will move in the line D*ra*F, which is the locus of the point *r*.   Q.E.D.

Cor. I. Therefore R*r* is equal to $\frac{DR \cdot AB}{N} - \frac{RDGT}{N}$; and therefore if RT be produced to X so that RX may be equal to $\dfrac{DR \cdot AB}{N}$, that is, if the parallel-ogram ACPY be completed, and DY cutting CP in Z be drawn, and RT be produced till it meets DY in X; Xr will be equal to $\dfrac{RDGT}{N}$, and therefore proportional to the time.

COR. II. Whence if innumerable lines CR, or, which is the same, innumerable lines ZX, be taken in a geometrical progression ,there will be as many lines Xr in an arithmetical progression. And hence the curve DraF is easily delineated by the table of logarithms.

COR. III. If a parabola be constructed to the vertex D, and the diameter DG produced downwards, and its latus rectum is to 2DP as the whole resistance at the beginning of the motion to the gravitating force, the velocity with which the body ought to go from the place D, in the direction of the right line DP, so

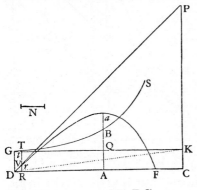

as in an uniform resisting medium to de-scribe the curve DraF, will be the same as that with which it ought to go from the same place D in the direction of the same right line DP, so as to describe a parabola in a nonresisting medium. For the latus rectum of this parabola, at the very be-ginning of the motion, is $\dfrac{DV^2}{V r}$; and Vr is $\dfrac{tGT}{N}$ or $\dfrac{DR \cdot Tt}{2N}$. But a right line which, if drawn, would touch the hyperbola GTS in G, is parallel to DK, and therefore Tt is $\dfrac{CK \cdot DR}{DC}$, and N is $\dfrac{QB \cdot DC}{CP}$. And therefore Vr is equal to $\dfrac{DR^2 \cdot CK \cdot CP}{2DC^2 \cdot QB}$, that is (because DR and DC, DV and DP are proportionals), to $\dfrac{DV^2 \cdot CK \cdot CP}{2DP^2 \cdot QB}$; and the latus rectum $\dfrac{DV^2}{V r}$ comes out $\dfrac{2DP^2 \cdot QB}{CK \cdot CP}$, that is (because QB and CK, DA and AC are proportionals), $\dfrac{2DP^2 \cdot DA}{AC \cdot CP}$, and therefore is to 2DP as DP$\cdot$DA to CP$\cdot$AC; that is, as the resistance to the gravity. Q.E.D.

COR. IV. Hence if a body be projected from any place D with a given velocity, in the direction of a right line DP given by position, and the resistance of the medium, at the beginning of the motion, be given, the curve DraF, which that body will describe, may be found. For the velocity being given, the latus rec-tum of the parabola is given, as is well known. And taking 2DP to that latus rectum, as the force of gravity to the resisting force, DP is also given. Then cutting DC in A, so that CP$\cdot$AC may be to DP$\cdot$DA in the same ratio of the gravity to the resistance, the point A will be given. And hence the curve DraF is also given.

COR. V. And conversely, if the curve DraF be given, there will be given both the velocity of the body and the resistance of the medium in each of the places r. For the ratio of CP$\cdot$AC to DP$\cdot$DA being given, there is given both the re-sistance of the medium at the beginning of the motion, and the latus rectum of the parabola; and thence the velocity at the beginning of the motion is given also. Then from the length of the tangent rL there is given both the velocity proportional to it, and the resistance proportional to the velocity in any place r.

Cor. vi. But since the length 2DP is to the latus rectum of the parabola as the gravity to the resistance in D, and, from the velocity augmented, the resistance is augmented in the same ratio, but the latus rectum of the parabola is augmented as the square of that ratio, it is plain that the length 2DP is augmented in that simple ratio only; and is therefore always proportional to the velocity; nor will it be augmented or diminished by the change of the angle CDP, unless the velocity be also changed.

Cor. vii. Hence appears the method of determining the curve DraF nearly from the phenomena, and thence finding the resistance and velocity with which the body is projected. Let two similar and equal bodies be projected with the same velocity, from the place D, in different angles CDP, CDp; and let the places F, f, where they fall upon the horizontal plane DC, be known. Then taking any length for DP or Dp suppose the resistance in D to be to the gravity in any ratio whatsoever, and let that ratio be represented by any length SM. Then, by computation, from that assumed length DP, find the lengths DF, Df; and from the ratio $\dfrac{Ff}{DF}$, found by calcu-

lation, subtract the same ratio as found by experiment; and let the difference be represented by the perpendicular MN. Repeat the same a second and a third time, by assuming always a new ratio SM of the resistance to the gravity, and collecting a new difference MN. Draw the positive differences on one side of the right line SM, and the negative on the other side; and through the points N, N, N, draw a regular curve NNN, cutting the right line SMMM in X, and SX will be the true ratio of the resistance to the gravity, which was to be found. From this ratio the length DF is to be found by calculation; and a length, which is to the assumed length DP as the length DF known by experiment to the length DF just now found, will be the true length DP. This being known, you will have both the curved line DraF which the body describes, and also the velocity and resistance of the body in each place.

Scholium

However, that the resistance of bodies is in the ratio of the velocity, is more a mathematical hypothesis than a physical one. In mediums void of all tenacity, the resistances made to bodies are as the square of the velocities. For by the action of a swifter body, a greater motion in proportion to a greater velocity is communicated to the same quantity of the medium in a less time; and in an equal time, by reason of a greater quantity of the disturbed medium, a motion is communicated as the square of the ratio greater; and the resistance (by Laws II and III) is as the motion communicated. Let us, therefore, see what motions arise from this law of resistance.

SECTION II

The motion of bodies that are resisted as the square of their velocities

Proposition 5. Theorem 3

If a body is resisted as the square of its velocity, and moves by its innate force only through an homogeneous medium; and the times be taken in a geometrical progression, proceeding from less to greater terms: I say, that the velocities at the beginning of each of the times are in the same geometrical progression inversely; and that the spaces are equal, which are described in each of the times.

For since the resistance of the medium is proportional to the square of the velocity, and the decrement of the velocity is proportional to the resistance: if the time be divided into innumerable equal intervals, the squares of the velocities at the beginning of each of the times will be proportional to the differences of the same velocities. Let those intervals of time be AK, KL, LM, &c., taken in the right line CD; and erect the perpendiculars AB, Kk, Ll, Mm, &c., meeting the hyperbola BklmG, described with the centre C, and the rectangular asymptotes CD, CH, in B, k, l, m, &c.; then AB will be to Kk as CK to CA, and, by division, AB − Kk to Kk as AK to CA, and alternately, AB − Kk to AK as Kk to CA; and therefore as AB·Kk to AB·CA. Therefore since AK and

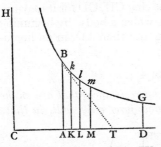

AB·CA are given, AB − Kk will be as AB·Kk; and, lastly, when AB and Kk coincide, as AB². And, by the like reasoning, Kk − Ll, Ll − Mm, &c., will be as Kk², Ll², &c. Therefore the squares of the lines AB, Kk, Ll, Mm, &c., are as their differences; and, therefore, since the squares of the velocities were shown above to be as their differences, the progression of both will be alike. This being demonstrated it follows also that the areas described by these lines are in a like progression with the spaces described by these velocities. Therefore if the velocity at the beginning of the first time AK be represented by the line AB, and the velocity at the beginning of the second time KL by the line K*k*, and the length described in the first time by the area AK*k*B, all the following velocities will be represented by the following lines L*l*, M*m*, &c., and the lengths described by the areas K*l*, L*m*, &c. And, by composition, if the whole time be represented by AM, the sum of its parts, the whole length described will be represented by AM*m*B, the sum of its parts. Now conceive the time AM to be divided into the parts AK, KL, LM, &c., so that CA, CK, CL, CM, &c., may be in a geometrical progression; and those parts will be in the same progression, and the velocities AB, K*k*, L*l*, M*m*, &c., will be in the same progression inversely, and the spaces described A*k*, K*l*, L*m*, &c., will be equal.   Q.E.D.

Cor. i. Hence it appears, that if the time be represented by any part AD of the asymptote, and the velocity in the beginning of the time by the ordinate AB, the velocity at the end of the time will be represented by the ordinate DG; and the whole space described by the adjacent hyperbolic area ABGD; and the space which any body can describe in the same time AD, with the first velocity AB, in a nonresisting medium, by the rectangle AB·AD.

Cor. ii. Hence the space described in a resisting medium is given, by taking it to the space described with the uniform velocity AB in a nonresisting medium, as the hyperbolic area ABGD to the rectangle AB·AD.

Cor. iii. The resistance of the medium is also given, by making it equal, in the very beginning of the motion, to an uniform centripetal force, which could generate, in a body falling through a nonresisting medium, the velocity AB in the time AC. For if BT be drawn touching the hyperbola in B, and meeting the asymptote in T, the right line AT will be equal to AC, and will express the time in which the first resistance, uniformly continued, may take away the whole velocity AB.

Cor. iv. And thence is also given the proportion of this resistance to the force of gravity, or any other given centripetal force.

Cor. v. And, conversely, if there is given the proportion of the resistance to any given centripetal force, the time AC is also given, in which a centripetal force equal to the resistance may generate any velocity as AB; and thence is given the point B, through which the hyperbola, having CH, CD for its asymptotes, is to be described; as also the space ABGD, which a body, by beginning its motion with that velocity AB, can describe in any time AD, in an homogeneous resisting medium.

Proposition 6. Theorem 4

Homogeneous and equal spherical bodies, opposed by resistances that are as the square of the velocities, and moving on by their innate force only, will, in times which are inversely as the velocities at the beginning,
describe equal spaces, and lose parts of their veloc-
ities proportional to the wholes.

To the rectangular asymptotes CD, CH describe any hyperbola B*b*E*e*, cutting the perpendiculars AB, *ab*, DE, *de* in B, *b*, E, *e*; let the initial velocities be represented by the perpendiculars AB, DE, and the times by the lines A*a*, D*d*. Therefore as A*a* is to D*d*, so (by the hypothesis) is DE to AB, and so (from the nature of the hy-

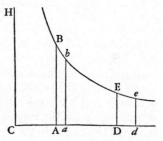

perbola) is CA to CD; and, by composition, so is C*a* to C*d*. Therefore the areas AB*ba*, DE*ed*, that is, the spaces described, are equal among themselves, and the first velocities AB, DE are proportional to the last *ab*, *de*; and therefore, by subtraction, proportional to the parts of the velocities lost, AB−*ab*, DE−*de*.   Q.E.D.

PROPOSITION 7. THEOREM 5

If spherical bodies are resisted as the squares of their velocities, in times which are directly as the first motions, and inversely as the first resistances, they will lose parts of their motions proportional to the wholes, and will describe spaces proportional to the product of those times and the first velocities.

For the parts of the motions lost are as the product of the resistances and times. Therefore, that those parts may be proportional to the wholes, the product of the resistance and time ought to be as the motion. Therefore the time will be as the motion directly and the resistance inversely. Therefore the intervals of the times being taken in that ratio, the bodies will always lose parts of their motions proportional to the wholes, and therefore will retain velocities always proportional to their first velocities. And because of the given ratio of the velocities, they will always describe spaces which are as the product of the first velocities and the times.   Q.E.D.

COR. I. Therefore if bodies equally swift are resisted as the square of their diameters, homogeneous globes moving with any velocities whatsoever, by describing spaces proportional to their diameters, will lose parts of their motions proportional to the wholes. For the motion of each globe will be as the product of its velocity and mass, that is, as the product of the velocity and the cube of its diameter; the resistance (by supposition) will be as the product of the square of the diameter and the square of the velocity; and the time (by this Proposition) is in the former ratio directly, and in the latter inversely, that is, as the diameter directly and the velocity inversely; and therefore the space, which is proportional to the time and velocity, is as the diameter.

COR. II. If bodies equally swift are resisted as the $\frac{3}{2}$th power of their diameters, homogeneous globes, moving with any velocities whatsoever, by describing spaces that are as the $\frac{3}{2}$th power of the diameters, will lose parts of their motions proportional to the wholes.

COR. III. And universally, if equally swift bodies are resisted in the ratio of any power of the diameters, the spaces, in which homogeneous globes, moving with any velocity whatsoever, will lose parts of their motions proportional to the wholes, will be as the cubes of the diameters applied to that power. Let those diameters be D and E; and if the resistances, where the velocities are supposed equal, are as D^n and E^n; the spaces in which the globes, moving with any velocities whatsoever, will lose parts of their motions proportional to the wholes, will be as D^{3-n} and E^{3-n}. And therefore homogeneous globes, in describing spaces proportional to D^{3-n} and E^{3-n}, will retain their velocities in the same ratio to one another as at the beginning.

COR. IV. Now if the globes are not homogeneous, the space described by the denser globe must be augmented in the ratio of the density. For the motion, with an equal velocity, is greater in the ratio of the density, and the time (by this Proposition) is augmented in the ratio of motion directly, and the space described in the ratio of the time.

Cor. v. And if the globes move in different mediums, the space, in a medium which, other things being equal, resists the most, must be diminished in the ratio of the greater resistance. For the time (by this Proposition) will be diminished in the ratio of the augmented resistance, and the space in the ratio of the time.

Lemma 2

The moment of any genitum *is equal to the moments of each of the generating sides multiplied by the indices of the powers of those sides, and by their coefficients continually.*

I call any quantity a *genitum* which is not made by addition or subtraction of divers parts, but is generated or produced in arithmetic by the multiplication, division, or extraction of the root of any terms whatsoever; in geometry by the finding of contents and sides, or of the extremes and means of proportionals. Quantities of this kind are products, quotients, roots, rectangles, squares, cubes, square and cubic sides, and the like. These quantities I here consider as variable and indetermined, and increasing or decreasing, as it were, by a continual motion or flux; and I understand their momentary increments or decrements by the name of moments; so that the increments may be esteemed as added or affirmative moments; and the decrements as subtracted or negative ones. But take care not to look upon finite particles as such. Finite particles are not moments, but the very quantities generated by the moments. We are to conceive them as the just nascent principles of finite magnitudes. Nor do we in this Lemma regard the magnitude of the moments, but their first proportion, as nascent. It will be the same thing, if, instead of moments, we use either the velocities of the increments and decrements (which may also be called the motions, mutations, and fluxions of quantities), or any finite quantities proportional to those velocities. The coefficient of any generating side is the quantity which arises by applying the *genitum* to that side.

Wherefore the sense of the Lemma is, that if the moments of any quantities A, B, C, &c., increasing or decreasing by a continual flux, or the velocities of the mutations which are proportional to them, be called a, b, c, &c., the moment or mutation of the generated rectangle AB will be $aB+bA$; the moment of the generated content ABC will be $aBC+bAC+cAB$; and the moments of the generated powers A^2, A^3, A^4, $A^{1/2}$, $A^{3/2}$, $A^{1/3}$, $A^{2/3}$, A^{-1}, A^{-2}, $A^{-1/2}$ will be $2aA$, $3aA^2$, $4aA^3$, $\frac{1}{2}aA^{-1/2}$, $\frac{3}{2}aA^{1/2}$, $\frac{1}{3}aA^{-2/3}$, $\frac{2}{3}aA^{-1/3}$, $-aA^{-2}$, $-2aA^{-3}$, $-\frac{1}{2}aA^{-3/2}$ respectively; and, in general, that the moment of any power $A^{\frac{n}{m}}$ will be $\frac{n}{m} aA^{\frac{n-m}{m}}$. Also, that the moment of the generated quantity A^2B will be $2aAB+bA^2$; the moment of the generated quantity $A^3B^4C^2$ will be $3aA^2B^4C^2+ 4bA^3B^3C^2+2cA^3B^4C$; and the moment of the generated quantity $\frac{A^3}{B^2}$ or A^3B^{-2} will be $3aA^2B^{-2}-2bA^3B^{-3}$; and so on. The Lemma is thus demonstrated.

Case 1. Any rectangle, as AB, augmented by a continual flux, when, as yet, there wanted of the sides A and B half their moments $\frac{1}{2}a$ and $\frac{1}{2}b$, was $A-\frac{1}{2}a$ into $B-\frac{1}{2}b$, or $AB-\frac{1}{2}a$ $B-\frac{1}{2}b$ $A+\frac{1}{4}ab$; but as soon as the sides A and B are augmented by the other half-moments, the rectangle becomes $A+\frac{1}{2}a$ into $B+\frac{1}{2}b$, or $AB+\frac{1}{2}a$ $B+\frac{1}{2}b$ $A+\frac{1}{4}ab$. From this rectangle subtract the former rectangle, and there will remain the excess $aB+bA$. Therefore with the whole increments a and b of the sides, the increment $aB+bA$ of the rectangle is generated. Q.E.D.

CASE 2. Suppose AB always equal to G, and then the moment of the content ABC or GC (by CASE 1) will be $gC+cG$, that is (putting AB and $aB+bA$ for G and g), $aBC+bAC+cAB$. And the reasoning is the same for contents under ever so many sides. Q.E.D.

CASE 3. Suppose the sides A, B, and C, to be always equal among themselves; and the moment $aB+bA$, of A^2, that is, of the rectangle AB, will be $2aA$; and the moment $aBC+bAC+cAB$ of A^3, that is, of the content ABC, will be $3aA^2$. And by the same reasoning the moment of any power A^n is naA^{n-1}. Q.E.D.

CASE 4. Therefore since $\frac{1}{A}$ into A is 1, the moment of $\frac{1}{A}$ multiplied by A, together with $\frac{1}{A}$ multiplied by a, will be the moment of 1, that is, nothing. Therefore the moment of $\frac{1}{A}$, or of A^{-1}, is $\frac{-a}{A^2}$. And generally since $\frac{1}{A^n}$ into A^n is 1, the moment of $\frac{1}{A^n}$ multiplied by A^n together with $\frac{1}{A^n}$ into naA^{n-1} will be nothing. And, therefore, the moment of $\frac{1}{A^n}$ or A^{-n} will be $-\frac{na}{A^{n+1}}$. Q.E.D.

CASE 5. And since $A^{1/2}$ into $A^{1/2}$ is A, the moment of $A^{1/2}$ multiplied by $2A^{1/2}$ will be a (by Case 3); and, therefore, the moment of $A^{1/2}$ will be $\frac{a}{2A^{1/2}}$ or $\frac{1}{2}aA^{-1/2}$. And generally, putting $A^{\frac{m}{n}}$ equal to B, then A^m will be equal to B^n, and therefore maA^{m-1} equal to nbB^{n-1}, and maA^{-1} equal to nbB^{-1}, or $nbA^{-\frac{m}{n}}$; and therefore $\frac{m}{n}aA^{\frac{n-m}{n}}$ is equal to b, that is, equal to the moment of $A^{\frac{m}{n}}$. Q.E.D.

CASE 6. Therefore the moment of any generated quantity A^mB^n is the moment of A^m multiplied by B^n, together with the moment of B^n multiplied by A^m, that is, $maA^{m-1}B^n+nbB^{n-1}A^m$; and that whether the indices m and n of the powers be whole numbers or fractions, affirmative or negative. And the reasoning is the same for higher powers. Q.E.D.

COR. I. Hence in quantities continually proportional, if one term is given, the moments of the rest of the terms will be as the same terms multiplied by the number of intervals between them and the given term. Let A, B, C, D, E, F be continually proportional; then if the term C is given, the moments of the rest of the terms will be among themselves as $-2A$, $-B$, D, 2E, 3F.

COR. II. And if in four proportionals the two means are given, the moments of the extremes will be as those extremes. The same is to be understood of the sides of any given rectangle.

COR. III. And if the sum or difference of two squares is given, the moments of the sides will be inversely as the sides.

SCHOLIUM

In a letter of mine to Mr. J. Collins, dated December 10, 1672, having described a method of tangents, which I suspected to be the same with Sluse's method, which at that time was not made public, I added these words: *This is one particular, or rather a Corollary, of a general method, which extends itself, without any troublesome calculation, not only to the drawing of tangents to any curved lines, whether geometrical or mechanical or in any manner respecting right lines or other curves, but also to the resolving other abstruser kinds of problems about the crookedness, areas, lengths, centres of gravity of curves, &c.; nor is it (as Hudden's method* de maximis et minimis) *limited to equations which are free from surd quantities. This method I have interwoven with that other of working in equations, by reducing them to infinite series.* So far that letter. And these last words relate to a treatise I composed on that subject in the year 1671. The foundation of that general method is contained in the preceding Lemma.

PROPOSITION 8. THEOREM 6

If a body in an uniform medium, being uniformly acted upon by the force of gravity, ascends or descends in a right line; and the whole space described be divided into equal parts, and in the beginning of each of the parts (by adding or subtracting the resisting force of the medium to or from the force of gravity, when the body ascends or descends) you derive the absolute forces: I say, that those absolute forces are in a geometrical progression.

Let the force of gravity be represented by the given line AC; the force of resistance by the indefinite line AK; the absolute force in the descent of the body by the difference KC; the velocity of the body by a line AP, which shall be a mean proportional between AK and AC, and therefore as the square root of the resistance; the increment of the resistance made in a given interval of time by the short line KL, and the contemporaneous increment of the velocity by the short line PQ; and with the centre C, and rectangular asymptotes CA, CH, describe any hyperbola BNS meeting the erected perpendiculars AB, KN, LO in B, N, and O. Because AK is as AP², the moment KL

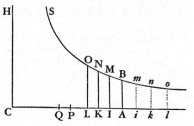

of the one will be as the moment 2AP·PQ of the other, that is, as AP·KC; for the increment PQ of the velocity is (by Law II) proportional to the generating force KC. Let the ratio of KL be multiplied by the ratio KN, and the rectangle KL·KN will become as AP·KC·KN; that is (because the rectangle KC·KN is given), as AP. But the ultimate ratio of the hyperbolic area KNOL to the rectangle KL·KN becomes, when the points K and L coincide, the ratio of equality. Therefore that hyperbolic evanescent area is as AP. Therefore the whole hyperbolic area ABOL is composed of intervals KNOL which are always proportional to the velocity AP; and therefore is itself proportional to the space described with that velocity. Let that area be now divided into equal parts, as ABMI, IMNK, KNOL, &c., and the absolute forces AC, IC, KC, LC, &c., will be in a geometrical progression. Q.E.D. And by a like reasoning, in the ascent of the body, taking, on the contrary side of the point A, the equal areas AB*mi*, *imnk*, *knol*, &c., it will appear that the absolute forces AC, *i*C, *k*C, *l*C, &c., are continually proportional. Therefore if all the spaces in the ascent and descent are taken equal, all the absolute forces *l*C, *k*C, *i*C, AC, IC, KC, LC, &c., will be continually proportional. Q.E.D.

COR. I. Hence if the space described be represented by the hyperbolic area ABNK, the force of gravity, the velocity of the body, and the resistance of the medium, may be represented by the lines AC, AP, and AK respectively; and conversely.

Cor. ii. And the greatest velocity which the body can ever acquire in an infinite descent will be represented by the line AC.

Cor. iii. Therefore if the resistance of the medium answering to any given velocity be known, the greatest velocity will be found, by taking it to that given velocity, as the square root of the ratio which the force of gravity bears to that known resistance of the medium.

Proposition 9. Theorem 7

Supposing what is above demonstrated, I say, that if the tangents of the angles of the sector of a circle, and of an hyperbola, be taken proportional to the velocities, the radius being of a fit magnitude, all the time of the ascent to the highest place will be as the sector of the circle, and all the time of descending from the highest place as the sector of the hyperbola.

To the right line AC, which expresses the force of gravity, let AD be drawn perpendicular and equal. From the centre D, with the semidiameter AD describe as well the quadrant A*t*E of a circle, as the rectangular hyperbola AVZ, whose axis is AK, principal vertex A, and asymptote DC. Let D*p*, DP

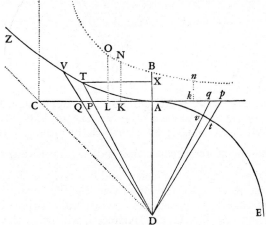

be drawn; and the circular sector A*t*D will be as all the time of the ascent to the highest place; and the hyperbolic sector ATD as all the time of descent from the highest place; if so be that the tangents A*p*, AP of those sectors be as the velocities.

Case 1. Draw D*vq* cutting off the moments or least intervals *t*D*v* and *q*D*p*, described in the same time, of the sector AD*t* and of the triangle AD*p*. Since those intervals (because of the common angle D) are as the square of the sides, the interval *t*D*v* will be as $\frac{qDp \cdot tD^2}{pD^2}$, that is (because *t*D is given), as $\frac{qDp}{pD^2}$. But pD^2 is $AD^2 + Ap^2$, that is, $AD^2 + AD \cdot Ak$, or $AD \cdot Ck$; and qDp is $\frac{1}{2}AD \cdot pq$. Therefore *t*D*v*, the interval of the sector, is as $\frac{pq}{Ck}$; that is, directly as the least decrement *pq* of the velocity, and inversely as the force C*k* which diminishes the velocity; and therefore as the interval of time answering to the decrement of the velocity. And, by composition, the sum of all the intervals tDv in the sector ADt will be as the sum of the intervals of time answering to each of the lost intervals pq of the decreasing velocity Ap, till that velocity, being diminished into nothing, vanishes; that is, the whole sector ADt is as the whole time of ascent to the highest place.   Q.E.D.

CASE 2. Draw DQV cutting off the least intervals TDV and PDQ of the sector DAV, and of the triangle DAQ; and these intervals will be to each other as DT^2 to DP^2, that is (if TX and AP are parallel), as DX^2 to DA^2 or TX^2 to

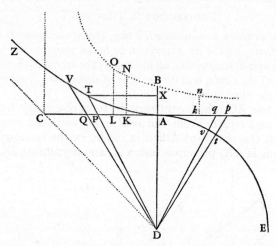

AP^2; and, by subtraction, as $DX^2 - TX^2$ to $DA^2 - AP^2$. But, from the nature of the hyperbola, $DX^2 - TX^2$ is AD^2; and, by the supposition, AP^2 is $AD \cdot AK$. Therefore the intervals are to each other as AD^2 to $AD^2 - AD \cdot AK$; that is, as AD to $AD - AK$ or AC to CK; and therefore the interval TDV of the sector is $\dfrac{PDQ \cdot AC}{CK}$; and therefore (because AC and AD are given) as $\dfrac{PQ}{CK}$; that is, directly as the increment of the velocity, and inversely as the force generating the increment; and therefore as the interval of the time answering to the increment. And, by composition, the sum of the intervals of time, in which all the intervals PQ of the velocity AP are generated, will be as the sum of the intervals of the sector ATD; that is, the whole time will be as the whole sector.

Q.E.D.

COR. I. Hence if AB be equal to a fourth part of AC, the space which a body will describe by falling in any time will be to the space which the body could describe, by moving uniformly on in the same time with its greatest velocity AC, as the area ABNK, which expresses the space described in falling to the area ATD, which expresses the time. For since

$$AC : AP = AP : AK,$$

and by Cor. I, Lem. 2, of this Book,

$$LK : PQ = 2AK : AP = 2AP : AC,$$

therefore $LK : \tfrac{1}{2}PQ = AP : \tfrac{1}{4}AC$ or AB,

and since $KN : AC$ or $AD = AD : CK$,

multiplying together corresponding terms,

$$LKNO : DPQ = AP : CK.$$

As shown above,
$$DPQ : DTV = CK : AC.$$
Hence, $$LKNO : DTV = AP : AC;$$
that is, as the velocity of the falling body to the greatest velocity which the body by falling can acquire. Since, therefore, the moments LKNO and DTV of the areas ABNK and ATD are as the velocities, all the parts of those areas generated in the same time will be as the spaces described in the same time; and therefore the whole areas ABNK and ADT, generated from the beginning, will be as the whole spaces described from the beginning of the descent. Q.E.D.

COR. II. The same is true also of the space described in the ascent. That is to say, that all that space is to the space described in the same time, with the uniform velocity AC, as the area ABnk is to the sector ADt.

COR. III. The velocity of the body, falling in the time ATD, is to the velocity which it would acquire in the same time in a nonresisting space, as the triangle APD to the hyperbolic sector ATD. For the velocity in a nonresisting medium would be as the time ATD, and in a resisting medium is as AP, that is, as the triangle APD. And those velocities, at the beginning of the descent, are equal among themselves, as well as those areas ATD, APD.

COR. IV. By the same argument, the velocity in the ascent is to the velocity with which the body in the same time, in a nonresisting space, would lose all its motion of ascent, as the triangle ApD to the circular sector AtD; or as the right line Ap to the arc At.

COR. V. Therefore the time in which a body, by falling in a resisting medium, would acquire the velocity AP, is to the time in which it would acquire its greatest velocity AC, by falling in a nonresisting space, as the sector ADT to the triangle ADC; and the time in which it would lose its velocity Ap, by ascending in a resisting medium, is to the time in which it would lose the same velocity by ascending in a nonresisting space, as the arc At to its tangent Ap.

COR. VI. Hence from the given time there is given the space described in the ascent or descent. For the greatest velocity of a body descending *in infinitum* is given (by Cor. II and III, Theor. 6, of this book); and thence the time is given in which a body would acquire that velocity by falling in nonresisting space. Taking the sector ADT or ADt to the triangle ADC in the ratio of the given time to the time just found, there will be given both the velocity AP or Ap, and the area ABNK or ABnk, which is to the sector ADT, or ADt as the space sought to that which would, in the given time, be uniformly described with that greatest velocity found just before.

COR. VII. And by going backwards, from the given space of ascent or descent ABnk or ABNK, there will be given the time ADt or ADT.

PROPOSITION 10. PROBLEM 3

Suppose the uniform force of gravity to tend directly to the plane of the horizon, and the resistance to be as the product of the density of the medium and the square of the velocity: it is proposed to find the density of the medium in each place, which shall make the body move in any given curved line, the velocity of the body, and the resistance of the medium in each place.

Let PQ be a plane perpendicular to the plane of the scheme itself; PFHQ a curved line meeting that plane in the points P and Q; G, H, I ,K four places of the body going on in this curve from F to Q; and GB, HC, ID, KE four parallel ordinates let fall from these points to the horizon, and standing on the horizontal line PQ at the points B, C, D, E; and let the distances BC, CD, DE of the ordinates be equal among themselves. From the points G and H let the right lines GL, HN be drawn touching the curve in G and H, and meeting the ordinates CH, DI, produced upwards, in L and N; and complete the parallelogram HCDM. And the times in which the body describes the arcs GH, HI, will be as the square root of the altitudes LH, NI, which the bodies would describe in those times, by falling from the tangents; and the velocities will be directly as the lengths described GH, HI, and inversely as the times. Let the times be represented by T and t,

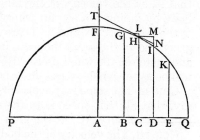

and the velocities by $\dfrac{GH}{T}$ and $\dfrac{HI}{t}$; and the decrement of the velocity produced

in the time t will be represented by $\dfrac{GH}{T} - \dfrac{HI}{t}$. This decrement arises from the resistance which retards the body, and from the gravity which accelerates it. Gravity, in a falling body, which in its fall describes the space NI, produces a velocity with which it would be able to describe twice that space in the same time, as Galileo hath demonstrated; that is, the velocity $\dfrac{2NI}{t}$: but if the body describes the arc HI, it augments that arc only by the length $HI - HN$ or $\dfrac{MI \cdot NI}{HI}$; and therefore generates only the velocity $\dfrac{2MI \cdot NI}{t \cdot HI}$. Let this velocity be added to the before-mentioned decrement, and we shall have the decrement of the velocity arising from the resistance alone, that is, $\dfrac{GH}{T} - \dfrac{HI}{t} + \dfrac{2MI \cdot NI}{t \cdot HI}$. Therefore since, in the same time, the action of gravity generates, in a falling body, the velocity $\dfrac{2NI}{t}$, the resistance will be to the gravity as

$$\frac{GH}{T} - \frac{HI}{t} + \frac{2MI \cdot NI}{t \cdot HI} \text{ to } \frac{2NI}{t} \text{ or as } \frac{t \cdot GH}{T} - HI + \frac{2MI \cdot NI}{HI} \text{ to } 2NI.$$

Now, for the abscissas CB, CD, CE, put $-o$, o, $2o$. For the ordinate CH put P; and for MI put any series $Qo + Ro^2 + So^3 +$, &c. And all the terms of the series after the first, that is, $Ro^2 + So^3 +$, &c., will be NI; and the ordinates DI, EK, and BG will be $P - Qo - Ro^2 - So^3 -$, &c., $P - 2Qo - 4Ro^2 - 8So^3 -$, &c., and $P + Qo - Ro^2 + So^3 -$, &c., respectively. And by squaring the differences of the ordinates $BG - CH$ and $CH - DI$, and to the squares thence produced adding the squares of BC and CD themselves, you will have $oo + QQoo - 2QRo^3 +$, &c., and $oo + QQoo + 2QRo^3 +$, &c., the squares of the arcs GH, HI; whose roots $o\sqrt{(1+QQ)} - \dfrac{QRoo}{\sqrt{(1+QQ)}}$ and $o\sqrt{(1+QQ)} + \dfrac{QRoo}{\sqrt{(1+QQ)}}$ are the arcs GH and HI. Moreover, if from the ordinate CH there be subtracted half the sum of the ordinates BG and DI, and from the ordinate DI there be subtracted half the sum of the ordinates CH and EK, there will remain Roo and $Roo + 3So^3$, the versed sines of the arcs GI and HK. And these are proportional to the short lines LH and NI, and therefore are as the squares of the infinitely small times T and t: and thence the ratio $\frac{t}{T}$ varies as the square root of $\frac{R+3So}{R}$

or $\frac{R+\frac{3}{2}So}{R}$; and $\frac{t\times GH}{T}-HI+\frac{2MI\times NI}{HI}$ by substituting the values of $\frac{t}{T}$, GH,

HI, MI, and NI just found, becomes $\frac{3Soo}{2R}\cdot\sqrt{(1+QQ)}$. And since 2NI is 2R$oo$,

the resistance will be now to the gravity as $\frac{3Soo}{2R}\sqrt{(1+QQ)}$ to 2Roo, that is, as

$3S\sqrt{(1+QQ)}$ to 4RR.

And the velocity will be such, that a body going off therewith from any place
H, in the direction of the tangent HN, would describe, in a vacuum, a parabola,

whose diameter is HC, and its latus rectum $\frac{HN^2}{NI}$ or $\frac{1+QQ}{R}$.

And the resistance is as the product of the density of the medium and the

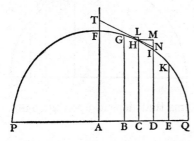

square of the velocity; and therefore the
density of the medium is directly as the resistance, and inversely as the square of the
velocity; that is, directly as $\frac{3S\sqrt{(1+QQ)}}{4RR}$

and inversely as $\frac{1+QQ}{R}$; that is, as

$\frac{S}{R\sqrt{(1+QQ)}}$.   Q.E.I.

COR. I. If the tangent HN be produced
both ways, so as to meet any ordinate AF in T, $\frac{HT}{AC}$ will be equal to $\sqrt{(1+}$

$QQ)$, and therefore in what has gone before may be put for $\sqrt{(1+QQ)}$. By
this means the resistance will be to the gravity as $3S\cdot HT$ to $4RR\cdot AC$; the

velocity will be as $\frac{HT}{AC\sqrt{R}}$, and the density of the medium will be as $\frac{S\cdot AC}{R\cdot HT}$.

COR. II. And hence, if the curved line PFHQ be defined by the relation between the base or abscissa AC and the ordinate CH, as is usual, and the value
of the ordinate be resolved into a converging series, the Problem will be expeditiously solved by the first terms of the series; as in the following Examples.

EXAM. 1. Let the line PFHQ be a semicircle described upon the diameter
PQ; to find the density of the medium that shall make a projectile move in
that line.

Bisect the diameter PQ in A; and call AQ, n; AC, a; CH, e; and CD, o; then
DI^2 or $AQ^2-AD^2=nn-aa-2ao-oo$, or $ee-2ao-oo$; and the root being
extracted by our method, will give

$$DI=e-\frac{ao}{e}-\frac{oo}{2e}-\frac{aaoo}{2e^3}-\frac{ao^3}{2e^3}-\frac{a^3o^3}{2e^5}, \&c.$$

Here put nn for $ee+aa$, and DI will become $=ee-\frac{ao}{e}-\frac{nnoo}{2e^3}-\frac{anno^3}{2e^5}-,\&c.$

In such a series I distinguish the successive terms after this manner: I call
that the first term in which the infinitely small quantity o is not found; the
second, in which that quantity is of one dimension only; the third, in which
it arises to two dimensions; the fourth, in which it is of three; and so ad
$infinitum$. And the first term, which here is e, will always denote the length of

the ordinate CH, erected at the starting point of the indefinite quantity o. The second term, which here is $\dfrac{ao}{e}$, will denote the difference between CH and DN; that is, the short line MN which is cut off by completing the parallelogram HCDM; and therefore always determines the position of the tangent HN; as, in this case, by taking MN : HM $= \dfrac{ao}{e} : o = a : e$. The third term, which here is $\dfrac{nnoo}{2e^3}$, will represent the short line IN, which lies between the tangent and the curve; and therefore determines the angle of contact IHN, or the curvature which the curved line has in H. If that short line IN is of a finite magnitude, it will be expressed by the third term, to-gether with those that follow *in infinitum*. But if that short line be diminished *in in-finitum*, the terms following become infin-itely less than the third term, and there-fore may be neglected. The fourth term determines the variation of the curvature; the fifth, the variation of the variation; and so on. From this, by the way, appears the use, not to be disdained, which may be made of these series in the solution of problems that depend upon tangents, and the curvature of curves.

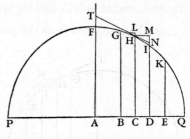

Now compare the series

$$e - \frac{ao}{e} - \frac{nnoo}{2e^3} - \frac{anno^3}{2e^5} - \&c.,$$

with the series

$$P - Qo - Roo - So^3 - \&c.,$$

and for P, Q, R and S, put $e, \dfrac{a}{e}, \dfrac{nn}{2e^3}$ and $\dfrac{ann}{2e^5}$, and for $\sqrt{(1+QQ)}$ put $\sqrt{\left(1 + \dfrac{aa}{ee}\right)}$ or $\dfrac{n}{e}$; and the density of the medium will come out as $\dfrac{a}{ne}$; that is (because n is given), as $\dfrac{a}{e}$ or $\dfrac{AC}{CH}$, that is, as that length of the tangent HT, which is term-inated at the semidiameter AF standing perpendicularly on PQ: and the resistance will be to the gravity as $3a$ to $2n$, that is, as 3AC to the diameter PQ of the circle; and the velocity will be as $\sqrt{CH}$. Therefore if the body goes from the place F, with a due velocity, in the direction of a line parallel to PQ, and the density of the medium in each of the places H is as the length of the tangent HT, and the resistance also in any place H is to the force of gravity as 3AC to PQ, that body will describe the quadrant FHQ of a circle.   Q.E.I.

But if the same body should go from the place P, in the direction of a line perpendicular to PQ, and should begin to move in an arc of the semicircle PFQ, we must take AC or a on the contrary side of the centre A; and therefore its sign must be changed, and we must put $-a$ for $+a$. Then the density of the medium would come out as $-\dfrac{a}{e}$. But Nature does not admit of a negative density, that is, a density which accelerates the motion of bodies; and therefore it cannot naturally come to pass that a body by ascending from P should describe the quadrant PF of a circle. To produce such an effect, a body ought to be accelerated by an impelling medium, and not impeded by a resisting one.

EXAM. 2. Let the line PFQ be a parabola, having its axis AF perpendicular to the horizon PQ; to find the density of the medium, which will make a projectile move in that line.

From the nature of the parabola, the rectangle $-$PD$\cdot$DQ is equal to the rectangle under the ordinate DI and some given right line; that is, if that right line be called b; PC, a; PQ, c; CH, e; and CD, o; the rectangle

$$(a+o)(c-a-o)=ac-aa-2ao+co-oo=b\cdot DI;$$

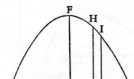

therefore $\quad DI=\dfrac{ac-aa}{b}+\dfrac{c-2a}{b}\cdot o-\dfrac{oo}{b}.$

Now the second term $\dfrac{c-2a}{b}\,o$ of this series is to be put for Qo, and the third term $\dfrac{oo}{b}$ for Roo. But since there are no more terms, the coefficient S of the fourth term will vanish; and therefore the quantity $\dfrac{S}{R\sqrt{(1+QQ)}}$, to which the density of the medium is proportional, will be nothing. Therefore, where the medium is of no density, the projectile will move in a parabola; as Galileo hath heretofore demonstrated. Q.E.I.

EXAM. 3. Let the line AGK be an hyperbola, having its asymptote NX perpendicular to the horizontal plane AK: to find the density of the medium that will make a projectile move in that line.

Let MX be the other asymptote, meeting the ordinate DG produced in V; and from the nature of the hyperbola, the rectangle of XV into VG will be given. There is also given the ratio of DN to VX, and therefore the rectangle of DN into VG is given. Let that be bb; and, completing the parallelogram DNXZ, let BN be called a; BD, o; NX, c; and let the given ratio of VZ to ZX or DN be $\dfrac{m}{n}$. Then DN will be equal to $a-o$, VG equal to $\dfrac{bb}{a-o}$, VZ equal to

$\dfrac{m}{n}\cdot(a-o)$ and GD or NX$-$VZ$-$VG equal to

$$c-\frac{m}{n}a+\frac{m}{n}o-\frac{bb}{a-o}.$$

Let the term $\dfrac{bb}{a-o}$ be resolved into the converging series

$$\frac{bb}{a}+\frac{bb}{aa}o+\frac{bb}{a^3}oo+\frac{bb}{a^4}o^3, \&c.,$$

and GD will become equal to

$$c-\frac{m}{n}a-\frac{bb}{a}+\frac{m}{n}o-\frac{bb}{aa}o-\frac{bb}{a^3}o^2-\frac{bb}{a^4}o^3, \&c.$$

The second term $\dfrac{m}{n}o-\dfrac{bb}{aa}o$ of this series is to be used for Qo; the third $\dfrac{bb}{a^3}o^2$, with its sign changed for Ro^2; and the fourth $\dfrac{bb}{a^4}o^3$, with

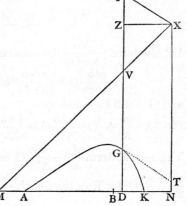

its sign changed also for So^3, and their coef-

ficients $\dfrac{m}{n} - \dfrac{bb}{aa}, \dfrac{bb}{a^3}$, and $\dfrac{bb}{a^4}$ are to be put

for Q, R, and S in the former rule. Which
being done, the density of the medium will
come out as

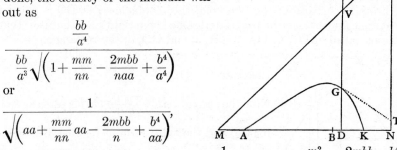

$$\frac{\dfrac{bb}{a^4}}{\dfrac{bb}{a^3}\sqrt{\left(1+\dfrac{mm}{nn}-\dfrac{2mbb}{naa}+\dfrac{b^4}{a^4}\right)}}$$

or

$$\frac{1}{\sqrt{\left(aa+\dfrac{mm}{nn}aa-\dfrac{2mbb}{n}+\dfrac{b^4}{aa}\right)}},$$

that is, if in VZ you take VY equal to VG, as $\dfrac{1}{XY}$. For aa and $\dfrac{m^2}{n^2}a^2-\dfrac{2mbb}{n}+\dfrac{b^4}{aa}$
are the squares of XZ and ZY. But the ratio of the resistance to gravity is
found to be that of 3XY to 2YG; and the velocity is that with which the body
would describe a parabola, whose vertex is G, diameter DG, latus rectum
$\dfrac{XY^2}{VG}$. Suppose, therefore, that the densities of the medium in each of the places
G are inversely as the distances XY, and that the resistance in any place G is
to the gravity as 3XY to 2YG; and a body let go from the place A, with a due
velocity, will describe that hyperbola AGK.   q.e.i.

Exam. 4. Suppose, indefinitely, the line AGK to be an hyperbola described
with the centre X, and the asymptotes MX, NX, so that, having constructed
the rectangle XZDN, whose side ZD cuts the hyperbola in G and its asymptote
in V, VG may be inversely as any power DN^n of the line ZX or DN, whose
index is the number n: to find the density of the medium in which a projected
body will describe this curve.

For BN, BD, NX, put A, O, C, respectively, and let VZ be to XZ or DN as
d to e, and VG be equal to $\dfrac{bb}{DN^n}$; then DN will be equal to $A-O$, $VG=\dfrac{bb}{(A-C)^n}$,

$VZ=\dfrac{d}{e}(A-O)$ and GD or $NX-VZ-VG$ equal to

$$C-\frac{d}{e}A+\frac{d}{e}O-\frac{bb}{(A-O)^n}.$$

Let the term $\dfrac{bb}{(A-O)^n}$ be resolved into an infinite series

$$\frac{bb}{A^n}+\frac{nbb}{A^{n+1}}\cdot O+\frac{nn+n}{2A^{n+2}}\cdot bbO^2+\frac{n^3+3nn+2n}{6A^{n+3}}\cdot bbO^3,\ \&c.,$$

and GD will be equal to

$$C-\frac{d}{e}A-\frac{bb}{A^n}+\frac{d}{e}O-\frac{nbb}{A^{n+1}}O-\frac{+nn+n}{2A^{n+2}}bbO^2-\frac{+n^3+3nn+2n}{6A^{n+3}}bbO^3,\ \&c.$$

The second term $\dfrac{d}{e}O-\dfrac{nbb}{A^{n+1}}O$ of this series is to be used for Qo, the third

$\dfrac{nn+n}{2A^{n+2}}bbO^2$ for Roo, the fourth $\dfrac{n^3+3nn+2n}{6A^{n+3}}bbO$ for So^3. And thence the density of the medium $\dfrac{S}{R\sqrt{(1+QQ)}}$, in any place G, will be

$$\frac{n+2}{3\sqrt{\left(A^2+\dfrac{dd}{ee}A^2-\dfrac{2dnbb}{eA^n}A+\dfrac{nnb^4}{A^{2n}}\right)}},$$

and therefore if in VZ you take VY equal to $n \cdot$ VG, that density is reciprocally as XY. For A^2 and $\dfrac{dd}{ee}A^2-\dfrac{2dnbb}{eA^n}A+\dfrac{nnb^4}{A^{2n}}$ are the squares of XZ and ZY. But the resistance in the same place G is to the force of gravity as $3S \cdot \dfrac{XY}{A}$ to 4RR, that is, as XY to $\dfrac{2nn+2n}{n+2}$ VG. And the velocity there is the same wherewith the projected body would move in a parabola, whose vertex is G, diameter GD, and latus rectum $\dfrac{1+QQ}{R}$ or $\dfrac{2XY^2}{(nn+n)\cdot VG}$.   Q.E.I.

SCHOLIUM

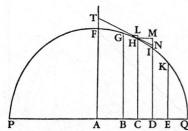

In the same manner that the density of the medium comes out to be as $\dfrac{S \cdot AC}{R \cdot HT}$, in Cor. I, if the resistance is put as any power V^n of the velocity V, the density of the medium will come out to be as

$$\frac{S}{R^{\frac{4-n}{2}}} \cdot \left(\frac{AC}{HT}\right)^{n-1}.$$

And therefore, if a curve can be found, such that the ratio of $\dfrac{S}{R^{\frac{4-n}{2}}}$ to $\left(\dfrac{HT}{AC}\right)^{n-1}$, or of $\dfrac{S^2}{R^{4-n}}$ to $(1+QQ)^{n-1}$ may be given; the body, in an uniform medium, whose resistance is as the power V^n of the velocity V, will move in this curve. But let us return to more simple curves.

Since there can be no motion in a parabola except in a nonresisting medium, but in the hyperbolas here described it is produced by a continual resistance; it is evident that the line which a projectile describes in an uniformly resisting

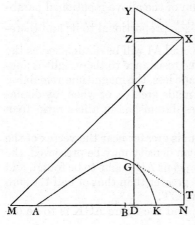

medium approaches nearer to these hyperbolas than to a parabola. That line is certainly of the hyperbolic kind, but about the vertex it is more distant from the asymptotes, and in the parts remote from the vertex draws nearer to them than these hyperbolas here described. The difference, however, is not so great between the one and the other but that these latter may be commodiously enough used in practice instead of the former. And perhaps these may prove more useful than an hyperbola that is more accurate, and at the same time more complex. They may be made use of, then, in this manner.

Complete the parallelogram XYGT, and the right line GT will touch the hyperbola in G, and therefore the density of the medium in G is inversely as the tangent GT, and the velocity there as $\sqrt{\dfrac{GT^2}{GV}}$; and the resistance is to the force of gravity as GT to $\dfrac{2nn+2n}{n+2}\cdot GV$.

Therefore if a body projected from the place A, in the direction of the right line AH, describes the hyperbola AGK, and AH produced meets the asymptote NX in H, and AI drawn parallel to it meets the other asymptote MX in I; the density of the medium in A will be inversely as AH and the velocity of the body as $\sqrt{\dfrac{AH^2}{AI}}$, and the resistance there to the force of gravity as AH to $\dfrac{2nn+2n}{n+2}\cdot AI$. Hence the following Rules are deduced.

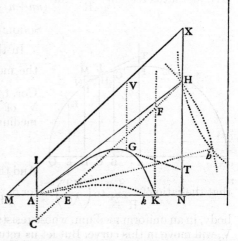

Rule 1. If the density of the medium at A, and the velocity with which the body is projected, remain the same, and the angle NAH be changed; the lengths AH, AI, HX will remain. Therefore if those lengths, in any one case, are found, the hyperbola may afterwards be easily determined from any given angle NAH.

Rule 2. If the angle NAH, and the density of the medium at A, remain the same, and the velocity with which the body is projected be changed, the length AH will continue the same; and AI will be changed inversely as the square of the velocity.

Rule 3. If the angle NAH, the velocity of the body at A, and the accelerative gravity remain the same, and the proportion of the resistance at A to the motive gravity be augmented in any ratio; the proportion of AH to AI will be augmented in the same ratio, the latus rectum of the above-mentioned parabola remaining the same, and also the length $\dfrac{AH^2}{AI}$ proportional to it; and therefore AH will be diminished in the same ratio, and AI will be diminished as the square of that ratio. But the proportion of the resistance to the weight is augmented, when either the specific gravity is made less, the magnitude remaining equal, or when the density of the medium is made greater, or when, by diminishing the magnitude, the resistance becomes diminished in a less ratio than the weight.

Rule 4. Because the density of the medium is greater near the vertex of the hyperbola than it is in the place A, that a mean density may be preserved, the ratio of the least of the tangents GT to the tangent AH ought to be found, and the density in A augmented in a ratio a little greater than that of half the sum of those tangents to the least of the tangents GT.

Rule 5. If the lengths AH, AI are given, and the figure AGK is to be de-

scribed, produce HN to X, so that HX may be to AI as $n+1$ to 1; and with
the centre X, and the asymptotes MX, NX, describe an hyperbola through the
point A, such that AI may be to any of the lines VG as XV^n to XI^n.

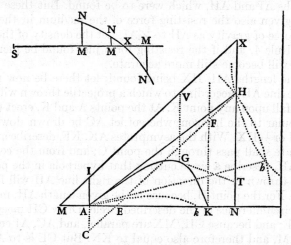

RULE 6. By how much the greater the number n is, so much the more accurate are these hyperbolas in the ascent of the body from A, and less accurate
in its descent to K; and conversely. The conic hyperbola keeps a mean ratio
between these, and is more simple than the rest. Therefore if the hyperbola be
of this kind, and you are to find the point K, where the projected body falls
upon any right line AN passing through the point A, let AN produced meet the
asymptotes MX, NX in M and N, and take NK equal to AM.

RULE 7. And hence appears an expeditious method of determining this hyperbola from the phenomena. Let two similar and equal bodies be projected
with the same velocity, in different angles HAK, hAk, and let them fall upon
the plane of the horizon in K and k; and note the proportion of AK to Ak. Let
it be as d to e. Then erecting a perpendicular AI of any length, assume any

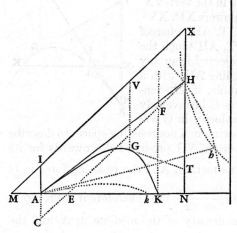

length AH or Ah, and thence graph-
ically, or by scale and compass,
collect the lengths AK, Ak (by Rule
6). If the ratio of AK to Ak be the
same with that of d to e, the length
of AH was rightly assumed. If not,
take on the indefinite right line SM,
the length SM equal to the assumed
AH; and erect a perpendicular MN
equal to the difference $\dfrac{AK}{Ak}-\dfrac{d}{e}$ of the
ratios multiplied by any given right
line. By the like method, from several
assumed lengths AH, you may find
several points N; and draw through
them all a regular curve NNXN,
cutting the right line SMMM in X.

Lastly, assume AH equal to the abscissa SX, and thence find again the length AK; and the lengths, which are to the assumed length AI, and this last AH, as the length AK known by experiment, to the length AK last found, will be the true lengths AI and AH, which were to be found. But these being given, there will be given also the resisting force of the medium in the place A, it being to the force of gravity as AH to $\frac{4}{3}$AI. Let the density of the medium be increased by Rule 4, and if the resisting force just found be increased in the same ratio, it will become still more accurate.

RULE 8. The lengths AH, HX being found; let there be now required the position of the line AH, according to which a projectile thrown with that given velocity shall fall upon any point K. At the points A and K, erect the lines AC, KF perpendicular to the horizon; whereof let AC be drawn downwards, and be equal to AI or $\frac{1}{2}$HX. With the asymptotes AK, KF, describe an hyperbola, whose conjugate shall pass through the point C; and from the centre A, with the interval AH, describe a circle cutting that hyperbola in the point H; then the projectile thrown in the direction of the right line AH will fall upon the point K. Q.E.I. For the point H, because of the given length AH, must be somewhere in the circumference of the described circle. Draw CH meeting AK and KF in E and F; and because CH, MX are parallel, and AC, AI equal, AE will be equal to AM, and therefore also equal to KN. But CE is to AE as FH to KN, and therefore CE and FH are equal. Therefore the point H falls upon the hyperbolic curve described with the asymptotes AK, KF whose conjugate passes through the point C; and is therefore found in the common intersection of this hyperbolic curve and the circumference of the described circle. Q.E.D. It is to be observed that this operation is the same, whether the right line AKN be parallel to the horizon, or inclined thereto in any angle; and that from two intersections H, h, there arise two angles NAH, NAh; and that in mechanical practice it is sufficient once to describe a circle, then to apply a ruler CH, of an indeterminate length, so to the point C, that its part FH, intercepted between the circle and the right line FK, may be equal to its part CE placed between the point C and the right line AK.

What has been said of hyperbolas may be easily applied to parabolas. For if a parabola be represented by XAGK, touched by a right line XV in the vertex X, and the ordinates IA, VG be as any powers XI^n, XV^n, of the abscissas XI, XV; draw XT, GT, AH, whereof let XT be parallel to VG, and let GT, AH touch the parabola in G and A: and a body projected from any place A, in the direction of the right line AH, with a due velocity, will describe this parabola, if the density of the medium in each of the places G be inversely as the tangent GT. In that case the velocity in G will

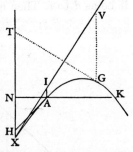

be the same as would cause a body, moving in a nonresisting space, to describe a conic parabola, having G for its vertex, VG produced downwards for its diameter, and $\dfrac{2GT^2}{(nn-n)\cdot VG}$ for its latus rectum. And the resisting force in G will be to the force of gravity as GT to $\dfrac{2nn-2n}{n-2}$ VG. Therefore if NAK represent an horizontal line, and both the density of the medium at A, and the velocity with which the body is projected, remaining the same, the angle NAH be anyhow altered, the lengths AH, AI, HX will remain; and thence will be given the vertex X of the parabola, and the position of the right line XI; and by taking VG to IA as XV^n to XI^n, there will be given all the points G of the parabola, through which the projectile will pass.

SECTION III

THE MOTION OF BODIES THAT ARE RESISTED PARTLY IN THE RATIO OF THE VELOCITIES, AND PARTLY AS THE SQUARE OF THE SAME RATIO

PROPOSITION 11. THEOREM 8

If a body be resisted partly in the ratio and partly as the square of the ratio of its velocity, and moves in a similar medium by its innate force only; and the times be taken in arithmetical progression: then quantities inversely proportional to the velocities, increased by a certain given quantity, will be in geometrical progression.

With the centre C, and the rectangular asymptotes CADd and CH, describe an hyperbola BEe, and let AB, DE, de be parallel to the asymptote CH. In

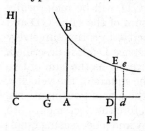

the asymptote CD let A, G be given points; and if the time be represented by the hyperbolic area ABED uniformly increasing, I say, that the velocity may be expressed by the length DF, whose reciprocal GD, together with the given line CG, compose the length CD increasing in a geometrical progression.

For let the small area DEed be the least given increment of the time, and Dd will be inversely as DE, and therefore directly as CD. Therefore the decre-

ment of $\frac{1}{GD}$, which (by Lem. 2, Book II) is $\frac{Dd}{GD^2}$, will be also as $\frac{CD}{GD^2}$ or $\frac{CG+GD}{GD^2}$, that is, as $\frac{1}{GD} + \frac{CG}{GD^2}$. Therefore, the time ABED uniformly in-

creasing by the addition of the given intervals EDde, it follows that $\frac{1}{GD}$ de-

creases in the same ratio with the velocity. For the decrement of the velocity is as the resistance, that is (by the supposition), as the sum of two quantities, whereof one is as the velocity, and the other as the square of the velocity; and

the decrement of $\frac{1}{GD}$ is as the sum of the quantities $\frac{1}{GD}$ and $\frac{CG}{GD^2}$, whereof the

first is $\frac{1}{GD}$ itself, and the last $\frac{CG}{GD^2}$ is as $\frac{1}{GD^2}$: therefore $\frac{1}{GD}$ is as the velocity, the decrements of both being analogous. And if the quantity GD inversely

proportional to $\frac{1}{GD}$, be augmented by the given quantity CG; the sum CD, the time ABED uniformly increasing, will increase in a geometrical progression. Q.E.D.

COR. I. Therefore, if, having the points A and G given, the time be repre-

sented by the hyperbolic area ABED, the velocity may be represented by $\frac{1}{GD}$

the reciprocal of GD.

COR. II. And by taking GA to GD as the reciprocal of the velocity at the beginning to the reciprocal of the velocity at the end of any time ABED, the point G will be found. And that point being found, the velocity may be found from any other time given.

PROPOSITION 12. THEOREM 9

The same things being supposed, I say, that if the spaces described are taken in arithmetical progression, the velocities augmented by a certain given quantity will be in geometrical progression.

In the asymptote CD let there be given the point R, and, erecting the perpendicular RS meeting the hyperbola in S, let the space described be represented by the hyperbolic area RSED; and the velocity will be as the length GD, which, together with the given line CG, composes a length CD decreasing in a geometrical progression, while the space RSED increases in an arithmetical progression.

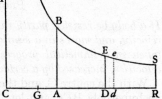

For, because the increment ED*de* of the space is given, the short line D*d*, which is the decrement of GD, will be reciprocally as ED, and therefore directly as CD; that is, as the sum of the same GD and the given length CG. But the decrement of the velocity, in a time inversely proportional thereto, in which the given interval of space D*de*E is described, is as the resistance and the time conjointly, that is, directly as the sum of two quantities, whereof one is as the velocity, the other as the square of the velocity, and inversely as the velocity; and therefore directly as the sum of two quantities, one of which is given, the other is as the velocity. Therefore the decrement both of the velocity and of the line GD is as a given quantity and a decreasing quantity conjointly; and, because the decrements are analogous, the decreasing quantities will always be analogous; viz., the velocity, and the line GD.   Q.E.D.

COR. I. If the velocity be represented by the length GD, the space described will be as the hyperbolic area DESR.

COR. II. And if the point R be assumed anywhere, the point G will be found, by taking GR to GD as the velocity at the beginning to the velocity after any space RSED is described. The point G being given, the space is given from the given velocity; and conversely.

COR. III. Whence since (by Prop. 11) the velocity is given from the given time, and (by this Proposition) the space is given from the given velocity, the space will be given from the given time; and conversely.

PROPOSITION 13. THEOREM 10

Supposing that a body attracted downwards by an uniform gravity ascends or descends in a right line; and that the same is resisted partly in the ratio of its velocity, and partly as the square of the ratio thereof: I say, that, if right lines parallel to the diameters of a circle and an hyperbola be drawn through the ends of the conjugate diameters, and the velocities be as some segments of those parallels drawn from a given point, the times will be as the sectors of the areas cut off by right lines drawn from the centre to the ends of the segments; and conversely.

CASE 1. Suppose first that the body is ascending, and from the centre D, with any semidiameter DB, describe a quadrant BETF of a circle, and through

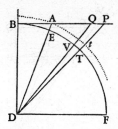

the end B of the semidiameter DB draw the indefinite line BAP, parallel to the semidiameter DF. In that line let there be given the point A, and take the segment AP proportional to the velocity. And since one part of the resistance is as the velocity, and another part as the square of the velocity, let the whole resistance be as $AP^2+2BA \cdot AP$. Join DA, DP, cutting the circle in E and T, and let the gravity be represented by DA^2, so that the gravity shall be to the resistance in P as DA^2 to $AP^2+2BA \cdot AP$; and the time of the whole ascent will be as the sector EDT of the circle.

For draw DVQ, cutting off the moment PQ of the velocity AP, and the moment DTV of the sector DET answering to a given moment of time; and that decrement PQ of the velocity will be as the sum of the forces of gravity DA^2 and of resistance $AP^2+2BA \cdot AP$; that is (by Prop. 12, Book II, *Elements* of Euclid), as DP^2. Then the area DPQ, proportional to PQ, is as DP^2, and the area DTV, which is to the area DPQ as DT^2 to DP^2, is as the given quantity DT^2. Therefore the area EDT decreases uniformly according to the rate of the future time, by subtraction of given intervals DTV, and is therefore proportional to the time of the whole ascent. Q.E.D.

CASE 2. If the velocity in the ascent of the body be represented by the length AP as before, and the resistance be made as $AP^2+2BA \cdot AP$; and if the force of gravity be less than can be expressed by DA^2; take BD of such a length, that AB^2-BD^2 may be proportional to the gravity, and let DF be perpendicular and equal to DB, and through the vertex F describe the hyperbola FTVE, whose conjugate semidiameters are DB and DF, and which cuts DA in E, and DP, DQ in

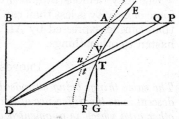

T and V; and the time of the whole ascent will be as the hyperbolic sector TDE.

For the decrement PQ of the velocity, produced in a given interval of time, is as the sum of the resistance $AP^2+2BA \cdot AP$ and of the gravity AB^2-BD^2, that is, as BP^2-BD^2. But the area DTV is to the area DPQ as DT^2 to DP^2; and, therefore, if GT be drawn perpendicular to DF, as GT^2 or GD^2-DF^2 to BD^2, and as GD^2 to BP^2, and, by subtraction, as DF^2 to BP^2-BD^2. Therefore since the area DPQ is as PQ, that is, as BP^2-BD^2, the area DTV will be as the given quantity DF^2. Therefore the area EDT decreases uniformly in each of the equal intervals of time, by the subtraction of so many given intervals DTV, and therefore is proportional to the time. Q.E.D.

CASE 3. Let AP be the velocity in the descent of the body, and $AP^2+2BA \cdot AP$ the force of resistance, and BD^2-AB^2 the force of gravity, the angle DBA being a right one. And if with the centre D, and the principal vertex B, there be described a rectangular hyperbola BETV cutting DA, DP, and DQ produced in E, T, and V; the sector DET of this hyperbola will be as the whole time of descent.

For the increment PQ of the velocity, and the area DPQ proportional to it, is as the excess of the gravity above the resistance, that is, as

$$BD^2-AB^2-2BA \cdot AP-AP^2$$

or $BD^2 - BP^2$. And the area DTV is to the area DPQ
as DT^2 to DP^2; and therefore as GT^2 or $GD^2 - BD^2$ to
BP^2; and as GD^2 to BD^2, and, by subtraction, as BD^2 to
$BD^2 - BP^2$. Therefore since the area DPQ is as $BD^2 -$
BP^2, the area DTV will be as the given quantity BD^2.
Therefore the area EDT increases uniformly in the several
equal intervals of time by the addition of as many given
intervals DTV, and therefore is proportional to the time
of the descent.   Q.E.D.

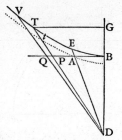

Cor. If with the centre D and the semidiameter DA
there be drawn through the vertex A an arc At similar to the arc ET, and
similarly subtending the angle ADT, the velocity AP will be to the velocity
which the body in the time EDT, in a nonresisting space, can lose in its ascent, or acquire in its descent, as the area of the triangle DAP to the area of
the sector DAt; and therefore is given from the time given. For the velocity
in a nonresisting medium is proportional to the time, and therefore to this
sector; in a resisting medium, it is as the triangle; and in both mediums,
where it is least, it approaches to the ratio of equality, as the sector and
triangle do.

SCHOLIUM

One may demonstrate also that case in the ascent of the body, where the
force of gravity is less than can be expressed by DA^2 or $AB^2 + BD^2$, and greater
than can be expressed by $AB^2 - DB^2$, and must be expressed by AB^2. But I
hasten to other things.

PROPOSITION 14. THEOREM 11

*The same things being supposed, I say, that the space described in the ascent or
descent is as the difference of the area by which the time is expressed, and of some
other area which is augmented or diminished in an arithmetical progression; if
the forces compounded of the resistance and the gravity be taken in a geometrical
progression.*

Take AC (in these three figures) proportional to the gravity, and AK to the
resistance; but take them on the same side of the point A, if the body is descending, otherwise on the contrary. Erect Ab, which make to DB as DB^2 to
$4BA \cdot CA$; and to the rectangular asymptotes CK, CH, describe the hyperbola
bN; and, erecting KN perpendicular to CK, the area AbNK will be augmented
or diminished in an arithmetical progression, while the forces CK are taken in
a geometrical progression. I say, therefore, that the distance of the body from
its greatest altitude is as the excess of the area AbNK above the area DET.

For since AK is as the resistance, that is, as $AP^2 \cdot 2BA \cdot AP$; assume any
given quantity Z, and put AK equal to $\dfrac{AP^2 + 2BA \cdot AP}{Z}$; then (by Lem. 2 of

this book) the moment KL of AK will be equal to $\dfrac{2PQ \cdot AP + 2BA \cdot PQ}{Z}$

or $\dfrac{2PQ \cdot BP}{Z}$, and the moment KLON of the area AbNK will be equal to

$\dfrac{2PQ \cdot BP \cdot LO}{Z}$ or $\dfrac{PQ \cdot BP \cdot BD^3}{2Z \cdot CK \cdot AB}$.

CASE 1. Now if the body ascends, and the gravity be as AB^2+BD^2, BET being a circle, the line AC, which is proportional to the gravity, will be $\frac{AB^2+BD^2}{Z}$, and DP^2 or $AP^2+2BA\cdot AP+AB^2+BD^2$ will be $AK\cdot Z+AC\cdot Z$ or $CK\cdot Z$; and therefore the area DTV will be to the area DPQ as DT^2 or DB^2 to $CK\cdot Z$.

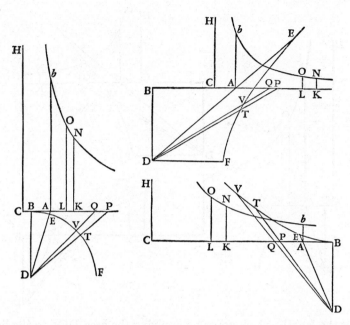

CASE 2. If the body ascends, and the gravity be as AB^2-BD^2, the line AC will be $\frac{AB^2-BD^2}{Z}$, and DT^2 will be to DP^2 as DF^2 or DB^2 to BP^2-BD^2 or $AP^2+2BA\cdot AP+AB^2-BD^2$, that is, to $AK\cdot Z+AC\cdot Z$ or $CK\cdot Z$. And therefore the area DTV will be to the area DPQ as DB^2 to $CK\cdot Z$.

CASE 3. And by the same reasoning, if the body descends, and therefore the gravity is as BD^2-AB^2, and the line AC becomes equal to $\frac{BD^2-AB^2}{Z}$; the area DTV will be to the area DPQ as DB^2 to $CK\cdot Z$: as above.

Since, therefore, these areas are always in this ratio, if for the area DTV, by which the moment of the time, always equal to itself, is expressed, there be put any determinate rectangle, as $BD\cdot m$, the area DPQ, that is, $\frac{1}{2}BD\cdot PQ$, will be to $BD\cdot m$ as $CK\cdot Z$ to BD^2. And thence $PQ\cdot BD^3$ becomes equal to $2BD\cdot m\cdot CK\cdot Z$, and the moment KLON of the area AbNK, found before, becomes $\frac{BP\cdot BD\cdot m}{AB}$. From the area DET subtract its moment DTV or $BD\cdot m$, and there will remain $\frac{AP\cdot BD\cdot m}{AB}$. Therefore the difference of the moments, that is, the moment of the difference of the areas, is equal to $\frac{AP\cdot BD\cdot m}{AB}$; and therefore (because of the given quantity $\dfrac{BD \cdot m}{AB}$) as the velocity AP; that is, as the moment of the space which the body describes in its ascent or descent. And therefore the difference of the areas, and that space, increasing or decreasing by proportional moments, and beginning together or vanishing together, are proportional.   Q.E.D

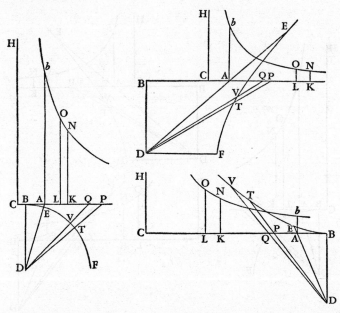

Cor. If the length, which arises by applying the area DET to the line BD, be called M; and another length V be taken in that ratio to the length M, which the line DA has to the line DE; the space which a body, in a resisting medium, describes in its whole ascent or descent, will be to the space which a body, in a nonresisting medium, falling from rest, can describe in the same time, as the difference of the aforesaid areas to $\dfrac{BD \cdot V^2}{AB}$; and therefore is given from the time given. For the space in a nonresisting medium is as the square of the time, or as V^2; and, because BD and AB are given, as $\dfrac{BD \cdot V^2}{AB}$. This area is equal to the area $\dfrac{DA^2 \cdot BD \cdot M^2}{DE^2 \cdot AB}$ and the moment of M is m; and therefore the moment of this area is $\dfrac{DA^2 \cdot BD \cdot 2M \cdot m}{DE^2 \cdot AB}$. But this moment is to the moment of the difference of the aforesaid areas DET and AbNK, viz., to $\dfrac{AP \cdot BD \cdot m}{AB}$, as $\dfrac{DA^2 \cdot BD \cdot M}{DE^2}$ to ½BD·AP, or as $\dfrac{DA^2}{DE^2}$ into DET to DAP; and, therefore, when the areas DET and DAP are least, in the ratio of equality. Therefore the area $\dfrac{BD \cdot V^2}{AB}$ and the difference of the areas DET and AbNK, when all these areas are least, have equal moments; and are therefore equal. Therefore since the velocities, and therefore also the spaces in both mediums described together, in the beginning of the descent, or the end of the ascent, approach to equality, and therefore are then one to another as the area $\dfrac{\text{BD} \cdot \text{V}^2}{\text{AB}}$, and the difference of the areas DET and AbNK; and moreover since the space, in a nonresisting medium, is continually as $\dfrac{\text{BD} \cdot \text{V}^2}{\text{AB}}$, and the space, in a resisting medium, is continually as the difference of the areas DET and AbNK; it necessarily follows, that the spaces, in both mediums, described in any equal times, are one to another as that area $\dfrac{\text{BD} \cdot \text{V}^2}{\text{AB}}$, and the difference of the areas DET and AbNK.   Q.E.D.

Scholium

The resistance of spherical bodies in fluids arises partly from the tenacity, partly from the attrition, and partly from the density of the medium. And that part of the resistance which arises from the density of the fluid is, as I said, as the square of the velocity; the other part, which arises from the tenacity of the fluid, is uniform, or as the moment of the time; and, therefore, we might now proceed to the motion of bodies, which are resisted partly by an uniform force, or in the ratio of the moments of the time, and partly as the square of the velocity. But it is sufficient to have cleared the way to this speculation in Props. 8 and 9 foregoing, and their Corollaries. For in those Propositions, instead of the uniform resistance made to an ascending body arising from its gravity, one may substitute the uniform resistance which arises from the tenacity of the medium, when the body moves by its inertia alone; and when the body ascends in a right line, add this uniform resistance to the force of gravity, and subtract it when the body descends in a right line. One might also go on to the motion of bodies which are resisted in part uniformly, in part in the ratio of the velocity, and in part as the square of the same velocity. And I have opened a way to this in Props. 13 and 14 foregoing, in which the uniform resistance arising from the tenacity of the medium may be substituted for the force of gravity, or be compounded with it as before. But I hasten to other things.

SECTION IV

The circular motion of bodies in resisting mediums

Lemma 3

Let PQR *be a spiral cutting all the radii* SP, SQ, SR, *&c., in equal angles. Draw the right line* PT *touching the spiral in any point* P, *and cutting the radius* SQ *in* T; *draw* PO, QO *perpendicular to the spiral, and meeting in* O, *and join* SO: *I say, that if the points* P *and* Q *approach and coincide, the angle* PSO *will become a right angle, and the ultimate ratio of the rectangle* TQ$\cdot$2PS *to* PQ^2 *will be the ratio of equality.*

For, from the right angles OPQ, OQR, subtract the equal angles SPQ, SQR, and there will remain the equal angles OPS, OQS. Therefore a circle which passes through the points OSP will pass also through the point Q. Let the points P and Q coincide, and this circle will touch the spiral in the place of coincidence PQ, and will therefore cut the right line OP perpendicularly. Therefore OP will become a diameter of this circle, and the angle OSP, being in a semicircle, becomes a right one.   Q.E.D.

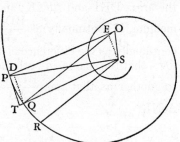

Draw QD, SE perpendicular to OP, and the ultimate ratios of the lines will be as follows:

TQ : PD = TS or PS : PE = 2PO : 2PS;
and   PD : PQ = PQ : 2PO;
multiplying together corresponding terms of equal ratios,

TQ : PQ = PQ : 2PS.

Whence PQ² becomes equal to TQ·2PS.

Q.E.D.

PROPOSITION 15. THEOREM 12

If the density of a medium in each place thereof be inversely as the distance of the places from an immovable centre, and the centripetal force be as the square of the density: I say, that a body may revolve in a spiral which cuts all the radii drawn from that centre in a given angle.

Suppose everything to be as in the foregoing Lemma, and produce SQ to V so that SV may be equal to SP. In any time let a body, in a resisting medium, describe the least arc PQ, and in double the time the least arc PR; and the decrements of those arcs arising from the resistance, or their differences from

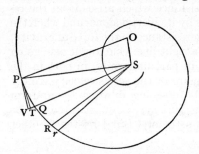

the arcs which would be described in a non-resisting medium in the same times, will be to each other as the squares of the times in which they are generated; therefore the decrement of the arc PQ is the fourth part of the decrement of the arc PR. Whence also if the area QSr be taken equal to the area PSQ, the decrement of the arc PQ will be equal to half the short line Rr; and therefore the force of resistance and the centripetal force are to each other as the short line

½Rr and TQ which they generate in the same time. Because the centripetal force with which the body is urged in P is inversely as SP², and (by Lem. 10, Book I) the short line TQ, which is generated by that force, is in a ratio compounded of the ratio of this force and the squared ratio of the time in which the arc PQ is described (for in this case I neglect the resistance, as being infinitely less than the centripetal force), it follows that TQ·SP², that is (by the last Lemma), ½PQ²·SP, will be as the square of the time, and therefore the time is as PQ·$\sqrt{SP}$; and the velocity of the body, with which the arc PQ is described in that time, as $\frac{PQ}{PQ·\sqrt{SP}}$ or $\frac{1}{\sqrt{SP}}$, that is, inversely as the square root of SP. And, by a like reasoning, the velocity with which the arc QR is described, is inversely as the square root of SQ. Now those arcs PQ and QR are as the describing velocities to each other; that is, as the square root of the ratio of

SQ to SP, or as SQ to $\sqrt{(SP \cdot SQ)}$; and, because of the equal angles SPQ, SQr, and the equal areas PSQ, QSr, the arc PQ is to the arc Qr as SQ to SP. Take the differences of the proportional consequents, and the arc PQ will be to the arc Rr as SQ to SP $- \sqrt{(SP \cdot SQ)}$, or $\frac{1}{2}$VQ. For, the points P and Q coinciding, the ultimate ratio of SP $- \sqrt{(SP \cdot SQ)}$ to $\frac{1}{2}$VQ is the ratio of equality. Since the decrement of the arc PQ arising from the resistance, or its double Rr, is as the resistance and the square of the time conjointly, the resistance will be as $\frac{Rr}{PQ^2 \cdot SP}$. But PQ was to Rr as SQ to $\frac{1}{2}$VQ, and thence $\frac{Rr}{PQ^2 \cdot SP}$ becomes as $\frac{\frac{1}{2}VQ}{PQ \cdot SP \cdot SQ}$, or as $\frac{\frac{1}{2}OS}{OP \cdot SP^2}$. For, the points P and Q coinciding, SP and SQ coincide also, and the angle PVQ becomes a right one; and, because of the similar triangles PVQ, PSO, PQ becomes to $\frac{1}{2}$ VQ as OP to $\frac{1}{2}$OS. Therefore $\frac{OS}{OP \cdot SP^2}$ is as the resistance, that is, in the ratio of the density of the medium in P and the squared ratio of the velocity conjointly. Subtract the squared ratio of the velocity, namely, the ratio $\frac{1}{SP}$, and there will remain the density of the medium in P, as $\frac{OS}{OP \cdot SP}$. Let the spiral be given, and, because of the given ratio of OS to OP, the density of the medium in P will be as $\frac{1}{SP}$. Therefore in a medium whose density is inversely as SP the distance from the centre, a body will revolve in this spiral.   Q.E.D.

Cor. I. The velocity in any place P, is always the same wherewith a body in a nonresisting medium with the same centripetal force would revolve in a circle, at the same distance SP from the centre.

Cor. II. The density of the medium, if the distance SP be given, is as $\frac{OS}{OP}$, but if that distance is not given, as $\frac{OS}{OP \cdot SP}$. And thence a spiral may be fitted to any density of the medium.

Cor. III. The force of the resistance in any place P is to the centripetal force in the same place as $\frac{1}{2}$OS to OP. For those forces are to each other as $\frac{1}{2}$Rr and TQ, or as $\frac{\frac{1}{4}VQ \cdot PQ}{SQ}$ and $\frac{\frac{1}{2}PQ^2}{SP}$, that is, as $\frac{1}{2}$VQ and PQ, or $\frac{1}{2}$OS and OP. The

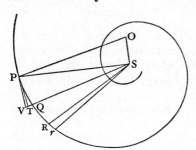

spiral therefore being given, there is given the proportion of the resistance to the centripetal force; and, conversely, from that proportion given the spiral is given.

Cor. IV. Therefore the body cannot revolve in this spiral, except where the force of resistance is less than half the centripetal force. Let the resistance be made equal to half the centripetal force, and the spiral will coincide with the right line PS, and in that right line the body will descend to the centre with a velocity that is to the velocity with which it was proved before in the case of the parabola (Theor. 10, Book I) that the descent would be made in a nonresisting medium, as the square root of the ratio of unity to the number 2. And the times of the descent will be here inversely as the velocities, and therefore given.

Cor. v. And because at equal distances from the centre the velocity is the same in the spiral PQR as it is in the right line SP, and the length of the spiral is to the length of the right line PS in a given ratio, namely, in the ratio of OP to OS; the time of the descent in the spiral will be to the time of the descent in the right line SP in the same given ratio, and therefore given.

Cor. vi. If from the centre S, with any two given radii, two circles are described; and these circles remaining, the angle which the spiral makes with the radius PS be changed in any manner; the number of revolutions which the body can complete in the space between the circumferences of those circles, going round in the spiral from one circumference to another, will be as $\frac{PS}{OS}$, or as the tangent of the angle which the spiral makes with the radius PS; and the time of the same revolutions will be as $\frac{OP}{OS}$, that is, as the secant of the same angle, or inversely as the density of the medium.

Cor. vii. If a body, in a medium whose density is inversely as the distances of places from the centre, revolves in any curve AEB about that centre, and cuts the first radius AS in the same angle in B as it did before in A, and that with a velocity that shall be to its first velocity in A inversely as the square root of the distances from the centre (that is, as AS to a mean proportional between AS and BS), that body will continue to describe innumerable similar revolutions BFC, CGD, &c., and by its intersections will divide the radius AS into parts AS, BS, CS, DS, &c., that are continually proportional. But the times of the revolutions will be directly as the perimeters of the orbits AEB, BFC, CGD, &c., and inversely as the velocities at the beginnings A, B, C of those orbits; that is, as $AS^{3/2}$, $BS^{3/2}$, $CS^{3/2}$. And the whole time in which the body will arrive at the centre, will be to the time of the first revolution as the sum of all the continued proportionals $AS^{3/2}$, $BS^{3/2}$, $CS^{3/2}$, going on *ad infinitum*, is to the first term $AS^{3/2}$; that is, as the first term $AS^{3/2}$ is to the difference of the two first $AS^{3/2} - BS^{3/2}$, or as $\frac{2}{3}AS$ is to AB, very nearly. Whence the whole time may be easily found.

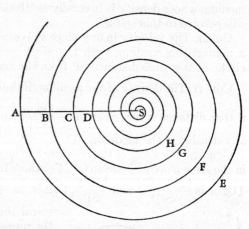

Cor. viii. From hence also may be deduced, near enough, the motions of bodies in mediums whose density is either uniform, or observes any other assigned law. From the centre S, with radii SA, SB, SC, &c., continually proportional, describe as many circles; and suppose the time of the revolutions between the perimeters of any two of those circles, in the medium whereof we treated, to be to the time of the revolutions between the same in the medium proposed as the mean density of the proposed medium between those circles is to the mean density of the medium whereof we treated, between the same circles, nearly; and that the secant of the angle in which the spiral above determined, in the medium whereof we treated, cuts the radius AS, is in the same ratio to the secant of the angle in which the new spiral, in the proposed medium, cuts the same radius; and also that the number of all the revolutions between the same two circles is nearly as the tangents of those angles. If this be done everywhere between every two circles, the motion will be continued through all the circles. And by this means one may without difficulty ascertain at what rate and in what time bodies ought to revolve in any regular medium.

COR. IX. And although these motions becoming eccentric should be performed in spirals approaching to an oval figure, yet, assuming the several revolutions of those spirals to be at the same distances from each other, and to approach to the centre by the same degrees as the spiral above described, we may also understand how the motions of bodies may be performed in spirals of that kind.

PROPOSITION 16. THEOREM 13

If the density of the medium in each of the places be inversely as the distance of the places from the immovable centre, and the centripetal force be inversely as any power of the same distance: I say, that the body may revolve in a spiral intersecting all the radii drawn from that centre in a given angle.

This is demonstrated in the same manner as the foregoing Proposition. For if the centripetal force in P be inversely as any power SP^{n+1} of the distance SP

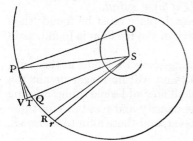

whose index is $n+1$; it will be concluded, as above, that the time in which the body describes any arc PQ, will be as $PQ \cdot PS^{1/2n}$; and the resistance in P as $\dfrac{Rr}{PQ^2 \cdot SP^n}$, or as $\dfrac{(1-\frac{1}{2}n)\cdot VQ}{PQ \cdot SP^n \cdot SQ}$, and therefore as $\dfrac{(1-\frac{1}{2}n)\cdot OS}{OP \cdot SP^{n+1}}$, that is (because $\dfrac{(1-\frac{1}{2}n)\cdot OS}{OP}$ is a given quantity), inversely as SP^{n+1}. And therefore, since the velocity is inversely as $SP^{1/2n}$, the density in P will be reciprocally as SP.

COR. I. The resistance is to the centripetal force as $(1-\frac{1}{2}n)\cdot OS$ to OP.

COR. II. If the centripetal force be inversely as SP^3, $1-\frac{1}{2}n$ will be $=0$; and therefore the resistance and density of the medium will be nothing, as in Prop. 9, Book I.

COR. III. If the centripetal force be inversely as any power of the radius SP, whose index is greater than the number 3, the positive resistance will be changed into a negative.

SCHOLIUM

This Proposition and the former, which relate to mediums of unequal density, are to be understood as applying only to the motion of bodies that are so small, that the greater density of the medium on one side of the body above that on the other is not to be considered. I suppose also the resistance, other things being equal, to be proportional to its density. Hence, in mediums whose force of resistance is not as the density, the density must be so much augmented or diminished, that either the excess of the resistance may be taken away, or the defect supplied.

PROPOSITION 17. PROBLEM 4

To find the centripetal force and the resisting force of the medium, by which a body, the law of the velocity being given, shall revolve in a given spiral.

Let that spiral be PQR. From the velocity, with which the body goes over the very small arc PQ, the time will be given; and from the altitude TQ, which is as the centripetal force, and the square of the time, that force will be given. Then from the difference RS*r* of the areas PSQ and QSR described in equal intervals of time, the retardation of the body will be given; and from the retardation will be found the resisting force and density of the medium.

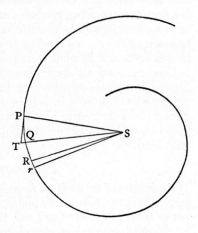

PROPOSITION 18. PROBLEM 5

The law of centripetal force being given, to find the density of the medium in each of the places thereof, by which a body may describe a given spiral.

From the centripetal force the velocity in each place must be found; then from the retardation of the velocity the density of the medium is found, as in the foregoing Proposition.

But I have explained the method of managing these Problems in the tenth Proposition and second Lemma of this book; and will no longer detain the reader in these complicated investigations. I shall now add some things relating to the forces of progressive bodies, and to the density and resistance of those mediums in which the motions hitherto discussed, and those akin to them, are performed.

SECTION V

THE DENSITY AND COMPRESSION OF FLUIDS; HYDROSTATICS.
THE DEFINITION OF A FLUID

A FLUID IS ANY BODY WHOSE PARTS YIELD TO ANY FORCE IMPRESSED ON IT, AND, BY YIELDING, ARE EASILY MOVED AMONG THEMSELVES

PROPOSITION 19. THEOREM 14

All the parts of an homogeneous and unmoved fluid included in any unmoved vessel, and compressed on every side (setting aside the consideration of condensation, gravity, and all centripetal forces), will be equally pressed on every side, and remain in their places without any motion arising from that pressure.

CASE 1. Let a fluid be included in the spherical vessel ABC, and uniformly compressed on every side: I say, that no part of it will be moved by that pressure. For if any part, as D, be moved, all such parts at the same distance from the centre on every side must necessarily be moved at the same time by a like

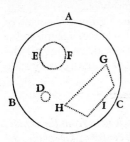

motion; because the pressure of them all is similar and equal; and all other motion is excluded that does not arise from that pressure. But if these parts come all of them nearer to the centre, the fluid must be condensed towards the centre, contrary to the supposition. If they recede from it, the fluid must be condensed towards the circumference; which is also contrary to the supposition. Neither can they move in any one direction retaining their distance from the centre, because, for the same reason, they may move in a contrary direction; but the same part cannot be moved contrary ways at the same time. Therefore no part of the fluid will be moved from its place.   Q.E.D.

Case 2. I say now, that all the spherical parts of this fluid are equally pressed on every side. For let EF be a spherical part of the fluid; if this be not pressed equally on every side, augment the lesser pressure till it be pressed equally on every side; and its parts (by Case 1) will remain in their places. But before the increase of the pressure, they would remain in their places (by Case 1); and by the addition of a new pressure they will be moved, by the definition of a fluid, from those places. Now these two conclusions contradict each other. Therefore it was false to say that the sphere EF was not pressed equally on every side.
                                                Q.E.D.

Case 3. I say besides, that different spherical parts have equal pressures. For the contiguous spherical parts press each other mutually and equally in the point of contact (by Law III). But (by Case 2) they are pressed on every side with the same force. Therefore any two spherical parts not contiguous, since an intermediate spherical part can touch both, will be pressed with the same force.   Q.E.D.

Case 4. I say now, that all the parts of the fluid are everywhere pressed equally. For any two parts may be touched by spherical parts in any points whatever; and there they will equally press those spherical parts (by Case 3), and are in reaction equally pressed by them (by Law III).   Q.E.D.

Case 5. Since, therefore, any part GHI of the fluid is inclosed by the rest of the fluid as in a vessel, and is equally pressed on every side; and also its parts equally press one another, and are at rest among themselves; it is manifest that all the parts of any fluid as GHI, which is pressed equally on every side, do press each other mutually and equally, and are at rest among themselves.
                                                Q.E.D.

Case 6. Therefore if that fluid be included in a vessel of a yielding substance, or that is not rigid, and be not equally pressed on every side, the same will give way to a stronger pressure, by the definition of fluidity.

Case 7. And therefore, in an inflexible or rigid vessel, a fluid will not sustain a stronger pressure on one side than on the other, but will give way to it, and that in a moment of time; because the rigid side of the vessel does not follow the yielding liquor. But the fluid, by thus yielding, will press against the opposite side, and so the pressure will tend on every side to equality. And because the fluid, as soon as it endeavors to recede from the part that is most pressed, is withstood by the resistance of the vessel on the opposite side, the pressure will on every side be reduced to equality, in a moment of time, without any local motion; and from thence the parts of the fluid (by Case 5) will press each other mutually and equally, and be at rest among themselves.   Q.E.D.

Cor. Hence neither will a motion of the parts of the fluid among themselves be changed by a pressure communicated to the external surface, except so far as either the figure of the surface may be somewhere altered, or that all the parts of the fluid, by pressing one another more intensely or remissly, may slide with more or less difficulty among themselves.

PROPOSITION 20. THEOREM 15

If all the parts of a spherical fluid, homogeneous at equal distances from the centre, lying on a spherical concentric bottom, gravitate towards the centre of the whole, the bottom will sustain the weight of a cylinder, whose base is equal to the surface of the bottom, and whose altitude is the same with that of the incumbent fluid.

Let DHM be the surface of the bottom, and AEI the upper surface of the fluid. Let the fluid be divided into concentric orbs of equal thickness, by the innumerable spherical surfaces BFK, CGL; and conceive the force of gravity to act only in the upper surface of every orb, and the actions to be equal on the equal parts of the surfaces. Therefore the upper surface AE is pressed by the single force of its own gravity, by which all the parts of the upper orb, and the second surface BFK, will (by Prop. 19), according to its measure, be equally pressed. The second surface BFK is pressed 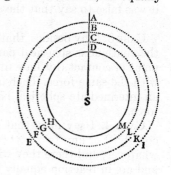 likewise by the force of its own gravity, which, added to the former force, makes the pressure double. The third surface CGL is, according to its measure, acted on by this pressure and the force of its own gravity besides, which makes its pressure triple. And in like manner the fourth surface receives a quadruple pressure, the fifth surface a quintuple, and so on. Therefore the pressure acting on every surface is not as the solid quantity of the incumbent fluid, but as the number of the orbs reaching to the upper surface of the fluid; and is equal to the gravity of the lowest orb multiplied by the number of orbs; that is, to the gravity of a solid whose ultimate ratio to the cylinder above mentioned (when the number of the orbs is increased and their thickness diminished, *ad infinitum*, so that the action of gravity from the lowest surface to the uppermost may become continued) is the ratio of equality. Therefore the lowest surface sustains the weight of the cylinder above determined. Q.E.D. And by a like reasoning the Proposition will be evident, where the gravity of the fluid decreases in any assigned ratio of the distance from the centre, and also where the fluid is more rare above and denser below.
          Q.E.D.

Cor. I. Therefore the bottom is not pressed by the whole weight of the incumbent fluid, but only sustains that part of it which is described in the Proposition; the rest of the weight being sustained archwise by the spherical figure of the fluid.

Cor. II. The quantity of the pressure is the same always at equal distances from the centre, whether the surface pressed be parallel to the horizon, or perpendicular, or oblique; or whether the fluid, continued upwards from the compressed surface, rises perpendicularly in a rectilinear direction, or creeps obliquely through crooked cavities and canals, whether those passages be regular or irregular, wide or narrow. That the pressure is not altered by any of these circumstances, may be inferred by applying the demonstration of this Theorem to the several cases of fluids.

Cor. iii. From the same demonstration it may also be concluded (by Prop. 19), that the parts of a heavy fluid acquire no motion among themselves by the pressure of the incumbent weight, except that motion which arises from condensation.

Cor. iv. And therefore if another body of the same specific gravity, incapable of condensation, be immersed in this fluid, it will acquire no motion by the pressure of the incumbent weight: it will neither descend nor ascend, nor change its figure. If it be spherical, it will remain so, notwithstanding the pressure; if it be square, it will remain square; and that, whether it be soft or fluid; whether it swims freely in the fluid, or lies at the bottom. For any internal part of a fluid is in the same state with the submersed body; and the case of all submersed bodies that have the same magnitude, figure, and specific gravity, is alike. If a submersed body, retaining its weight, should dissolve and put on the form of a fluid, this body, if before it should have ascended, descended, or from any pressure assumed a new figure, would now likewise ascend, descend, or put on a new figure; and that, because its gravity and the other causes of its motion remain. But (by Case 5, Prop. 19) it would now be at rest, and retain its figure. Therefore also in the former case.

Cor. v. Therefore a body that is specifically heavier than a fluid contiguous to it will sink; and that which is specifically lighter will ascend, and attain so much motion and change of figure as that excess or defect of gravity is able to produce. For that excess or defect is the same thing as an impulse, by which a body, otherwise in equilibrium with the parts of the fluid, is acted on; and may be compared with the excess or defect of a weight in one of the scales of a balance.

Cor. vi. Therefore bodies placed in fluids have a twofold gravity: the one true and absolute, the other apparent, common, and comparative. Absolute gravity is the whole force with which the body tends downwards; relative and common gravity is the excess of gravity with which the body tends downwards more than the ambient fluid. By the first kind of gravity the parts of all fluids and bodies gravitate in their proper places; and therefore their weights taken together compose the weight of the whole. For the whole taken together is heavy, as may be experienced in vessels full of liquor; and the weight of the whole is equal to the weights of all the parts, and is therefore composed of them. By the other kind of gravity bodies do not gravitate in their places; that is, compared with one another, they do not preponderate, but, hindering one another's endeavor to descend, remain in their proper places as if they were not heavy. Those things which are in the air, and do not preponderate, are commonly looked on as not heavy. Those which do preponderate are commonly reckoned heavy, inasmuch as they are not sustained by the weight of the air. The common weights are nothing else but the excess of the true weights above the weight of the air. Hence also, commonly, those things are called light which are less heavy, and, by yielding to the preponderating air, mount upwards. But these are only comparatively light, and not truly so, because they descend in a vacuum. Thus, in water, bodies which, by their greater or less gravity, descend or ascend, are comparatively and apparently heavy or light; and their comparative and apparent gravity or levity is the excess or defect by which their true gravity either exceeds the gravity of the water or is exceeded by it. But those things which neither by preponderating descend, nor, by yielding to the preponderating fluid, ascend, although by their true weight they do increase the weight of the whole, yet comparatively, and as commonly understood, they do not gravitate in the water. For these cases are alike demonstrated.

COR. VII. These things which have been demonstrated concerning gravity take place in any other centripetal forces.

COR. VIII. Therefore if the medium in which any body moves be acted on either by its own gravity, or by any other centripetal force, and the body be urged more powerfully by the same force; the difference of the forces is that very motive force, which, in the foregoing Proposition, I have considered as a centripetal force. But if the body be more lightly urged by that force, the difference of the forces becomes a centrifugal force, and is to be considered as such.

COR. IX. But since fluids by pressing the included bodies do not change their external figures, it appears also (by Cor., Prop. 19) that they will not change the situation of their internal parts in relation to one another; and therefore if animals were immersed therein, and if all sensation did arise from the motion of their parts, the fluid would neither hurt the immersed bodies, nor excite any sensation, unless so far as those bodies might be condensed by the compression. And the case is the same of any system of bodies encompassed with a compressing fluid. All the parts of the system will be agitated with the same motions as if they were placed in a vacuum, and would only retain their comparative gravity; unless so far as the fluid may somewhat resist their motions, or be requisite to unite them by compression.

PROPOSITION 21. THEOREM 16

Let the density of any fluid be proportional to the compression, and its parts be attracted downwards by a centripetal force inversely proportional to the distances from the centre: I say, that, if those distances be taken continually proportional, the densities of the fluid at the same distances will be also continually proportional.

Let ATV denote the spherical bottom of the fluid, S the centre, SA, SB, SC, SD, SE, SF, &c., distances continually proportional. Erect the perpendiculars AH, BI, CK, DL, EM, FN, &c., which shall be as the densities of the medium in the places A, B, C, D, E, F; and the specific gravities in those places will be as $\frac{AH}{AS}, \frac{BI}{BS}, \frac{CK}{CS}$, &c., or, which is all one, as $\frac{AH}{AB}, \frac{BI}{BC}, \frac{CK}{CD}$, &c. Suppose, first, these gravities to be uniformly continued from A to B, from B to C, from C to D, &c., the decrements in the points B, C, D, &c., being taken by steps. And these gravities multiplied by the altitudes AB, BC, CD, &c., will give the pressures AH, BI, CK, &c., by which the bottom ATV is acted on (by Theor. 15). Therefore the particle A sustains all the pressures AH, BI, CK, DL, &c., proceeding *in infinitum;* and the particle B sustains the pressures of all but the first AH; and the particle C all but the two first AH, BI; and so on: and therefore the density AH of the first particle A is to the density BI of the second

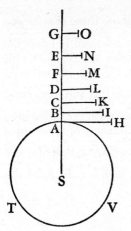

particle B as the sum of all AH+BI+CK+DL, *in infinitum*, to the sum of all BI+CK+DL, &c. And BI the density of the second particle B is to CK the density of the third C, as the sum of all BI+CK+DL, &c., to the sum of all CK+DL, &c. Therefore these sums are proportional to their differences AH, BI, CK, &c., and therefore continually proportional (by Lem. 1 of this book); and therefore the differences AH, BI, CK, &c., proportional to the sums, are also continually proportional. Therefore since the densities in the places A, B, C, &c., are as AH, BI, CK, &c., they will also be continually proportional. Proceed intermissively, and, at the distances SA, SC, SE, continually proportional, the densities AH, CK, EM will be continually proportional. And by the same reasoning, at any distances SA, SD, SG, continually proportional, the densities AH, DL, GO will be continually proportional. Let now the points A, B, C, D, E, &c., coincide, so that the progression of the specific gravities from the bottom A to the top of the fluid may be made continual; and at any distances SA, SD, SG, continually proportional, the densities AH, DL, GO, being all along continually proportional, will still remain continually proportional.

Q.E.D.

Cor. Hence if the density of the fluid in two places, as A and E, be given, its density in any other place Q may be obtained. With the centre S, and the rectangular asymptotes SQ, SX, describe an hyperbola cutting the perpendiculars AH, EM, QT in *a*, *e*, and *q*, as also the

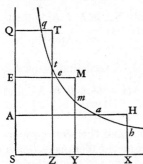

perpendiculars HX, MY, TZ, let fall upon the asymptote SX, in *h*, *m*, and *t*. Make the area Y*mt*Z to the given area Y*mh*X as the given area E*eq*Q to the given area E*ea*A; and the line Z*t* produced will cut off the line QT proportional to the density. For if the lines SA, SE, SQ are continually proportional, the areas E*eq*Q, E*ea*A will be equal, and thence the areas Y*mt*Z, X*hm*Y, proportional to them, will be also equal; and the lines SX, SY, SZ, that is, AH, EM, QT continually proportional, as they ought to be. And if the lines SA, SE, SQ obtain any other order in the series of continued proportionals, the lines AH, EM, QT, because of the proportional hyperbolic areas, will obtain the same order in another series of quantities continually proportional.

PROPOSITION 22. THEOREM 17

Let the density of any fluid be proportional to the compression, and its parts be attracted downwards by a gravitation inversely proportional to the squares of the distances from the centre: I say, that if the distances be taken in harmonic progression, the densities of the fluid at those distances will be in a geometrical progression.

Let S denote the centre, and SA, SB, SC, SD, SE the distances in geometrical progression. Erect the perpendiculars AH, BI, CK, &c., which shall be as the densities of the fluid in the places A, B, C, D, E, &c., and the specific gravities thereof in those places will be as $\dfrac{AH}{SA^2}$, $\dfrac{BI}{SB^2}$, $\dfrac{CK}{SC^2}$, &c. Suppose these gravities to be uniformly continued, the first from A to B, the second from B to C, the third from C to D, &c. And these multiplied by the altitudes AB, BC, CD, DE, &c., or, which is the same thing, by the distances SA, SB, SC, &c., proportional to those altitudes, will give $\dfrac{AH}{SA}$, $\dfrac{BI}{SB}$, $\dfrac{CK}{SC}$, &c., representing the pressures. Therefore since the densities are as the sums of those pressures, the differences $AH-BI$, $BI-CK$, &c., of the densities will be as the differences of those sums $\dfrac{AH}{SA}$, $\dfrac{BI}{SB}$, $\dfrac{CK}{SC}$, &c. With the centre S, and the asymptotes SA, Sx, describe any hyperbola, cutting the perpendiculars AH, BI, CK, &c., in a, b, c, &c., and the

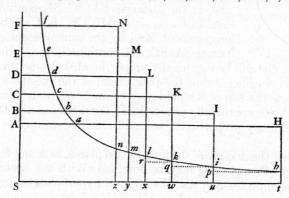

perpendiculars Ht, Iu, Kw, let fall upon the asymptote Sx, in h, i, k; and the differences of the densities, tu, uw, &c., will be as $\dfrac{AH}{SA}$, $\dfrac{BI}{SB}$, &c. And the rectangles $tu \cdot th$, $uw \cdot ui$, &c., or tp, uq, &c., as $\dfrac{AH \cdot th}{SA}$, $\dfrac{BI \cdot ui}{SB}$, &c., that is, as Aa, Bb, &c. For, by the nature of the hyperbola, SA is to AH or St as th to Aa, and therefore $\dfrac{AH \cdot th}{SA}$ is equal to Aa. And, by a like reasoning, $\dfrac{BI \cdot ui}{SB}$ is equal to Bb, &c. But Aa, Bb, Cc, &c., are continually proportional, and therefore proportional to their differences A$a-$Bb, B$b-$Cc, &c., therefore the rectangles tp, uq, &c., are proportional to those differences; as also the sums of the rectangles $tp+uq$ or $tp+uq+wr$ to the sums of the differences A$a-$Cc or A$a-$Dd. Suppose several of these terms, and the sum of all the differences, as A$a-$Ff, will be proportional to the sum of all the rectangles, as $zthn$. Increase the number of terms, and diminish the distances of the points A, B, C, &c., *in infinitum*, and those rectangles will become equal to the hyperbolic area $zthn$, and therefore the difference A$a-$Ff is proportional to this area. Take now any distances, as SA, SD, SF, in harmonic progression, and the differences A$a-$Dd, D$d-$Ff will be equal; and therefore the areas $thlx$, $xlnz$, proportional to those differences, will be equal among themselves, and the densities St, Sx, Sz, that is, AH, DL, FN, continually proportional.   Q.E.D.

Cor. Hence if any two densities of the fluid, as AH and BI, be given, the area $thiu$, answering to their difference tu, will be given; and thence the density

FN will be found at any height SF, by taking the area *thnz* to that given area *thiu* as the difference Aa−Ff to the difference Aa−Bb.

SCHOLIUM

By a like reasoning it may be proved, that if the gravity of the particles of a fluid diminishes as the cube of the distances from the centre, and the reciprocals of the squares of the distances SA, SB, SC, &c., (namely, $\frac{SA^3}{SA^2}$, $\frac{SA^3}{SB^2}$, $\frac{SA^3}{SC^2}$) be taken in an arithmetical progression, the densities AH, BI, CK, &c., will be in a geometrical progression. And if the gravity be diminished as the fourth power of the distances, and the reciprocals of the cubes of the distances (as $\frac{SA^4}{SA^3}$, $\frac{SA^4}{SB^3}$, $\frac{SA^4}{SC^3}$, &c.) be taken in arithmetical progression, the densities AH, BI, CK, &c., will be in geometrical progression. And so *in infinitum*. Again; if the gravity of the particles of the fluid be the same at all distances, and the distances be in arithmetical progression, the densities will be in a geometrical progression, as Dr. Halley hath found. If the gravity be as the distance, and the squares of the distances be in arithmetical progression, the densities will be in geometrical progression. And so *in infinitum*. These things will be so, when the density of the fluid condensed by compression is as the force of compression; or, which is the same thing, when the space possessed by the fluid is inversely as this force. Other laws of condensation may be supposed, as that the cube of the compressing force may be as the fourth power of the density, or the cube of the ratio of the force the same with the fourth power of the ratio of the density: in which case, if the gravity be inversely as the square of the distance from the centre, the density will be inversely as the cube of the distance. Suppose that the cube of the compressing force be as the fifth power of the density; and if the gravity be inversely as the square of the distance, the density will be inversely as the $\frac{3}{2}$th power of the distance. Suppose the compressing force to be as the square of the density, and the gravity inversely as the square of the distance, then the density will be inversely as the distance. To run over all the cases that might be offered would be tedious. But as to our own air, this is certain from experiment, that its density is either accurately, or very nearly at least, as the compressing force; and therefore the density of the air in the atmosphere of the earth is as the weight of the whole incumbent air, that is, as the height of the mercury in the barometer.

PROPOSITION 23. THEOREM 18

If a fluid be composed of particles fleeing from each other, and the density be as the compression, the centrifugal forces of the particles will be inversely proportional to the distances of their centres. And, conversely, particles fleeing from each other, with forces that are inversely proportional to the distances of their centres, compose an elastic fluid, whose density is as the compression.

Let the fluid be supposed to be included in a cubic space ACE, and then to be reduced by compression into a lesser cubic space *ace*; and the distances of the particles retaining a like situation with respect to each other in both the spaces, will be as the sides AB, *ab* of the cubes; and the densities of the mediums will be inversely as the containing spaces AB³, *ab*³. In the plane side of the

greater cube ABCD take the square DP
equal to the plane side *db* of the lesser cube;
and, by the supposition, the pressure with
which the square DP urges the inclosed fluid
will be to the pressure with which that square
db urges the inclosed fluid as the densities of
the mediums are to each other, that is, as *ab*³

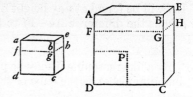

to AB³. But the pressure with which the square DB urges the included fluid is
to the pressure with which the square DP urges the same fluid as the square DB
to the square DP, that is, as AB² to *ab*². Therefore, multiplying together corresponding terms of the proportions, the pressure with which the square DB
urges the fluid is to the pressure with which the square *db* urges the fluid as *ab*
to AB. Let the planes FGH, *fgh* be drawn through the interior of the two cubes,
and divide the fluid into two parts. These parts will press each other with the
same forces with which they are themselves pressed by the planes AC, *ac*, that
is, in the proportion of *ab* to AB: and therefore the centrifugal forces by which
these pressures are sustained are in the same ratio. The number of the particles
being equal, and the situation alike, in both cubes, the forces which all the
particles exert, according to the planes FGH, *fgh*, upon all, are as the forces
which each exerts on each. Therefore the forces which each exerts on each,
according to the plane FGH in the greater cube, are to the forces which each
exerts on each, according to the plane *fgh* in the lesser cube, as *ab* to AB, that
is, inversely as the distances of the particles from each other.   Q.E.D.

And, conversely, if the forces of the single particles are inversely as the
distances, that is, inversely as the sides of the cubes AB, *ab*; the sums of the
forces will be in the same ratio, and the pressures of the sides DB, *db* as the
sums of the forces; and the pressure of the square DP to the pressure of
the side DB as *ab*² to AB². And, multiplying together corresponding terms
of the proportions, one obtains the pressure of the square DP to the pressure of
the side *db* as *ab*³ to AB³; that is, the force of compression in the one is to the
force of compression in the other as the density in the former to the density
in the latter.   Q.E.D.

SCHOLIUM

By a like reasoning, if the centrifugal forces of the particles are inversely as
the square of the distances between the centres, the cubes of the compressing
forces will be as the fourth power of the densities. If the centrifugal forces be
inversely as the third or fourth power of the distances, the cubes of the compressing forces will be as the fifth or sixth power of the densities. And universally, if D be put for the distance, and E for the density of the compressed fluid,
and the centrifugal forces be inversely as any power D^n of the distance, whose
index is the number n, the compressing forces will be as the cube roots of the
power E^{n+2}, whose index is the number $n+2$; and conversely. All these things
are to be understood of particles whose centrifugal forces terminate in those
particles that are next them, or are diffused not much farther. We have an
example of this in magnetic bodies. Their attractive force is terminated nearly
in bodies of their own kind that are next them. The force of the magnet is
reduced by the interposition of an iron plate, and is almost terminated at it:
for bodies farther off are not attracted by the magnet so much as by the iron

plate. If in this manner particles repel others of their own kind that lie next them, but do not exert their force on the more remote, particles of this kind will compose such fluids as are treated of in this Proposition. If the force of any particle diffuse itself every way *in infinitum*, there will be required a greater force to produce an equal condensation of a greater quantity of the fluid. But whether elastic fluids do really consist of particles so repelling each other, is a physical question. We have here demonstrated mathematically the property of fluids consisting of particles of this kind, that hence philosophers may take occasion to discuss that question.

SECTION VI

The motion and resistance of pendulous bodies

Proposition 24. Theorem 19

The quantities of matter in pendulous bodies, whose centres of oscillation are equally distant from the centre of suspension, are in a ratio compounded of the ratio of the weights and the squared ratio of the times of the oscillations in a vacuum.

For the velocity which a given force can generate in a given matter in a given time is directly as the force and the time, and inversely as the matter. The greater the force or the time is, or the less the matter, the greater the velocity generated. This is manifest from the second Law of Motion. Now if pendulums are of the same length, the motive forces in places equally distant from the perpendicular are as the weights: and therefore if two bodies by oscillating describe equal arcs, and those arcs are divided into equal parts; since the times in which the bodies describe each of the correspondent parts of the arcs are as the times of the whole oscillations, the velocities in the correspondent parts of the oscillations will be to each other directly as the motive forces and the whole times of the oscillations, and inversely as the quantities of matter: and therefore the quantities of matter are directly as the forces and the times of the oscillations, and inversely as the velocities. But the velocities are inversely as the times, and therefore the times are directly and the velocities inversely as the squares of the times; and therefore the quantities of matter are as the motive forces and the squares of the times, that is, as the weights and the squares of the times.   Q.E.D.

Cor. i. Therefore if the times are equal, the quantities of matter in each of the bodies are as the weights.

Cor. ii. If the weights are equal, the quantities of matter will be as the squares of the times.

Cor. iii. If the quantities of matter are equal, the weights will be inversely as the squares of the times.

Cor. iv. Since the squares of the times, other things being equal, are as the lengths of the pendulums, therefore if both the times and the quantities of matter are equal, the weights will be as the lengths of the pendulums.

Cor. v. And, in general, the quantity of matter in the pendulous body is directly as the weight and the square of the time, and inversely as the length of the pendulum.

Cor. vi. But in a nonresisting medium, the quantity of matter in the pendulous body is directly as the comparative weight and the square of the time, and inversely as the length of the pendulum. For the comparative weight is the motive force of the body in any heavy medium, as was shown above; and therefore does the same thing in such a nonresisting medium as the absolute weight does in a vacuum.

Cor. vii. And hence appears a method both of comparing bodies one with another, as to the quantity of matter in each; and of comparing the weights of the same body in different places, to know the variation of its gravity. And by experiments made with the greatest accuracy, I have always found the quantity of matter in bodies to be proportional to their weight.

Proposition 25. Theorem 20

Pendulous bodies that are, in any medium, resisted in the ratio of the moments of time, and pendulous bodies that move in a nonresisting medium of the same specific gravity, perform their oscillations in a cycloid in the same time, and describe proportional parts of arcs together.

Let AB be an arc of a cycloid, which a body D, by vibrating in a nonresisting medium, shall describe in any time. Bisect that arc in C, so that C may be the lowest point thereof; and the accelerative force with which the body is urged in any place D, or *d*, or E, will be as the length of the arc CD, or C*d*, or CE. Let that force be expressed by that same arc; and since the resistance is as the moment of the time, and therefore given, let it be expressed by the given part CO of the cycloidal arc, and take the arc O*d* in the same ratio to the arc CD that the arc OB has to the arc CB: and the force with which the body in *d* is urged in a resisting medium, being the excess of the force C*d* above the resistance CO, will be expressed by the arc O*d*, and will therefore be to the force with which the body D is urged in a non-resisting medium in the place D, as the arc O*d* to the arc CD; and therefore also in the place B, as the arc OB to the arc CB. Therefore if two bodies D, *d* go from the place B, and are urged by these forces; since the forces at the beginning are as the arcs CB and OB, the first velocities and arcs first described will be in the same ratio. Let those arcs be BD and B*d*, and the remain-

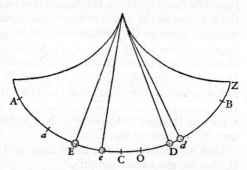

ing arcs CD, O*d* will be in the same ratio. Therefore the forces, being proportional to those arcs CD, O*d*, will remain in the same ratio as at the beginning, and therefore the bodies will continue describing together arcs in the same ratio. Therefore the forces and velocities and the remaining arcs CD, O*d*, will be always as the whole arcs CB, OB, and therefore those remaining arcs will be described together. Therefore the two bodies D and *d* will arrive together at the places C and O; that which moves in the nonresisting medium, at the place C, and the other, in the resisting medium, at the place O. Now since the velocities in C and O are as the arcs CB, OB, the arcs which the bodies describe when they go farther will be in the same ratio. Let those arcs be CE and O*e*.

The force with which the body D in a nonresisting medium is retarded in E is as CE, and the force with which the body d in the resisting medium is retarded in e, is as the sum of the force Ce and the resistance CO, that is, as Oe; and therefore the forces with which the bodies are retarded are as the arcs CB, OB, proportional to the arcs CE, Oe; and therefore the velocities, retarded in that given ratio, remain in the same given ratio. Therefore the velocities and the arcs described with those velocities are always to each other in that given ratio of the arcs CB and OB; and therefore if the entire arcs AB, aB are taken in the same ratio, the bodies D and d will describe those arcs together, and in the places A and a will lose all their motion together. Therefore the whole oscillations are isochronal, or are performed in equal times; and any parts of the arcs, as BD, Bd, or BE, Be, that are described together, are proportional to the whole arcs BA, Ba.   Q.E.D.

Cor. Therefore the swiftest motion in a resisting medium does not fall upon the lowest point C, but is found in that point O, in which the whole arc described Ba is bisected. And the body, proceeding from thence to a, is retarded at the same rate with which it was accelerated before in its descent from B to O.

PROPOSITION 26. THEOREM 21

Pendulous bodies, that are resisted in the ratio of the velocity, have their oscillations in a cycloid isochronal.

For if two bodies, equally distant from their centres of suspension, describe, in oscillating, unequal arcs, and the velocities in the correspondent parts of the arcs be to each other as the whole arcs; the resistances, proportional to the velocities, will be also to each other as the same arcs. Therefore if these resistances be subtracted from or added to the motive forces arising from gravity which are as the same arcs, the differences or sums will be to each other in the same ratio of the arcs; and since the increments and decrements of the velocities are as these differences or sums, the velocities will be always as the whole arcs; therefore if the velocities are in any one case as the whole arcs, they will remain always in the same ratio. But at the beginning of the motion, when the bodies begin to descend and describe those arcs, the forces, which at that time are proportional to the arcs, will generate velocities proportional to the arcs. Therefore the velocities will be always as the whole arcs to be described, and therefore those arcs will be described in the same time.   Q.E.D.

PROPOSITION 27. THEOREM 22

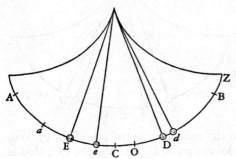

If pendulous bodies are resisted as the square of their velocities, the differences between the times of the oscillations in a resisting medium, and the times of the oscillations in a nonresisting medium of the same specific gravity, will be proportional to the arcs described in oscillating, nearly.

For let equal pendulums in a resisting medium describe the unequal arcs A, B; and the resistance of the body in the arc A will be to the resistance of the body in the correspondent part of the arc B as the square of the velocities, that is, as AA to BB, nearly. If the resistance in the arc B were to the resistance in the arc A as AB to AA, the times in the arcs A and B would be equal (by the last Proposition). Therefore the resistance AA in the arc A, or AB in the arc B, causes the excess of the time in the arc A above the time in a nonresisting medium; and the resistance BB causes the excess of the time in the arc B above the time in a nonresisting medium. But those excesses are as the efficient forces AB and BB nearly, that is, as the arcs A and B.   Q.E.D.

COR. I. Hence from the times of the oscillations in unequal arcs in a resisting medium, may be known the times of the oscillations in a nonresisting medium of the same specific gravity. For the difference of the times will be to the excess of the time in the shorter arc above the time in a nonresisting medium as the difference of the arcs is to the shorter arc.

COR. II. The shorter oscillations are more isochronal, and very short ones are performed nearly in the same times as in a nonresisting medium. But the times of those which are performed in greater arcs are a little greater, because the resistance in the descent of the body, by which the time is prolonged, is greater, in proportion to the length described in the descent than the resistance in the subsequent ascent, by which the time is contracted. But the time of the oscillations, both short and long, seems to be prolonged in some measure by the motion of the medium. For retarded bodies are resisted somewhat less in proportion to the velocity, and accelerated bodies somewhat more than those that proceed uniformly forwards; because the medium, by the motion it has received from the bodies, going forwards the same way with them, is more agitated in the former case, and less in the latter; and so conspires more or less with the bodies moved. Therefore it resists the pendulums in their descent more, and in their ascent less, than in proportion to the velocity; and these two causes concurring prolong the time.

PROPOSITION 28. THEOREM 23

If a pendulous body, oscillating in a cycloid, be resisted in the ratio of the moments of the time, its resistance will be to the force of gravity, as the excess of the arc described in the whole descent above the arc described in the subsequent ascent is to twice the length of the pendulum.

Let BC represent the arc described in the descent, Ca the arc described in the ascent, and Aa the difference of the arcs: and things remaining as they were constructed and demonstrated in Prop. 25, the force with which the oscillating body is urged in any place D will be to the force of resistance as the arc CD to the arc CO, which is half of that difference Aa. Therefore the force with which the oscillating body is urged at the beginning or the highest point of the cycloid, that is, the force of gravity, will be to the resistance as the arc of the cycloid, between that highest point and the lowest point C, is to the arc CO; that is

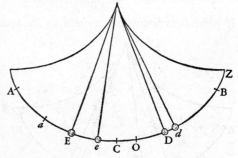

(doubling those arcs), as the whole cycloidal arc, or twice the length of the pendulum, is to the arc Aa.   Q.E.D.

PROPOSITION 29. PROBLEM 6

Supposing that a body oscillating in a cycloid is resisted as the square of the velocity; to find the resistance in each place.

Let Ba be an arc described in one entire oscillation, C the lowest point of the cycloid, and CZ half the whole cycloidal arc, equal to the length of the pendulum; and let it be required to find the resistance of the body in any place D. Cut the indefinite right line OQ in the points O, S, P, Q, so that (erecting the perpendiculars OK, ST, PI, QE, and with the centre O, and the asymptotes OK, OQ, describing the hyperbola TIGE cutting the perpendiculars ST, PI, QE in T, I, and E, and through the point I drawing KF, parallel to the asymptote, OQ, meeting the asymptote OK in K, and the perpendiculars ST and QE in L and F) the hyperbolic area PIEQ may be to the hyperbolic area PITS as the arc BC, described in the descent of the body, is to the arc Ca described in the ascent; and that the area IEF may be to the area ILT as OQ to OS. Then

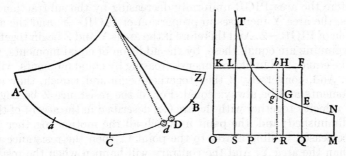

with the perpendicular MN cut off the hyperbolic area PINM, and let that area be to the hyperbolic area PIEQ as the arc CZ to the arc BC described in the descent. And if the perpendicular RG cuts off the hyperbolic area PIGR, which shall be to the area PIEQ as any arc CD is to the arc BC described in the whole descent, the resistance in any place D will be to the force of gravity as the area $\frac{OR}{OQ}$ IEF$-$IGH is to the area PINM.

For since the forces arising from gravity with which the body is urged in the places Z, B, D, a are as the arcs CZ, CB, CD, Ca, and those arcs are as the areas PINM, PIEQ, PIGR, PITS; let those areas represent both the arcs and the forces respectively. Let Dd be a very small space described by the body in its descent; and let it be expressed by the very small area RGgr, comprehended between the parallels RG, rg; and produce rg to h, so that GHhg and RGgr may be the contemporaneous decrements of the areas IGH, PIGR. And the increment GH$hg-\frac{Rr}{OQ}$ IEF, or Rr·HG$-\frac{Rr}{OQ}$ IEF, of the area $\frac{OR}{OQ}$ IEF$-$IGH will be to the decrement RGgr, or Rr·RG, of the area PIGR, as HG$-\frac{IEF}{OQ}$ is to RG; and therefore as OR·HG$-\frac{OR}{OQ}$ IEF is to OR·GR or OP·PI, that is (because of the equal quantities OR·HG, OR·HR$-$OR·GR, ORHK$-$OPIK,

PIHR and PIGR+IGH), as PIGR+IGH$-\frac{OR}{OQ}$ IEF is to OPIK. Therefore if

the area $\frac{OR}{OQ}$ IEF$-$IGH be called Y, and RGgr the decrement of the area

PIGR be given, the increment of the area Y will be as PIGR$-$Y.

Then if V represent the force arising from the gravity, proportional to the arc CD to be described, by which the body is acted upon in D, and R be put for the resistance, V$-$R will be the whole force with which the body is urged in D. Therefore the increment of the velocity is as V$-$R and the interval of time in which it is generated conjointly. But the velocity itself is directly as the contemporaneous increment of the space described and inversely as the same interval of time. Therefore, since the resistance is, by the supposition, as the square of the velocity, the increment of the resistance will (by Lem. 2) be as the velocity and the increment of the velocity conjointly, that is, as the moment of the space and V$-$R conjointly; and, therefore, if the moment of the space be given, as V$-$R; that is, if for the force V we put its expression PIGR, and the resistance R be expressed by any other area Z, as PIGR$-$Z.

Therefore the area PIGR uniformly decreasing by the subtraction of given moments, the area Y increases in proportion of PIGR$-$Y, and the area Z in proportion of PIGR$-$Z. And therefore if the areas Y and Z begin together, and at the beginning are equal, these, by the addition of equal moments, will continue to be equal; and in like manner decreasing by equal moments, will vanish together. And, conversely, if they together begin and vanish, they will have equal moments and be always equal. For, if the resistance Z be augmented, then the velocity together with the arc Ca, described in the ascent of the body, will be diminished; and, the point in which all the motion together with the resistance ceases, coming nearer to the point C, then the resistance vanishes sooner than the area Y. And the contrary will happen when the resistance is diminished.

Now the area Z begins and ends where the resistance is nothing, that is, at the beginning of the motion where the arc CD is equal to the arc CB, and the right line RG falls upon the right line QE; and at the end of the motion where the arc CD is equal to the arc Ca, and RG falls upon the right line ST. And the

area Y or $\frac{OR}{OQ}$ IEF$-$IGH begins and ends also where the resistance is nothing,

and therefore where $\frac{OR}{OQ}$ IEF and IGH are equal; that is (by the construction),

where the right line RG falls successively upon the right lines QE and ST. Therefore those areas begin and vanish together, and are therefore always

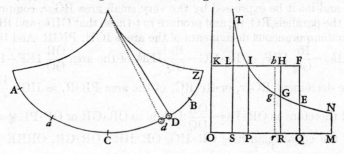

equal. Hence, the area $\frac{OR}{OQ}$ IEF $-$ IGH is equal to the area Z, by which the resistance is expressed, and therefore is to the area PINM, by which the gravity is expressed, as the resistance is to the gravity. Q.E.D.

COR. I. Therefore the resistance in the lowest place C is to the force of gravity as the area $\frac{OP}{OQ}$ IEF is to the area PINM.

COR. II. But it becomes greatest where the area PIHR is to the area IEF as OR is to OQ. For in that case its moment (that is, PIGR $-$ Y) becomes nothing.

COR. III. Hence also may be known the velocity in each place, as varying as the square root of the resistance, and at the beginning of the motion being equal to the velocity of the body oscillating in the same cycloid without any resistance.

However, by reason of the difficulty of the calculation by which the resistance and the velocity are found by this Proposition, we have thought fit to subjoin the Proposition following.

PROPOSITION 30. THEOREM 24

If a right line aB *be equal to the arc of a cycloid which an oscillating body describes, and at each of its points* D *the perpendiculars* DK *be erected, which shall be to the length of the pendulum as the resistance of the body in the corresponding points of the arc is to the force of gravity: I say, that the difference between the arc described in the whole descent and the arc described in the whole subsequent ascent multiplied by half the sum of the same arcs will be equal to the area* BKa *which all those perpendiculars take up.*

Let the arc of the cycloid, described in one entire oscillation, be expressed by the right line aB, equal to it, and the arc which would have been described in a vacuum by the length AB. Bisect AB in C, and the point C will represent the lowest point of the cycloid, and CD will be as the force arising from gravity, with which the body in D is urged in the direction of the tangent of the cycloid, and will have the same ratio to the length of the pendulum as the force in D has

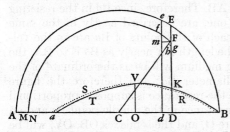

to the force of gravity. Let that force, therefore, be expressed by that length CD, and the force of gravity by the length of the pendulum; and if in DE you take DK in the same ratio to the length of the pendulum as the resistance is to the gravity, DK will be the exponent of the resistance. From the centre C with the interval CA or CB describe a semicircle BEeA. Let the body describe, in the least time, the space Dd; and, erecting the perpendiculars DE, de, meeting the circumference in E and e, they will be as the velocities which the body descending in a vacuum from the point B would acquire in the places D and d. This appears by Prop. 52, Book I. Let, therefore, these velocities be expressed by those perpendiculars DE, de; and let DF be the velocity which it acquires in D by falling from B in the resisting medium. And if from the centre C with the interval CF we describe the circle FfM meeting the right lines de and AB in f and M, then M will be the place to which it would thenceforward, without further resistance, ascend, and df the velocity it would acquire in d. Hence, also, if Fg represent the moment of the velocity which the body D, in describing the least space Dd, loses by the resistance of the medium; and CN be taken equal to Cg; then will N be the place to which the body, if it met no further resistance, would thenceforward ascend, and MN will be the decrement of the ascent arising from the loss of that velocity. Draw Fm perpendicular to df, and the decrement Fg of the velocity DF generated by the resistance DK will be to the increment fm of the same velocity, generated by the force CD, as the generating force DK to the generating force CD. But because of the similar triangles F$m f$, Fhg, FDC, fm is to Fm or Dd as CD to DF; and, by multiplication of corresponding terms, Fg to Dd as DK to DF. Also Fh is to Fg as DF to CF; and, again by multiplication of corresponding terms, Fh or MN to Dd as DK to CF or CM; and therefore the sum of all the MN$\cdot$CM will be equal to the sum of all the D$d\cdot$DK. At the movable point M suppose always a rectangular ordinate erected equal to the indeterminate CM, which by a continual motion is multiplied by the whole length Aa; and the trapezium described by that motion, or its equal, the rectangle A$a\cdot\frac{1}{2}a$B, will be equal to the sum of all the MN$\cdot$CM, and therefore to the sum of all the D$d\cdot$DK, that is, to the area BKVTa.   q.e.d.

Cor. Hence from the law of resistance, and the difference Aa of the arcs Ca, CB, may be derived the proportion of the resistance to the gravity, nearly.

For if the resistance DK be uniform, the figure BKTa will be a rectangle under Ba and DK; and hence the rectangle under $\frac{1}{2}$Ba and Aa will be equal to the rectangle under Ba and DK, and DK will be equal to $\frac{1}{2}$Aa. Therefore since DK represents the resistance, and the length of the pendulum represents the gravity, the resistance will be to the gravity as $\frac{1}{2}$Aa is to the length of the pendulum; altogether as in Prop. 28 is demonstrated.

If the resistance be as the velocity, the figure BKTa will be nearly an ellipse. For if a body, in a nonresisting medium, by one entire oscillation, should describe the length BA, the velocity in any place D would be as the ordinate DE of the circle described on the diameter AB. Therefore since Ba in the resisting medium, and BA in the nonresisting one, are described nearly in the same times; and therefore the velocities in each of the points of Ba are to the velocities in the corresponding points of the length BA nearly as Ba is to BA, the velocity in the point D in the resisting medium will be as the ordinate of the circle or ellipse described upon the diameter Ba; and therefore the figure BKVTa will be nearly an ellipse. Since the resistance is supposed proportional to the velocity, let OV represent the resistance in the middle point O; and an ellipse BRVSa described with the centre O, and the semiaxes OB, OV, will be nearly equal to the figure BKVTa, and to its equal the rectangle A$a\cdot$BO. Therefore A$a\cdot$BO is to OV$\cdot$BO as the area of this ellipse to OV$\cdot$BO; that is, Aa is to OV as the area of the semicircle is to the square of the radius, or as 11 to 7 nearly; and, therefore, $\frac{7}{11}$ Aa is to the length of the pendulum as the resistance of the oscillating body in O is to its gravity.

Now if the resistance DK varies as the square of the velocity, the figure BKVTa will be almost a parabola having V for its vertex and OV for its axis, and therefore will be nearly equal to the rectangle under $\frac{2}{3}$Ba and OV. Therefore the rectangle under $\frac{1}{2}$Ba and Aa is equal to the rectangle $\frac{2}{3}$B$a\cdot$OV, and therefore OV is equal to $\frac{3}{4}$Aa; and therefore the resistance in O made to the oscillating body is to its gravity as $\frac{3}{4}$Aa is to the length of the pendulum.

And I take these conclusions to be accurate enough for practical uses. For since an ellipse or parabola BRVSa falls in with the figure BKVTa in the middle point V, that figure, if greater towards the part BRV or VSa, is less towards the contrary part, and is therefore nearly equal to it.

Proposition 31. Theorem 25

If the resistance made to an oscillating body in each of the proportional parts of the arcs described be augmented or diminished in a given ratio, the difference between the arc described in the descent and the arc described in the subsequent ascent will be augmented or diminished in the same ratio.

For that difference arises from the retardation of the pendulum by the resistance of the medium, and therefore is as the whole retardation and the retarding

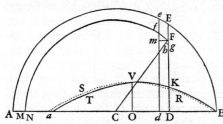

resistance proportional thereto. In the foregoing Proposition the rectangle under the right line $\frac{1}{2}a$B and the difference Aa of the arcs CB, Ca, was equal to the area BKTa. And that area, if the length aB remains, is augmented or diminished in the ratio of the ordinates DK; that is, in the ratio of the resistance, and is therefore as the length aB and the resistance conjointly. And therefore the rectangle under Aa and $\frac{1}{2}a$B is as aB and the resistance conjointly, and therefore Aa is as the resistance.   Q.E.D.

Cor. i. Hence if the resistance be as the velocity, the difference of the arcs in the same medium will be as the whole arc described; and conversely.

Cor. ii. If the resistance varies as the square of the velocity, that difference will vary as the square of the whole arc; and conversely.

Cor. iii. And generally, if the resistance varies as the third or any other power of the velocity, the difference will vary as the same power of the whole arc; and conversely.

Cor. iv. If the resistance varies partly as the first power of the velocity and partly as the square of the same, the difference will vary partly as the first power and partly as the square of the whole arc; and conversely. So that the law and ratio of the resistance will be the same for the velocity as the law and ratio of that difference for the length of the arc.

Cor. v. And therefore if a pendulum describe successively unequal arcs, and we can find the ratio of the increment or decrement of this difference for the length of the arc described, there will be had also the ratio of the increment or decrement of the resistance for a greater or less velocity.

General Scholium

From these Propositions we may find the resistance of mediums by pendulums oscillating therein. I found the resistance of the air by the following experiments. I suspended a wooden globe or ball weighing $57\frac{7}{22}$ ounces troy, its diameter $6\frac{7}{8}$ London inches, by a fine thread on a firm hook, so that the distance between the hook and the centre of oscillation of the globe was $10\frac{1}{2}$

feet. I marked on the thread a point 10 feet and 1 inch distant from the centre of suspension; and even with that point I placed a ruler divided into inches, by the help of which I observed the lengths of the arcs described by the pendulum. Then I numbered the oscillations in which the globe would lose $\frac{1}{8}$ part of its motion. If the pendulum was drawn aside from the perpendicular to the distance of 2 inches, and then let go, so that in its whole descent it described an arc of 2 inches, and in the first whole oscillation, compounded of the descent and subsequent ascent, an arc of almost 4 inches, the pendulum in 164 oscillations lost $\frac{1}{8}$ part of its motion, so as in its last ascent to describe an arc of $1\frac{3}{4}$ inches. If in the first descent it described an arc of 4 inches, it lost $\frac{1}{8}$ part of its motion in 121 oscillations, so as in its last ascent to describe an arc of $3\frac{1}{2}$ inches. If in the first descent it described an arc of 8, 16, 32, or 64 inches, it lost $\frac{1}{8}$ part of its motion in 69, $35\frac{1}{2}$, $18\frac{1}{2}$, $9\frac{2}{3}$ oscillations, respectively. Therefore the difference between the arcs described in the first descent and the last ascent was in the 1st, 2d, 3d, 4th, 5th, 6th cases, $\frac{1}{4}$, $\frac{1}{2}$, 1, 2, 4, 8 inches, respectively. Divide those differences by the number of oscillations in each case, and in one mean oscillation, in which an arc of $3\frac{3}{4}$, $7\frac{1}{2}$, 15, 30, 60, 120 inches was described, the difference of the arcs described in the descent and subsequent ascent will be $\frac{1}{656}$, $\frac{1}{242}$, $\frac{1}{69}$, $\frac{4}{71}$, $\frac{8}{37}$, $\frac{24}{29}$ parts of an inch, respectively. But these differences in the greater oscillations are as the square of the arcs described, nearly, but in lesser oscillations somewhat greater than in that ratio; and therefore (by Cor. II, Prop. 31 of this Book) the resistance of the globe, when it moves very swiftly, varies as the square of the velocity, nearly; and when it moves slowly, in a somewhat greater ratio.

Now let V represent the greatest velocity in any oscillation, and let A, B, and C be given quantities, and let us suppose the difference of the arcs to be $AV + BV^{3/2} + CV^2$. Since the greatest velocities are in the cycloid as $\frac{1}{2}$ the arcs described in oscillating, and in the circle as $\frac{1}{2}$ the chords of those arcs; and therefore in equal arcs are greater in the cycloid than in the circle in the ratio of $\frac{1}{2}$ the arcs to their chords; but the times in the circle are greater than in the cycloid, in a ratio inversely as the velocity; it is plain that the differences of the arcs (which are as the resistance and the square of the time conjointly) are nearly the same in both curves: for in the cycloid those differences must be on the one hand augmented, with the resistance, in about the squared ratio of the arc to the chord, because of the velocity augmented in the simple ratio of the same; and on the other hand diminished, with the square of the time, in the same squared ratio. Therefore to reduce these observations to the cycloid, we must take the same differences of the arcs as were observed in the circle, and suppose the greatest velocities analogous to the half, or the whole arcs, that is, to the numbers $\frac{1}{2}$, 1, 2, 4, 8, 16. Therefore in the 2d, 4th, and 6th cases put 1, 4, and 16 for V; and the difference of the arcs in the 2d case will become $\frac{\frac{1}{2}}{121} = A$ $+B+C$; in the 4th case, $\frac{2}{35\frac{1}{2}} = 4A + 8B + 16C$; in the 6th case, $\frac{8}{9\frac{2}{3}} = 16A + 64B$ $+256C$. These equations reduced give $A = 0.0000916$, $B = 0.0010847$, and $C = 0.0029558$. Therefore the difference of the arcs is as $0.0000916V + 0.0010847V^{3/2}$ $+0.0029558V^2$; and therefore since (by Cor., Prop. 30, applied to this case) the resistance of the globe in the middle of the arc described in oscillating, where the velocity is V, is to its weight as $\frac{7}{11}AV + \frac{7}{10}BV^{3/2} + \frac{3}{4}CV^2$ is to the length of the pendulum, if for A, B, and C you put the numbers found, the resistance of the globe will be to its weight as $0.0000583V + 0.0007593V^{3/2} + 0.0022169V^2$

is to the length of the pendulum between the centre of suspension and the ruler, that is, to 121 inches. Therefore since V in the second case represents 1, in the 4th case 4 and in the 6th case 16, the resistance will be to the weight of the globe, in the 2d case, as 0.0030345 is to 121; in the 4th, as 0.041748 is to 121; in the 6th, as 0.61705 is to 121.

The arc, which the point marked in the thread described in the 6th case, was $120 - \frac{8}{9\frac{2}{3}}$, or $119\frac{5}{29}$ inches. And therefore since the radius was 121 inches, and the length of the pendulum between the point of suspension and the centre of the globe was 126 inches, the arc which the centre of the globe described was $124\frac{3}{31}$ inches. Because the greatest velocity of the oscillating body, by reason of the resistance of the air, does not fall on the lowest point of the arc described, but near the middle place of the whole arc, this velocity will be nearly the same as if the globe in its whole descent in a nonresisting medium should describe $62\frac{3}{62}$ inches, the half of that arc, and that in a cycloid, to which we have above reduced the motion of the pendulum; and therefore that velocity will be equal to that which the globe would acquire by falling perpendicularly from a height equal to the versed sine of that arc. But that versed sine in the cycloid is to that arc $62\frac{3}{32}$ as the same arc to twice the length of the pendulum 252, and therefore equal to 15.278 inches. Therefore the velocity of the pendulum is the same which a body would acquire by falling, and in its fall describing a space of 15.278 inches. Therefore with such a velocity the globe meets with a resistance which is to its weight as 0.61705 is to 121, or (if we take that part only of the resistance which is in the squared ratio of the velocity) as 0.56752 to 121.

I found, by an hydrostatical experiment, that the weight of this wooden globe was to the weight of a globe of water of the same magnitude as 55 to 97; and therefore since 121 is to 213.4 in the same ratio, the resistance made to this globe of water, moving forwards with the above-mentioned velocity, will be to its weight as 0.56752 to 213.4, that is, as 1 to $376\frac{1}{50}$. Since the weight of a globe of water, in the time in which the globe with a velocity uniformly continued describes a length of 30.556 inches, will generate all that velocity in the falling globe, it is manifest that the force of resistance uniformly continued in the same time will take away a velocity, which will be less than the other in the ratio of 1 to $376\frac{1}{50}$, that is, the $\frac{1}{376\frac{1}{50}}$ part of the whole velocity. And therefore in the time that the globe, with the same velocity uniformly continued, would describe the length of its semidiameter, or $3\frac{7}{16}$ inches, it would lose the $\frac{1}{3342}$ part of its motion.

I also counted the oscillations in which the pendulum lost $\frac{1}{4}$ part of its motion. In the following table the upper numbers denote the length of the arc described in the first descent, expressed in inches and parts of an inch; the middle numbers denote the length of the arc described in the last ascent; and in the lowest place are the numbers of the oscillations. I give an account of this experiment, as being more accurate than that in which only $\frac{1}{8}$ part of the motion was lost. I leave the calculation to such as are disposed to make it.

First descent	2	4	8	16	32	64
Last ascent	$1\frac{1}{2}$	3	6	12	24	48
No. of oscillations	374	272	$162\frac{1}{2}$	$83\frac{1}{3}$	$41\frac{2}{3}$	$22\frac{2}{3}$

I afterwards suspended a leaden globe of 2 inches in diameter, weighing $26\frac{1}{4}$ ounces troy by the same thread, so that between the centre of the globe and the point of suspension there was an interval of $10\frac{1}{2}$ feet, and I counted the oscillations in which a given part of the motion was lost. The first of the following tables exhibits the number of oscillations in which $\frac{1}{8}$ part of the whole motion was lost; the second the number of oscillations in which there was lost $\frac{1}{4}$ part of the same.

First descent	1	2	4	8	16	32	64
Last ascent	$\frac{7}{8}$	$\frac{7}{4}$	$3\frac{1}{2}$	7	14	28	56
No. of oscillations	226	228	193	140	$90\frac{1}{2}$	53	30
First descent	1	2	4	8	16	32	64
Last ascent	$\frac{3}{4}$	$1\frac{1}{2}$	3	6	12	24	48
No. of oscillations	510	518	420	318	204	121	70

Selecting in the first table the 3d, 5th, and 7th observations, and expressing the greatest velocities in these observations particularly by the numbers 1, 4, 16, respectively, and generally by the quantity V as above, there will come out in the 3d observation $\frac{1}{193} = A + B + C$, in the 5th observation $\frac{2}{90\frac{1}{2}} = 4A + 8B + 16C$, in the 7th observation $\frac{8}{30} = 16A + 64B + 256C$. These equations reduced give A = 0.001414, B = 0.000297, C = 0.000879. And thence the resistance of the globe moving with the velocity V will be to its weight $26\frac{1}{4}$ ounces in the same ratio as $0.0009V + 0.000208V^{3/2} + 0.000659V^2$ to 121 inches, the length of the pendulum. And if we regard that part only of the resistance which is as the square of the velocity, it will be to the weight of the globe as $0.000659V^2$ to 121 inches. But this part of the resistance in the first experiment was to the weight of the wooden globe of $57\frac{7}{22}$ ounces as $0.002217V^2$ to 121; hence the resistance of the wooden globe is to the resistance of the leaden one (their velocities being equal) as $57\frac{7}{22}$ into 0.002217 to $26\frac{1}{4}$ into 0.000659, that is, as $7\frac{1}{3}$ to 1. The diameters of the two globes were $6\frac{7}{8}$ and 2 inches, and the squares of these are to each other as $47\frac{1}{4}$ and 4, or $11\frac{13}{16}$ and 1, nearly. Therefore the resistances of these equally swift globes were in less than a squared ratio of the diameters. But we have not yet considered the resistance of the thread, which was certainly very considerable, and ought to be subtracted from the resistance of the pendulums here found. I could not determine this accurately, but I found it greater than $\frac{1}{8}$ part of the whole resistance of the lesser pendulum; hence I gathered that the resistances of the globes, when the resistance of the thread is subtracted, are nearly in the squared ratio of their diameters. For the ratio of $7\frac{1}{2} - \frac{1}{8}$ to $1 - \frac{1}{8}$, or $10\frac{1}{2}$ to 1 is not very different from the squared ratio of the diameters $11\frac{13}{16}$ to 1.

Since the resistance of the thread is of less moment in greater globes, I tried the experiment also with a globe whose diameter was $18\frac{3}{4}$ inches. The length of the pendulum between the point of suspension and the centre of oscillation was $122\frac{1}{2}$ inches, and between the point of suspension and the knot in the thread $109\frac{1}{2}$ inches. The arc described by the knot at the first descent of the pendulum was 32 inches. The arc described by the same knot in the last ascent after five oscillations was 28 inches. The sum of the arcs, or the whole arc described in one mean oscillation, was 60 inches; the difference of the arcs, 4 inches. The $\frac{1}{10}$ part of this, or the difference between the descent and ascent in one mean oscillation, is $\frac{2}{5}$ of an inch. Then as the radius $109\frac{1}{2}$ is to the radius $122\frac{1}{2}$, so is the whole arc of 60 inches described by the knot in one mean oscillation to the whole arc of $67\frac{1}{8}$ inches described by the centre of the globe in one mean oscillation; and so is the difference $\frac{2}{5}$ to a new difference 0.4475. If the length of the arc described were to remain, and the length of the pendulum should be augmented in the ratio of 126 to $122\frac{1}{2}$, the time of the oscillation would be augmented, and the velocity of the pendulum would be diminished as the square root of that ratio; so that the difference 0.4475 of the arcs described in the descent and subsequent ascent would remain. Then if the arc described be augmented in the ratio of $124\frac{3}{31}$ to $67\frac{1}{8}$, that difference 0.4475 would be augmented as the square of that ratio, and so would become 1.5295. These things would be so upon the supposition that the resistance of the pendulum were as the square of the velocity. Therefore if the pendulum describe the whole arc of $124\frac{3}{31}$ inches, and its length between the point of suspension and the centre of oscillation be 126 inches, the difference of the arcs described in the descent and subsequent ascent would be 1.5295 inches. And this difference multiplied by the weight of the pendulous globe, which was 208 ounces, produces 318.136. Again, in the pendulum above mentioned, made of a wooden globe, when its centre of oscillation, being 126 inches from the point of suspension, described the whole arc of $124\frac{3}{31}$ inches, the difference of the arcs described in the descent and ascent was $\frac{126}{121}$ into $\frac{8}{9\frac{2}{3}}$. This multiplied by the weight of the globe, which was $57\frac{1}{22}$ ounces, produces 49.396. But I multiply these differences by the weights of the globes, in order to find their resistances. For the differences arise from the resistances, and are as the resistances directly and the weights inversely. Therefore the resistances are as the numbers 318.136 and 49.396. But that part of the resistance of the lesser globe, which is as the square of the velocity, was to the whole resistance as 0.56752 to 0.61675, that is, as 45.453 to 49.396, whereas that part of the resistance of the greater globe is almost equal to its whole resistance, and so those parts are nearly as 318.136 and 45.453, that is, as 7 and 1. But the diameters of the globes are $18\frac{3}{4}$ and $6\frac{7}{8}$; and their squares $351\frac{9}{16}$ and $47\frac{17}{64}$ are as 7.438 and 1, that is, nearly as the resistances of the globes 7 and 1. The difference of these ratios is barely greater than may arise from the resistance of the thread. Therefore those parts of the resistances which are, when the globes are equal, as the squares of the velocities, are also, when the velocities are equal, as the squares of the diameters of the globes.

But the greatest of the globes I used in these experiments was not perfectly spherical, and therefore in this calculation I have, for brevity's sake, neglected some little niceties; being not very solicitous for an accurate calculus in an experiment that was not very accurate. So that I could wish that these experiments were tried again with other globes, of a larger size, more in number, and more accurately formed; since the demonstration of a vacuum depends thereon. If the globes be taken in a geometrical proportion, whose diameters, let us suppose, are 4, 8, 16, 32 inches; one may infer from the progression observed in the experiments what would happen if the globes were still larger.

In order to compare the resistances of different fluids with each other, I made the following trials. I procured a wooden vessel 4 feet long, 1 foot broad, and 1 foot high. This vessel, being uncovered, I filled with spring water, and, having immersed pendulums therein, I made them oscillate in the water. And I found that a leaden globe weighing $166\frac{1}{6}$ ounces, and in diameter $3\frac{5}{8}$ inches, moved therein as it is set down in the following table; the length of the pendulum from the point of suspension to a certain point marked in the thread being 126 inches, and to the centre of oscillation 134⅜ inches.

The arc described in the first descent, by a point marked in the thread was inches	64	. 32	. 16	. 8	. 4	. 2	. 1	. ½	. ¼
The arc described in the last ascent was inches	48	. 24	. 12	. 6	. 3	. 1½	. ¾	. ⅜	. 3/16
The difference of the arcs, proportional to the motion lost, was inches	16	. 8	. 4	. 2	. 1	. ½	. ¼	. ⅛	. 1/16
The number of the oscillations in water			²⁹⁄₆₀	. 1⅕	. 3	. 7	. 11¼	. 12⅔	. 13⅓
The number of the oscillations in air	85½	. 287	. 535						

In the experiments of the 4th column there were equal motions lost in 535 oscillations made in the air, and 1⅕ in water. The oscillations in the air were indeed a little swifter than those in the water. But if the oscillations in the water were accelerated in such a ratio that the motions of the pendulums might be equally swift in both mediums, there would be still the same number of 1⅕ oscillations in the water, and by these the same quantity of motion would be lost as before; because the resistance is increased, and the square of the time diminished in the same squared ratio. The pendulums, therefore, being of equal velocities, there were equal motions lost in 535 oscillations in the air, and 1⅕ in the water; and therefore the resistance of the pendulum in the water is to its resistance in the air as 535 to 1⅕. This is the proportion of the whole resistances in the case of the 4th column.

Now let $AV + CV^2$ represent the difference of the arcs described in the descent and subsequent ascent by the globe moving in air with the greatest velocity V; and since the greatest velocity is in the case of the 4th column to the greatest velocity in the case of the 1st column as 1 is to 8; and that difference of the arcs in the case of the 4th column to the difference in the case of the 1st column as $\frac{2}{535}$ to $\frac{16}{535}$, or as 85½ to 4280; put in these cases 1 and 8 for the velocities, and 85½ and 4280 for the differences of the arcs, and $A + C$ will be $= 85½$, and $8A + 64C = 4280$ or $A + 8C = 535$; and then, by reducing these equations, there will come out $7C = 449½$ and $C = 64\frac{3}{14}$ and $A = 21\frac{2}{7}$; and therefore the resistance, which is as $\frac{7}{11}AV + \frac{3}{4}CV^2$, will become as $13\frac{6}{11}V + 48\frac{9}{56}V^2$. Therefore in the case of the 4th column, where the velocity was 1, the whole resistance is to its part proportional to the square of the velocity as $13\frac{6}{11} + 48\frac{9}{56}$ or $61\frac{12}{17}$ to $48\frac{9}{56}$; and therefore the resistance of the pendulum in water is to that part of the resistance in air, which is proportional to the square of the velocity, and which in swift motions is the only part that deserves consideration, as $61\frac{12}{17}$ to $48\frac{9}{56}$ and 535 to 1⅕ conjointly, that is, as 571 to 1. If the whole thread of the pendulum oscillating in the water had been immersed, its resistance would have been still greater; so that the resistance of the pendulum oscillating in the water, that is, that part which is proportional to the square of the velocity, and which only needs to be considered in swift bodies, is to the resistance of the same whole pendulum, oscillating in air with the same velocity, as about 850 to 1, that is, as the density of water is to the density of air, nearly.

In this calculation we ought also to have taken in that part of the resistance of the pendulum in the water which was as the square of the velocity; but I found (which will perhaps seem strange) that the resistance in the water was augmented in more than a squared ratio of the velocity. In searching after the cause, I thought upon this, that the vessel was too narrow for the magnitude of the pendulous globe, and by its narrowness obstructed the motion of the water as it yielded to the oscillating globe. For when I immersed a pendulous globe, whose diameter was one inch only, the resistance was augmented nearly as the square of the velocity. I tried this by making a pendulum of two globes, of which the lesser and lower oscillated in the water, and the greater and higher was fastened to the thread just above the water, and, by oscillating in the air, assisted the motion of the pendulum, and continued it longer. The experiments made by this contrivance resulted as shown in the following table.

Arc described in first descent	16	.	8	.	4	.	2	.	1	.	$\frac{1}{2}$	.	$\frac{1}{4}$
Arc described in last ascent	12	.	6	.	3	.	$1\frac{1}{2}$	.	$\frac{3}{4}$	.	$\frac{3}{8}$	.	$\frac{3}{16}$
Difference of arcs, proportional to motion lost	4	.	2	.	1	.	$\frac{1}{2}$	.	$\frac{1}{4}$	.	$\frac{1}{8}$	.	$\frac{1}{16}$
Number of oscillations	$3\frac{3}{8}$	.	$6\frac{1}{2}$	.	$12\frac{1}{12}$	.	$21\frac{1}{5}$	.	34	.	53	.	$62\frac{1}{5}$

In comparing the resistances of the mediums with each other, I also caused iron pendulums to oscillate in quicksilver. The length of the iron wire was about 3 feet, and the diameter of the pendulous globe about $\frac{1}{3}$ of an inch. To the wire, just above the quicksilver, there was fixed another leaden globe of a bigness sufficient to continue the motion of the pendulum for some time. Then a vessel, that would hold about 3 pounds of quicksilver, was filled by turns with quicksilver and common water, so that, by making the pendulum oscillate successively in these two different fluids, I might find the proportion of their resistances; and the resistance of the quicksilver proved to be to the resistance of water as about 13 or 14 to 1; that is, as the density of quicksilver to the density of water. When I made use of a pendulous globe something bigger, as of one whose diameter was about $\frac{1}{2}$ or $\frac{2}{3}$ of an inch, the resistance of the quicksilver proved to be to the resistance of the water as about 12 or 10 to 1. But the former experiment is more to be relied on, because in the latter the vessel was too narrow in proportion to the magnitude of the immersed globe; for the vessel ought to have been enlarged together with the globe. I intended to repeat these experiments with larger vessels, and in melted metals, and other liquors both cold and hot; but I had not leisure to try all; and besides, from what is already described, it appears sufficiently that the resistance of bodies moving swiftly is nearly proportional to the densities of the fluids in which they move. I do not say accurately; for more tenacious fluids, of equal density, will undoubtedly resist more than those that are more liquid; as cold oil more than warm, warm oil more than rain water, and water more than spirit of wine. But in liquors, which are sensibly fluid enough, as in air, in salt and fresh water, in spirit of wine, of turpentine, and salts, in oil cleared of its feces by distillation and warmed, in oil of vitriol, and in mercury, and melted metals, and any other such like, that are fluid enough to retain for some time the motion impressed upon them by the agitation of the vessel, and which being poured out are easily resolved into drops, I doubt not that the rule already laid down may be accurate enough, especially if the experiments be made with larger pendulous bodies and more swiftly moved.

Lastly, since it is the opinion of some that there is a certain ethereal medium extremely rare and subtile, which freely pervades the pores of all bodies; and from such a medium, so pervading the pores of bodies, some resistance must needs arise; in order to try whether the resistance, which we experience in bodies in motion, be made upon their outward surfaces only, or whether their internal parts meet with any considerable resistance upon their surfaces, I thought of the following experiment. I suspended a round deal box by a thread 11 feet long, on a steel hook, by means of a ring of the same metal, so as to make a pendulum of the aforesaid length. The hook had a sharp hollow edge on its upper part, so that the upper arc of the ring pressing on the edge might move the more freely; and the thread was fastened to the lower arc of the ring. The pendulum being thus prepared, I drew it aside from the perpendicular to the distance of about 6 feet, and that in a plane perpendicular to the edge of the hook, lest the ring, while the pendulum oscillated, should slide to and fro on the edge of the hook; for the point of suspension, in which the ring touches the hook, ought to remain immovable. I therefore accurately noted the place to which the pendulum was brought, and letting it go, I marked three other places, to which it returned at the end of the 1st, 2d, and 3d oscillation. This I often repeated, that I might find those places as accurately as possible. Then I filled the box with lead and other heavy metals that were near at hand. But first, I weighed the box when empty, and that part of the thread that went round it, and half the remaining part, extended between the hook and the suspended box; for the thread so extended always acts upon the pendulum, when drawn aside from the perpendicular, with half its weight. To this weight I added the weight of the air contained in the box. And this whole weight was about $\frac{1}{78}$ of the weight of the box when filled with the metals. Then because the box when full of the metals, by extending the thread with its weight, increased the length of the pendulum, I shortened the thread so as to make the length of the pendulum, when oscillating, the same as before. Then drawing aside the pendulum to the place first marked, and letting it go, I reckoned about 77 oscillations before the box returned to the second mark, and as many afterwards before it came to the third mark, and as many after that before it came to the fourth mark. From this I conclude that the whole resistance of the box, when full, had not a greater proportion to the resistance of the box, when empty, than 78 to 77. For if their resistances were equal, the box, when full, by reason of its inertia, which was 78 times greater than the inertia of the same when empty, ought to have continued its oscillating motion so much the longer, and therefore to have returned to those marks at the end of 78 oscillations. But it returned to them at the end of 77 oscillations.

Let, therefore, A represent the resistance of the box upon its external surface, and B the resistance of the empty box on its internal surface, and if the resistances to the internal parts of bodies equally swift be as the matter, or the number of particles that are resisted, then 78B will be the resistance made to the internal parts of the box, when full; and therefore the whole resistance A+B of the empty box will be to the whole resistance A+78B of the full box as 77 to 78, and, by subtraction, A+B to 77B as 77 to 1; and thence A+B to

B as 77·77 to 1, and, by subtraction, again, A to B as 5928 to 1. Therefore the resistance of the empty box in its internal parts will be above 5000 times less than the resistance on its external surface. This reasoning depends upon the supposition that the greater resistance of the full box arises not from any other latent cause, but only from the action of some subtile fluid upon the included metal.

This experiment is related by memory, the paper being lost in which I had described it; so that I have been obliged to omit some fractional parts, which are slipped out of my memory; and I have no leisure to try it again. The first time I made it, the hook being weak, the full box was retarded sooner. The cause I found to be, that the hook was not strong enough to bear the weight of the box; so that, as it oscillated to and fro, the hook was bent sometimes this and sometimes that way. I therefore procured a hook of sufficient strength, so that the point of suspension might remain unmoved, and then all things happened as is above described.

SECTION VII

The motion of fluids, and the resistance made to projected bodies

Proposition 32. Theorem 26

Suppose two similar systems of bodies consisting of an equal number of particles, and let the correspondent particles be similar and proportional, each in one system to each in the other, and have a like situation among themselves, and the same given ratio of density to each other; and let them begin to move among themselves in proportional times, and with like motions (that is, those in one system among one another, and those in the other among one another). And if the particles that are in the same system do not touch one another, except in the moments of reflection; nor attract, nor repel each other, except with accelerative forces that are inversely as the diameters of the correspondent particles, and directly as the squares of the velocities: I say, that the particles of those systems will continue to move among themselves with like motions and in proportional times.

Like bodies in like situations are said to be moved among themselves with like motions and in proportional times, when their situations at the end of those times are always found alike in respect of each other; as suppose we compare the particles in one system with the correspondent particles in the other. Hence the times will be proportional, in which similar and proportional parts of similar figures will be described by correspondent particles. Therefore if we suppose two systems of this kind, the correspondent particles, by reason of the similitude of the motions at their beginning, will continue to be moved with like motions, so long as they move without meeting one another; for if they are acted on by no forces, they will go on uniformly in right lines, by the first Law. But if they agitate one another with some certain forces, and those forces are inversely as the diameters of the correspondent particles and directly as the squares of the velocities, then, because the particles are in like situations, and their forces are proportional, the whole forces with which correspondent particles are agitated, and which are compounded of each of the agitating forces (by Cor. II of the Laws), will have like directions, and have the same effect as if they respected centres places alike among the particles; and those whole forces will be to each other as the several forces which compose them, that is, inversely as the diameters of the correspondent particles and directly as the squares of the velocities: and therefore will cause correspondent particles to continue to describe like figures. These things will be so (by Cor. I and VIII, Prop. 4, Book I), if those centres are at rest; but if they are moved, yet, by reason of the similitude of the translations, their situations among the particles of the system will remain similar, so that the changes introduced into the figures described by the particles will still be similar. So that the motions of correspondent and similar particles will continue similar till their first meeting with each other; and thence will arise similar collisions, and similar reflections; which will again beget similar motions of the particles among themselves (by what was just now shown), till they mutually fall upon one another again, and so on *ad infinitum*.   Q.E.D.

COR. I. Hence if any two bodies, which are similar and in like situations to the correspondent particles of the systems, begin to move amongst them in like manner and in proportional times, and their magnitudes and densities be to each other as the magnitudes and densities of the corresponding particles, these bodies will continue to be moved in like manner and in proportional times; for the case of the greater parts of both systems and of the particles is the very same.

COR. II. And if all the similar and similarly situated parts of both systems be at rest among themselves; and two of them, which are greater than the rest, and mutually correspondent in both systems, begin to move in lines alike posited, with any similar motion whatsoever, they will excite similar motions in the rest of the parts of the systems, and will continue to move among those parts in like manner and in proportional times; and will therefore describe spaces proportional to their diameters.

PROPOSITION 33. THEOREM 27

The same things being supposed, I say, that the greater parts of the systems are resisted in a ratio compounded of the squared ratio of their velocities, and the squared ratio of their diameters, and the simple ratio of the density of the parts of the systems.

For the resistance arises partly from the centripetal or centrifugal forces with which the particles of the system act on each other, partly from the collisions and reflections of the particles and the greater parts. The resistances of the first kind are to each other as the whole motive forces from which they arise, that is, as the whole accelerative forces and the quantities of matter in corresponding parts; that is (by the supposition), directly as the squares of the velocities and inversely as the distances of the corresponding particles, and directly as the quantities of matter in the correspondent parts: and therefore since the distances of the particles in one system are to the correspondent distances of the particles in the other, as the diameter of one particle or part in the former system to the diameter of the correspondent particle or part in the other, and since the quantities of matter are as the densities of the parts and the cubes of the diameters, the resistances are to each other as the squares of the velocities and the squares of the diameters and the densities of the parts of the systems. Q.E.D. The resistances of the latter sort are as the number of correspondent reflections and the forces of those reflections conjointly; but the number of the reflections are to each other directly as the velocities of the corresponding parts and inversely as the spaces between their reflections. And the forces of the reflections are as the velocities and the magnitudes and the densities of the corresponding parts conjointly; that is, as the velocities and the cubes of the diameters and the densities of the parts. And, joining all these ratios, the resistances of the corresponding parts are to each other as the squares of the velocities and the squares of the diameters and the densities of the parts conjointly.

Q.E.D.

COR. I. Therefore if those systems are two elastic fluids, like our air, and their parts are at rest among themselves; and two similar bodies proportional in magnitude and density to the parts of the fluids, and similarly situated among those parts, be in any manner projected in the direction of lines similarly posited; and the accelerative forces with which the particles of the fluids act upon each other are inversely as the diameters of the bodies projected and directly as the squares of their velocities; those bodies will excite similar motions in the fluids in proportional times, and will describe similar spaces and proportional to their diameters.

COR. II. Therefore in the same fluid a projected body that moves swiftly meets with a resistance that is as the square of its velocity, nearly. For if the forces with which distant particles act upon one another should be augmented as the square of the velocity, the projected body would be resisted in the same squared ratio accurately; and therefore in a medium, whose parts when at a distance do not act with any force on one another, the resistance is as the square of the velocity, accurately. Let there be, therefore, three mediums A, B, C, consisting of similar and equal parts regularly disposed at equal distances. Let the parts of the mediums A and B recede from each other with forces that are among themselves as T and V; and let the parts of the medium C be entirely destitute of any such forces. And if four equal bodies D, E, F, G move in these mediums, the two first D and E in the two first A and B, and the other two F and G in the third C; and if the velocity of the body D be to the velocity of the body E, and the velocity of the body F to the velocity of the body G, as the square root of the ratio of the force T to the force V; then the resistance of the body D to the resistance of the body E, and the resistance of the body F to the resistance of the body G, will be as the square of the velocities; and therefore the resistance of the body D will be to the resistance of the body F as the resistance of the body E to the resistance of the body G. Let the bodies D and F be equally swift, as also the bodies E and G; and, augmenting the velocities of the bodies D and F in any ratio, and diminishing the forces of the particles of the medium B as the square of the same ratio, the medium B will approach to the form and condition of the medium C at pleasure; and therefore the resistances of the equal and equally swift bodies E and G in these mediums will continually approach to equality, so that their difference will at last become less than any given. Therefore since the resistances of the bodies D and F are to each other as the resistances of the bodies E and G, those will also in like manner approach to the ratio of equality. Therefore the bodies D and F, when they move with very great swiftness, meet with resistances very nearly equal; and therefore since the resistance of the body F is in a squared ratio of the velocity, the resistance of the body D will be nearly in the same ratio.

Cor. III. Hence the resistance of a body moving very swiftly in an elastic fluid is almost the same as if the parts of the fluid were destitute of their centrifugal forces, and did not fly from each other; provided only that the elasticity of the fluid arise from the centrifugal forces of the particles, and the velocity be so great as not to allow the particles time enough to act.

Cor. IV. Since the resistances of similar and equally swift bodies, in a medium whose distant parts do not fly from each other, are as the squares of the diameters, therefore the resistances made to bodies moving with very great and equal velocities in an elastic fluid will be as the squares of the diameters, nearly.

Cor. V. And since similar, equal, and equally swift bodies, moving through mediums of the same density, whose particles do not fly from each other, will strike against an equal quantity of matter in equal times, whether the particles of which the medium consists be more and smaller, or fewer and greater, and therefore impress on that matter an equal quantity of motion, and in return (by the third Law of Motion) suffer an equal reaction from the same, that is, are equally resisted; it is manifest, also, that in elastic fluids of the same density, when the bodies move with extreme swiftness, their resistances are nearly equal, whether the fluids consist of gross parts, or of parts ever so subtile. For the resistance of projectiles moving with exceedingly great celerities is not much diminished by the subtilty of the medium.

Cor. VI. All these things are so in fluids whose elastic force takes its rise from the centrifugal forces of the particles. But if that force arise from some other cause, as from the expansion of the particles after the manner of wool, or the boughs of trees, or any other cause, by which the particles are hindered from moving freely among themselves, the resistance, by reason of the lesser fluidity of the medium, will be greater than in the Corollaries above.

PROPOSITION 34. THEOREM 28

If in a rare medium, consisting of equal particles freely disposed at equal distances from each other, a globe and a cylinder described on equal diameters move with equal velocities in the direction of the axis of the cylinder, the resistance of the globe will be but half as great as that of the cylinder.

For since the action of the medium upon the body is the same (by Cor. V of the Laws) whether the body move in a quiescent medium, or whether the particles of the medium impinge with the same velocity upon the quiescent body, let us consider the body as if it were quiescent, and see with what force it would be impelled by the moving medium. Let, therefore, ABKI represent a spherical body described from the centre C with the semidiameter CA, and let the particles of the medium impinge with a given velocity upon that spherical body in the directions of right lines parallel to AC; and let FB be one of those right lines. In FB take LB equal to the semidiameter CB, and draw BD touching the sphere in B. Upon KC and BD let fall the

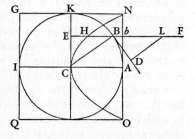

perpendiculars BE, LD; and the force with which a particle of the medium, impinging on the globe obliquely in the direction FB, would strike the globe in B, will be to the force with which the same particle, meeting the cylinder ONGQ described about the globe with the axis ACI, would strike it perpendicularly in *b*, as LD is to LB, or BE to BC. Again; the efficacy of this force to move the globe, according to the direction of its incidence FB or AC, is to the efficacy of the same to move the globe, according to the direction of its determination, that is, in the direction of the right line BC in which it impels the globe directly, as BE to BC. And, joining these ratios, the efficacy of a particle, falling upon the globe obliquely in the direction of the right line FB, to move the globe in the direction of its incidence, is to the efficacy of the same particle falling in the same line perpendicularly on the cylinder, to move it in the same direction, as BE^2 to BC^2. Therefore if in *b*E, which is perpendicular to the circular base of the cylinder NAO, and equal to the radius AC, we take *b*H equal to $\dfrac{BE^2}{CB}$;

then *b*H will be to *b*E as the effect of the particle upon the globe to the effect of the particle upon the cylinder. And therefore the solid which is formed by all the right lines *b*H will be to the solid formed by all the right lines *b*E as the effect of all the particles upon the globe to the effect of all the particles upon the cylinder. But the former of these solids is a paraboloid whose vertex is C, its axis CA, and latus rectum CA, and the latter solid is a cylinder circumscribing the paraboloid; and it is known that a paraboloid is half its circumscribed cylinder. Therefore the whole force of the medium upon the globe is half the entire force of the same upon the cylinder. And therefore if the particles of the medium are at rest, and the cylinder and globe move with equal velocities, the resistance of the globe will be half the resistance of the cylinder.   Q.E.D.

Scholium

By the same method other figures may be compared together as to their resistance; and those may be found which are most apt to continue their mo-

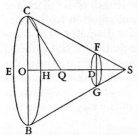

tions in resisting mediums. As if upon the circular base CEBH from the centre O, with the radius OC, and the altitude OD, one would construct a frustum CBGF of a cone, which should meet with less resistance than any other frustum constructed with the same base and altitude, and going forwards towards D in the direction of its axis: bisect the altitude OD in Q, and produce OQ to S, so that QS may be equal to QC, and S will be the vertex of the cone whose frustum is sought.

Incidentally, since the angle CSB is always acute, it follows from the above that, if the solid ADBE be generated by the convolution of an elliptical or oval figure ADBE about its axis AB, and the generating figure be touched by three right lines FG, GH, HI, in the points F, B, and I, so that GH shall be perpendicular to the axis in the point of contact B, and FG, HI may be inclined to GH

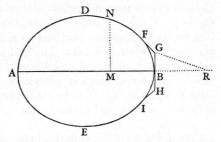

in the angles FGB, BHI of 135 degrees: the solid arising from the convolution of the figure ADFGHIE about the same axis AB will be less resisted than the former solid, provided that both move forwards in the direction of their axis AB, and that the extremity B of each go foremost. This Proposition I conceive may be of use in the building of ships.

If the figure DNFG be such a curve, that if, from any point thereof, as N, the perpendicular NM be let fall on the axis AB, and from the given point G there be drawn the right line GR parallel to a right line touching the figure in N, and cutting the axis produced in R, MN becomes to GR as GR^3 to $4BR \cdot GB^2$, the solid described by the revolution of this figure about its axis AB, moving in the before-mentioned rare medium from A towards B, will be less resisted than any other circular solid whatsoever, described of the same length and breadth.

PROPOSITION 35. PROBLEM 7

If a rare medium consist of very small quiescent particles of equal magnitudes, and freely disposed at equal distances from one another: to find the resistance of a globe moving uniformly forwards in this medium.

CASE 1. Let a cylinder described with the same diameter and altitude be conceived to go forwards with the same velocity in the direction of its axis through the same medium; and let us suppose that the particles of the medium, on which the globe or cylinder falls, fly back with as great a force of reflection as possible. Then since the resistance of the globe (by the last Proposition) is but half the resistance of the cylinder, and since the globe is to the cylinder as 2 to 3, and since the cylinder by falling perpendicularly on the particles, and reflecting them with the utmost force, communicates to them a velocity double to its own: it follows that the cylinder in moving forwards uniformly half the length of its axis, will communicate a motion to the particles which is to the whole motion of the cylinder as the density of the medium to the density of the cylinder; and that the globe, in the time it describes one length of its diameter in moving uniformly forwards, will communicate the same motion to the particles; and, in the time that it describes two-thirds of its diameter, will communicate a motion to the particles which is to the whole motion of the globe as the density of the medium to the density of the globe. And therefore the globe meets with a resistance, which is to the force by which its whole motion may be either taken away or generated in the time in which it describes two-thirds of its diameter moving uniformly forwards, as the density of the medium is to the density of the globe.

CASE 2. Let us suppose that the particles of the medium incident on the globe or cylinder are not reflected; and then the cylinder falling perpendicularly on the particles will communicate its own simple velocity to them, and therefore meets a resistance but half so great as in the former case, and the globe also meets with a resistance but half so great.

CASE 3. Let us suppose the particles of the medium to fly back from the globe with a force which is neither the greatest, nor yet none at all, but with a certain mean force; then the resistance of the globe will be in the same mean ratio between the resistance in the first case and the resistance in the second.

Q.E.I.

COR. I. Hence if the globe and the particles are infinitely hard, and destitute of all elastic force, and therefore of all force of reflection, the resistance of the globe will be to the force by which its whole motion may be destroyed or generated, in the time that the globe describes four third parts of its diameter, as the density of the medium is to the density of the globe.

COR. II. The resistance of the globe, other things being equal, varies as the square of the velocity.

COR. III. The resistance of the globe, other things being equal, varies as the square of the diameter.

COR. IV. The resistance of the globe, other things being equal, varies as the density of the medium.

COR. V. The resistance of the globe varies jointly as the square of the velocity, as the square of the diameter, and as the density of the medium.

COR. VI. The motion of the globe and its resistance may be thus represented. Let AB be the time in which the globe may, by its resistance uniformly continued, lose its whole motion. Erect AD, BC perpendicular to AB. Let BC be that whole motion, and through the point C, the asymptotes being AD, AB,

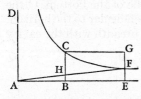

describe the hyperbola CF. Produce AB to any point E. Erect the perpendicular EF meeting the hyperbola in F. Complete the parallelogram CBEG, and draw AF meeting BC in H. Then if the globe in any time BE, with its first motion BC uniformly continued, describes in a nonresisting medium the space CBEG represented by the area of the parallelogram, the same in a resisting medium will describe the space CBEF, represented by the area of the hyperbola; and its motion at the end of that time will be represented by EF, the ordinate of the hyperbola, there being lost of its motion the part FG. And its resistance at the end of the same time will be represented by the length BH, there being lost of its resistance the part CH. All these things appear by Cor. I and III, Prop. 5, Book II.

COR. VII. Hence if the globe in the time T by the resistance R uniformly continued to lose its whole motion M, the same globe in the time t in a resisting medium, wherein the resistance R decreases as the square of the velocity, will lose out of its motion M the part $\dfrac{tM}{T+t}$, the part $\dfrac{TM}{T+t}$ remaining; and will describe a space which is to the space described in the same time t, with the uniform motion M, as the logarithm of the number $\dfrac{T+t}{T}$ multiplied by the number 2.302585092994 is to the number $\dfrac{t}{T}$, because the hyperbolic area BCFE is to the rectangle BCGE in that proportion.

SCHOLIUM

I have exhibited in this Proposition the resistance and retardation of spherical projectiles in mediums that are not continued, and shown that this resistance is to the force by which the whole motion of the globe may be destroyed or produced in the time in which the globe can describe two-thirds of its diameter, with a velocity uniformly continued, as the density of the medium is to the density of the globe, provided the globe and the particles of the medium be perfectly elastic, and are endued with the utmost force of reflection; and that this force, where the globe and particles of the medium are infinitely hard and void of any reflecting force, is diminished one-half. But in continued mediums, as water, hot oil, and quicksilver, the globe as it passes through them does not immediately strike against all the particles of the fluid that generate the resistance made to it, but presses only the particles that lie next to it, which press the particles beyond, which press other particles, and so on; and in these mediums the resistance is diminished one other half. A globe in these extremely fluid mediums meets with a resistance that is to the force by which its whole motion may be destroyed or generated in the time wherein it can describe, with that motion uniformly continued, eight third parts of its diameter, as the density of the medium is to the density of the globe. This I shall endeavor to show in what follows.

PROPOSITION 36. PROBLEM 8

To find the motion of water running out of a cylindrical vessel through a hole made at the bottom.

Let ACDB be a cylindrical vessel, AB the mouth of it, CD the bottom parallel to the horizon, EF a circular hole in the middle of the bottom, G the centre of the hole, and GH the axis of the cylinder perpendicular to the horizon. And suppose a cylinder of ice APQB to be of the same breadth with the cavity

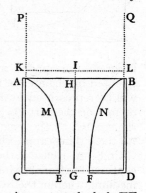

of the vessel, and to have the same axis, and to descend continually with an uniform motion, and that its parts, as soon as they touch the surface AB, dissolve into water, and flow down by their weight into the vessel, and in their fall compose the cataract or column of water ABNFEM, passing through the hole EF, and filling up the same exactly. Let the uniform velocity of the descending ice and of the contiguous water in the circle AB be that which the water would acquire by falling through the space IH; and let IH and HG lie in the same right line; and through the point I let there be drawn the right line KL parallel to the horizon, and meeting the ice on both the sides thereof in K and L. Then the velocity of the water running out at the hole EF will be the same that it would acquire by falling from I through the space IG. Therefore, by Galileo's Theorems, IG will be to IH as the square of the velocity of the water that runs out at the hole to the velocity of the water in the circle AB, that is, as the square of the ratio of the circle AB to the circle EF; those circles being inversely as the velocities of the water which in the same time and in equal quantities passes through each of them, and completely fills them both. We are now considering the velocity with which the water tends to the plane of the horizon. But the motion parallel to the same, by which the parts of the falling water approach to each other, is not here taken notice of; since it is neither produced by gravity, nor at all changes the motion perpendicular to the horizon which the gravity produces. We suppose, indeed, that the parts of the water cohere a little, that by their cohesion they may in falling approach to each other with motions parallel to the horizon in order to form one single cataract, and to prevent their being divided into several; but the motion parallel to the horizon arising from this cohesion does not come under our present consideration.

CASE 1. Conceive now the whole cavity in the vessel, which surrounds the falling water ABNFEM, to be full of ice, so that the water may pass through the ice as through a funnel. Then if the water pass very near to the ice only, without touching it; or, which is the same thing, if by reason of the perfect smoothness of the surface of the ice, the water, though touching it, glides over it with the utmost freedom, and without the least resistance; the water will run through the hole EF with the same velocity as before, and the whole weight of the column of water ABNFEM will be taken up as before in forcing out the water, and the bottom of the vessel will sustain the weight of the ice surrounding that column.

Let now the ice in the vessel dissolve into water; but the efflux of the water will remain, as to its velocity, the same as before. It will not be less, because the ice now dissolved will endeavor to descend; it will not be greater, because the ice, now become water, cannot descend without hindering the descent of other water equal to its own descent. The same force ought always to generate the same velocity in the effluent water.

But the hole at the bottom of the vessel, by reason of the oblique motions of the particles of the effluent water, must be a little greater than before. For now the particles of the water do not all of them pass through the hole perpendicularly, but, flowing down on all parts from the sides of the vessel, and converging towards the hole, pass through it with oblique motions; and in tending downwards they meet in a stream whose diameter is a little smaller below the hole than at the hole itself; its diameter being to the diameter of the hole as 5 to 6, or as $5\frac{1}{2}$ to $6\frac{1}{2}$, very nearly, if I measured those diameters rightly. I procured a thin flat plate, having a hole pierced in the middle, the diameter of the circular hole being five eighth parts of an inch. And that the stream of running water might not be accelerated in falling, and by that acceleration become narrower, I fixed this plate not to the bottom, but to the side of the vessel, so as to make the water go out in the direction of a line parallel to the horizon. Then, when the vessel was full of water, I opened the hole to let it run out; and the diameter of the stream, measured with great accuracy at the distance of about half an inch from the hole, was $^{21}\!/_{40}$ of an inch. Therefore the diameter of this circular hole was to the diameter of the stream very nearly as 25 to 21. So that the water in passing through the hole converges on all sides, and, after it has run out of the vessel, becomes smaller by converging in that manner, and by becoming smaller is accelerated till it comes to the distance of half an inch from the hole, and at that distance flows in a smaller stream and with greater celerity than in the hole itself, and this in the ratio of $25 \cdot 25$ to $21 \cdot 21$, or 17 to 12, very nearly; that is, in about the ratio of $\sqrt{2}$ to 1. Now it is certain from experiments, that the quantity of water running out in a given time through a circular hole made in the bottom of a vessel is equal to the quantity, which, flowing freely with the aforesaid velocity, would run out in the same time through another circular hole, whose diameter is to the diameter of the former as 21 to 25. And therefore this running water in passing through the hole itself has a velocity downwards nearly equal to that which a heavy body would acquire in falling through half the height of the stagnant water in the vessel. But then, after it has run out, it is still accelerated by converging, till it arrives at a distance from the hole that is nearly equal to its diameter, and acquires a velocity greater than the other in about the ratio of $\sqrt{2}$ to 1; this velocity a heavy body would nearly acquire by falling freely through the whole height of the stagnant water in the vessel.

Therefore in what follows let the diameter of the stream be represented by that lesser hole which we shall call EF. And imagine another plane VW above the hole EF, and parallel to the plane thereof, to be placed at a distance equal to the diameter of the same hole, and to be pierced through with a greater hole ST, of such a magnitude that a stream which will exactly fill the lower hole EF may pass through it; the diameter of this hole will therefore be to the diameter of the lower hole nearly as 25 to 21. By this means the water will run perpendicularly out at the lower hole; and the quantity of the water running out will be, according to the magnitude of this last hole, very nearly the same as that which the solution of the Problem requires. The space included between the two planes and the falling stream may be considered as the bottom of the vessel.

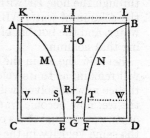

But to make the solution more simple and mathematical, it is better to take the lower plane alone for the bottom of the vessel, and to suppose that the water which flowed through the ice as through a funnel, and ran out of the vessel through the hole EF made in the lower plane, preserves its motion continually, and that the ice continues at rest. Therefore in what follows let ST be the diameter of a circular hole described from the centre Z, and let the stream run out of the vessel through that hole, when the water in the vessel is all fluid. And let EF be the diameter of the hole, which the stream, in falling through, exactly fills up, whether the water runs out of the vessel by that upper hole ST, or flows through the middle of the ice in the vessel, as through a funnel. And let the diameter of the upper hole ST be to the diameter of the lower EF as about 25 to 21, and let the perpendicular distance between the planes of the holes be equal to the diameter of the lesser hole EF. Then the velocity of the water downwards, in running out of the vessel through the hole ST, will be in that hole the same that a body may acquire by falling freely from half the height IZ; and the velocity of both the falling streams will be in the hole EF, the same which a body would acquire by falling freely from the whole height IG.

CASE 2. If the hole EF be not in the middle of the bottom of the vessel, but in some other part thereof, the water will still run out with the same velocity as before, if the magnitude of the hole be the same. For though a heavy body takes a longer time in descending to the same depth, by an oblique line, than by a perpendicular line, yet in both cases it acquires in its descent the same velocity; as Galileo hath demonstrated.

CASE 3. The velocity of the water is the same when it runs out through a hole in the side of the vessel. For if the hole be small, so that the interval between the surfaces AB and KL may vanish as to sense, and the stream of water horizontally issuing out may form a parabolic figure; from the latus rectum of this parabola one may see, that the velocity of the effluent water is that which a body may acquire by falling the height IG or HG of the stagnant water in the vessel. For, by making an experiment, I found that if the height of the stagnant water above the hole were 20 inches, and the height of the hole above a plane parallel to the horizon were also 20 inches, a stream of water springing out from thence would fall upon the plane, at the distance of very nearly 37 inches, from a perpendicular let fall upon that plane from the hole. For without resistance the stream would have fallen upon the plane at the distance of 40 inches, the latus rectum of the parabolic stream being 80 inches.

CASE 4. If the effluent water tend upwards, it will still issue forth with the same velocity. For the small stream of water springing upwards, ascends with a perpendicular motion to GH or GI, the height of the stagnant water in the vessel; except so far as its ascent is hindered a little by the resistance of the air; and therefore it springs out with the same velocity that it would acquire in falling from that height. Every particle of the stagnant water is equally pressed on all sides (by Prop. 19, Book II), and, yielding to the pressure, tends always with an equal force, whether it descends through the hole in the bottom of the vessel, or gushes out in an horizontal direction through a hole in the side, or passes into a canal, and springs up from thence through a little hole made in the upper part of the canal. And it may not only be inferred from reasoning, but is manifest also from the well-known experiments just mentioned, that the velocity with which the water runs out is the very same that is assigned in this Proposition.

CASE 5. The velocity of the effluent water is the same, whether the figure of the hole be circular, or square, or triangular, or of any other figure whatever equal to the circular; for the velocity of the effluent water does not depend upon the figure of the hole, but arises from such depth of the hole as it may have below the plane KL.

CASE 6. If the lower part of the vessel ABDC be immersed into stagnant water, and the height of the stagnant water above the bottom of the vessel be

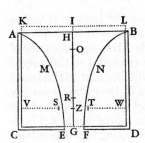

GR, the velocity with which the water that is in the vessel will run out at the hole EF into the stagnant water will be the same which the water would acquire by falling from the height IR; for the weight of all the water in the vessel that is below the surface of the stagnant water will be sustained in equilibrium by the weight of the stagnant water, and therefore does not at all accelerate the motion of the descending water in the vessel. This case will also become evident from experiments, measuring the times in which the water will run out.

COR. I. Hence if CA, the depth of the water, be produced to K, so that AK may be to CK as the square of the ratio of the area of a hole made in any part of the bottom to the area of the circle AB, the velocity of the effluent water will be equal to the velocity which the water would acquire by falling freely from the height KC.

COR. II. And the force with which the whole motion of the effluent water may be generated is equal to the weight of a cylindric column of water, whose base is the hole EF, and its altitude 2GI or 2CK. For the effluent water, in the time it becomes equal to this column, may acquire, by falling by its own weight from the height GI, a velocity equal to that with which it runs out.

COR. III. The weight of all the water in the vessel ABDC is to that part of the weight which is employed in forcing out the water as the sum of the circles AB and EF is to twice the circle EF. For let IO be a mean proportional between IH and IG, and the water running out at the hole EF will, in the time that a drop falling from I would describe the altitude IG, become equal to a cylinder whose base is the circle EF and its altitude 2IG, that is, to a cylinder whose base is the circle AB, and whose altitude is 2IO. For the circle EF is to the circle AB as the square root of the ratio of the altitude IH to the altitude IG; that is, in the simple ratio of the mean proportional IO to the altitude IG. Moreover, in the time that a drop falling from I can describe the altitude IH, the water that runs out will have become equal to a cylinder whose base is the circle AB, and its altitude 2IH; and in the time that a drop falling from I through H to G describes HG, the difference of the altitudes, the effluent water, that is, the water contained within the solid ABNFEM, will be equal to the difference of the cylinders, that is, to a cylinder whose base is AB, and its altitude 2HO. And therefore all the water contained in the vessel ABDC is to the whole falling water contained in the said solid ABNFEM as HG is to 2HO, that is, as HO+OG to 2HO, or IH+IO to 2IH. But the weight of all the water in the solid ABNFEM is employed in forcing out the water; and therefore the weight of all the water in the vessel is to that part of the weight that is employed in forcing out the water as IH+IO is to 2IH, and therefore as the sum of the circles EF and AB is to twice the circle EF.

Cor. iv. And hence the weight of all the water in the vessel ABDC is to the other part of the weight which is sustained by the bottom of the vessel as the sum of the circles AB and EF is to the difference of the same circles.

Cor. v. And that part of the weight which the bottom of the vessel sustains is to the other part of the weight employed in forcing out the water as the difference of the circles AB and EF is to twice the lesser circle EF, or as the area of the bottom to twice the hole.

Cor. vi. That part of the weight which presses upon the bottom is to the whole weight of the water perpendicularly incumbent thereon as the circle AB is to the sum of the circles AB and EF, or as the circle AB is to the excess of twice the circle AB above the area of the bottom. For that part of the weight which presses upon the bottom is to the weight of the whole water in the vessel as the difference of the circles AB and EF is to the sum of the same circles (by Cor. iv); and the weight of the whole water in the vessel is to the weight of the whole water perpendicularly incumbent on the bottom as the circle AB is to the difference of the circles AB and EF. Therefore, multiplying together corresponding terms of the two proportions, that part of the weight which presses upon the bottom is to the weight of the whole water perpendicularly incumbent thereon as the circle AB to the sum of the circles AB and EF, or the excess of twice the circle AB above the bottom.

Cor. vii. If in the middle of the hole EF there be placed the little circle PQ described about the centre G, and parallel to the horizon, the weight of water which that little circle sustains is greater than the weight of a third part of a cylinder of water whose base is that little circle and its height GH. For let ABNFEM be the cataract or column of falling water whose axis is GH, as above, and let all the water, whose fluidity is not requisite for the ready and quick descent of the water, be supposed to be congealed, as well round about the cataract, as above the little circle. And let PHQ be the column of water congealed above

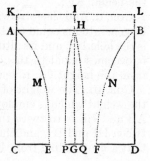

the little circle, whose vertex is H, and its altitude GH. And suppose this cataract to fall with its whole weight downwards, and not in the least to lie against or to press PHQ, but to glide freely by it without any friction, unless, perhaps, just at the very vertex of the ice, where the cataract at the beginning of its fall may tend to a concave figure. And as the congealed water AMEC, BNFD, lying round the cataract, is convex in its internal surfaces AME, BNF towards the falling cataract, so this column PHQ will be convex towards the cataract also, and will therefore be greater than a cone whose base is that little circle PQ and its altitude GH; that is, greater than a third part of a cylinder described with the same base and altitude. Now that little circle sustains the weight of this column, that is, a weight greater than the weight of the cone, or a third part of the cylinder.

COR. VIII. The weight of water which the circle PQ, when very small, sustains, seems to be less than the weight of two-thirds of a cylinder of water whose base is that little circle, and its altitude HG. For, things standing as above supposed, imagine the half of a spheroid described whose base is that little circle, and its semiaxis or altitude HG. This figure will be equal to two-thirds of that cylinder, and will comprehend within it the column of congealed water PHQ, the weight of which is sustained by that little circle. For though the motion of the water tends directly downwards, the external surfaces of that column must yet meet the base PQ in an angle somewhat acute, because the water in its fall is continually accelerated, and by reason of that acceleration becomes narrower. Therefore, since that angle is less than a right one, this column in the lower parts thereof will lie within the hemispheroid. In the upper parts also it will be acute or pointed; because to make it otherwise, the horizontal motion of the water must be at the vertex infinitely more swift than its motion towards the horizon. And the less this circle PQ is, the more acute will the vertex of this column be; and the circle being diminished *in infinitum*, the angle PHQ will be diminished *in infinitum*, and therefore the column will lie within the hemispheroid. Therefore that column is less than that hemispheroid, or than two third parts of the cylinder whose base is that little circle, and its altitude GH. Now the little circle sustains a force of water equal to the weight of this column, the weight of the ambient water being employed in causing its efflux out at the hole.

COR. IX. The weight of water which the little circle PQ sustains, when it is very small, is very nearly equal to the weight of a cylinder of water whose base is that little circle, and its altitude $\frac{1}{2}$GH; for this weight is an arithmetical mean between the weights of the cone and the hemispheroid above mentioned. But if that little circle be not very small, but on the contrary increased till it be equal to the hole EF, it will sustain the weight of all the water lying perpendicularly above it, that is, the weight of a cylinder of water whose base is that little circle, and its altitude GH.

COR. X. And (as far as I can judge) the weight which this little circle sustains is always to the weight of a cylinder of water whose base is that little circle, and its altitude $\frac{1}{2}$GH, as EF^2 is to $EF^2 - \frac{1}{2}PQ^2$, or as the circle EF is to the excess of this circle above half the little circle PQ, very nearly.

Lemma 4

If a cylinder moves uniformly forwards in the direction of its length, the resistance made thereto is not at all changed by augmenting or diminishing that length; and is therefore the same with the resistance of a circle, described with the same diameter, and moving forwards with the same velocity in the direction of a right line perpendicular to its plane.

For the sides are not at all opposed to the motion; and a cylinder becomes a circle when its length is diminished *in infinitum.*

Proposition 37. Theorem 29

If a cylinder moves uniformly forwards in a compressed, infinite, and nonelastic fluid, in the direction of its length, the resistance arising from the magnitude of its transverse section is to the force by which its whole motion may be destroyed or generated, in the time that it moves four times its length, as the density of the medium is to the density of the cylinder, nearly.

For let the vessel ABDC touch the surface of stagnant water with its bottom CD, and let the water run out of this vessel into the stagnant water through the cylindric canal EFTS perpendicular to the horizon; and let the little circle PQ be placed parallel to the horizon anywhere in the middle of the canal; and produce CA to K, so that AK may be to CK as the square of the ratio, which the excess of the orifice of the canal EF above the little circle PQ bears to the circle AB. Then it is manifest (by Case 5, Case 6, and Cor. i, Prop. 36) that the velocity of the water passing through the annular space between the little circle and the sides of the vessel will be the very same as that which the water would acquire by falling, and in its fall describing the altitude KC or IG.

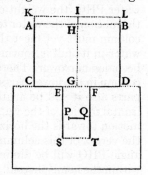

And (by Cor. x, Prop. 36) if the breadth of the vessel be infinite, so that the short line HI may vanish, and the altitudes IG, HG become equal; the force of the water that flows down and presses upon the circle will be to the weight of a cylinder whose base is that little circle, and the altitude ½IG, as EF² is to EF² − ½PQ², very nearly. For the force of the water flowing downwards uniformly through the whole canal will be the same upon the little circle PQ in whatsoever part of the canal it be placed.

Let now the orifices of the canal EF, ST be closed, and let the little circle ascend in the fluid compressed on every side, and by its ascent let it oblige the water that lies above it to descend through the annular space between the little circle and the sides of the canal. Then will the velocity of the ascending little circle be to the velocity of the descending water as the difference of the circles EF and PQ is to the circle PQ; and the velocity of the ascending little circle will be to the sum of the velocities, that is, to the relative velocity of the descending water with which it passes by the little circle in its ascent, as the difference of the circles EF and PQ is to the circle EF, or as EF² − PQ² to EF². Let that relative velocity be equal to the velocity with which it was shown above that the water would pass through the annular space, if the circle were to remain unmoved, that is, to the velocity which the water would acquire by falling, and in its fall describing the altitude IG; and the force of the water upon the ascending circle will be the same as before (by Cor. v of the Laws of Motion); that is, the resistance of the ascending little circle will be to the weight of a cylinder of water whose base is that little circle, and its altitude $\frac{1}{2}$IG, as EF^2 is to $EF^2 - \frac{1}{2}PQ^2$, nearly. But the velocity of the little circle will be to the velocity which the water acquires by falling, and in its fall describing the altitude IG, as $EF^2 - PQ^2$ is to EF^2.

Let the breadth of the canal be increased *in infinitum;* and the ratios between $EF^2 - PQ^2$ and EF^2, and between EF^2 and $EF^2 - \frac{1}{2}PQ^2$, will become at last ratios of equality. And therefore the velocity of the little circle will now be the same as that which the water would acquire in falling, and in its fall describing the altitude IG; and the resistance will become equal to the weight of a cylinder whose base is that little circle, and its altitude half the altitude IG, from which the cylinder must fall to acquire the velocity of the ascending circle; and with this velocity the cylinder in the time of its fall will describe four times its length. But the resistance of the cylinder moving forwards with this velocity in the direction of its length is the same with the resistance of the little circle (by Lem. 4), and is therefore nearly equal to the force by which its motion may be generated while it describes four times its length.

If the length of the cylinder be augmented or diminished, its motion, and the time in which it describes four times its length, will be augmented or diminished in the same ratio, and therefore the force by which the motion, so increased or diminished, may be destroyed or generated, will continue the same; because the time is increased or diminished in the same proportion; and therefore that force remains still equal to the resistance of the cylinder, because (by Lem. 4) that resistance will also remain the same.

If the density of the cylinder be augmented or diminished, its motion, and the force by which its motion may be generated or destroyed in the same time, will be augmented or diminished in the same ratio. Therefore the resistance of any cylinder whatsoever will be to the force by which its whole motion may be generated or destroyed, in the time during which it moves four times its length, as the density of the medium is to the density of the cylinder, nearly.   Q.E.D.

A fluid must be compressed to become continued; it must be continued and nonelastic, that all the pressure arising from its compression may be propagated in an instant; and so, acting equally upon all parts of the body moved, may produce no change of the resistance. The pressure arising from the motion of the body is spent in generating a motion in the parts of the fluid, and this creates the resistance. But the pressure arising from the compression of the fluid, be it ever so forcible, if it be propagated in an instant, generates no motion in the parts of a continued fluid, produces no change at all of motion therein; and therefore neither augments nor lessens the resistance. This is certain, that the action of the fluid arising from the compression cannot be stronger on the hinder parts of the body moved than on its fore parts, and therefore cannot lessen the resistance described in this Proposition. And if its propagation be infinitely swifter than the motion of the body pressed, it will not be stronger on the fore parts than on the hinder parts. But that action will be infinitely swifter, and propagated in an instant, if the fluid be continued and nonelastic.

COR. I. The resistances, made to cylinders going uniformly forwards in the direction of their lengths through continued infinite mediums, are in a ratio compounded of the square of the ratio of the velocities and the square of the ratio of the diameters, and the ratio of the density of the mediums.

Cor. ii. If the breadth of the canal be not infinitely increased, but the cylinder go forwards in the direction of its length through an included quiescent medium, its axis all the while coinciding with the axis of the canal, its resistance

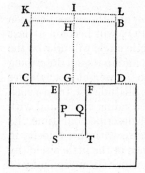

will be to the force by which its whole motion, in the time in which it describes four times its length, may be generated or destroyed, in a ratio compounded of the ratio of EF^2 to $EF^2 - \frac{1}{2}PQ^2$, and the square of the ratio of EF^2 to $EF^2 - PQ^2$, and the ratio of the density of the medium to the density of the cylinder.

Cor. iii. The same thing supposed, and that a length L is to four times the length of the cylinder in a ratio compounded of the ratio $EF^2 - \frac{1}{2}PQ^2$ to EF^2, and the square of the ratio of $EF^2 - PQ^2$ to EF^2: the resistance of the cylinder will be to the force by which its whole motion, in the time during which it describes the length L, may be destroyed or generated, as the density of the medium is to the density of the cylinder.

<h2 style="text-align:center">Scholium</h2>

In this Proposition we have investigated that resistance alone which arises from the magnitude of the transverse section of the cylinder, neglecting that part of the same which may arise from the obliquity of the motions. For as, in Case 1 of Prop. 36, the obliquity of the motions with which the parts of the water in the vessel converged on every side to the hole EF hindered the efflux of the water through the hole, so, in this Proposition, the obliquity of the motions, with which the parts of the water, pressed by the antecedent extremity of the cylinder, yield to the pressure, and diverge on all sides, retards their passage through the places that lie round that antecedent extremity, towards the hinder parts of the cylinder, and causes the fluid to be moved to a greater distance; which increases the resistance, and that in the same ratio almost in which it diminished the efflux of the water out of the vessel, that is, in the squared ratio of 25 to 21, nearly. And as, in Case 1 of that Proposition, we made the parts of the water pass through the hole EF perpendicularly and in the greatest plenty, by supposing all the water in the vessel lying round the cataract to be frozen, and that part of the water whose motion was oblique and useless to remain without motion, so in this Proposition, that the obliquity of the motions may be taken away, and the parts of the water may give the freest passage to the cylinder, by yielding to it with the most direct and quick motion possible, so that only so much resistance may remain as arises from the magnitude of the transverse section, and as is incapable of diminution, unless by diminishing the diameter of the cylinder; we must conceive those parts of the fluid whose motions are oblique and useless, and produce resistance, to be at rest among themselves at both extremities of the cylinder, and there to cohere, and be joined to the cylinder. Let ABCD be a rectangle, and let AE and BE be two parabolic arcs, described with the axis AB, and with a latus rectum that is to the space HG, which must be described by the cylinder in falling, in order to acquire the velocity with which it moves, as HG to ½AB. Let CF and DF be two other parabolic arcs described with the axis CD, and a latus rectum four times the former; and by the revolution of the figure about the axis EF let there be generated a solid, whose middle part ABDC is the cylinder we are here speaking of, and whose extreme parts ABE and CDF contain the parts of the fluid at rest among themselves, and concreted into two hard bodies, adhering to the cylinder at each end like a head and tail. Then if this solid EACFDB move in the direction of the length of its axis FE towards the parts beyond E, the resistance will be nearly the same as that which we have here determined in this Proposition; that is, it will have the same ratio to the force with which the whole motion of the cylinder may be destroyed or generated, in the time that it is describing the length 4AC with that motion uniformly continued, as the density of the fluid has to the density of the cylinder, nearly. And (by Cor. vii, Prop. 36) the resistance must be to this force in the ratio of 2 to 3, at the least.

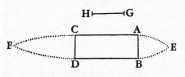

Lemma 5

If a cylinder, a sphere, and a spheroid, of equal breadths be placed successively in the middle of a cylindric canal, so that their axes may coincide with the axis of the canal, these bodies will equally hinder the passage of the water through the canal.

For the spaces lying between the sides of the canal, and the cylinder, sphere, and spheroid, through which the water passes, are equal; and the water will pass equally through equal spaces.

This is true, upon the supposition that all the water above the cylinder, sphere, or spheroid, whose fluidity is not necessary to make the passage of the water the quickest possible, is congealed, as was explained above in Cor. vii, Prop. 36.

Lemma 6

The same supposition remaining, the fore-mentioned bodies are equally acted on by the water flowing through the canal.

This appears by Lem. 5 and the third Law. For the water and the bodies act upon each other mutually and equally.

Lemma 7

If the water be at rest in the canal, and these bodies move with equal velocity and in opposite directions through the canal, their resistances will be equal among themselves.

This appears from the last Lemma, for the relative motions remain the same among themselves.

Scholium

The case is the same for all convex and round bodies, whose axes coincide with the axis of the canal. Some difference may arise from a greater or less friction; but in these Lemmas we suppose the bodies to be perfectly smooth, and the medium to be void of all tenacity and friction; and that those parts of the fluid which by their oblique and superfluous motions may disturb, hinder, and retard the flux of the water through the canal, are at rest among themselves; being fixed like water by frost, and adhering to the force and hinder parts of the bodies in the manner explained in the Scholium of the last Proposition; for in what follows we consider the very least resistance that round bodies described with the greatest given transverse sections can possibly meet with.

Bodies swimming upon fluids, when they move straight forwards, cause the fluid to ascend at their fore parts and subside at their hinder parts, especially if they are of an obtuse figure; and hence they meet with a little more resistance than if they were acute at the head and tail. And bodies moving in elastic fluids, if they are obtuse behind and before, condense the fluid a little more at their fore parts, and relax the same at their hinder parts; and therefore meet also with a little more resistance than if they were acute at the head and tail. But in these Lemmas and Propositions we are not treating of elastic but nonelastic fluids; not of bodies floating on the surface of the fluid, but deeply immersed therein. And when the resistance of bodies in nonelastic fluids is once known, we may then augment this resistance a little in elastic fluids, as our air; and in the surfaces of stagnating fluids, as lakes and seas.

Proposition 38. Theorem 30

If a globe move uniformly forwards in a compressed, infinite, and nonelastic fluid, its resistance is to the force by which its whole motion may be destroyed or generated, in the time that it describes eight third parts of its diameter, as the density of the fluid is to the density of the globe, very nearly.

For the globe is to its circumscribed cylinder as 2 to 3; and therefore the force which can destroy all the motion of the cylinder, while the same cylinder is describing the length of four of its diameters, will destroy all the motion of the globe, while the globe is describing two-thirds of this length, that is, eight third parts of its own diameter. Now the resistance of the cylinder is to this force very nearly as the density of the fluid is to the density of the cylinder or globe (by Prop. 37), and the resistance of the globe is equal to the resistance of the cylinder (by Lems. 5, 6, 7).   q.e.d.

Cor. i. The resistances of globes in infinite compressed mediums are in a ratio compounded of the squared ratio of the velocity, and the squared ratio of the diameter, and the ratio of the density of the mediums.

Cor. ii. The greatest velocity, with which a globe can descend by its comparative weight through a resisting fluid, is the same as that which it may acquire by falling with the same weight, and without any resistance, and in its fall describing a space that is to four third parts of its diameter as the density of the globe is to the density of the fluid. For the globe in the time of its fall, moving with the velocity acquired in falling, will describe a space that will be to eight third parts of its diameter as the density of the globe is to the density of the fluid; and the force of its weight which generates this motion will be to the force that can generate the same motion, in the time that the globe describes eight third parts of its diameter, with the same velocity as the density of the fluid is to the density of the globe; and therefore (by this Proposition) the force of weight will be equal to the force of resistance, and therefore cannot accelerate the globe.

Cor. iii. If there be given both the density of the globe and its velocity at the beginning of the motion, and the density of the compressed quiescent fluid in which the globe moves, there is given at any time both the velocity of the globe and its resistance, and the space described by it (by Cor. VII, Prop. 35).

COR. IV. A globe moving in a compressed quiescent fluid of the same density with itself will lose half its motion before it can describe the length of two of its diameters (by the same Cor. VII).

PROPOSITION 39. THEOREM 31

If a globe move uniformly forwards through a fluid inclosed and compressed in a cylindric canal, its resistance is to the force by which its whole motion may be generated or destroyed, in the time in which it describes eight third parts of its diameter, in a ratio compounded of the ratio of the orifice of the canal to the excess of that orifice above half the greatest circle of the globe; and the squared ratio of the orifice of the canal to the excess of that orifice above the greatest circle of the globe; and the ratio of the density of the fluid to the density of the globe, nearly.

This appears by Cor. II, Prop. 37, and the demonstration proceeds in the same manner as in the foregoing Proposition.

SCHOLIUM

In the last two Propositions we suppose (as was done before in Lem. 5) that all the water which precedes the globe, and whose fluidity increases the resistance of the same, is congealed. Now if that water becomes fluid, it will somewhat increase the resistance. But in these Propositions that increase is so small, that it may be neglected, because the convex surface of the globe produces the very same effect almost as the congelation of the water.

PROPOSITION 40. PROBLEM 9

To find by experiment the resistance of a globe moving through a perfectly fluid compressed medium.

Let A be the weight of the globe in a vacuum, B its weight in the resisting medium, D the diameter of the globe, F a space which is to $\frac{4}{3}$D as the density of the globe is to the density of the medium, that is, as A is to A−B, G the time in which the globe falling with the weight B without resistance describes the space F, and H the velocity which the body acquires by that fall. Then H will be the greatest velocity with which the globe can possibly descend with the weight B in the resisting medium, by Cor. II, Prop. 38; and the resistance which the globe meets with, when descending with that velocity, will be equal to its weight B; and the resistance it meets with in any other velocity will be to the weight B as the square of the ratio of that velocity to the greatest velocity H, by Cor. I, Prop. 38.

This is the resistance that arises from the inactivity of the matter of the fluid. That resistance which arises from the elasticity, tenacity, and friction of its parts, may be thus investigated.

Let the globe be let fall so that it may descend in the fluid by the weight B; and let P be the time of falling, and let that time be expressed in seconds, if the time G be given in seconds. Find the absolute number N agreeing to the logarithm 0.4342944819 $\frac{2P}{G}$, and let L be the logarithm of the number $\frac{N+1}{N}$; and the velocity acquired in falling will be $\frac{N-1}{N+1}H$, and the height described will be $\frac{2PF}{G} - 1.3862943611F + 4.605170186LF$. If the fluid be of a sufficient depth, we may neglect the term $4.605170186LF$; and $\frac{2PF}{G} - 1.3862943611F$ will be the altitude described, nearly. These things appear by Prop. 9, Book II, and its Corollaries, and are true upon this supposition, that the globe meets with no other resistance but that which arises from the inactivity of matter. Now if it really meet with any resistance of another kind, the descent will be slower, and from the amount of that retardation will be known the amount of this new resistance.

That the velocity and descent of a body falling in a fluid might more easily be known, I have composed the following table, the first column of which

The Times P	Velocities of the body falling in the fluid	The spaces described in falling in the fluid	The spaces described with the greatest motion	The spaces described by falling in a vacuum
0.001G	$99999^{29}/_{30}$	0.000001F	0.002F	0.000001F
0.01G	999967	0.0001F	0.02F	0.0001F
0.1G	9966799	0.0099834F	0.2F	0.01F
0.2G	19737532	0.0397361F	0.4F	0.04F
0.3G	29131261	0.0886815F	0.6F	0.09F
0.4G	37994896	0.1559070F	0.8F	0.16F
0.5G	46211716	0.2402290F	1.0F	0.25F
0.6G	53704957	0.3402706F	1.2F	0.36F
0.7G	60436778	0.4545405F	1.4F	0.49F
0.8G	66403677	0.5815071F	1.6F	0.64F
0.9G	71629787	0.7196609F	1.8F	0.81F
1G	76159416	0.8675617F	2F	1F
2G	96402758	2.6500055F	4F	4F
3G	99505475	4.6186570F	6F	9F
4G	99932930	6.6143765F	8F	16F
5G	99990920	8.6137964F	10F	25F
6G	99998771	10.6137179F	12F	36F
7G	99999834	12.6137073F	14F	49F
8G	99999980	14.6137059F	16F	64F
9G	99999997	16.6137057F	18F	81F
10G	$99999999^{3}/_{5}$	18.6137056F	20F	100F

denotes the times of descent; the second shows the velocities acquired in falling, the greatest velocity being 100,000,000; the third exhibits the spaces described by falling in those times, 2F being the space which the body describes in the time G with the greatest velocity; and the fourth gives the spaces described with the greatest velocity in the same times. The numbers in the fourth column are $\frac{2P}{G}$, and by subtracting the number $1.3862944 - 4.6051702L$, are found the numbers in the third column; and these numbers must be multiplied by the space F to obtain the spaces described in falling. A fifth column is added to all these, containing the spaces described in the same times by a body falling in a vacuum with the force of B its comparative weight.

SCHOLIUM

In order to investigate the resistances of fluids from experiments, I procured a square wooden vessel, whose length and breadth on the inside was 9 inches English measure, and its depth $9\frac{1}{2}$ feet; this I filled with rain water; and having provided globes made up of wax, and lead included therein, I noted the times of the descents of these globes, the height through which they descended being 112 inches. A solid cubic foot of English measure contains 76 pounds troy weight of rain water; and a solid inch contains $\frac{19}{36}$ ounces troy weight, or $253\frac{1}{3}$ grains; and a globe of water of one inch in diameter contains 132.645 grains in air, or 132.8 grains in a vacuum; and any other globe will be as the excess of its weight in a vacuum above its weight in water.

EXPER. 1. A globe whose weight was $156\frac{1}{4}$ grains in air, and 77 grains in water, described the whole height of 112 inches in 4 seconds. And, upon repeating the experiment, the globe spent again the very same time of 4 seconds in falling.

The weight of this globe in a vacuum is $156\frac{13}{38}$ grains; and the excess of this weight above the weight of the globe in water is $79\frac{13}{38}$ grains. Hence the diameter of the globe appears to be 0.84224 parts of an inch. Then it will be, as that excess to the weight of the globe in a vacuum, so is the density of the water to the density of the globe; and so is $\frac{8}{3}$ parts of the diameter of the globe (viz., 2.24597 inches) to the space 2F, which will be therefore 4.4256 inches. Now a globe falling in a vacuum with its whole weight of $156\frac{13}{38}$ grains in one second of time will describe $193\frac{1}{3}$ inches; and falling in water in the same time with the weight of 77 grains without resistance, will describe 95.219 inches; and in the time G, which is to one second of time as the square root of the ratio of the space F, or of 2.2128 inches to 95.219 inches, will describe 2.2128 inches, and will acquire the greatest velocity H with which it is capable of descending in water. Therefore the time G is 0.15244 seconds. And in this time G, with that greatest velocity H, the globe will describe the space 2F, which is 4.4256 inches; and therefore in 4 seconds will describe a space of 116.1245 inches. Subtract the space $1.3862944 \cdot F$, or 3.0676 inches, and there will remain a space of 113.0569 inches, which the globe falling through water in a very wide vessel will describe in 4 seconds. But this space, by reason of the narrowness of the wooden vessel before mentioned, ought to be diminished in a ratio compounded of the square root of the ratio of the orifice of the vessel to the excess of this orifice above half a great circle of the globe, and of the simple ratio of the same orifice to its excess above a great circle of the globe, that is, in a ratio of 1 to 0.9914. This done, we have a space of 112.08 inches, which a globe falling through the water in this wooden vessel in 4 seconds of time ought nearly to describe by this theory; but it described 112 inches by the experiment.

EXPER. 2. Three equal globes, whose weights were severally $76\frac{1}{3}$ grains in air, and $5\frac{1}{16}$ grains in water, were let fall successively; and every one fell through the water in 15 seconds of time, describing in its fall a height of 112 inches.

By computation, the weight of each globe in a vacuum is $76\frac{5}{12}$ grains; the excess of this weight above the weight in water is $71\frac{17}{48}$ grains; the diameter of the globe 0.81296 of an inch; $\frac{8}{3}$ parts of this diameter 2.16789 inches; the space 2F is 2.3217 inches; the space which a globe of $5\frac{1}{16}$ grains in weight would describe in one second without resistance, 12.808 inches, and the time G

0.301056 seconds. Therefore the globe, with the greatest velocity it is capable of receiving from a weight of $5\frac{1}{16}$ grains in its descent through water, will describe in the time 0.301056 seconds the space 2.3217 inches; and in 15 seconds the space 115.678 inches. Subtract the space 1.3862944F, or 1.609 inches, and there remains the space 114.069 inches; which therefore the falling globe ought to describe in the same time, if the vessel were very wide. But because our vessel was narrow, the space ought to be diminished by about 0.895 of an inch. And so the space will remain 113.174 inches, which a globe falling in this vessel ought nearly to describe in 15 seconds. But by the experiment it described 112 inches. The difference is not sensible.

EXPER. 3. Three equal globes, whose weights were severally 121 grains in air, and 1 grain in water, were successively let fall; and they fell through the water in the times 46 seconds, 47 seconds, and 50 seconds, describing a height of 112 inches.

By the theory, these globes ought to have fallen in about 40 seconds. Now whether their falling more slowly were occasioned from the consideration that in slow motions the resistance arising from the force of inactivity does really bear a less proportion to the resistance arising from other causes; or whether it is to be attributed to little bubbles that might chance to stick to the globes, or to the rarefaction of the wax by the warmth of the weather, or of the hand that let them fall; or, lastly, whether it proceeded from some insensible errors in weighing the globes in the water, I am not certain. Therefore the weight of the globe in water should be of several grains, that the experiment may be certain, and to be depended on.

EXPER. 4. I began the foregoing Experiments to investigate the resistances of fluids, before I was acquainted with the theory laid down in the Propositions immediately preceding. Afterwards, in order to examine the theory after it was discovered, I procured a wooden vessel, whose breadth on the inside was $8\frac{2}{3}$ inches, and its depth $15\frac{1}{3}$ feet. Then I made four globes of wax, with lead included, each of which weighed $139\frac{1}{4}$ grains in air, and $7\frac{1}{8}$ grains in water. These I let fall, measuring the times of their falling in the water with a pendulum oscillating to half-seconds. The globes were cold, and had remained so some time, both when they were weighed and when they were let fall; because warmth rarefies the wax, and by rarefying it diminishes the weight of the globe in the water; and wax, when rarefied, is not instantly reduced by cold to its former density. Before they were let fall, they were totally immersed under water, lest, by the weight of any part of them that might chance to be above the water, their descent should be accelerated in its beginning. Then, when after their immersion they were perfectly at rest, they were let go with the greatest care, that they might not receive any impulse from the hand that let them down. And they fell successively in the times of $47\frac{1}{2}$, $48\frac{1}{2}$, 50, and 51 oscillations, describing a height of 15 feet and 2 inches. But the weather was now a little colder than when the globes were weighed, and therefore I repeated the experiment another day; and then the globes fell in the times of 49, $49\frac{1}{2}$, 50, and 53; and at a third trial in the times of $49\frac{1}{2}$, 50, 51, and 53 oscillations. And by making the experiment several times over, I found that the globes fell mostly in the times of $49\frac{1}{2}$ and 50 oscillations. When they fell slower, I suspect them to have been retarded by striking against the sides of the vessel.

Now, computing from the theory, the weight of the globe in a vacuum is $139\frac{2}{5}$ grains; the excess of this weight above the weight of the globe in water $132\frac{11}{40}$ grains; the diameter of the globe 0.99868 of an inch; $\frac{8}{3}$ parts of the diameter 2.66315 inches; the space 2F 2.8066 inches; the space which a globe weighing $7\frac{1}{8}$ grains falling without resistance describes in a second of time 9.88164 inches; and the time G 0.376843 seconds. Therefore the globe with the greatest velocity with which it is capable of descending through the water by the force of a weight of $7\frac{1}{8}$ grains, will in the time 0.376843 seconds describe a space of 2.8066 inches, and in one second of time a space of 7.44766 inches, and in the time 25 seconds, or in 50 oscillations, the space 186.1915 inches. Subtract the space 1.386294F, or 1.9454 inches, and there will remain the space 184.2461 inches which the globe will describe in that time in a very wide vessel. Because our vessel was narrow, let this space be diminished in a ratio compounded of the square root of the ratio of the orifice of the vessel to the excess of this orifice above half a great circle of the globe, and of the simple ratio of the same orifice to its excess above a great circle of the globe; and we shall have the space of 181.86 inches, which the globe ought by the theory to describe in this vessel in the time of 50 oscillations, nearly. But it described the space of 182 inches, by experiment, in $49\frac{1}{2}$ or 50 oscillations.

Exper. 5. Four globes weighing $154\frac{3}{8}$ grains in air, and $21\frac{1}{2}$ grains in water, being let fall several times, fell in the times of $28\frac{1}{2}$, 29, $29\frac{1}{2}$, and 30, and sometimes of 31, 32, and 33 oscillations, describing a height of 15 feet and 2 inches.

They ought by the theory to have fallen in the time of 29 oscillations, nearly.

Exper. 6. Five globes, weighing $212\frac{3}{8}$ grains in air, and $79\frac{1}{2}$ in water, being several times let fall, fell in the times of 15, $15\frac{1}{2}$, 16, 17, and 18 oscillations, describing a height of 15 feet and 2 inches.

By the theory they ought to have fallen in the time of 15 oscillations, nearly.

Exper. 7. Four globes, weighing $293\frac{3}{8}$ grains in air, and $35\frac{7}{8}$ grains in water, being let fall several times, fell in the times of $29\frac{1}{2}$, 30, $30\frac{1}{2}$, 31, 32, and 33 oscillations, describing a height of 15 feet and $1\frac{1}{2}$ inches.

By the theory they ought to have fallen in the time of 28 oscillations, nearly.

In searching for the cause that occasioned these globes of the same weight and magnitude to fall, some swifter and some slower, I hit upon this: that the globes, when they were first let go and began to fall, oscillated about their centres; that side which chanced to be the heavier descending first, and producing an oscillating motion. Now by oscillating thus, the globe communicates a greater motion to the water than if it descended without any oscillations; and by this communication loses part of its own motion with which it should descend; and therefore as this oscillation is greater or less, it will be more or less retarded. Besides, the globe always recedes from that side of itself which is descending in the oscillation, and by so receding comes nearer to the sides of the vessel, so as even to strike against them sometimes. And the heavier the globes are, the stronger this oscillation is; and the greater they are, the more is the water agitated by it. Therefore to diminish this oscillation of the globes, I made new ones of lead and wax, sticking the lead in one side of the globe very near its surface; and I let fall the globe in such a manner, that, as near as possible, the heavier side might be lowest at the beginning of the descent. By this means the oscillations became much less than before, and the times in which the globes fell were not so unequal: as in the following Experiments.

EXPER. 8. Four globes weighing 139 grains in air, and $6\frac{1}{2}$ in water, were let fall several times, and fell mostly in the time of 51 oscillations, never in more than 52, or in fewer than 50, describing a height of 182 inches.

By the theory they ought to fall in about the time of 52 oscillations.

EXPER. 9. Four globes weighing $273\frac{1}{4}$ grains in air, and $140\frac{3}{4}$ in water, being several times let fall, fell in never fewer than 12, and never more than 13 oscillations, describing a height of 182 inches.

These globes by the theory ought to have fallen in the time of $11\frac{1}{3}$ oscillations, nearly.

EXPER. 10. Four globes, weighing 384 grains in air, and $119\frac{1}{2}$ in water, being let fall several times, fell in the times of $17\frac{3}{4}$, 18, $18\frac{1}{2}$, and 19 oscillations, describing a height of $181\frac{1}{2}$ inches. And when they fell in the time of 19 oscillations, I sometimes heard them hit against the sides of the vessel before they reached the bottom.

By the theory they ought to have fallen in the time of $15\frac{5}{9}$ oscillations, nearly.

EXPER. 11. Three equal globes, weighing 48 grains in air, and $3\frac{29}{32}$ in water, being several times let fall, fell in the times of $43\frac{1}{2}$, 44, $44\frac{1}{2}$, 45, and 46 oscillations, and mostly in 44 and 45, describing a height of $182\frac{1}{2}$ inches, nearly.

By the theory they ought to have fallen in the time of $46\frac{5}{9}$ oscillations, nearly.

EXPER. 12. Three equal globes, weighing 141 grains in air, and $4\frac{3}{8}$ in water, being let fall several times, fell in the times of 61, 62, 63, 64, and 65 oscillations, describing a space of 182 inches.

And by the theory they ought to have fallen in $64\frac{1}{2}$ oscillations, nearly.

From these Experiments it is manifest, that when the globes fell slowly, as in the second, fourth, fifth, eighth, eleventh, and twelfth Experiments, the times of falling are rightly exhibited by the theory; but when the globes fell more swiftly, as in the sixth, ninth, and tenth Experiments, the resistance was somewhat greater than the square of the velocity. For the globes in falling oscillate a little; and this oscillation, in those globes that are light and fall slowly, soon ceases by the weakness of the motion; but in greater and heavier globes, the motion being strong, it continues longer, and is not to be checked by the ambient water till after several oscillations. Besides, the more swiftly the globes move, the less are they pressed by the fluid at their hinder parts; and if the velocity be continually increased, they will at last leave an empty space behind them, unless the compression of the fluid be increased at the same time. For the compression of the fluid ought to be increased (by Props. 32 and 33) as the square of the velocity, in order to maintain the resistance in the same squared ratio. But because this is not done, the globes that move swiftly are not so much pressed at their hinder parts as the others; and by the defect of this pressure it comes to pass that their resistance is a little greater than the square of their velocity.

So that the theory agrees with the experiments on bodies falling in water. It remains that we examine the observations of bodies falling in air.

EXPER. 13. From the top of St. Paul's Church in London, in June, 1710, there were let fall together two glass globes, one full of quicksilver, the other

of air; and in their fall they described a height of 220 English feet. A wooden
table was suspended upon iron hinges on one side, and the other side of the
table was supported by a wooden pin. The two globes lying upon this table
were let fall together by pulling out the pin by means of an iron wire reaching
thence down to the ground; so that, the pin being removed, the table, which
had then no support but the iron hinges, fell downwards, and turning round
upon the hinges, gave leave to the globes to drop off from it. At the same instant, with the same pull of the iron wire that took out the pin, a pendulum
oscillating to seconds was let go, and began to oscillate. The diameters and
weights of the globes, and their times of falling, are exhibited in the accom-
panying table.

The globes filled with mercury			The globes full of air		
Weights	*Diameters*	*Times in falling*	*Weights*	*Diameters*	*Times in falling*
grains	inches	seconds	grains	inches	seconds
908	0.8	4	510	5.1	$8\frac{1}{2}$
983	0.8	4−	642	5.2	8
866	0.8	4	599	5.1	8
747	0.75	4+	515	5.0	$8\frac{1}{4}$
808	0.75	4	483	5.0	$8\frac{1}{2}$
784	0.75	4+	641	5.2	8

But the times observed must be corrected; for the globes of mercury (by
Galileo's theory), in 4 seconds of time, will describe 257 English feet, and 220
feet in only 3 seconds 42 thirds. So that the wooden table, when the pin was
taken out, did not turn upon its hinges so quickly as it ought to have done;
and the slowness of that revolution hindered the descent of the globes at the
beginning. For the globes lay about the middle of the table, and indeed were
rather nearer to the axis upon which it turned than to the pin. And hence the
times of falling were prolonged about 18 thirds; and therefore ought to be
corrected by subtracting that excess, especially in the larger globes, which, by
reason of the largeness of their diameters, lay longer upon the revolving table
than the others. This being done, the times in which the six larger globes fell
will come forth 8 seconds 12 thirds, 7 seconds 42 thirds, 7 seconds 42 thirds,
7 seconds 57 thirds, 8 seconds 12 thirds, and 7 seconds 42 thirds.

Therefore the fifth in order among the globes that were full of air being 5
inches in diameter, and 483 grains in weight, fell in 8 seconds 12 thirds, describing a space of 220 feet. The weight of a bulk of water equal to this globe
is 16,600 grains; and the weight of an equal bulk of air is $\frac{16600}{860}$ grains, or $19\frac{3}{10}$
grains; and therefore the weight of the globe in a vacuum is $502\frac{3}{10}$ grains; and
this weight is to the weight of a bulk of air equal to the globe as $502\frac{3}{10}$ is to
$19\frac{3}{10}$; and so is 2F to $\frac{8}{3}$ of the diameter of the globe, that is, to $13\frac{1}{3}$ inches.
Hence 2F becomes 28 feet 11 inches. A globe, falling in a vacuum with its
whole weight of $502\frac{3}{10}$ grains, will in one second of time describe $193\frac{1}{3}$ inches
as above; and with the weight 483 grains will describe 185.905 inches; and with
that weight 483 grains in a vacuum will describe the space F, or 14 feet $5\frac{1}{2}$
inches, in the time of 57 thirds and 58 fourths, and acquire the greatest velocity it is capable of descending with in the air. With this velocity the globe in

8 seconds 12 thirds of time will describe 245 feet and $5\frac{1}{3}$ inches. Subtract
$1.3863 \cdot F$, or 20 feet and $\frac{1}{2}$ an inch, and there remain 225 feet 5 inches. This
space, therefore, the falling globe ought by the theory to describe in 8 seconds
12 thirds. But by the experiment it described a space of 220 feet. The difference is inappreciable.

By like calculations applied to the other globes full of air, I composed the
following table.

The weights of the globes	The diameters	The times of falling from a height of 220 feet		The spaces which they would describe by the theory		The excesses	
grains	inches	seconds	thirds	feet	inches	feet	inches
510	5.1	8	12	226	11	6	11
642	5.2	7	42	230	9	10	9
599	5.1	7	42	227	10	7	0
515	5	7	57	224	5	4	5
483	5	8	12	225	5	5	5
641	5.2	7	42	230	7	10	7

EXPER. 14. In the year 1719, in the month of July, Dr. Desaguliers made
some experiments of this kind again, by forming hogs' bladders into spherical
orbs; which was done by means of a concave wooden sphere, which the bladders, being wetted well first, were put into. After that, being blown full of air,
they were obliged to fill up the spherical cavity that contained them; and then,
when dry, were taken out. These were let fall from the lantern on the top of the
cupola of the same church, namely, from a height of 272 feet; and at the same
moment of time there was let fall a leaden globe, whose weight was about 2
pounds troy weight. And in the meantime some persons standing in the upper
part of the church where the globes were let fall observed the whole times of
falling; and others standing on the ground observed the differences of the
times between the fall of the leaden weight and the fall of the bladder. The
times were measured by pendulums oscillating to half-seconds. And one of
those that stood upon the ground had a machine vibrating four times in one
second; and another had another machine accurately made with a pendulum
vibrating four times in a second also. One of those also who stood at the top of
the church had a like machine; and these instruments were so contrived, that
their motions could be stopped or renewed at pleasure. Now the leaden globe
fell in about $4\frac{1}{4}$ seconds of time; and from the addition of this time to the
difference of time above spoken of, was obtained the whole time in which the
bladder was falling. The times which the five bladders spent in falling, after
the leaden globe had reached the ground, were, the first time, $14\frac{3}{4}$ seconds,
$12\frac{3}{4}$ seconds, $14\frac{5}{8}$ seconds, $17\frac{3}{4}$ seconds, and $16\frac{7}{8}$ seconds; and the second time,
$14\frac{1}{2}$ seconds, $14\frac{1}{4}$ seconds, 14 seconds, 19 seconds, and $16\frac{3}{4}$ seconds. Add to
these $4\frac{1}{4}$ seconds, the time in which the leaden globe was falling, and the
whole times in which the five bladders fell were, the first time, 19 seconds, 17
seconds, $18\frac{7}{8}$ seconds, 22 seconds, and $21\frac{1}{8}$ seconds; and the second time,
$18\frac{3}{4}$ seconds, $18\frac{1}{2}$ seconds, $18\frac{1}{4}$ seconds, $23\frac{1}{4}$ seconds, and 21 seconds. The
times observed at the top of the church were, the first time, $19\frac{3}{8}$ seconds, $17\frac{1}{4}$
seconds, $18\frac{3}{4}$ seconds, $22\frac{1}{8}$ seconds, and $21\frac{5}{8}$ seconds; and the second time,

19 seconds, 18⅝ seconds, 18⅜ seconds, 24 seconds, and 21¼ seconds. But the bladders did not always fall directly down, but sometimes fluttered a little in the air, and waved to and fro, as they were descending. And by these motions the times of their falling were prolonged, and increased by half a second sometimes, and sometimes by a whole second. The second and fourth bladders fell most directly the first time, and the first and third the second time. The fifth bladder was wrinkled, and by its wrinkles was a little retarded. I found their diameters by their circumferences measured with a very fine thread wound about them twice. In the following table I have compared the experiments with the theory; making the density of air to be to the density of rain water as 1 to 860, and computing the spaces which by the theory the globes ought to describe in falling.

The weights of the bladders	The diameters	The times of falling from a height of 272 feet	The spaces which by the theory ought to have been described in those times		The difference between the theory and the experiments	
grains	inches	seconds	feet	inches	feet	inches
128	5.28	19	271	11	− 0	1
156	5.19	17	272	0½	+ 0	0½
137½	5.3	18	272	7	+ 0	7
97½	5.26	22	277	4	+ 5	4
99⅛	5	21⅛	282	0	+10	0

Our theory, therefore, exhibits rightly, within a very little, all the resistance that globes moving either in air or in water meet with; which appears to be proportional to the densities of the fluids in globes of equal velocities and magnitudes.

In the Scholium subjoined to the sixth Section, we showed, by experiments of pendulums, that the resistances of equal and equally swift globes moving in air, water, and quicksilver, are as the densities of the fluids. We here prove the same more accurately by experiments of bodies falling in air and water. For pendulums at each oscillation excite a motion in the fluid always contrary to the motion of the pendulum in its return; and the resistance arising from this motion, as also the resistance of the thread by which the pendulum is suspended, makes the whole resistance of a pendulum greater than the resistance deduced from the experiments of falling bodies. For by the experiments of pendulums described in that Scholium, a globe of the same density as water in describing the length of its semidiameter in air would lose the $\frac{1}{3342}$ part of its motion. But by the theory delivered in this seventh Section, and confirmed by experiments of falling bodies, the same globe in describing the same length would lose only a part of its motion equal to $\frac{1}{4586}$, supposing the density of water to be to the density of air as 860 to 1. Therefore the resistances were found greater by the experiments of pendulums (for the reasons just mentioned) than by the experiments of falling globes; and that in the ratio of about 4 to 3. But yet since the resistances of pendulums oscillating in air, water, and quicksilver, are alike increased by like causes, the proportion of the resistances in these mediums will be rightly enough exhibited by the experiments of pendulums, as well as by the experiments of falling bodies. And from all this it may be concluded, that the resistances of bodies, moving in any fluids whatsoever, though of the most extreme fluidity, are, other things being equal, as the densities of the fluids.

These things being thus established, we may now determine what part of its motion any globe projected in any fluid whatsoever would nearly lose in a given time. Let D be the diameter of the globe, and V its velocity at the beginning of its motion, and T the time in which a globe with the velocity V can describe in a vacuum a space that is to the space $\frac{8}{3}$D as the density of the globe to the density of the fluid; and the globe projected in that fluid will, in any other time t lose the part $\frac{tV}{T+t}$, the part $\frac{TV}{T+t}$ remaining; and will describe a space, which will be to that described in the same time in a vacuum with the uniform velocity V, as the logarithm of the number $\frac{T+t}{T}$ multiplied by the number 2.302585093 is to the number $\frac{t}{T}$ by Cor. VII, Prop. 35. In slow motions the resistance may be a little less, because the figure of a globe is more adapted to motion than the figure of a cylinder described with the same diameter. In swift motions the resistance may be a little greater, because the elasticity and compression of the fluid do not increase as the square of the velocity. But these little niceties I take no notice of.

And though air, water, quicksilver, and the like fluids, by the division of their parts *in infinitum*, should be subtilized, and become mediums infinitely fluid, nevertheless, the resistance they would make to projected globes would be the same. For the resistance considered in the preceding Propositions arises from the inactivity of the matter; and the inactivity of matter is essential to bodies, and always proportional to the quantity of matter. By the division of the parts of the fluid the resistance arising from the tenacity and friction of the parts may be indeed diminished; but the quantity of matter will not be at all diminished by this division; and if the quantity of matter be the same, its force of inactivity will be the same; and therefore the resistance here spoken of will be the same, as being always proportional to that force. To diminish this resistance, the quantity of matter in the spaces through which the bodies move must be diminished; and therefore the celestial spaces, through which the globes of the planets and comets are continually passing towards all parts, with the utmost freedom, and without the least sensible diminution of their motion, must be utterly void of any corporeal fluid, excepting, perhaps, some extremely rare vapors and the rays of light.

Projectiles excite a motion in fluids as they pass through them, and this motion arises from the excess of the pressure of the fluid at the fore parts of the projectile above the pressure of the same at the hinder parts; and cannot be less in mediums infinitely fluid than it is in air, water, and quicksilver, in proportion to the density of matter in each. Now this excess of pressure does, in proportion to its quantity, not only excite a motion in the fluid, but also acts upon the projectile so as to retard its motion; and therefore the resistance in every fluid is as the motion excited by the projectile in the fluid; and cannot be less in the most subtile ether in proportion to the density of that ether, than it is in air, water, and quicksilver, in proportion to the densities of those fluids.

SECTION VIII

The motion propagated through fluids

Proposition 41. Theorem 32

A pressure is not propagated through a fluid in rectilinear directions except where the particles of the fluid lie in a right line.

If the particles *a, b, c, d, e* lie in a right line, the pressure may be indeed directly propagated from *a* to *e*; but then the particle *e* will urge the obliquely posited particles *f* and *g* obliquely, and those particles *f* and *g* will not sustain
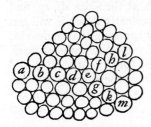
this pressure, unless they be supported by the particles *h* and *k* lying beyond them; but the particles that support them are also pressed by them; and those particles cannot sustain that pressure, without being supported by, and pressing upon, those particles that lie still farther, as *l* and *m*, and so on *in infinitum.* Therefore the pressure, as soon as it is propagated to particles that lie out of right lines, begins to deflect towards one hand and the other,
and will be propagated obliquely *in infinitum;* and after it has begun to be propagated obliquely, if it reaches more distant particles lying out of the right line, it will deflect again on each hand; and this it will do as often as it lights on particles that do not lie exactly in a right line.   Q.E.D.

Cor. If any part of a pressure, propagated through a fluid from a given point, be intercepted by any obstacle, the remaining part, which is not intercepted, will deflect into the spaces behind the obstacle. This may be demonstrated also after the following manner. Let a pressure be propagated from the point A towards any part, and, if it be possible, in rectilinear directions; and the obstacle NBCK being perforated in BC, let all the pressure be intercepted

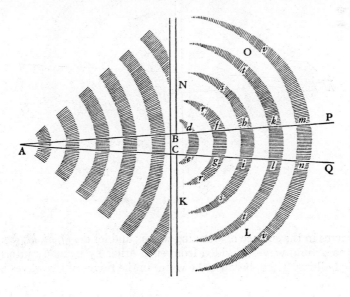

but the coniform part APQ passing through the circular hole BC. Let the cone APQ be divided into frustums by the transverse planes, *de, fg, hi*. Then while the cone ABC, propagating the pressure, urges the conic frustum *degf* beyond it on the surface *de*, and this frustum urges the next frustum *fgih* on the surface *fg*, and that frustum urges a third frustum, and so *in infinitum;* it is manifest (by the third Law) that the first frustum *defg* is, by the reaction of the second frustum *fghi*, as much urged and pressed on the surface *fg*, as it urges and presses that second frustum. Therefore the frustum *degf* is compressed on both sides, that is, between the cone A*de* and the frustum *fhig;* and therefore (by Case 6, Prop. 19) cannot preserve its figure, unless it be compressed with the same force on all sides. Therefore with the same force with which it is pressed on the surfaces *de, fg*, it will endeavor to break forth at the sides *df, eg;* and there (being not in the least tenacious or hard, but perfectly fluid) it will run out, expanding itself, unless there be an ambient fluid opposing that endeavor. Therefore, by the effort it makes to run out, it will press the ambient fluid, at its sides *df, eg*, with the same force that it does the frustum *fghi;* and therefore, the pressure will be propagated as much from the sides *df, eg*, into the spaces NO, KL this way and that way, as it is propagated from the surface *fg* towards PQ.   Q.E.D.

PROPOSITION 42. THEOREM 33

All motion propagated through a fluid diverges from a rectilinear progress into the unmoved spaces.

CASE 1. Let a motion be propagated from the point A through the hole BC, and, if it be possible, let it proceed in the conic space BCQP according to right lines diverging from the point A. And let us first suppose this motion to be

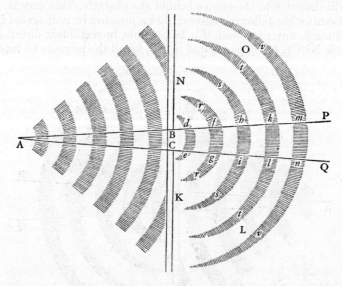

that of waves in the surface of standing water; and let *de, fg, hi, kl*, &c., be the tops of the several waves, divided from each other by as many intermediate valleys or hollows. Then, because the water in the ridges of the waves is higher than in the unmoved parts of the fluid KL, NO, it will run down from off the tops of those ridges, *e, g, i, l,* &c., *d, f, h, k,* &c., this way and that way towards KL and NO; and because the water is more depressed in the hollows of the waves than in the unmoved parts of the fluid KL, NO, it will run down into those hollows out of those unmoved parts. By the first deflux the ridges of the waves will dilate themselves this way and that way, and be propagated towards KL and NO. And because the motion of the waves from A towards PQ is carried on by a continual deflux from the ridges of the waves into the hollows next to them, and therefore cannot be swifter than in proportion to the celerity of the descent; and the descent of the water on each side towards KL and NO must be performed with the same velocity: it follows that the dilatation of the waves on each side towards KL and NO will be propagated with the same velocity as the waves themselves go forwards directly from A to PQ. And therefore the whole space this way and that way towards KL and NO will be filled by the dilated waves *rfgr, shis, tklt, vmnv,* &c. Q.E.D. That these things are so, anyone may find by making the experiment in still water.

CASE 2. Let us suppose that *de, fg, hi, kl, mn* represent pulses successively propagated from the point A through an elastic medium. Conceive the pulses to be propagated by successive condensations and rarefactions of the medium, so that the densest part of every pulse may occupy a spherical surface described about the centre A, and that equal intervals intervene between the successive pulses. Let the lines *de, fg, hi, kl,* &c., represent the densest parts of the pulses, propagated through the hole BC; and because the medium is denser there than in the spaces on either side towards KL and NO, it will dilate itself as well towards those spaces KL, NO, on each hand, as towards the rare intervals between the pulses; and hence the medium, becoming always more rare next the intervals, and more dense next the pulses, will partake of their motion. And because the progressive motion of the pulses arises from the continual relaxation of the denser parts towards the antecedent rare intervals; and since the pulses will relax themselves on each hand towards the quiescent parts of the medium KL, NO with very near the same celerity; therefore the pulses will dilate themselves on all sides into the unmoved parts KL, NO with almost the same celerity with which they are propagated directly from the centre A; and therefore will fill up the whole space KLON. Q.E.D. And we find the same by experience also in sounds which are heard through a mountain interposed; and, if they come into a chamber through the window, dilate themselves into all the parts of the room, and are heard in every corner; and not as reflected from the opposite walls, but directly propagated from the window, as far as our sense can judge.

CASE 3. Let us suppose, lastly, that a motion of any kind is propagated from A through the hole BC. Then since the cause of this propagation is that the parts of the medium that are near the centre A disturb and agitate those which lie farther from it; and since the parts which are urged are fluid, and therefore recede every way towards those spaces where they are less pressed: they will by consequence recede towards all the parts of the quiescent medium, as well to the parts on each hand, as KL and NO, as to those right before, as PQ; and by this means all the motion, as soon as it has passed through the hole BC, will begin to dilate itself, and from thence, as from its principle and centre, will be propagated directly every way. Q.E.D.

PROPOSITION 43. THEOREM 34

Every tremulous body in an elastic medium propagates the motion of the pulses on every side straight forwards; but in a nonelastic medium excites a circular motion.

CASE 1. The parts of the tremulous body, alternately going and returning, do in going urge and drive before them those parts of the medium that lie nearest, and by that impulse compress and condense them; and in returning suffer those compressed parts to recede again, and expand themselves. Therefore the parts of the medium that lie nearest to the tremulous body move to and fro by turns, in like manner as the parts of the tremulous body itself do; and for the same cause that the parts of this body agitate these parts of the medium, these parts, being agitated by like tremors, will in their turn agitate others next to themselves; and these others, agitated in like manner, will agitate those that lie beyond them, and so on *in infinitum.* And in the same manner as the first parts of the medium were condensed in going, and relaxed in returning, so will the other parts be condensed every time they go, and expand themselves every time they return. And therefore they will not be all going and all returning at the same instant (for in that case they would always maintain determined distances from each other, and there could be no alternate condensation and rarefaction); but since, in the places where they are condensed, they approach to, and, in the places where they are rarefied, recede from each other, therefore some of them will be going while others are returning; and so on *in infinitum.* The parts so going, and in their going condensed, are pulses, by reason of the progressive motion with which they strike obstacles in their way; and therefore the successive pulses produced by a tremulous body will be propagated in rectilinear directions; and that at nearly equal distances from each other, because of the equal intervals of time in which the body, by its several tremors, produces the several pulses. And though the parts of the tremulous body go and return in some certain and determinate direction, yet the pulses propagated from thence through the medium will dilate themselves towards the sides, by the foregoing Proposition; and will be propagated on all sides from that tremulous body, as from a common centre, in surfaces nearly spherical and concentric, as in waves excited by shaking a finger in water, which proceed not only forwards and backwards agreeably to the motion of the finger, but spread themselves in the manner of concentric circles all round the finger, and are propagated on every side. For the gravity of the water supplies the place of elastic force.

CASE 2. If the medium be not elastic, then, because its parts cannot be condensed by the pressure arising from the vibrating parts of the tremulous body, the motion will be propagated in an instant towards the parts where the medium yields most easily, that is, to the parts which the tremulous body would otherwise leave vacuous behind it. The case is the same with that of a body projected in any medium whatever. A medium yielding to projectiles does not recede *in infinitum,* but with a circular motion comes round to the spaces which the body leaves behind it. Therefore as often as a tremulous body tends to any part, the medium yielding to it comes round in a circle to the parts which the body leaves; and as often as the body returns to the first place, the medium will be driven from the place it came round to, and return to its original place. And though the tremulous body be not firm and hard, but every way flexible, yet if it continue of a given magnitude, since it cannot impel the medium by its tremors anywhere without yielding to it somewhere else, the medium receding from the parts of the body where it is pressed will always come round in a circle to the parts that yield to it.   Q.E.D.

COR. Hence it is a mistake to think that the agitation of the parts of flame conduces to the propagation of a pressure in rectilinear directions through an ambient medium. Such a pressure must be derived not from the agitation only of the parts of flame, but from the dilatation of the whole.

PROPOSITION 44. THEOREM 35

If water ascend and descend alternately in the erected legs KL, MN of a canal or pipe; and a pendulum be constructed whose length between the point of suspension and the centre of oscillation is equal to half the length of the water in the canal: I say, that the water will ascend and descend in the same times in which the pendulum oscillates.

I measure the length of the water along the axes of the canal and its legs, and make it equal to the sum of those axes; and take no notice of the resistance of the water arising from its attrition by the sides of the canal. Let, therefore, AB, CD represent the mean height of the water in both legs; and when the water in the leg KL ascends to the height EF, the water will descend in the

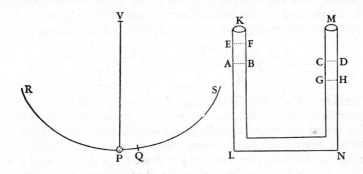

leg MN to the height GH. Let P be a pendulous body, VP the thread, V the point of suspension, RPQS the cycloid which the pendulum describes, P its lowest point, PQ an arc equal to the height AE. The force with which the motion of the water is accelerated and retarded alternately is the excess of the weight of the water in one leg above the weight in the other; and, therefore, when the water in the leg KL ascends to EF, and in the other leg descends to GH, that force is double the weight of the water EABF, and therefore is to the weight of the whole water as AE or PQ to VP or PR. The force also with which the body P is accelerated or retarded in any place, as Q, of a cycloid, is (by Cor., Prop. 51, Book I) to its whole weight as its distance PQ from the lowest place P to the length PR of the cycloid. Therefore the motive forces of the water and pendulum, describing the equal spaces AE, PQ, are as the weights to be moved; and therefore if the water and pendulum are quiescent at first, those forces will move them in equal times, and will cause them to go and return together with a reciprocal motion.   Q.E.D.

COR. I. Therefore the reciprocations of the water in ascending and descending are all performed in equal times, whether the motion be more or less intense or remiss.

COR. II. If the length of the whole water in the canal be of $6\frac{1}{9}$ feet of French measure, the water will descend in one second of time, and will ascend in another second, and so on by turns *in infinitum;* for a pendulum of $3\frac{1}{18}$ such feet in length will oscillate in one second of time.

COR. III. But if the length of the water be increased or diminished, the time of the reciprocation will be increased or diminished as the square root of the length.

PROPOSITION 45. THEOREM 36

The velocity of waves varies as the square root of the breadths.
This follows from the construction of the following Proposition.

PROPOSITION 46. PROBLEM 10

To find the velocity of waves.
Let a pendulum be constructed, whose length between the point of suspension and the centre of oscillation is equal to the breadth of the waves, and in the time that the pendulum will perform one single oscillation the waves will advance forwards nearly a space equal to their breadth.

That which I call the breadth of waves is the transverse measure lying between the deepest part of the hollows, or the tops of the ridges. Let ABCDEF represent the surface of stagnant water ascending and descending in successive

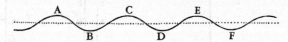

waves; and let A, C, E, &c., be the tops of the waves; and let B, D, F, &c., be the intermediate hollows. Because the motion of the waves is carried on by the successive ascent and descent of the water, so that the parts thereof, as A, C, E, &c., which are highest at one time, become lowest immediately after; and because the motive force, by which the highest parts descend and the lowest ascend, is the weight of the elevated water, that alternate ascent and descent will be analogous to the reciprocal motion of the water in the canal, and will observe the same laws as to the times of ascent and descent; and therefore (by Prop. 44) if the distances between the highest places of the waves A, C, E and the lowest B, D, F be equal to twice the length of any pendulum, the highest parts A, C, E will become the lowest in the time of one oscillation, and in the time of another oscillation will ascend again. Therefore with the passage of each wave, the time of two oscillations will occur; that is, the wave will describe its breadth in the time that pendulum will oscillate twice; but a pendulum of four times that length, and therefore equal to the breadth of the waves, will just oscillate once in that time. Q.E.I.

COR. I. Therefore, waves whose breadth is equal to $3\frac{1}{18}$ French feet, will advance through a space equal to their breadth in one second of time; and therefore in one minute will go over a space of $183\frac{1}{3}$ feet; and in an hour, a space of 11,000 feet, nearly.

COR. II. And the velocity of greater or less waves will be augmented or diminished as the square root of their breadth.

These things are true upon the supposition that the parts of water ascend or descend in a straight line; but, in truth, that ascent and descent is rather performed in a circle; and therefore I give the time defined by this Proposition as only approximate.

PROPOSITION 47. THEOREM 37

If pulses are propagated through a fluid, the several particles of the fluid, going and returning with the shortest reciprocal motion, are always accelerated or retarded according to the law of the oscillating pendulum.

Let AB, BC, CD, &c., represent equal distances of successive pulses; ABC the line of direction of the motion of the successive pulses propagated from A to B; E, F, G three physical points of the quiescent medium situate in the right line AC at equal distances from each other; E*e*, F*f*, G*g* equal spaces of extreme shortness, through which those points go and return with a reciprocal motion in each vibration; ϵ, ϕ, γ any intermediate places of the same points; EF, FG physical short lines, or linear parts of the medium lying between those points, and successively transferred into the places ϵϕ, ϕγ, and *ef*, *fg*. Let there be drawn the right line PS equal to the right line E*e*. Bisect the same in O, and from the centre O, with the radius OP, describe the circle SIP*i*. Let the whole time of one vibration, with its proportional parts, be represented by the whole circumference of this circle and its parts, in such sort, that, when any time PH or PHS*h* is completed, if there be let fall to PS the perpendicular HL or *hl*, and there be taken E*ϵ* equal to PL or P*l*, the physical point E may be found in ϵ. A point, as E, moving according to this law with a reciprocal motion, in its going from E through ϵ to *e*, and returning again through ϵ to E, will perform its several vibrations with the same degrees of acceleration and retardation with those of an oscillating pendulum. We are now to prove that the several physical points of the medium will be agitated with such a kind of motion. Let us suppose, then, that a medium hath such a motion excited in it from any cause whatsoever, and consider what will follow from thence.

In the circumference PHS*h* let there be taken the equal arcs, HI, IK, or *hi*, *ik*, having the same ratio to the whole circumference as the equal right lines EF, FG have to BC, the whole interval of the pulses. Let fall the perpendiculars IM, KN, or *im*, *kn;* then because the points E, F, G are successively agitated with like motions, and perform their entire vibrations composed of their going and return, while the pulse is transferred from B to C; if PH or PHS*h* be the time elapsed since the beginning of the motion of the point E, then will PI or PHS*i* be the time elapsed since the beginning of the motion of the point F, and PK or PHS*k* the time elapsed since the beginning of the motion of the point G; and therefore E*ϵ*, F*ϕ*, G*γ* will be respectively equal to PL, PM, PN, while the points

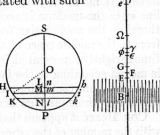

are going, and to P*l*, P*m*, P*n*, when the points are returning. Therefore $\epsilon\gamma$ or EG+Gγ−Eϵ will, when the points are going, be equal to EG−LN, and in their return equal to EG+*ln*. But $\epsilon\gamma$ is the breadth or expansion of the part EG of the medium in the place $\epsilon\gamma$; and therefore the expansion of that part in its going is to its mean expansion as EG−LN to EG; and in its return, as EG+*ln* or EG+LN is to EG. Therefore since LN is to KH as IM to the radius OP, and KH to EG as the circumference PHS*h*P to BC; that is, if we put V for the radius of a circle whose circumference is equal to BC, the interval of the pulses, as OP is to V; and, multiplying together corresponding terms of the proportions, we obtain LN to EG as IM to V; the expansion of the part EG, or of the physical point F in the place $\epsilon\gamma$, is to the mean expansion of the same part in its first place EG, as V−IM is to V in going, and as V+*im* is to V in its return. Hence the elastic force of the point F in the place $\epsilon\gamma$ is to its mean elastic force in the place EG as $\dfrac{1}{V-IM}$ is to $\dfrac{1}{V}$ in its going, and as $\dfrac{1}{V+im}$ is to $\dfrac{1}{V}$ in its return. And by the same reasoning the elastic forces of the physical points E and G in going are as $\dfrac{1}{V-HL}$ and $\dfrac{1}{V-KN}$ is to $\dfrac{1}{V}$; and the difference of the forces is to the mean elastic force of the medium as $\dfrac{HL-KN}{VV-V\cdot HL-V\cdot KN+HL\cdot KN}$ is to $\dfrac{1}{V}$; that is, as $\dfrac{HL-KN}{VV}$ is to $\dfrac{1}{V}$, or as HL−KN is to V; if we suppose (by reason of the very short extent of the vibrations) HL and KN to be indefinitely less than the quantity V. Therefore since the quantity V is given, the difference of the forces is as HL−KN; that is (because HL−KN is proportional to HK, and OM to OI or OP; and because HK and OP are given), as OM; that is, if F*f* be bisected in Ω, as $\Omega\phi$. And for the same reason the difference of the elastic forces of the physical points ϵ and γ, in the return of the physical short line $\epsilon\gamma$, is as $\Omega\phi$. But that difference (that is, the excess of the elastic force of the point ϵ above the elastic force of the point γ) is the very force by which the intervening physical short line $\epsilon\gamma$ of the medium is accelerated in going, and retarded in returning; and therefore the accelerative force of the physical short line $\epsilon\gamma$ is as its distance from Ω, the middle place of the vibration. Therefore (by Prop. 38, Book I) the time is rightly represented by the arc PI; and the linear part of the medium $\epsilon\gamma$ is moved according to the law above mentioned, that is, according to the law of a pendulum oscillating; and the case is the same of all the linear parts of which the whole medium is compounded.　　　　　　　　　　　　　　　　Q.E.D.

COR. Hence it appears that the number of the pulses propagated is the same with the number of the vibrations of the tremulous body, and is not multiplied in their progress. For the physical short line $\epsilon\gamma$ as soon as it returns to its first place is at rest; neither will it move again, unless it receives a new motion either from the impulse of the tremulous body, or of the pulses propagated from that body. As soon, therefore, as the pulses cease to be propagated from the tremulous body, it will return to a state of rest, and move no more.

PROPOSITION 48. THEOREM 38

The velocities of pulses propagated in an elastic fluid are in a ratio compounded of the square root of the ratio of the elastic force directly, and the square root of the ratio of the density inversely; supposing the elastic force of the fluid to be proportional to its condensation.

CASE 1. If the mediums be homogeneous, and the distances of the pulses in those mediums be equal amongst themselves, but the motion in one medium is more intense than in the other, the contractions and dilatations of the corresponding parts will be as those motions; not that this proportion is perfectly accurate. However, if the contractions and dilatations are not exceedingly intense, the error will not be sensible; and therefore this proportion may be considered as physically exact. Now the motive elastic forces are as the contractions and dilatations; and the velocities generated in the same time in equal parts are as the forces. Therefore equal and corresponding parts of corresponding pulses will go and return together, through spaces proportional to their contractions and dilatations, with velocities that are as those spaces; and therefore the pulses, which in the time of one going and returning advance forwards a space equal to their breadth, and are always succeeding into the places of the pulses that immediately go before them, will, by reason of the equality of the distances, go forwards in both mediums with equal velocity.

CASE 2. If the distances of the pulses or their lengths are greater in one medium than in another, let us suppose that the correspondent parts describe spaces, in going and returning, each time proportional to the breadths of the pulses; then will their contractions and dilatations be equal; and therefore if the mediums are homogeneous, the motive elastic forces, which agitate them with a reciprocal motion, will be equal also. Now the matter to be moved by these forces is as the breadth of the pulses; and the space through which they move every time they go and return is in the same ratio. And, moreover, the time of one going and returning is in a ratio compounded of the square root of the matter and the square root of the space; and therefore is as the space. But the pulses advance a space equal to their breadths in the times of going once and returning once; that is, they go over spaces proportional to the times, and therefore are equally swift.

CASE 3. And therefore in mediums of equal density and elastic force, all the pulses are equally swift. Now if the density or the elastic force of the medium were augmented, then, because the motive force is increased in the ratio of the elastic force, and the matter to be moved is increased in the ratio of the density, the time which is necessary for producing the same motion as before will be increased as the square root of the ratio of the density, and will be diminished as the square root of the ratio of the elastic force. And therefore the velocity of the pulses will be in a ratio compounded of the square root of the inverse ratio of the density of the medium, and the square root of the direct ratio of the elastic force. Q.E.D.

This Proposition will be made clearer from the construction of the following Problem.

Proposition 49. Problem 11

The density and elastic force of a medium being given, to find the velocity of the pulses.

Suppose the medium to be pressed by an incumbent weight after the manner of our air; and let A be the height of an homogeneous medium, whose weight is equal to the incumbent weight, and whose density is the same with the density of the compressed medium in which the pulses are propagated. Suppose a pendulum to be constructed whose length between the point of suspension and the centre of oscillation is A: and in the time in which that pendulum will perform one entire oscillation composed of its going and returning, the pulse will be propagated right onwards through a space equal to the circumference of a circle described with the radius A.

For, letting those things stand which were constructed in Prop. 47, if any physical line, as EF, describing the space PS in each vibration, be acted on in the extremities P and S of every going and return that it makes by an elastic force that is equal to its weight, it will perform its several vibrations in the time in which the same might oscillate in a cycloid whose whole perimeter is equal to the length PS; and that because equal forces will impel equal corpuscles through equal spaces in the same or equal times. Therefore since the times of the oscillations are as the square root of the lengths of the pendulums, and the length of the pendulum is equal to half the arc of the whole cycloid, the time of one vibration would be to the time of the oscillation of a pendulum whose length is A as the square root of the length ½PS or PO to the length A. But the elastic force with which the physical short line EG is urged, when it is found in its extreme places P, S, was (in the demonstration of Prop. 47) to its whole elastic force as HL−KN is to V, that is (since the point K now falls upon P), as HK to V; and all that force,

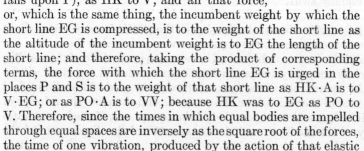

or, which is the same thing, the incumbent weight by which the short line EG is compressed, is to the weight of the short line as the altitude of the incumbent weight is to EG the length of the short line; and therefore, taking the product of corresponding terms, the force with which the short line EG is urged in the places P and S is to the weight of that short line as HK·A is to V·EG; or as PO·A is to VV; because HK was to EG as PO to V. Therefore, since the times in which equal bodies are impelled through equal spaces are inversely as the square root of the forces, the time of one vibration, produced by the action of that elastic force, will be to the time of a vibration, produced by the impulse of the weight, as the square root of the ratio of VV to PO·A, and therefore to the time of the oscillation of a pendulum whose length is A as the square root of the ratio of VV to PO·A, and as the square root of the ratio of PO to A conjointly; that is, in the entire ratio of V to A. But in the time of one vibration composed of the going and returning of the pendulum, the pulse will be propagated right onwards through a space equal to its breadth BC. Therefore the time in which a pulse runs over the space BC is to the time of one oscillation composed of the going and returning of the pendulum as V is to A, that is, as BC is to the circumference of a circle whose radius is A. But the time in which the pulse will run over the space BC is to the time in which it will run over a length equal to that circumference in the same ratio; and therefore in the time of such an oscillation the pulse will run over a length equal to that circumference.   Q.E.D.

Cor. I. The velocity of the pulses is equal to that which heavy bodies acquire by falling with an equally accelerated motion, and in their fall describing half the altitude A. For the pulse will, in the time of this fall, supposing it to move with the velocity acquired by that fall, run over a space that will be equal to the whole altitude A; and therefore in the time of one oscillation composed of one going and return, will go over a space equal to the circumference of a circle described with the radius A; for the time of the fall is to the time of oscillation as the radius of a circle to its circumference.

Cor. II. Therefore since that altitude A is directly as the elastic force of the fluid, and inversely as the density of the same, the velocity of the pulses will be in a ratio compounded of the square root of the ratio of the density inversely, and the square root of the ratio of the elastic force directly.

PROPOSITION 50. PROBLEM 12

To find the distances of the pulses.

Let the number of the vibrations of the body, by whose tremor the pulses are produced, be found to any given time. By that number divide the space which a pulse can go over in the same time, and the part found will be the breadth of one pulse.   Q.E.I.

SCHOLIUM

The last Propositions respect the motions of light and sounds; for since light is propagated in right lines, it is certain that it cannot consist in action alone (by Props. 41 and 42). As to sounds, since they arise from tremulous bodies, they can be nothing else but pulses of the air propagated through it (by Prop. 43); and this is confirmed by the tremors which sounds, if they be loud and deep, excite in the bodies near them, as we experience in the sound of drums; for quick and short tremors are less easily excited. But it is well known that any sounds, falling upon strings in unison with the sonorous bodies, excite tremors in those strings. This is also confirmed from the velocity of sounds; for since the specific gravities of rain water and quicksilver are to one another as about 1 to 13⅔, and when the mercury in the barometer is at the height of 30 inches of our measure, the specific gravities of the air and of rain water are to one another as about 1 to 870, therefore the specific gravities of air and quicksilver are to each other as 1 to 11,890. Therefore when the height of the quicksilver is at 30 inches, a height of uniform air, whose weight would be sufficient to compress our air to the density we find it to be of, must be equal to 356,700 inches, or 29,725 feet of our measure; and this is that very height of the medium, which I have called A in the construction of the foregoing Proposition. A circle whose radius is 29,725 feet is 186,768 feet in circumference. And since a pendulum 39⅕ inches in length completes one oscillation, composed of its going and return, in two seconds of time, as is commonly known, it follows that a pendulum 29,725 feet, or 356,700 inches in length will perform a like oscillation in 190¾ seconds. Therefore in that time a sound will go right onwards 186,768 feet, and therefore in one second, 979 feet.

But in this computation we have made no allowance for the crassitude of the solid particles of the air, by which the sound is propagated instantaneously. Because the weight of air is to the weight of water as 1 to 870, and because salts are almost twice as dense as water; if the particles of air are supposed to be of about the same density as those of water or salt, and the rarity of the air arises from the intervals of the particles, the diameter of one particle of air will be to the interval between the centres of the particles as 1 to about 9 or 10, and to the interval between the particles themselves as 1 to 8 or 9. Therefore to 979 feet, which, according to the above calculation, a sound will advance forwards in one second of time, we may add $\frac{979}{9}$, or about 109 feet, to compensate for the crassitude of the particles of the air: and then a sound will go forwards about 1088 feet in one second of time.

Moreover, the vapors floating in the air being of another spring, and a different tone, will hardly, if at all, partake of the motion of the true air in which the sounds are propagated. Now if these vapors remain unmoved, that motion will be propagated the swifter through the true air alone, and that as the square root of the defect of the matter. So if the atmosphere consist of ten parts of true air and one part of vapors, the motion of sounds will be swifter as the square root of the ratio of 11 to 10, or very nearly in the entire ratio of 21 to 20 than if it were propagated through eleven parts of true air: and therefore the motion of sounds above discovered must be increased in that ratio. By this means the sound will pass through 1142 feet in one second of time.

These things will be found true in spring and autumn, when the air is rarefied by the gentle warmth of those seasons, and by that means its elastic force becomes somewhat more intense. But in winter, when the air is condensed by the cold, and its elastic force is somewhat remitted, the motion of sounds will be slower as the square root of the density; and, on the other hand, swifter in the summer.

Now by experiments it actually appears that sounds do really advance in one second of time about 1142 feet of English measure, or 1070 feet of French measure.

The velocity of sounds being known, the intervals of the pulses are known also. For M. Sauveur, by some experiments that he made, found that an open pipe about five Paris feet in length gives a sound of the same tone with a viol string that vibrates a hundred times in one second. Therefore there are near 100 pulses in a space of 1070 Paris feet, which a sound runs over in a second of time; and therefore one pulse fills up a space of about $10\frac{7}{10}$ Paris feet, that is, about twice the length of the pipe. From this it is probable that the breadths of the pulses, in all sounds made in open pipes, are equal to twice the length of the pipes.

Moreover, from the Corollary of Prop. 47 appears the reason why the sounds immediately cease with the motion of the sonorous body, and why they are heard no longer when we are at a great distance from the sonorous bodies than when we are very near them. And besides, from the foregoing principles, it plainly appears how it comes to pass that sounds are so mightily increased in speaking-trumpets; for all reciprocal motion tends to be increased by the generating cause at each return. And in tubes hindering the dilatation of the sounds, the motion decays more slowly, and recurs more forcibly; and therefore is the more increased by the new motion impressed at each return. And these are the principal phenomena of sounds.

SECTION IX

THE CIRCULAR MOTION OF FLUIDS

HYPOTHESIS

The resistance arising from the want of lubricity in the parts of a fluid, is, other things being equal, proportional to the velocity with which the parts of the fluid are separated from one another.

PROPOSITION 51. THEOREM 39

If a solid cylinder infinitely long, in an uniform and infinite fluid, revolves with an uniform motion about an axis given in position, and the fluid be forced round by only this impulse of the cylinder, and every part of the fluid continues uniformly in its motion: I say, that the periodic times of the parts of the fluid are as their distances from the axis of the cylinder.

Let AFL be a cylinder turning uniformly about the axis S, and let the concentric circles BGM, CHN, DIO, EKP, &c., divide the fluid into innumerable concentric cylindric solid orbs of the same thickness. Then, because the fluid is homogeneous, the impressions which the contiguous orbs make upon each

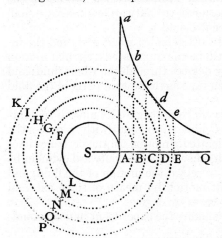

other will be (by the Hypothesis) as their translations from each other, and as the contiguous surfaces upon which the impressions are made. If the impression made upon any orb be greater or less on its concave than on its convex side, the stronger impression will prevail, and will either accelerate or retard the motion of the orb, according as it agrees with, or is contrary to, the motion of the same. Therefore, that every orb may continue uniformly in its motion, the impressions made on both sides must be equal and their directions contrary. Therefore since the impressions are as the contiguous surfaces, and as their translations from one another, the translations will be inversely as the surfaces, that is, inversely as the distances of the surfaces from the axis. But the differences of the angular motions about the axis are as those translations applied to the distances, or directly as the translations and inversely as the distances; that is, joining these ratios together, inversely as the squares of the distances. Therefore if there be erected the lines Aa, Bb, Cc, Dd, Ee, &c., perpendicular to the several parts of the infinite right line SABCDEQ, and inversely proportional to the squares of SA, SB, SC, SD, SE, &c., and through the extremities of those perpendiculars there be supposed to pass an hyperbolic curve, the sums of the differences, that is, the whole angular motions, will be as the correspondent sums of the lines Aa, Bb, Cc, Dd, Ee, that is (if to constitute a medium uniformly fluid the number of the orbs be increased and their breadth diminished *in infinitum*), as the hyperbolic areas AaQ, BbQ, CcQ, DdQ, EeQ, &c., analogous to the sums; and the times, inversely proportional to the angular motions, will be also inversely proportional to those areas. Therefore the periodic time of any particle, as D, is inversely as the area DdQ, that is (as appears from the known methods of quadratures of curves), directly as the distance SD.   Q.E.D.

COR. I. Hence the angular motions of the particles of the fluid are inversely as their distances from the axis of the cylinder, and the absolute velocities are equal.

COR. II. If a fluid be contained in a cylindric vessel of an infinite length, and contain another cylinder within, and both the cylinders revolve about one common axis, and the times of their revolutions be as their semidiameters, and every part of the fluid continues in its motion, the periodic times of the several parts will be as the distances from the axis of the cylinders.

COR. III. If there be added or taken away any common quantity of angular motion from the cylinder and fluid moving in this manner, yet because this new motion will not alter the mutual attrition of the parts of the fluid, the motion of the parts among themselves will not be changed; for the translations of the parts from one another depend upon the attrition. Any part will continue in that motion, which, by the attrition made on both sides with contrary directions, is no more accelerated than it is retarded.

COR. VI. Therefore if there be taken away from this whole system of the cylinders and the fluid all the angular motion of the outward cylinder, we shall have the motion of the fluid in a quiescent cylinder.

COR. V. Therefore if the fluid and outward cylinder are at rest, and the inward cylinder revolve uniformly, there will be communicated a circular motion to the fluid, which will be propagated by degrees through the whole fluid; and will go on continually increasing, till such time as the several parts of the fluid acquire the motion determined in Cor. IV.

COR. VI. And because the fluid endeavors to propagate its motion still farther, its impulse will carry the outmost cylinder also about with it, unless the cylinder be forcibly held back; and accelerate its motion till the periodic times of both cylinders become equal with each other. But if the outward cylinder be forcibly held fast, it will make an effort to retard the motion of the fluid; and unless the inward cylinder preserve that motion by means of some external force impressed thereon, it will make it cease by degrees.

All these things will be found true by making the experiment in deep standing water.

PROPOSITION 52. THEOREM 40

If a solid sphere, in an uniform and infinite fluid, revolves about an axis given in position with an uniform motion, and the fluid be forced round by only this impulse of the sphere; and every part of the fluid continues uniformly in its motion: I say, that the periodic times of the parts of the fluid are as the squares of their distances from the centre of the sphere.

CASE 1. Let AFL be a sphere turning uniformly about the axis S, and let the concentric circles BGM, CHN, DIO, EKP, &c., divide the fluid into innumerable concentric orbs of the same thickness. Suppose those orbs to be solid; and, because the fluid is homogeneous, the impressions which the contiguous orbs make one upon another will be (by the supposition) as their translations from one another, and the contiguous surfaces upon which the impressions are made. If the impression upon any orb be greater or less upon its concave than upon its convex side, the more forcible impression will prevail, and will either ac-

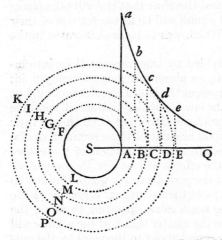

celerate or retard the velocity of the orb, according as it is directed with a conspiring or contrary motion to that of the orb. Therefore that every orb may continue uniformly in its motion, it is necessary that the impressions made upon both sides of the orb should be equal, and have contrary directions. Therefore since the impressions are as the contiguous surfaces, and as their translations from one another, the translations will be inversely as the surfaces, that is, inversely as the squares of the distances of the surfaces from the centre. But the differences of the angular motions about the axis are as those translations applied to the distances, or directly as the translations and inversely as the distances; that is, by compounding those ratios, inversely as the cubes of the distances. Therefore, if upon the several parts of the infinite right line SABCDEQ there be erected the perpendiculars Aa, Bb, Cc, Dd, Ee, &c., inversely proportional to the cubes of SA, SB, SC, SD, SE, &c., the sums of the differences, that is, the whole angular motions, will be as the corresponding sums of the lines Aa, Bb, Cc, Dd, Ee, &c., that is (if to constitute an uniformly fluid medium the number of the orbs be increased and their thickness diminished *in infinitum*), as the hyperbolic areas AaQ, BbQ, CcQ, DdQ, EeQ, &c., analogous to the sums; and the periodic times being inversely proportional to the angular motions, will be also inversely proportional to those areas. Therefore the periodic time of any orb DIO is inversely as the area DdQ, that is (by the known methods of quadratures), directly as the square of the distance SD. Which was first to be demonstrated.

CASE 2. From the centre of the sphere let there be drawn a great number of indefinite right lines, making given angles with the axis, exceeding one another by equal differences; and, by these lines revolving about the axis, conceive the orbs to be cut into innumerable annuli; then will every annulus have four annuli contiguous to it, that is, one on its inside, one on its outside, and two on each hand. Now each of these annuli cannot be impelled equally and with contrary directions by the attrition of the interior and exterior annuli, unless the motion be communicated according to the law which we demonstrated in Case 1. This appears from that demonstration. And therefore any series of annuli, taken in any right line extending itself *in infinitum* from the globe, will move according to the law of Case 1, except we should imagine it hindered by the attrition of the annuli on each side of it. But now in a motion, according to this law, no such is, and therefore cannot be, any obstacle to the motions continuing according to that law. If annuli at equal distances from the centre revolve either more swiftly or more slowly near the poles than near the ecliptic they will be accelerated if slow, and retarded if swift, by their mutual attrition; and so the periodic times will continually approach to equality, according to the law of Case 1. Therefore this attrition will not at all hinder the motion from going on according to the law of Case 1, and therefore that law will take place; that is, the periodic times of the several annuli will be as the squares of their distances from the centre of the globe. Which was to be demonstrated in the second place.

CASE 3. Let now every annulus be divided by transverse sections into innumerable particles constituting a substance absolutely and uniformly fluid; and because these sections do not at all respect the law of circular motion, but only serve to produce a fluid substance, the law of circular motion will continue the same as before. All the very small annuli will either not at all change their asperity and force of mutual attrition upon account of these sections, or else they will change the same equally. Therefore the proportion of the causes remaining the same, the proportion of the effects will remain the same also; that is, the proportion of the motions and the periodic times. Q.E.D. But now as the circular motion, and the centrifugal force thence arising, is greater at the ecliptic than at the poles, there must be some cause operating to retain the several particles in their circles; otherwise the matter that is at the ecliptic will always recede from the centre, and come round about to the poles by the outside of the vortex, and from thence return by the axis to the ecliptic with a continual circulation.

COR. I. Hence the angular motions of the parts of the fluid about the axis of the globe are inversely as the squares of the distances from the centre of the globe, and the absolute velocities are inversely as the same squares applied to the distances from the axis.

COR. II. If a globe revolve with an uniform motion about an axis of a given position in a similar and infinite quiescent fluid with an uniform motion, it will communicate a whirling motion to the fluid like that of a vortex, and that motion will by degrees be propagated onwards *in infinitum;* and this motion will be increased continually in every part of the fluid, till the periodical times of the several parts become as the squares of the distances from the centre of the globe.

COR. III. Because the inward parts of the vortex are by reason of their greater velocity continually pressing upon and driving forwards the external parts, and by that action are continually communicating motion to them, and at the same time those exterior parts communicate the same quantity of motion to those that lie still beyond them, and by this action preserve the quantity of their motion continually unchanged, it is plain that the motion is continually transferred from the centre to the circumference of the vortex, till it is quite swallowed up and lost in the boundless extent of that circumference. The matter between any two spherical surfaces concentric to the vortex will never be accelerated; because that matter will be always transferring the motion it receives from the matter nearer the centre to that matter which lies nearer the circumference.

COR. IV. Therefore, in order to continue a vortex in the same state of motion, some active principle is required from which the globe may receive continually the same quantity of motion which it is always communicating to the matter of the vortex. Without such a principle it will undoubtedly come to pass that the globe and the inward parts of the vortex, being always propagating their motion to the outward parts, and not receiving any new motion, will gradually move slower and slower, and at last be carried round no longer.

COR. V. If another globe should be swimming in the same vortex at a certain distance from its centre, and in the meantime by some force revolve constantly about an axis of a given inclination, the motion of this globe will drive the fluid round after the manner of a vortex; and at first this new and small vortex will revolve with its globe about the centre of the other; and in the meantime its motion will creep on farther and farther, and by degrees be propagated *in infinitum*, after the manner of the first vortex. And for the same reason that the globe of the new vortex was carried about before by the motion of the other vortex, the globe of this other will be carried about by the motion of this new vortex, so that the two globes will revolve about some intermediate point, and by reason of that circular motion mutually fly from each other, unless some force restrains them. Afterwards, if the constantly impressed forces, by which the globes continue in their motions, should cease, and everything be left to act according to the laws of mechanics, the motion of the globes will languish by degrees (for the reason assigned in Cor. III and IV), and the vortices at last will quite stand still.

COR. VI. If several globes in given places should constantly revolve with determined velocities about axes given in position, there would arise from them as many vortices going on *in infinitum*. For upon the same account that any one globe propagates its motion *in infinitum*, each globe apart will propagate its motion *in infinitum* also; so that every part of the infinite fluid will be agitated with a motion resulting from the actions of all the globes. Therefore the vortices will not be confined by any certain limits, but by degrees run into each other; and by the actions of the vortices on each other, the globes will be continually moved from their places, as was shown in the last Corollary; neither can they possibly keep any certain position among themselves, unless some force restrains them. But if those forces, which are constantly impressed upon the globes to continue these motions, should cease, the matter (for the reason assigned in Cor. III and IV) will gradually stop, and cease to move in vortices.

COR. VII. If a similar fluid be inclosed in a spherical vessel, and, by the uniform rotation of a globe in its centre, be driven round in a vortex; and the globe and vessel revolve the same way about the same axis, and their periodic times be as the squares of the semidiameters: the parts of the fluid will not go on in their motions without acceleration or retardation, till their periodical times are as the squares of their distances from the centre of the vortex. No constitution of a vortex can be permanent but this.

COR. VIII. If the vessel, the inclosed fluid, and the globe, retain this motion, and revolve besides with a common angular motion about any given axis, because the mutual attrition of the parts of the fluid is not changed by this motion, the motions of the parts among themselves will not be changed; for the translations of the parts among themselves depend upon this attrition. Any part will continue in that motion in which its attrition on one side retards it just as much as its attrition on the other side accelerates it.

COR. IX. Therefore if the vessel be quiescent, and the motion of the globe be given, the motion of the fluid will be given. For conceive a plane to pass through the axis of the globe, and to revolve with a contrary motion; and suppose the sum of the time of this revolution and of the revolution of the globe to be to the time of the revolution of the globe as the square of the semidiameter of the vessel to the square of the semidiameter of the globe; and the periodic times of the parts of the fluid in respect of this plane will be as the squares of their distances from the centre of the globe.

COR. X. Therefore if the vessel move about the same axis with the globe, or with a given velocity about a different one, the motion of the fluid will be given. For if from the whole system we take away the angular motion of the vessel, all the motions will remain the same among themselves as before, by Cor. VIII, and those motions will be given by Cor. IX.

COR. XI. If the vessel and the fluid are quiescent, and the globe revolves with an uniform motion, that motion will be propagated by degrees through the whole fluid to the vessel, and the vessel will be carried round by it, unless forcibly held back; and the fluid and the vessel will be continually accelerated till their periodic times become equal to the periodic times of the globe. If the vessel be either restrained by some force, or revolve with any constant and uniform motion, the medium will come little by little to the state of motion defined in Cor. VIII, IX, X, nor will it ever continue in any other state. But if then the forces, by which the globe and vessel revolve with certain motions, should cease, and the whole system be left to act according to the mechanical laws, the vessel and globe, by means of the intervening fluid, will act upon each other, and will continue to propagate their motions through the fluid to each other, till their periodic times become equal among themselves, and the whole system revolves together like one solid body.

SCHOLIUM

In all these reasonings I suppose the fluid to consist of matter of uniform density and fluidity; I mean, that the fluid is such, that a globe placed anywhere therein may propagate with the same motion of its own, at distances from itself continually equal, similar and equal motions in the fluid in the same interval of time. The matter by its circular motion endeavors to recede from the axis of the vortex, and therefore presses all the matter that lies beyond. This pressure makes the attrition greater, and the separation of the parts more difficult; and by consequence diminishes the fluidity of the matter. Again; if the parts of the fluid are in any one place denser or larger than in the others, the fluidity will be less in that place, because there are fewer surfaces where the parts can be separated from each other. In these cases I suppose the defect of the fluidity to be supplied by the smoothness or softness of the parts, or some other condition; otherwise the matter where it is less fluid will cohere more, and be more sluggish, and therefore will receive the motion more slowly, and propagate it farther than agrees with the ratio above assigned. If the vessel be not spherical, the particles will move in lines not circular, but answering to the figure of the vessel; and the periodic times will be nearly as the squares of the mean distances from the centre. In the parts between the centre and the circumference the motions will be slower where the spaces are wide, and swifter where narrow; nevertheless, the particles will not tend to the circumference at all the more because of their greater swiftness; for they then describe arcs of less curvity, and the tendency to recede from the centre is as much diminished by the lessening of this curvature as it is augmented by the increase of the velocity. As they go out of narrow into wide spaces, they recede a little farther from the centre, but in doing so are retarded; and when they come out of wide into narrow spaces, they are again accelerated; and so each particle is retarded and accelerated by turns forever. These things will come to pass in a rigid vessel; for the state of vortices in an infinite fluid is known by Cor. VI of this Proposition.

I have endeavored in this Proposition to investigate the properties of vortices, that I might find whether the celestial phenomena can be explained by them; for the phenomenon is this, that the periodic times of the planets revolving about Jupiter are as the $\frac{3}{2}$th power of their distances from Jupiter's centre; and the same rule obtains also among the planets that revolve about the sun. And these rules obtain also with the greatest accuracy, as far as has been yet discovered by astronomical observation. Therefore if those planets are carried round in vortices revolving about Jupiter and the sun, the vortices must revolve according to that law. But here we found the periodic times of the parts of the vortex to be as the square of the distances from the centre of motion; and this ratio cannot be diminished and reduced to the $\frac{3}{2}$th power, unless either the matter of the vortex be more fluid the farther it is from the centre, or the resistance arising from the want of lubricity in the parts of the fluid should, as the velocity with which the parts of the fluid are separated goes on increasing, be augmented with it in a greater ratio than that in which the velocity increases. But neither of these suppositions seems reasonable. The more gross and less fluid parts will tend to the circumference, unless they are heavy towards the centre. And though, for the sake of demonstration, I proposed, at the beginning of this Section, an Hypothesis that the resistance is proportional to the velocity, nevertheless, it is in truth probable that the resistance is in a less ratio than that of the velocity; which granted, the periodic times of the parts of the vortex will be in a greater ratio than the square of the distances from its centre. If, as some think, the vortices move more swiftly near the centre, then slower to a certain limit, then again swifter near the circumference, certainly neither the $\frac{3}{2}$th power, nor any other certain and determinate power, can obtain in them. Let philosophers then see how that phenomenon of the $\frac{3}{2}$th power can be accounted for by vortices.

PROPOSITION 53. THEOREM 41

Bodies carried about in a vortex, and returning in the same orbit, are of the same density with the vortex, and are moved according to the same law with the parts of the vortex, as to velocity and direction of motion.

For if any small part of the vortex, whose particles or physical points continue a given situation among themselves, be supposed to be congealed, this particle will move according to the same law as before, since no change is made either in its density, inertia, or figure. And again; if a congealed or solid part of the vortex be of the same density with the rest of the vortex, and be resolved into a fluid, this will move according to the same law as before, except so far as its particles, now become fluid, may be moved among themselves. Neglect, therefore, the motion of the particles among themselves as not at all concerning the progressive motion of the whole, and the motion of the whole will be the same as before. But this motion will be the same with the motion of other parts of the vortex at equal distances from the centre; because the solid, now resolved into a fluid, is become exactly like the other parts of the vortex. Therefore a solid, if it be of the same density with the matter of the vortex, will move with the same motion as the parts thereof, being relatively at rest in the matter that surrounds it. If it be more dense, it will endeavor more than before to recede from the centre; and therefore overcoming that force of the vortex, by which, being, as it were, kept in equilibrium, it was retained in its orbit, it will recede from the centre, and in its revolution describe a spiral, returning no longer into the same orbit. And, by the same argument, if it be more rare, it will approach to the centre. Therefore it can never continually go round in the same orbit, unless it be of the same density with the fluid. But we have shown in that case that it would revolve according to the same law with those parts of the fluid that are at the same or equal distances from the centre of the vortex.

Cor. i. Therefore a solid revolving in a vortex, and continually going round in the same orbit, is relatively quiescent in the fluid that carries it.

Cor. ii. And if the vortex be of an uniform density, the same body may revolve at any distance from the centre of the vortex.

Scholium

Hence it is manifest that the planets are not carried round in corporeal vortices; for, according to the Copernican hypothesis, the planets going round the sun revolve in ellipses, having the sun in their common focus; and by radii drawn to the sun describe areas proportional to the times. But the parts of a vortex can never revolve with such a motion. For, let AD, BE, CF represent three orbits described about the sun S, of which let the outmost circle CF be concentric to the sun; let the aphelions of the two innermost be A, B; and their perihelions D, E. Hence a body revolving in the orb CF, describing, by a radius drawn to the sun, areas proportional to the times, will move with an uniform motion. And, according to the laws of astronomy, the body revolving in the orbit BE will move slower in its aphelian B, and swifter in its perihelion E; whereas, according to the laws of mechanics, the matter of the vortex ought to move more swiftly in the narrow space between A and C than in the wide space between D and F; that is, more swiftly in the aphelion than in the perihelion. Now these two conclusions contradict each other. So at the beginning of the sign of Virgo, where the aphelion of Mars is at present, the distance between the orbits of Mars and Venus is to the distance between the same orbits, at the beginning of the sign of Pisces, as about 3 to 2; and therefore the matter of the vortex between those orbits ought to be swifter at the beginning of Pisces than at the beginning of Virgo in the ratio of 3 to 2; for the narrower the space is through which the same quantity of matter passes in the same time of one revolution, the greater will be the velocity with which it passes through it. Therefore if the earth

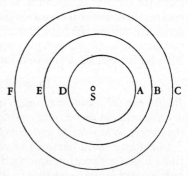

being relatively at rest in this celestial matter should be carried round by it, and revolve together with it about the sun, the velocity of the earth at the beginning of Pisces would be to its velocity at the beginning of Virgo in the ratio of 3 to 2. Therefore the sun's apparent diurnal motion at the beginning of Virgo ought to be above 70 minutes, and at the beginning of Pisces less than 48 minutes; whereas, on the contrary, that apparent motion of the sun is really greater at the beginning of Pisces than at the beginning of Virgo, as experience testifies; and therefore the earth is swifter at the beginning of Virgo than at the beginning of Pisces; so that the hypothesis of vortices is utterly irreconcilable with astronomical phenomena, and rather serves to perplex than explain the heavenly motions. How these motions are performed in free spaces without vortices, may be understood by the first book; and I shall now more fully treat of it in the following book.

BOOK THREE

SYSTEM OF THE WORLD

(IN MATHEMATICAL TREATMENT)

IN the preceding books I have laid down the principles of philosophy; principles not philosophical but mathematical: such, namely, as we may build our reasonings upon in philosophical inquiries. These principles are the laws and conditions of certain motions, and powers or forces, which chiefly have respect to philosophy; but, lest they should have appeared of themselves dry and barren, I have illustrated them here and there with some philosophical scholiums, giving an account of such things as are of more general nature, and which philosophy seems chiefly to be founded on; such as the density and the resistance of bodies, spaces void of all bodies, and the motion of light and sounds. It remains that, from the same principles, I now demonstrate the frame of the System of the World. Upon this subject I had, indeed, composed the third book in a popular method, that it might be read by many; but afterwards, considering that such as had not sufficiently entered into the principles could not easily discern the strength of the consequences, nor lay aside the prejudices to which they had been many years accustomed, therefore, to prevent the disputes which might be raised upon such accounts, I chose to reduce the substance of this book into the form of Propositions (in the mathematical way), which should be read by those only who had first made themselves masters of the principles established in the preceding books: not that I would advise anyone to the previous study of every Proposition of those books; for they abound with such as might cost too much time, even to readers of good mathematical learning. It is enough if one carefully reads the Definitions, the Laws of Motion, and the first three sections of the first book. He may then pass on to this book, and consult such of the remaining Propositions of the first two books, as the references in this, and his occasions, shall require.

RULES OF REASONING IN PHILOSOPHY

RULE I

We are to admit no more causes of natural things than such as are both true and sufficient to explain their appearances.

To this purpose the philosophers say that Nature does nothing in vain, and more is in vain when less will serve; for Nature is pleased with simplicity, and affects not the pomp of superfluous causes.

RULE II

Therefore to the same natural effects we must, as far as possible, assign the same causes.

As to respiration in a man and in a beast; the descent of stones in Europe and in America; the light of our culinary fire and of the sun; the reflection of light in the earth, and in the planets.

RULE III

The qualities of bodies, which admit neither intensification nor remission of degrees, and which are found to belong to all bodies within the reach of our experiments, are to be esteemed the universal qualities of all bodies whatsoever.

For since the qualities of bodies are only known to us by experiments, we are to hold for universal all such as universally agree with experiments; and such as are not liable to diminution can never be quite taken away. We are certainly not to relinquish the evidence of experiments for the sake of dreams and vain fictions of our own devising; nor are we to recede from the analogy of Nature, which is wont to be simple, and always consonant to itself. We no other way know the extension of bodies than by our senses, nor do these reach it in all bodies; but because we perceive extension in all that are sensible, therefore we ascribe it universally to all others also. That abundance of bodies are hard, we learn by experience; and because the hardness of the whole arises from the hardness of the parts, we therefore justly infer the hardness of the undivided particles not only of the bodies we feel but of all others. That all bodies are impenetrable, we gather not from reason, but from sensation. The bodies which we handle we find impenetrable, and thence conclude impenetrability to be an universal property of all bodies whatsoever. That all bodies are movable, and endowed with certain powers (which we call the inertia) of persevering in their motion, or in their rest, we only infer from the like properties observed in the bodies which we have seen. The extension, hardness, impenetrability, mobility, and inertia of the whole, result from the extension, hardness, impenetrability, mobility, and inertia of the parts; and hence we conclude the least particles of all bodies to be also all extended, and hard and impenetrable, and movable, and endowed with their proper inertia. And this is the foundation of all philosophy. Moreover, that the divided but contiguous particles of bodies may be

270

separated from one another, is matter of observation; and, in the particles that remain undivided, our minds are able to distinguish yet lesser parts, as is mathematically demonstrated. But whether the parts so distinguished, and not yet divided, may, by the powers of Nature, be actually divided and separated from one another, we cannot certainly determine. Yet, had we the proof of but one experiment that any undivided particle, in breaking a hard and solid body, suffered a division, we might by virtue of this rule conclude that the undivided as well as the divided particles may be divided and actually separated to infinity.

Lastly, if it universally appears, by experiments and astronomical observations, that all bodies about the earth gravitate towards the earth, and that in proportion to the quantity of matter which they severally contain; that the moon likewise, according to the quantity of its matter, gravitates towards the earth; that, on the other hand, our sea gravitates towards the moon; and all the planets one towards another; and the comets in like manner towards the sun; we must, in consequence of this rule, universally allow that all bodies whatsoever are endowed with a principle of mutual gravitation. For the argument from the appearances concludes with more force for the universal gravitation of all bodies than for their impenetrability; of which, among those in the celestial regions, we have no experiments, nor any manner of observation. Not that I affirm gravity to be essential to bodies: by their *vis insita* I mean nothing but their inertia. This is immutable. Their gravity is diminished as they recede from the earth.

RULE IV

In experimental philosophy we are to look upon propositions inferred by general induction from phenomena as accurately or very nearly true, notwithstanding any contrary hypotheses that may be imagined, till such time as other phenomena occur, by which they may either be made more accurate, or liable to exceptions.

This rule we must follow, that the argument of induction may not be evaded by hypotheses.

PHENOMENA[1]

PHENOMENON I

That the circumjovial planets, by radii drawn to Jupiter's centre, describe areas proportional to the times of description; and that their periodic times, the fixed stars being at rest, are as the ³⁄₂th power of their distances from its centre.

This we know from astronomical observations. For the orbits of these planets differ but insensibly from circles concentric to Jupiter; and their motions in those circles are found to be uniform. And all astronomers agree that their periodic times are as the ³⁄₂th power of the semidiameters of their orbits; and so it manifestly appears from the following table.

The periodic times of the satellites of Jupiter.

$1^d. 18^h. 27^m. 34^s., 3^d. 13^h. 13^m. 42^s., 7^d. 3^h. 42^m. 36^s., 16^d. 16^h. 32^m. 9^s.$

The distances of the satellites from Jupiter's centre.

	1	2	3	4	
From the observations of:					
Borelli	5⅔	8⅔	14	24⅔	
Townly *by the micrometer*	5.52	8.78	13.47	24.72	*Semi-*
Cassini *by the telescope*	5	8	13	23	*diameter of*
Cassini *by the eclipse of the satel-*					*Jupiter*
lites	5⅔	9	$14^{23}/_{60}$	$25^3/_{10}$	
From the periodic times	5.667	9.017	14.384	25.299	

Mr. Pound hath determined, by the help of excellent micrometers, the diameters of Jupiter and the elongation of its satellites after the following manner. The greatest heliocentric elongation of the fourth satellite from Jupiter's centre was taken with a micrometer in a 15-foot telescope, and at the mean distance of Jupiter from the earth was found about 8′ 16″. The elongation of the third satellite was taken with a micrometer in a telescope of 123 feet, and at the same distance of Jupiter from the earth was found 4′ 42″. The greatest elongations of the other satellites, at the same distance of Jupiter from the earth, are found from the periodic times to be 2′ 56″ 47‴, and 1′ 51″ 6‴.

The diameter of Jupiter taken with the micrometer in a 123-foot telescope several times, and reduced to Jupiter's mean distance from the earth, proved always less than 40″, never less than 38″, generally 39″. This diameter in shorter telescopes is 40″, or 41″; for Jupiter's light is a little dilated by the unequal refrangibility of the rays, and this dilatation bears a less ratio to the diameter of Jupiter in the longer and more perfect telescopes than in those which are shorter and less perfect. The times in which two satellites, the first

[1][In the following parts of Book III, scattered words and phrases in italics (except in Latin expressions and in names of writings) are, in Motte's translation, interpolations of words and phrases not in the Latin text of the *Principles;* and a few are departures from a literal translation of the Latin].

and the third, passed over Jupiter's body, were observed, from the beginning of the ingress to the beginning of the egress, and from the complete ingress to the complete egress, with the long telescope. And from the transit of the first satellite, the diameter of Jupiter at its mean distance from the earth came forth $37\frac{1}{8}''$, and from the transit of the third $37\frac{3}{8}''$. There was observed also the time in which the shadow of the first satellite passed over Jupiter's body, and thence the diameter of Jupiter at its mean distance from the earth came out about $37''$. Let us suppose its diameter to be $37\frac{1}{4}''$, very nearly, and then the greatest elongations of the first, second, third, and fourth satellite will be respectively equal to 5.965, 9.494, 15.141, and 26.63 semidiameters of Jupiter.

PHENOMENON II

That the circumsaturnal planets, by radii drawn to Saturn's centre, describe areas proportional to the times of description; and that their periodic times, the fixed stars being at rest, are as the $\frac{3}{2}$th power of their distances from its centre.

For, as Cassini from his own observations hath determined, their distances from Saturn's centre and their periodic times are as follows:

The periodic times of the satellites of Saturn.

$1^{\mathrm{d}}.\ 21^{\mathrm{h}}.\ 18^{\mathrm{m}}.\ 27^{\mathrm{s}}.,\ 2^{\mathrm{d}}.\ 17^{\mathrm{h}}.\ 41^{\mathrm{m}}.\ 22^{\mathrm{s}}.,\ 4^{\mathrm{d}}.\ 12^{\mathrm{h}}.\ 25^{\mathrm{m}}.\ 12^{\mathrm{s}}.,\ 15^{\mathrm{d}}.\ 22^{\mathrm{h}}.\ 41^{\mathrm{m}}.\ 14^{\mathrm{s}}.,$
$79^{\mathrm{d}}.\ 7^{\mathrm{h}}.\ 48^{\mathrm{m}}.\ 00^{\mathrm{s}}.$

The distances of the satellites from Saturn's centre, in semidiameters of its ring.

From observations	$1^{19}\!/_{20}$	$2\frac{1}{2}$	$3\frac{1}{2}$	8	24
From the periodic times	1.93	2.47	3.45	8	23.35

The greatest elongation of the fourth satellite from Saturn's centre is commonly determined from the observations to be eight of those semidiameters, very nearly. But the greatest elongation of this satellite from Saturn's centre, when taken with an excellent micrometer in Mr. Huygens' telescope of 123 feet, appeared to be eight semidiameters and $\frac{7}{10}$ of a semidiameter. And from this observation and the periodic times the distances of the satellites from Saturn's centre in semidiameters of the ring are 2.1, 2.69, 3.75, 8.7, and 25.35. The diameter of Saturn observed in the same telescope was found to be to the diameter of the ring as 3 to 7; and the diameter of the ring, May 28-29, 1719, was found to be $43''$; and hence the diameter of the ring when Saturn is at its mean distance from the earth is $42''$, and the diameter of Saturn $18''$. These things appear so in very long and excellent telescopes, because in such telescopes the apparent magnitudes of the heavenly bodies bear a greater proportion to the dilatation of light in the extremities of those bodies than in shorter telescopes. If, then, we reject all the spurious light, the diameter of Saturn will not amount to more than $16''$.

PHENOMENON III

That the five primary planets, Mercury, Venus, Mars, Jupiter, and Saturn, with their several orbits, encompass the sun.

That Mercury and Venus revolve about the sun, is evident from their moon-like appearances. When they shine out with a full face, they are, in respect of us, beyond or above the sun; when they appear half full, they are about the same height on one side or other of the sun; when horned, they are below or between us and the sun; and they are sometimes, *when directly under*, seen like spots traversing the sun's disk. That Mars surrounds the sun, is as plain from its full face when near its conjunction with the sun, and from the gibbous figure which it shows in its quadratures. And the same thing is demonstrable of Jupiter and Saturn, from their appearing full in all situations; for the shadows of their satellites that appear sometimes upon their disks make it plain that the light they shine with is not their own, but borrowed from the sun.

PHENOMENON IV

That the fixed stars being at rest, the periodic times of the five primary planets, and (whether of the sun about the earth, or) of the earth about the sun, are as the $\frac{3}{2}$th power of their mean distances from the sun.

This proportion, first observed by Kepler, is now received by all astronomers; for the periodic times are the same, and the dimensions of the orbits are the same, whether the sun revolves about the earth, or the earth about the sun. And as to the measures of the periodic times, all astronomers are agreed about them. But for the dimensions of the orbits, Kepler and Boulliau, above all others, have determined them from observations with the greatest accuracy; and the mean distances corresponding to the periodic times differ but insensibly from those which they have assigned, and for the most part fall in between them; as we may see from the following table.

The periodic times, with respect to the fixed stars, of the planets and earth revolving about the sun, in days and decimal parts of a day.

♄	♃	♂	♁	♀	☿
10759.275	4332.514	686.9785	365.2565	224.6176	87.9692

The mean distances of the planets and of the earth from the sun.

	♄	♃	♂
According to Kepler	951,000	519,650	152,350
" " Boulliau	954,198	522,520	152,350
" " the periodic times	954,006	520,096	152,369
	♁	♀	☿
According to Kepler	100,000	72,400	38,806
" " Boulliau	100,000	72,398	38,585
" " the periodic times	100,000	72,333	38,710

As to Mercury and Venus, there can be no doubt about their distances from the sun; for they are determined by the elongations of those planets from the sun; and for the distances of the superior planets, all dispute is cut off by the eclipses of the satellites of Jupiter. For by those eclipses the position of the shadow which Jupiter projects is determined; from this we have the heliocentric longitude of Jupiter. And from its heliocentric and geocentric longitudes compared together, we determine its distance.

PHENOMENON V

Then the primary planets, by radii drawn to the earth, describe areas in no wise proportional to the times; but the areas which they describe by radii drawn to the sun are proportional to the times of description.

For to the earth they appear sometimes direct, sometimes stationary, nay, and sometimes retrograde. But from the sun they are always seen direct, and to proceed with a motion nearly uniform, that is to say, a little swifter in the perihelion and a little slower in the aphelion distances, so as to maintain an equality in the description of the areas. This is a noted proposition among astronomers, and particularly demonstrable in Jupiter, from the eclipses of his satellites; by the help of these eclipses, as we have said, the heliocentric longitudes of that planet, and its distances from the sun, are determined.

PHENOMENON VI

That the moon, by a radius drawn to the earth's centre, describes an area proportional to the time of description.

This we gather from the apparent motion of the moon, compared with its apparent diameter. It is true that the motion of the moon is a little disturbed by the action of the sun: but in laying down these Phenomena, I neglect those small and inconsiderable errors.

PROPOSITIONS

PROPOSITION 1. THEOREM 1

That the forces by which the circumjovial planets are continually drawn off from rectilinear motions, and retained in their proper orbits, tend to Jupiter's centre; and are inversely as the squares of the distances of the places of those planets from that centre.

The former part of this Proposition appears from Phen. i, and Prop. 2 or 3, Book i; the latter from Phen. i, and Cor. vi, Prop. 4, of the same book.

The same thing we are to understand of the planets which encompass Saturn, by Phen. ii.

PROPOSITION 2. THEOREM 2

That the forces by which the primary planets are continually drawn off from rectilinear motions, and retained in their proper orbits, tend to the sun; and are inversely as the squares of the distances of the places of those planets from the sun's centre.

The former part of the Proposition is manifest from Phen. v, and Prop. 2, Book i; the latter from Phen. iv, and Cor. vi, Prop. 4, of the same book. But this part of the Proposition is, with great accuracy, demonstrable from the quiescence of the aphelion points; for a very small aberration from the proportion according to the inverse square of the distances would (by Cor. i, Prop. 45, Book i) produce a motion of the apsides sensible enough in every single revolution, and in many of them enormously great.

PROPOSITION 3. THEOREM 3

That the force by which the moon is retained in its orbit tends to the earth; and is inversely as the square of the distance of its place from the earth's centre.

The former part of the Proposition is evident from Phen. vi, and Prop. 2 or 3, Book i; the latter from the very slow motion of the moon's apogee; which in every single revolution amounting but to 3° 3′ forwards, may be neglected. For (by Cor. i, Prop. 45, Book i) it appears that, if the distance of the moon from the earth's centre is to the semidiameter of the earth as D to 1, the force, from which such a motion will result, is inversely as $D^{2\frac{4}{243}}$, i.e., inversely as the power of D, whose exponent is $2\frac{4}{243}$; that is to say, in the proportion of the distance somewhat greater than the inverse square, but which comes $59\frac{3}{4}$ times nearer to the proportion according to the square than to the cube. But since this increase is due to the action of the sun (as we shall afterwards show), it is here to be neglected. The action of the sun, attracting the moon from the earth, is nearly as the moon's distance from the earth; and therefore (by what we have shown in Cor. ii, Prop. 45, Book i) is to the centripetal force of the moon as 2 to 357.45, or nearly so; that is, as 1 to $178\frac{29}{40}$. And if we neglect so inconsiderable a force of the sun, the remaining force, by which the moon is retained in its orb, will be inversely as D^2. This will yet more fully appear from comparing this force with the force of gravity, as is done in the next Proposition.

COR. If we augment the mean centripetal force by which the moon is retained in its orb, first in the proportion of $177^{29}\!/_{40}$ to $178^{29}\!/_{40}$, and then in the proportion of the square of the semidiameter of the earth to the mean distance of the centres of the moon and earth, we shall have the centripetal force of the moon at the surface of the earth; supposing this force, in descending to the earth's surface, continually to increase inversely as the square of the height.

PROPOSITION 4. THEOREM 4

That the moon gravitates towards the earth, and by the force of gravity is continually drawn off from a rectilinear motion, and retained in its orbit.

The mean distance of the moon from the earth in the syzygies in semidiameters of the earth, is, according to Ptolemy and most astronomers, 59; according to Vendelin and Huygens, 60; to Copernicus, $60\frac{1}{3}$; to Street, $60\frac{2}{5}$; and to Tycho, $56\frac{1}{2}$. But Tycho, and all that follow his tables of refraction, making the refractions of the sun and moon (altogether against the nature of light) to exceed the refractions of the fixed stars, and that by four or five minutes *near the horizon*, did thereby increase the moon's *horizontal* parallax by a like number of minutes, that is, by a twelfth or fifteenth part of the whole parallax. Correct this error, and the distance will become about $60\frac{1}{2}$ semidiameters of the earth, near to what others have assigned. Let us assume the mean distance of 60 diameters in the syzygies; and suppose one revolution of the moon, in respect of the fixed stars, to be completed in $27^d \cdot 7^h \cdot 43^m$., as astronomers have determined; and the circumference of the earth to amount to 123,249,600 Paris feet, as the French have found by mensuration. And now if we imagine the moon, deprived of all motion, to be let go, so as to descend towards the earth with the impulse of all that force by which (by Cor. Prop. 3) it is retained in its orb, it will in the space of one minute of time, describe in its fall $15\frac{1}{12}$ Paris feet. This we gather by a calculus, founded either upon Prop. 36, Book I, or (which comes to the same thing) upon Cor. IX, Prop. 4, of the same book. For the versed sine of that arc, which the moon, in the space of one minute of time, would by its mean motion describe at the distance of 60 semidiameters of the earth, is nearly $15\frac{1}{12}$ Paris feet, or more accurately 15 feet, 1 inch, and 1 line $\frac{4}{9}$. Wherefore, since that force, in approaching to the earth, increases in the proportion of the inverse square of the distance, and, upon that account, at the surface of the earth, is $60 \cdot 60$ times greater than at the moon, a body in our regions, falling with that force, ought in the space of one minute of time, to describe $60 \cdot 60 \cdot 15\frac{1}{12}$ Paris feet; and, in the space of one second of time, to describe $15\frac{1}{12}$ of those feet; or more accurately 15 feet, 1 inch, and 1 line $\frac{4}{9}$. And with this very force we actually find that bodies here upon earth do really descend; for a pendulum oscillating seconds in the latitude of Paris will be 3 Paris feet, and 8 lines $\frac{1}{2}$ in length, as Mr. Huygens has observed. And the space which a heavy body describes by falling in one second of time is to half the length of this pendulum as the square of the ratio of the circumference of a circle to its diameter (as Mr. Huygens has also shown), and is therefore 15 Paris feet, 1 inch, 1 line $\frac{7}{9}$. And therefore the force by which the moon is retained in its orbit becomes, at the very surface of the earth, equal to the force of gravity which we observe in heavy bodies there. And therefore (by Rules 1 and 2) the force by which the moon is retained in its orbit is that very same force which we commonly call gravity; for, were gravity another force different from that, then bodies descending to the earth with the joint impulse of both forces would fall with a double velocity, and in the space of one second of time would describe $30\frac{1}{6}$ Paris feet; altogether against experience.

This calculus is founded on the hypothesis of the earth's standing still; for if both earth and moon move about the sun, and at the same time about their common centre of gravity, the distance of the centres of the moon and earth from one another will be $60\frac{1}{2}$ semidiameters of the earth; as may be found by a computation from Prop. 60, Book I.

SCHOLIUM

The demonstration of this Proposition may be more diffusely explained after the following manner. Suppose several moons to revolve about the earth, as in the system of Jupiter or Saturn; the periodic times of these moons (by the argument of induction) would observe the same law which Kepler found to obtain among the planets; and therefore their centripetal forces would be inversely as the squares of the distances from the centre of the earth, by Prop. 1, of this book. Now if the lowest of these were very small, and were so near the earth as almost to touch the tops of the highest mountains, the centripetal force thereof, retaining it in its orbit, would be nearly equal to the weights of any terrestrial bodies that should be found upon the tops of those mountains, as may be known by the foregoing computation. Therefore if the same little moon should be deserted by its centrifugal force that carries it through its orbit, and be disabled from going onward therein, it would descend to the earth; and that with the same velocity, with which heavy bodies actually fall upon the tops of those very mountains, because of the equality of the forces that oblige them both to descend. And if the force by which that lowest moon would descend were different from gravity, and if that moon were to gravitate towards the earth, as we find terrestrial bodies do upon the tops of mountains, it would then descend with twice the velocity, as being impelled by both these forces conspiring together. Therefore since both these forces, that is, the gravity of heavy bodies, and the centripetal forces of the moons, are directed to the centre of the earth, and are similar and equal between themselves, they will (by Rules 1 and 2) have one and the same cause. And therefore the force which retains the moon in its orbit is that very force which we commonly call gravity; because otherwise this little moon at the top of a mountain must either be without gravity, or fall twice as swiftly as heavy bodies are wont to do.

PROPOSITION 5. THEOREM 5

That the circumjovial planets gravitate towards Jupiter; the circumsaturnal towards Saturn; the circumsolar towards the sun; and by the forces of their gravity are drawn off from rectilinear motions, and retained in curvilinear orbits.

For the revolutions of the circumjovial planets about Jupiter, of the circumsaturnal about Saturn, and of Mercury and Venus, and the other circumsolar planets, about the sun, are appearances of the same sort with the revolution of the moon about the earth; and therefore, by Rule 2, must be owing to the same sort of causes; especially since it has been demonstrated, that the forces upon which those revolutions depend tend to the centres of Jupiter, of Saturn, and of the sun; and that those forces, in receding from Jupiter, from Saturn, and from the sun, decrease in the same proportion, and according to the same law, as the force of gravity does in receding from the earth.

Cor. i. There is, therefore, a power of gravity tending to all the planets; for, doubtless, Venus, Mercury, and the rest, are bodies of the same sort with Jupiter and Saturn. And since all attraction (by Law iii) is mutual, Jupiter will therefore gravitate towards all his own satellites, Saturn towards his, the earth towards the moon, and the sun towards all the primary planets.

Cor. ii. The force of gravity which tends to any one planet is inversely as the square of the distance of places from that planet's centre.

Cor. iii. All the planets do gravitate towards one another, by Cor. i and ii. And hence it is that Jupiter and Saturn, when near their conjunction, by their mutual attractions sensibly disturb each other's motions. So the sun disturbs the motions of the moon; and both sun and moon disturb our sea, as we shall hereafter explain.

Scholium

The force which retains the celestial bodies in their orbits has been hitherto called centripetal force; but it being now made plain that it can be no other than a gravitating force, we shall hereafter call it gravity. For the cause of that centripetal force which retains the moon in its orbit will extend itself to all the planets, by Rules 1, 2, and 4.

Proposition 6. Theorem 6

That all bodies gravitate towards every planet; and that the weights of bodies towards any one planet, at equal distances from the centre of the planet, are proportional to the quantities of matter which they severally contain.

It has been, now for a long time, observed by others, that all sorts of heavy bodies (allowance being made for the inequality of retardation which they suffer from a small power of resistance in the air) descend to the earth *from equal heights* in equal times; and that equality of times we may distinguish to a great accuracy, by the help of pendulums. I tried experiments with gold, silver, lead, glass, sand, common salt, wood, water, and wheat. I provided two wooden boxes, round and equal: I filled the one with wood, and suspended an equal weight of gold (as exactly as I could) in the centre of oscillation of the other. The boxes, hanging by equal threads of 11 feet, made a couple of pendulums perfectly equal in weight and figure, and equally receiving the resistance of the air. And, placing the one by the other, I observed them to play together forwards and backwards, for a long time, with equal vibrations. And therefore the quantity of matter in the gold (by Cor. i and vi, Prop. 24, Book ii) was to the quantity of matter in the wood as the action of the motive force (or *vis motrix*) upon all the gold to the action of the same upon all the wood; that is, as the weight of the one to the weight of the other: and the like happened in the other bodies. By these experiments, in bodies of the same weight, I could manifestly have discovered a difference of matter less than the thousandth part of the whole, had any such been. But, without all doubt, the nature of gravity towards the planets is the same as towards the earth. For, should we imagine our terrestrial bodies taken to the orbit of the moon, and there, together with the moon, deprived of all motion, to be let go, so as to fall together towards the earth, it is certain, from what we have demonstrated before, that, in equal times, they would describe equal spaces with the moon, and of consequence are to the moon, in quantity of matter, as their weights to its weight. Moreover, since the satellites of Jupiter perform their revolutions in times which observe the $\frac{3}{2}$th power of the proportion of their distances from Jupiter's centre, their accelerative gravities towards Jupiter will be inversely as the squares of their distances from Jupiter's centre; that is, equal, at equal distances. And, therefore, these satellites, if supposed to fall *towards Jupiter* from equal heights, would describe equal spaces in equal times, in like manner as heavy bodies do on our earth. And, by the same argument, if the circumsolar planets were supposed to be let fall at equal distances from the sun, they would, in their descent towards the sun, describe equal spaces in equal times. But forces which equally accelerate unequal bodies must be as those bodies: that is to say, the weights of the planets *towards the sun* must be as their quantities of matter. Further, that the weights of Jupiter and of his satellites towards the sun are proportional to the several quantities of their matter, appears from the exceedingly regular motions of the satellites (by Cor. III, Prop. 65, Book I). For if some of those bodies were more strongly attracted to the sun in proportion to their quantity of matter than others, the motions of the satellites would be disturbed by that inequality of attraction (by Cor. II, Prop. 65, Book I). If, at equal distances from the sun, any satellite, in proportion to the quantity of its matter, did gravitate towards the sun with a force greater than Jupiter in proportion to his, according to any given proportion, suppose of *d* to *e;* then the distance between the centres of the sun and of the satellite's orbit would be always greater than the distance between the centres of the sun and of Jupiter, nearly as the square root of that proportion: as by some computations I have found. And if the satellite did gravitate towards the sun with a force, less in the proportion of *e* to *d*, the distance of the centre of the satellite's orbit from the sun would be less than the distance of the centre of Jupiter from the sun as the square root of the same proportion. Therefore if, at equal distances from the sun, the accelerative gravity of any satellite towards the sun were greater or less than the accelerative gravity of Jupiter towards the sun but by one $\frac{1}{1000}$ part of the whole gravity, the distance of the centre of the satellite's orbit from the sun would be greater of less than the distance of Jupiter from the sun by one $\frac{1}{2000}$ part of the whole distance; that is, by a fifth part of the distance of the utmost satellite from the centre of Jupiter; an eccentricity of the orbit which would be very sensible. But the orbits of the satellites are concentric to Jupiter, and therefore the accelerative gravities of Jupiter, and of all its satellites towards the sun, are equal among themselves. And by the same argument, the weights of Saturn and of his satellites towards the sun, at equal distances from the sun, are as their several quantities of matter; and the weights of the moon and of the earth towards the sun are either none, or accurately proportional to the masses of matter which they contain. But some weight they have, by Cor. I and III, Prop. 5.

But further; the weights of all the parts of every planet towards any other planet are one to another as the matter in the several parts; for if some parts did gravitate more, others less, than for the quantity of their matter, then the whole planet, according to the sort of parts with which it most abounds, would gravitate more or less than in proportion to the quantity of matter in the whole. Nor is it of any moment whether these parts are external or internal; for if, for example, we should imagine the terrestrial bodies with us to be raised to the orbit of the moon, to be there compared with its body; if the weights of such bodies were to the weights of the external parts of the moon as the quantities of matter in the one and in the other respectively, but to the weights of the internal parts in a greater or less proportion, then likewise the weights of those bodies would be to the weight of the whole moon in a greater or less proportion; against what we have shown above.

COR. I. Hence the weights of bodies do not depend upon their forms and textures; for if the weights could be altered with the forms, they would be greater or less, according to the variety of forms, in equal matter; altogether against experience.

COR. II. Universally, all bodies about the earth gravitate towards the earth; and the weights of all, at equal distances from the earth's centre, are as the quantities of matter which they severally contain. This is the quality of all bodies within the reach of our experiments; and therefore (by Rule 3) to be affirmed of all bodies whatsoever. If the ether, or any other body, were either altogether void of gravity, or were to gravitate less in proportion to its quantity of matter, then, because (according to Aristotle, Descartes, and others) there is no difference between that and other bodies but in *mere* form of matter, by a successive change from form to form, it might be changed at last into a body of the same condition with those which gravitate most in proportion to their quantity of matter; and, on the other hand, the heaviest bodies, acquiring the first form of that body, might by degrees quite lose their gravity. And therefore the weights would depend upon the forms of bodies, and with those forms, might be changed: contrary to what was proved in the preceding Corollary.

COR. III. All spaces are not equally full; for if all spaces were equally full, then the specific gravity of the fluid which fills the region of the air, on account of the extreme density of the matter, would fall nothing short of the specific gravity of quicksilver, or gold, or any other the most dense body; and, therefore, neither gold, nor any other body, could descend in air; for bodies do not descend in fluids, unless they are specifically heavier than the fluids. And if the quantity of matter in a given space can, by any rarefaction, be diminished, what should hinder a diminution to infinity?

COR. IV. If all the solid particles of all bodies are of the same density, and cannot be rarefied without pores, then a void, space, or vacuum must be granted. By bodies of the same density, I mean those whose inertias are in the proportion of their bulks.

COR. V. The power of gravity is of a different nature from the power of magnetism; for the magnetic attraction is not as the matter attracted. Some bodies are attracted more by the magnet; others less; most bodies not at all. The power of magnetism in one and the same body may be increased and diminished; and is sometimes far stronger, for the quantity of matter, than the power of gravity; and in receding from the magnet decreases not as the square but almost as the cube of the distance, as nearly as I could judge from some rude observations.

PROPOSITION 7. THEOREM 7

That there is a power of gravity pertaining to all bodies, proportional to the several quantities of matter which they contain.

That all the planets gravitate one towards another, we have proved before; as well as that the force of gravity towards every one of them, considered apart, is inversely as the square of the distance of places from the centre of the planet. And thence (by Prop. 69, Book I, and its Corollaries) it follows that the gravity tending towards all the planets is proportional to the matter which they contain.

Moreover, since all the parts of any planet A gravitate towards any other planet B; and the gravity of every part is to the gravity of the whole as the matter of the part to the matter of the whole; and (by Law III) to every action corresponds an equal reaction; therefore the planet B will, on the other hand, gravitate towards all the parts of the planet A; and its gravity towards any one part will be to the gravity towards the whole as the matter of the part to the matter of the whole.   Q.E.D.

Cor. I. Therefore the force of gravity towards any whole planet arises from, and is compounded of, the forces of gravity towards all its parts. Magnetic and electric attractions afford us examples of this; for all attraction towards the whole arises from the attractions towards the several parts. The thing may be easily understood in gravity, if we consider a greater planet, as formed of a number of lesser planets, meeting together in one globe; for *hence it would appear* that the force of the whole must arise from the forces of the component parts. If it is objected that, according to this law, all bodies with us must gravitate one towards another, whereas no such gravitation anywhere appears, I answer, that since the gravitation towards these bodies is to the gravitation towards the whole earth as these bodies are to the whole earth, the gravitation towards them must be far less than to fall under the observation of our senses.

Cor. II. The force of gravity towards the several equal particles of any body is inversely as the square of the distance of places from the particles; as appears from Cor. III, Prop. 74, Book I.

Proposition 8. Theorem 8

In two spheres gravitating each towards the other, if the matter in places on all sides round about and equidistant from the centres is similar, the weight of either sphere towards the other will be inversely as the square of the distance between their centres.

After I had found that the force of gravity towards a whole planet did arise from and was compounded of the forces of gravity towards all its parts, and towards every one part was in the inverse proportion of the squares of the distances from the part, I was yet in doubt whether that proportion inversely as the square of the distance did accurately hold, or but nearly so, in the total force compounded of so many partial ones; for it might be that the proportion which accurately enough took place in greater distances should be wide of the truth near the surface of the planet, where the distances of the particles are unequal, and their situation dissimilar. But by the help of Props. 75 and 76, Book I, and their Corollaries, I was at last satisfied of the truth of the Proposition, as it now lies before us.

Cor. I. Hence we may find and compare together the weights of bodies towards different planets; for the weights of bodies revolving in circles about planets are (by Cor. II, Prop. 4, Book I) directly as the diameters of the circles and inversely as the squares of their periodic times; and their weights at the surfaces of the planets, or at any other distances from their centres, are (by this Proposition) greater or less inversely as the square of the distances. Thus from the periodic times of Venus, revolving about the sun, in $224^{d} \cdot 16\frac{3}{4}^{h}$.; of the utmost circumjovial satellite revolving about Jupiter, in 16^{d}., $16\frac{8}{15}^{h}$.; of the Huygenian satellite about Saturn, in 15^{d}. $22\frac{2}{3}^{h}$.; and of the moon about the earth, in 27^{d}. 7^{h}. 43^{m}.; compared with the mean distance of Venus from the sun, and with the greatest heliocentric elongations of the outmost circumjovial satellite from Jupiter's centre, $8'\ 16''$; of the Huygenian satellite from the centre of Saturn, $3'\ 4''$; and of the moon from the earth, $10'\ 33''$; by computation I found that the weight of equal bodies, at equal distances from the centres of the sun, of Jupiter, of Saturn, and of the earth, towards the sun, Jupiter, Saturn, and the earth, were one to another, as 1, $\frac{1}{1067}$, $\frac{1}{3021}$, and $\frac{1}{169282}$ respectively. Then because as the distances are increased or diminished, the weights are diminished or increased in a squared ratio, the weights of equal bodies towards the sun, Jupiter, Saturn, and the earth, at the distances $10,000$, 997, 791, and 109 from their centres, that is, at their very surfaces, will be as $10,000$, 943, 529, and 435 respectively. How much the weights of bodies are at the surface of the moon, will be shown hereafter.

COR. II. Hence likewise we discover the quantity of matter in the several planets; for their quantities of matter are as the forces of gravity at equal distances from their centres; that is, in the sun, Jupiter, Saturn, and the earth, as 1, $\frac{1}{1067}$, $\frac{1}{3021}$, and $\frac{1}{169282}$ respectively. If the parallax of the sun be taken greater or less than $10''\ 30'''$, the quantity of matter in the earth must be augmented or diminished as the cube of that proportion.

COR. III. Hence also we find the densities of the planets; for (by Prop. 72, Book I) the weights of equal and similar bodies towards similar spheres are, at the surfaces of those spheres, as the diameters of the spheres; and therefore the densities of dissimilar spheres are as those weights applied to the diameters of the spheres. But the true diameters of the sun, Jupiter, Saturn, and the earth, were one to another as $10,000$, 997, 791, and 109; and the weights towards the same as $10,000$, 943, 529, and 435 respectively; and therefore their densities are as 100, $94\frac{1}{2}$, 67, and 400. The density of the earth, which comes out by this computation, does not depend upon the parallax of the sun, but is determined by the parallax of the moon, and therefore is here truly defined. The sun, therefore, is a little denser than Jupiter, and Jupiter than Saturn, and the earth four times denser than the sun; for the sun, by its great heat, is kept in a sort of rarefied state. The moon is denser than the earth, as shall appear afterwards.

COR. IV. The smaller the planets are, they are, other things being equal, of so much the greater density; for so the powers of gravity on their several surfaces come nearer to equality. They are likewise, other things being equal, of the greater density, as they are nearer to the sun. So Jupiter is more dense than Saturn, and the earth than Jupiter; for the planets were to be placed at different distances from the sun, that, according to their degrees of density, they might enjoy a greater or less proportion of the sun's heat. Our water, if it were removed as far as the orbit of Saturn, would be turned into ice, and in that of Mercury would quickly fly away in vapor; for the light of the sun, to which its heat is proportional, is seven times denser in the orb of Mercury than with us: and by the thermometer I have found that a sevenfold heat of our summer sun will make water boil. Nor are we to doubt that the matter of Mercury is adapted to its heat, and is therefore more dense than the matter of our earth; since, in a denser matter, the operations of Nature require a stronger heat.

Proposition 9. Theorem 9

That the force of gravity, considered downwards from the surface of the planets, decreases nearly in the proportion of the distances from the centre of the planets.

If the matter of the planet were of an uniform density, this Proposition would be accurately true (by Prop. 73, Book I). The error, therefore, can be no greater than what may arise from the inequality of the density.

Proposition 10. Theorem 10

That the motions of the planets in the heavens may subsist an exceedingly long time.

In the Scholium of Prop. 40, Book II, I have shown that a globe of water frozen into ice, and moving freely in our air, in the time that it would describe the length of its semidiameter, would lose by the resistance of the air $\frac{1}{4586}$ part of its motion; and the same proportion holds nearly in all globes, however great, and moved with whatever velocity. But that our globe of earth is of greater density than it would be if the whole consisted of water only, I thus make out. If the whole consisted of water only, whatever was of less density than water, because of its less specific gravity, would emerge and float above. And upon this account, if a globe of terrestrial matter, covered on all sides with water, was less dense than water, it would emerge somewhere; and, the subsiding water falling back, would be gathered to the opposite side. And such is the condition of our earth, which in a great measure is covered with seas. The earth, if it was not for its greater density, would emerge from the seas, and, according to its degree of levity, would be raised more or less above their surface, the water of the seas flowing backwards to the opposite side. By the same argument, the spots of the sun, which float upon the lucid matter thereof, are lighter than that matter; and, however the planets have been formed while they were yet in fluid masses, all the heavier matter subsided to the centre. Since, therefore, the common matter of our earth on the surface thereof is about twice as heavy as water, and a little lower, in mines, is found about three, or four, or even five times heavier, it is probable that the quantity of the whole matter of the earth may be five or six times greater than if it consisted all of water; especially since I have before shown that the earth is about four times more dense than Jupiter. If, therefore, Jupiter is a little more dense than water, in the space of thirty days, in which that planet describes the length of 459 of its semidiameters, it would, in a medium of the same density with our air, lose almost a tenth part of its motion. But since the resistance of mediums decreases in proportion to their weight or density, so that water, which is $13\frac{3}{5}$ times lighter than quicksilver, resists less in that proportion; and air, which is 860 times lighter than water, resists less in the same proportion; therefore in the heavens, where the weight of the medium in which the planets move is immensely diminished, the resistance will almost vanish.

It is shown in the Scholium of Prop. 22, Book II, that at the height of 200 miles above the earth the air is more rare than it is at the surface of the earth in the ratio of 30 to 0.0000000000003998, or as 75,000,000,000,000 to 1, nearly. And hence the planet Jupiter, revolving in a medium of the same density with that superior air, would not lose by the resistance of the medium the 1,000,000th part of its motion in 1,000,000 years. In the spaces near the earth the resistance is produced only by the air, exhalations, and vapors. When these are carefully

exhausted by the air pump from under the receiver, heavy bodies fall within
the receiver with perfect freedom, and without the least sensible resistance:
gold itself, and the lightest down, let fall together, will descend with equal
velocity; and though they fall through a space of four, six, and eight feet, they
will come to the bottom at the same time; as appears from experiments. And
therefore, the celestial regions being perfectly void of air and exhalations, the
planets and comets meeting no sensible resistance in those spaces will continue
their motions through them for an immense tract of time.

HYPOTHESIS I

THAT THE CENTRE OF THE SYSTEM OF THE WORLD IS IMMOVABLE.

This is acknowledged by all, while some contend that the earth, others that
the sun, is fixed in that centre. Let us see what may from hence follow.

PROPOSITION 11. THEOREM 11

*That the common centre of gravity of the earth, the sun, and all the planets, is
immovable.*

For (by Cor. IV of the Laws) that centre either is at rest, or moves uniformly
forwards in a right line; but if that centre moved, the centre of the world would
move also, against the Hypothesis.

PROPOSITION 12. THEOREM 12

*That the sun is agitated by a continual motion, but never recedes far from the
common centre of gravity of all the planets.*

For since (by Cor. II, Prop. 8) the quantity of matter in the sun is to the
quantity of matter in Jupiter as 1067 to 1; and the distance of Jupiter from the
sun is to the semidiameter of the sun in a proportion but a small matter greater,
the common centre of gravity of Jupiter and the sun will fall upon a point a
little without the surface of the sun. By the same argument, since the quantity
of matter in the sun is to the quantity of matter in Saturn as 3021 to 1, and the
distance of Saturn from the sun is to the semidiameter of the sun in a proportion but a small matter less, the common centre of gravity of Saturn and the
sun will fall upon a point a little within the surface of the sun. And, pursuing
the principles of this computation, we should find that though the earth and all
the planets were placed on one side of the sun, the distance of the common
centre of gravity of all from the centre of the sun would scarcely amount to one
diameter of the sun. In other cases, the distances of those centres are always
less; and therefore, since that centre of gravity is continually at rest, the sun,
according to the various positions of the planets, must continually be moved
every way, but will never recede far from that centre.

COR. Hence the common centre of gravity of the earth, the sun, and all the
planets, is to be esteemed the centre of the world; for since the earth, the sun,
and all the planets gravitate one towards another, and are, therefore, according
to their powers of gravity, in continual agitation, as the Laws of Motion require, it is plain that their movable centres cannot be taken for the immovable
centre of the world. If that body were to be placed in the centre, towards which
other bodies gravitate most (according to common opinion), that privilege
ought to be allowed to the sun; but since the sun itself is moved, a fixed point
is to be chosen from which the centre of the sun recedes least, and from which

it would recede yet less if the body of the sun were denser and greater, and therefore less apt to be moved.

Proposition 13. Theorem 13

The planets move in ellipses which have their common focus in the centre of the sun; and, by radii drawn to that centre, they describe areas proportional to the times of description.

We have discoursed above on these motions from the Phenomena. Now that we know the principles on which they depend, from those principles we deduce the motions of the heavens *a priori*. Because the weights of the planets towards the sun are inversely as the squares of their distances from the sun's centre, if the sun were at rest, and the other planets did not act one upon another, their orbits would be ellipses, having the sun in their common focus; and they would describe areas proportional to the times *of description*, by Props. 1 and 11, and Cor. I, Prop. 13, Book I. But the actions of the planets one upon another are so very small, that they may be neglected; and by Prop. 66, Book I, they disturb the motions of the planets around the sun in motion, less than if those motions were performed about the sun at rest.

It is true, that the action of Jupiter upon Saturn is not to be neglected; for the force of gravity towards Jupiter is to the force of gravity towards the sun (at equal distances, Cor. II, Prop. 8) as 1 to 1067; and therefore in the conjunction of Jupiter and Saturn, because the distance of Saturn from Jupiter is to the distance of Saturn from the sun almost as 4 to 9, the gravity of Saturn towards Jupiter will be to the gravity of Saturn towards the sun as 81 to 16·1067; or, as 1 to about 211. And hence arises a perturbation of the orbit of Saturn in every conjunction of this planet with Jupiter, so sensible, that astronomers are puzzled with it. As the planet is differently situated in these conjunctions, its eccentricity is sometimes augmented, sometimes diminished; its aphelion is sometimes carried forwards, sometimes backwards, and its mean motion is by turns accelerated and retarded; yet the whole error in its motion about the sun, though arising from so great a force, may be almost avoided (except in the mean motion) by placing the lower focus of its orbit in the common centre of gravity of Jupiter and the sun (according to Prop. 67, Book I), and therefore that error, when it is greatest, scarcely exceeds two minutes; and the greatest error in the mean motion scarcely exceeds two minutes yearly. But in the conjunction of Jupiter and Saturn, the accelerative forces of gravity of the sun towards Saturn, of Jupiter towards Saturn, and of Jupiter towards the sun, are almost as 16, 81, and $\dfrac{16 \cdot 81 \cdot 3021}{25}$, or 156,609; and therefore the difference of the forces of gravity of the sun towards Saturn, and of Jupiter towards Saturn, is to the force of gravity of Jupiter towards the sun as 65 to 156,609, or as 1 to 2409. But the greatest power of Saturn to disturb the motion of Jupiter is proportional to this difference; and therefore the perturbation of the orbit of Jupiter is much less than that of Saturn's. The perturbations of the other orbits are yet far less, except that the orbit of the earth is sensibly disturbed by the moon. The common centre of gravity of the earth and moon moves in an ellipse about the sun in the focus thereof, and, by a radius drawn to the sun, describes areas proportional to the times of description. But the earth in the meantime by a menstrual motion is revolved about this common centre.

Proposition 14. Theorem 14

The aphelions and nodes of the orbits of the planets are fixed.

The aphelions are immovable by Prop. 11, Book I; and so are the planes of the orbits, by Prop. 1 of the same book. And if the planes are fixed, the nodes must be so too. It is true that some inequalities may arise from the mutual actions of the planets and comets in their revolutions, but these will be so small, that they may be here passed by.

Cor. I. The fixed stars are immovable, seeing they keep the same position to the aphelions and nodes of the planets.

Cor. II. And since these stars are liable to no sensible parallax from the annual motion of the earth, they can have no force, because of their immense distance, to produce any sensible effect in our system. Not to mention that the fixed stars, everywhere promiscuously dispersed in the heavens, by their contrary attractions destroy their mutual actions, by Prop. 70, Book I.

Scholium

Since the planets near the sun (viz., Mercury, Venus, the earth, and Mars) are so small that they can act with but little force upon one another, therefore their aphelions and nodes must be fixed, except so far as they are disturbed by the actions of Jupiter and Saturn, and other higher bodies. And hence we may find, by the theory of gravity, that their aphelions move forwards a little, in respect of the fixed stars, and that as the $\frac{3}{2}$th power of their several distances from the sun. So that if the aphelion of Mars, in the space of a hundred years, is carried forwards 33′ 20″, in respect of the fixed stars, the aphelions of the earth, of Venus, and of Mercury, will in a hundred years be carried forwards 17′ 40″, 10′ 53″, and 4′ 16″, respectively. But these motions are so inconsiderable, that we have neglected them in this Proposition.

Proposition 15. Problem 1

To find the principal diameters of the orbits of the planets.

They are to be taken as the $\frac{2}{3}$th power of the periodic times, by Prop. 15, Book I, and then to be severally augmented in the proportion of the sum of the masses of matter in the sun and each planet to the first of two mean proportionals between that sum and the quantity of matter in the sun, by Prop. 60, Book I.

Proposition 16. Problem 2

To find the eccentricities and aphelions of the planets.

This Problem is resolved by Prop. 18, Book I.

Proposition 17. Theorem 15

That the diurnal motions of the planets are uniform, and that the libration of the moon arises from its diurnal motion.

The Proposition is proved from the first Law of Motion, and Cor. XXII, Prop. 66, Book I. Jupiter, with respect to the fixed stars, revolves in 9^h. 56^m.; Mars in 24^h. 39^m.; Venus in about 23^h.; the earth in 23^h. 56^m.; the sun in 25$\frac{1}{2}$^{d}., and the moon in 27^d. 7^h. 43^m. These things appear by the Phenomena. The spots in the sun's body return to the same situation on the sun's disk, with respect to the earth, in $27\frac{1}{2}$ days; and therefore with respect to the fixed stars the sun revolves in about $25\frac{1}{2}$ days. But because the lunar day, arising from its uniform revolution about its axis, is menstrual, *that is, equal to the time of its periodic revolution in its orbit*, hence the same face of the moon will be always nearly turned to the upper focus of its orbit; but, as the situation of that focus requires, will deviate a little to one side and to the other from the earth in the lower focus; and this is the libration in longitude; for the libration in latitude arises from the moon's latitude, and the inclination of its axis to the plane of the ecliptic. This theory of the libration of the moon, Mr. N. Mercator, in his *Astronomy*, published at the beginning of the year 1676, explained more fully out of the letters I sent him. The utmost satellite of Saturn seems to revolve about its axis with a motion like this of the moon, respecting Saturn continually with the same face; for in its revolution round Saturn, as often as it comes to the eastern part of its orbit, it is scarcely visible, and generally quite disappears; this is probably occasioned by some spots in that part of its body, which is then turned towards the earth, as M. Cassini has observed. So also the utmost satellite of Jupiter seems to revolve about its axis with a like motion, because in that part of its body which is turned from Jupiter it has a spot, which always appears as if it were in Jupiter's own body, whenever the satellite passes between Jupiter and our eye.

Proposition 18. Theorem 16

That the axes of the planets are less than the diameters drawn perpendicular to the axes.

The equal gravitation of the parts on all sides would give a spherical figure to the planets, if it was not for their diurnal revolution in a circle. By that circular motion it comes to pass that the parts receding from the axis endeavor to ascend about the equator; and therefore if the matter is in a fluid state, by its ascent towards the equator it will enlarge the diameters there, and by its descent towards the poles it will shorten the axis. So the diameter of Jupiter (by the concurring observations of astronomers) is found shorter between pole and pole than from east to west. And, by the same argument, if our earth was not higher about the equator than at the poles, the seas would subside about the poles, and, rising towards the equator, would lay all things there under water.

Proposition 19. Problem 3

To find the proportion of the axis of a planet to the diameters perpendicular thereto.

Our countryman, Mr. Norwood, measuring a distance of 905,751 feet of London measure between London and York, in 1635, and observing the difference of latitudes to be $2° 28'$, determined the measure of one degree to be 367,196 feet of London measure, that is, 57,300 Paris toises. M. Picard, measuring an arc of one degree, and $22' 55''$ of the meridian between Amiens and Malvoisine, found an arc of one degree to be 57,060 Paris toises. M. Cassini, the father, measured the distance upon the meridian from the town of Collioure in Roussillon to the Observatory of Paris; and his son added the distance from the Observatory to the Citadel of Dunkirk. The whole distance was $486156\frac{1}{2}$ toises and the difference of the latitudes of Collioure and Dunkirk was 8 degrees, and $31' 11\frac{5}{6}''$. Hence an arc of one degree appears to be 57,061 Paris toises. And from these measures we conclude that the circumference of the

earth is 123,249,600, and its semidiameter 19,615,800 Paris feet, upon the supposition that the earth is of a spherical figure.

In the latitude of Paris a heavy body falling in a second of time describes 15
Paris feet, 1 inch, $1\frac{7}{9}$ lines, as above, that is, $2173\frac{7}{9}$ lines. The weight of the
body is diminished by the weight of the ambient air. Let us suppose the weight
lost thereby to be $\frac{1}{11000}$ part of the whole weight; then that heavy body falling in a vacuum will describe a height of 2174 lines in one second of time.

A body in every sidereal day of 23^{h}. 56^{m}. 4^{s}. uniformly revolving in a circle
at the distance of 19,615,800 feet from the centre, in one second of time describes
an arc of 1433.46 feet; the versed sine of which is 0.05236561 feet, or 7.54064
lines. And therefore the force with which bodies descend in the latitude of Paris
is to the centrifugal force of bodies in the equator arising from the diurnal
motion of the earth as 2174 to 7.54064.

The centrifugal force of bodies in the equator is to the centrifugal force with
which bodies recede directly from the earth in the latitude of Paris, 48° 50′ 10″,
as the square of the ratio of the radius to the cosine of the latitude, that is, as
7.54064 to 3.267. Add this force to the force with which bodies descend by their
weight in the latitude of Paris, and a body, in the latitude of Paris, falling by
its whole undiminished force of gravity, in the time of one second, will describe
2177.267 lines, or 15 Paris feet, 1 inch, and 5.267 lines. And the total force of
gravity in that latitude will be to the centrifugal force of bodies in the equator
of the earth as 2177.267 to 7.54064, or as 289 to 1.

Therefore if APBQ represent the figure of the earth, now no longer spherical,
but generated by the rotation of an ellipse about its lesser axis PQ; and ACQ*qca*
a canal full of water, reaching from the pole Q*q* to the centre C*c*, and thence
rising to the equator A*a*; the weight of the water in the leg of the canal AC*ca*

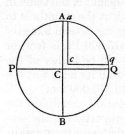

will be to the weight of water in the other leg QC*cq* as
289 to 288, because the centrifugal force arising from the
circular motion sustains and takes off one of the 289
parts of the weight (in the one leg), and the weight of
288 in the other sustains the rest. But by computation
(from Cor. ii, Prop. 91, Book i) I find, that, if the matter of the earth was all uniform, and without any motion,
and its axis PQ were to the diameter AB as 100 to 101,
the force of gravity in the place Q towards the earth
would be to the force of gravity in the same place Q
towards a sphere described about the centre C with the radius PC, or QC, as
126 to 125. And, by the same argument, the force of gravity in the place A
towards the spheroid generated by the rotation of the ellipse APBQ about the
axis AB is to the force of gravity in the same place A, towards the sphere described about the centre C with the radius AC, as 125 to 126. But the force of
gravity in the place A towards the earth is a mean proportional between the
forces of gravity towards the spheroid and this sphere; because the sphere, by
having its diameter PQ diminished in the proportion of 101 to 100, is transformed into the figure of the earth; and this figure, by having a third diameter
perpendicular to the two diameters AB and PQ diminished in the same proportion, is converted into the said spheroid; and the force of gravity in A, in
either case, is diminished nearly in the same proportion. Therefore the force of
gravity in A towards the sphere described about the centre C with the radius

AC, is to the force of gravity in A towards the earth as 126 is to $125\frac{1}{2}$. And the force of gravity in the place Q towards the sphere described about the centre C with the radius QC, is to the force of gravity in the place A towards the sphere described about the centre C with the radius AC, in the proportion of the diameters (by Prop. 72, Book I), that is, as 100 to 101. If, therefore, we compound those three proportions 126 to 125, 126 to $125\frac{1}{2}$, and 100 to 101, into one, the force of gravity in the place Q towards the earth will be to the force of gravity in the place A towards the earth as $126 \cdot 126 \cdot 100$ to $125 \cdot 125\frac{1}{2} \cdot 101$; or as 501 to 500.

Now since (by Cor. III, Prop. 91, Book I) the force of gravity in either leg of the canal ACca, or QCcq, is as the distance of the places from the centre of the earth, if those legs are conceived to be divided by transverse, parallel, and equidistant surfaces, into parts proportional to the wholes, the weights of any number of parts in the one leg ACca will be to the weights of the same number of parts in the other leg as their magnitudes and the accelerative forces of their gravity conjointly, that is, as 101 to 100, and 500 to 501, or as 505 to 501. And therefore if the centrifugal force of every part in the leg ACca, arising from the diurnal motion, was to the weight of the same part as 4 to 505, so that from the weight of every part, conceived to be divided into 505 parts, the centrifugal force might take off four of those parts, the weights would remain equal in each leg, and therefore the fluid would rest in an equilibrium. But the centrifugal force of every part is to the weight of the same part as 1 to 289; that is, the centrifugal force, which should be $\frac{4}{505}$ parts of the weight, is only $\frac{1}{289}$ part thereof. And, therefore, I say, by the rule of proportion, that if the centrifugal force $\frac{4}{505}$ make the height of the water in the leg ACca to exceed the height of the water in the leg QCcq by $\frac{1}{100}$ part of its whole height the centrifugal force $\frac{1}{289}$ will make the excess of the height in the leg ACca only $\frac{1}{289}$ part of the height of the water in the other leg QCcq; and therefore the diameter of the earth at the equator is to its diameter from pole to pole as 230 to 229. And since the mean semidiameter of the earth, according to Picard's mensuration, is 19,615,800 Paris feet, or 3923.16 miles (reckoning 5000 feet to a mile), the earth will be higher at the equator than at the poles by 85,472 feet, or $17\frac{1}{10}$ miles. And its height at the equator will be about 19,658,600 feet, and at the poles 19,573,000 feet.

If, the density and periodic time of the diurnal revolution remaining the same, the planet was greater or less than the earth, the proportion of the centrifugal force to that of gravity, and therefore also of the diameter between the poles to the diameter at the equator, would likewise remain the same. But if the diurnal motion was accelerated or retarded in any proportion, the centrifugal force would be augmented or diminished nearly in the same proportion squared; and therefore the difference of the diameters will be increased or diminished in the same squared ratio, very nearly. And if the density of the planet was augmented or diminished in any proportion, the force of gravity tending towards it would also be augmented or diminished in the same proportion: and the difference of the diameters on the contrary would be diminished in proportion as the force of gravity is augmented, and augmented in proportion as the force of gravity is diminished. Therefore, since the earth, in respect of the fixed stars, revolves in 23^h. 56^m., but Jupiter in 9^h. 56^m., and the squares of their periodic times are as 29 to 5, and their densities as 400 to $94\frac{1}{2}$, the difference of the diameters of Jupiter will be to its lesser diameter as

$\frac{29}{5} \cdot \frac{400}{94\frac{1}{2}} \cdot \frac{1}{229}$ to 1, or as 1 to $9\frac{1}{3}$, nearly. Therefore the diameter of Jupiter from east to west is to its diameter from pole to pole nearly as $10\frac{1}{3}$ to $9\frac{1}{3}$. Therefore, since its greatest diameter is 37″, its lesser diameter lying between the poles will be 33″ 25‴. Add thereto about 3″ for the irregular refraction of light, and the apparent diameters of this planet will become 40″ and 36″ 25‴; which are to each other as $11\frac{1}{6}$ to $10\frac{1}{6}$, very nearly. These things are so upon the supposition that the body of Jupiter is uniformly dense. But now if its body be denser towards the plane of the equator than towards the poles, its diameters may be to each other as 12 to 11, or 13 to 12, or perhaps as 14 to 13.

And Cassini observed, in the year 1691, that the diameter of Jupiter reaching from east to west is greater by about a fifteenth part than the other diameter. Mr. Pound with his 123-foot telescope, and an excellent micrometer, measured the diameters of Jupiter in the year 1719, and found them as follows:

The times			Greatest diameter	Lesser diameter	The diameters to each other
	days	hours	Parts	Parts	
January	28	6	13.40	12.28	As 12 to 11
March	6	7	13.12	12.20	$13\frac{3}{4}$ to $12\frac{3}{4}$
March	9	7	13.12	12.08	$12\frac{2}{3}$ to $11\frac{2}{3}$
April	9	9	12.32	11.48	$14\frac{1}{2}$ to $13\frac{1}{2}$

So that the theory agrees with the phenomena; for the planets are more heated by the sun's rays towards their equators, and therefore are a little more condensed by that heat than towards their poles.

Moreover, that there is a diminution of gravity occasioned by the diurnal rotation of the earth, and therefore the earth rises higher there than it does at the poles (supposing that its matter is uniformly dense), will appear by the experiments of pendulums related under the following Proposition.

Proposition 20. Problem 4

To find and compare together the weights of bodies in the different regions of our earth.

Because the weights of the unequal legs of the canal of water ACQqca are equal; and the weights of the parts proportional to the whole legs, and alike situated in them, are one to another as the weights of the wholes, and therefore equal between themselves; the weights of equal parts, and alike situated in the

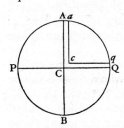

legs, will be inversely as the legs, that is, inversely as 230 to 229. And the case is the same in all homogeneous equal bodies alike situated in the legs of the canal. Their weights are inversely as the legs, that is, inversely as the distances of the bodies from the centre of the earth. Therefore if the bodies are situated in the uppermost parts of the canals, or on the surface of the earth, their weights will be one to another inversely as their distances from the centre. And, by the same argument, the weights in all other places round the whole surface of the earth are inversely as the distances of the places from the centre; and, therefore, on the hypothesis of the earth's being a spheroid, are given in proportion.

From this arises the theorem that the increase of weight in passing from the equator to the poles is nearly as the versed sine of double the latitude; or, which comes to the same thing, as the square of the sine of the latitude; and the arcs of the degrees of latitude in the meridian increase nearly in the same proportion. And, therefore, since the latitude of Paris is 48° 50', that of places under the equator 00°00', and that of places under the poles 90°; and the versed sines of double those arcs are 1,133,400,000 and 20,000, the radius being 10,000; and the force of gravity at the pole is to the force of gravity at the equator as 230 to 229; and the excess of the force of gravity at the pole to the force of gravity at the equator is as 1 to 229; the excess of the force of gravity in the latitude of Paris will be to the force of gravity at the equator as $1 \cdot \frac{11334}{20000}$ to 229, or as 5667 to 2,290,000. And therefore the whole forces of gravity in those places will be one to the other as 2,295,667 to 2,290,000. Therefore, since the lengths of pendulums vibrating in equal times are as the forces of gravity, and in the latitude of Paris the length of a pendulum vibrating seconds is 3 Paris feet and $8\frac{1}{2}$ lines, or rather, because of the weight of the air, $8\frac{5}{9}$ lines, the length of a pendulum vibrating in the same time under the equator will be shorter by 1.087 lines. And by a like calculus the following table is made.

Latitude of the place	Length of the pendulum		Measure of one degree in the meridian	Latitude of the place	Length of the pendulum		Measure of one degree in the meridian
degrees	feet	lines	toises	degrees	feet	lines	toises
0	3	. 7.468	56637	6	3	. 8.461	57022
5	3	. 7.482	56642	7	3	. 8.494	57035
10	3	. 7.526	56659	8	3	. 8.528	57048
15	3	. 7.596	56687	9	3	. 8.561	57061
20	3	. 7.692	56724	50	3	. 8.594	57074
25	3	. 7.812	56769	55	3	. 8.756	57137
30	3	. 7.948	56823	60	3	. 8.907	57196
35	3	. 8.099	56882	65	3	. 9.044	57250
40	3	. 8.261	56945	70	3	. 9.162	57295
1	3	. 8.294	56958	75	3	. 9.258	57332
2	3	. 8.327	56971	80	3	. 9.329	57360
3	3	. 8.361	56984	85	3	. 9.372	57377
4	3	. 8.394	56997	90	3	. 9.387	57382
45	3	. 8.428	57010				

By this table, therefore, it appears that the inequality of degrees is so small that the figure of the earth, in geographical matters, may be considered as spherical; especially if the earth be a little denser towards the plane of the equator than towards the poles.

Now several astronomers, sent into remote countries to make astronomical observations, have found that pendulum clocks do accordingly move slower near the equator than in our climates. And, first of all, in the year 1672, M. Richer took notice of it in the island of Cayenne; for when, in the month of August, he was observing the transits of the fixed stars over the meridian, he found his clock to go slower than it ought in respect of the mean motion of the sun at the rate of 2^m. 28^s. a day. Therefore, fitting up a simple pendulum to vibrate in seconds, which were measured by an excellent clock, he observed the length of that simple pendulum; and this he did over and over every week for ten months together. And upon his return to France, comparing the length of that pendulum with the length of the pendulum at Paris (which was 3 Paris feet and $8\frac{3}{5}$ lines), he found it shorter by $1\frac{1}{4}$ lines.

Afterwards, our friend Dr. Halley, about the year 1677, arriving at the island of St. Helena, found his pendulum clock to go slower there than at London without marking the difference. But he shortened the rod of his clock by more than $\frac{1}{8}$ of an inch, or $1\frac{1}{2}$ lines; and, to effect this, because the length of the screw at the lower end of the rod was not sufficient, he interposed a wooden ring between the nut and the ball.

Then, in the year 1682, M. Varin and M. des Hayes found the length of a simple pendulum vibrating in seconds at the Royal Observatory of Paris to be 3 feet and $8\frac{5}{9}$ lines. And by the same method in the island of Goree, they found the length of an isochronal pendulum to be 3 feet and $6\frac{5}{9}$ lines, differing from the former by two lines. And in the same year, going to the islands of Guadaloupe and Martinico, they found that the length of an isochronal pendulum in those islands was 3 feet and $6\frac{1}{2}$ lines.

After this, M. Couplet, the son, in the month of July, 1697, at the Royal Observatory of Paris, so fitted his pendulum clock to the mean motion of the sun, that for a considerable time together the clock agreed with the motion of the sun. In November following, upon his arrival at Lisbon, he found his clock to go slower than before at the rate of $2^{m}. 13^{s}.$ in 24 hours. And the following March, coming to Paraiba, he found his clock to go slower than at Paris, and at the rate $4^{m}. 12^{s}.$ in 24 hours; and he affirms that the pendulum vibrating in seconds was shorter at Lisbon by $2\frac{1}{2}$ lines, and at Paraiba by $3\frac{2}{3}$ lines, than at Paris. He would have done better to have reckoned those differences $1\frac{1}{3}$ and $2\frac{5}{9}$: for these differences correspond to the differences of the times $2^{m}. 13^{s}.$ and $4^{m}. 12^{s}.$ But this gentleman's observations are so gross, that we cannot confide in them.

In the following years, 1699 and 1700, M. des Hayes, making another voyage to America, determined that in the islands of Cayenne and Granada the length of the pendulum vibrating in seconds was a small matter less than 3 feet and $6\frac{1}{2}$ lines; that in the island of St. Christopher it was 3 feet and $6\frac{3}{4}$ lines; and in the island of St. Domingo 3 feet and 7 lines.

And, in the year 1704, Feuillé, at Puerto Bello in America, found that the length of the pendulum vibrating in seconds was 3 Paris feet and only $5\frac{7}{12}$ lines, that is, almost 3 lines shorter than at Paris; but the observation was faulty. For afterwards, going to the island of Martinico, he found the length of the isochronal pendulum there 3 Paris feet and $5\frac{10}{12}$ lines.

Now the latitude of Paraiba is 6° 38′ south; that of Puerto Bello, 9° 33′ north; and the latitudes of the islands Cayenne, Goree, Guadaloupe, Martinico, Granada, St. Christopher, and St. Domingo, are respectively 4° 55′, 14° 40″, 15° 00′, 14° 44′, 12° 06′, 17° 19′, and 19° 48′, north. And the excesses of the length of the pendulum at Paris above the lengths of the isochronal pendulums observed in those latitudes are a little greater than by the table of the lengths of the pendulum before computed. And therefore the earth is a little higher under the equator than by the preceding calculus, and a little denser at the centre than in mines near the surface, unless, perhaps, the heats of the torrid zone have a little extended the length of the pendulums.

For M. Picard has observed that a rod of iron, which in frosty weather in the winter season was one foot long, when heated by fire, was lengthened into one foot and ¼ line. Afterwards M. de la Hire found that a rod of iron, which in the like winter season was 6 feet long, when exposed to the heat of the summer sun, was extended into 6 feet and ⅔ line. In the former case the heat was greater than in the latter; but in the latter it was greater than the heat of the external parts of a human body; for metals exposed to the summer sun acquire a very considerable degree of heat. But the rod of a pendulum clock is never exposed to the heat of the summer sun, nor ever acquires a heat equal to that of the external parts of a human body; and, therefore, though the 3-foot rod of a pendulum clock will indeed be a little longer in the summer than in the winter season, yet the difference will scarcely amount to ¼ line. Therefore the total difference of the lengths of isochronal pendulums in different climates cannot be ascribed to the difference of heat; nor indeed to the mistakes of the French astronomers. For although there is not a perfect agreement between their observations, yet the errors are so small that they may be neglected; and in this they all agree, that isochronal pendulums are shorter under the equator than at the Royal Observatory of Paris, by a difference not less than 1¼ lines, nor greater than 2⅔ lines. By the observations of M. Richer, in the island of Cayenne, the difference was 1¼ lines. That difference being corrected by those of M. des Hayes, becomes 1½ lines or 1¾ lines. By the less accurate observations of others, the same was made about 2 lines. And this disagreement might arise partly from the errors of the observations, partly from the dissimilitude of the internal parts of the earth, and the height of mountains; partly from the different temperatures of the air.

I take an iron rod 3 feet long to be shorter by a sixth part of one line in winter time with us here in England than in the summer. Because of the great heats under the equator, subtract this quantity from the difference of 1¼ lines observed by M. Richer, and there will remain 1¹⁄₁₂ lines, which agrees very well with $1\frac{87}{1000}$ lines, obtained earlier by the theory. M. Richer repeated his observations, made in the island of Cayenne, every week for ten months together, and compared the lengths of the pendulum which he had there noted in the iron rods with the lengths thereof which he observed in France. This diligence and care seems to have been wanting to the other observers. If this gentleman's observations are to be depended on, the earth is higher under the equator than at the poles, and that by an excess of about 17 miles; as appeared above by the theory.

Proposition 21. Theorem 17

That the equinoctial points go backwards, and that the axis of the earth, by a nutation in every annual revolution, twice vibrates towards the ecliptic, and as often returns to its former position.

The Proposition appears from Cor. xx, Prop. 66, Book I; but that motion of nutation must be very small, and, indeed, scarcely perceptible.

Proposition 22. Theorem 18

That all the motions of the moon, and all the inequalities of those motions, follow from the principles which we have laid down.

That the greater planets, while they are carried about the sun, may in the meantime carry other lesser planets, revolving about them, and that those lesser planets must move in ellipses which have their foci in the centres of the greater, appears from Prop. 65, Book I. But then their motions will be in several ways disturbed by the action of the sun, and they will suffer such inequalities as are observed in our moon. Thus our moon (by Cor. II, III, IV, and V, Prop. 66, Book I) moves faster, and, by a radius drawn to the earth, describes an area greater for the time, and has its orbit less curved, and therefore approaches nearer to the earth in the syzygies than in the quadratures, excepting so far as these effects are hindered by the motion of eccentricity; for (by Cor. IX, Prop. 66, Book I) the eccentricity is greatest when the apogee of the moon is in the syzygies, and least when the same is in the quadratures; and upon this account the perigean moon is swifter, and nearer to us, but the apogean moon slower and farther from us, in the syzygies than in the quadratures. Moreover, the apogee goes forwards, and the nodes backwards; and this is done not with a regular but an unequal motion. For (by Cor. VII and VIII, Prop. 66, Book I) the apogee goes more swiftly forwards in its syzygies, more slowly backwards in its quadratures; and, by the excess of its progress above its regress, advances yearly forwards. But the nodes, on the contrary (by Cor. XI, Prop. 66, Book I), are quiescent in their syzygies, and go fastest back in their quadratures. Further, the greatest latitude of the moon (by Cor. X, Prop. 66, Book I) is greater in the quadratures of the moon than in its syzygies. And (by Cor. VI, Prop. 66, Book I) the mean motion of the moon is slower in the perihelion of the earth than in its aphelion. And these are the principal inequalities (of the moon) taken notice of by astronomers.

But there are yet other inequalities not observed by former astronomers, by which the motions of the moon are so disturbed that to this day we have not been able to bring them under any certain rule. For the velocities or hourly motions of the apogee and nodes of the moon, and their equations, as well as the difference between the greatest eccentricity in the syzygies and the least eccentricity in the quadratures, and that inequality which we call the variation, are (by Cor. XIV, Prop. 66, Book I) in the course of the year augmented and diminished as the cube of the sun's apparent diameter. And besides (by Cor. I and II, Lem. 10, and Cor. XVI, Prop. 66, Book I) the variation is augmented and diminished nearly as the square of the time between the quadratures. But, in astronomical calculations, this inequality is commonly thrown into and combined with the equation of the moon's centre.

PROPOSITION 23. PROBLEM 5

To derive the unequal motions of the satellites of Jupiter and Saturn from the motions of our moon.

From the motions of our moon we deduce the corresponding motions of the moons or satellites of Jupiter in this manner, by Cor. XVI, Prop. 66, Book I. The mean motion of the nodes of the outmost satellite of Jupiter is to the mean motion of the nodes of our moon in a proportion compounded of the squared ratio of the periodic times of the earth about the sun to the periodic times of Jupiter about the sun, and the simple ratio of the periodic time of the satellite about Jupiter to the periodic time of our moon about the earth; and therefore, those nodes, in the space of an hundred years, are carried 8° 24′ backwards or forwards. The mean motions of the nodes of the inner satellites are to the mean motion of the nodes of the outmost as their periodic times are to the periodic time of the former, by the same Corollary, and are thence given. And the forward motion of the apse of every satellite is to the backward motion of its nodes as the motion of the apogee of our moon to the motion of its nodes (by the same Corollary), and is thence given. But the motions of the apsides thus found must be diminished in the proportion of 5 to 9, or of about 1 to 2, on account of a cause which I cannot here stop to explain. The greatest equations of the nodes, and of the apse of every satellite, are to the greatest equations of the nodes, and apogee of our moon respectively, as the motions of the nodes and apsides of the satellites, in the time of one revolution of the former equations, to the motions of the nodes and apogee of our moon, in the time of one revolution of the latter equations. The variation of a satellite seen from Jupiter is to the variation of our moon in the same proportion as the whole motions of their nodes respectively during the times in which the satellite and our moon (after parting from) are revolved (again) to the sun, by the same Corollary; and therefore in the outmost satellite the variation does not exceed 5^s 12th.

Proposition 24. Theorem 19

That the flux and reflux of the sea arise from the actions of the sun and moon.

By Cor. xix and xx, Prop. 66, Book i, it appears that the waters of the sea ought twice to rise and twice to fall every day, as well lunar as solar; and that the greatest height of the waters in the open and deep seas ought to follow the approach of the luminaries to the meridian of the place by a less interval than six hours; as happens in all that eastern tract of the Atlantic and Ethiopic seas between *France* and the Cape of Good Hope; and on the coasts of Chile and Peru in the South Sea; in all which shores the flood falls out about the second, third, or fourth hour, unless where the motion propagated from the deep ocean is by the shallowness of the channels, through which it passes to some particular places, retarded to the fifth, sixth, or seventh hour, and even later. The hours I reckon from the approach of each luminary to the meridian of the place, as well under as above the horizon; and by the hours of the lunar day I understand the 24th parts of that time which the moon, by its apparent diurnal motion, employs to come about again to the meridian of the place which it left the day before. The force of the sun or moon in raising the sea is greatest in the approach of the luminary to the meridian of the place; but the force impressed upon the sea at that time continues a little while after the impression, and is afterwards increased by a new though less force still acting upon it. This makes the sea rise higher and higher, till, this new force becoming too weak to raise it any more, the sea rises to its greatest height. And this will come to pass, perhaps, in one or two hours, but more frequently near the shores in about three hours, or even more, where the sea is shallow.

The two luminaries excite two motions, which will not appear distinctly, but between them will arise one mixed motion compounded out of both. In the conjunction or opposition of the luminaries their forces will be conjoined, and bring on the greatest flood and ebb. In the quadratures the sun will raise the waters which the moon depresses, and depress the waters which the moon raises, and from the difference of their forces the smallest of all tides will follow. And because (as experience tells us) the force of the moon is greater than that of the sun, the greatest height of the waters will happen about the third lunar hour. Out of the syzygies and quadratures, the greatest tide, which by the single force of the moon ought to fall out at the third lunar hour, and by the single force of the sun at the third solar hour, by the compounded forces of both must fall out in an intermediate time that approaches nearer to the third hour of the moon than to that of the sun. And, therefore, while the moon is passing from the syzygies to the quadratures, during which time the third hour of the sun precedes the third hour of the moon, the greatest height of the waters will also precede the third hour of the moon, and that, by the greatest interval, a little after the octants of the moon; and, by like intervals, the greatest tide will follow the third lunar hour, while the moon is passing from the quadratures to the syzygies. Thus it happens in the open sea; for in the mouths of rivers the greater tides come later to their height.

But the effects of the luminaries depend upon their distances from the earth; for when they are less distant, their effects are greater, and when more distant, their effects are less, and that as the cube of their apparent diameter. Therefore it is that the sun, in the winter time, being then in its perigee, has a greater effect, and makes the tides in the syzygies somewhat greater, and those in the quadratures somewhat less than in the summer season; and every month the moon, while in the perigee, raises greater tides than at the distance of fifteen days before or after, when it is in its apogee. From this it comes to pass that two highest tides do not follow one the other in two immediately succeeding syzygies.

The effect of either luminary doth likewise depend upon its declination or distance from the equator; for if the luminary was placed at the pole, it would constantly attract all the parts of the waters without any intensification or remission of its action, and could cause no reciprocation of motion. And, therefore, as the luminaries decline from the equator towards either pole they will, by degrees, lose their force, and on this account will excite lesser tides in the solstitial than in the equinoctial syzygies. But in the solstitial quadratures they will raise greater tides than in the quadratures about the equinoxes; because the force of the moon, then situated in the equator, most exceeds the force of the sun. Therefore the greatest tides occur in those syzygies, and the least in those quadratures, which happen about the time of both equinoxes; and the greatest tide in the syzygies is always succeeded by the least tide in the quadratures, as we find by experience. But, because the sun is less distant from the earth in winter than in summer, it comes to pass that the greatest and least tides more frequently appear before than after the vernal equinox, and more frequently after than before the autumnal.

Moreover, the effects of the luminaries depend upon the latitudes of places. Let ApEP represent the earth covered with deep waters; C its centre; P, p its poles; AE the equator; F any place without the equator; Ff the parallel of the

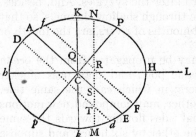

place; Dd the correspondent parallel on the other side of the equator; L the place of the moon three hours before; H the place of the earth directly under it; h the opposite place; K, k the places at 90 degrees distance; CH, Ch, the greatest heights of the sea from the centre of the earth; and CK, Ck its least heights: and if with the axes Hh, Kk, an ellipse is described, and by the revolution of that ellipse about its longer axis H*h* a spheroid HPK*hpk* is formed, this spheroid will nearly represent the figure of the sea; and CF, C*f*, CD, C*d*, will represent the heights of the sea in the places F*f*, D*d*. But further; in the said revolution of the ellipse any point N describes the circle NM cutting the parallels F*f*, D*d*, in any places RT, and the equator AE in S; CN will represent the height of the sea in all those places, R, S, T, situated in this circle. Therefore, in the diurnal revolution of any place F, the greatest flood will be in F, at the third hour after the appulse of the moon to the meridian above the horizon; and afterwards the greatest ebb in Q, at the third hour after the setting of the moon; and then the greatest flood in *f*, at the third hour after the appulse of the moon to the meridian under the horizon; and, lastly, the greatest ebb in Q, at the third hour after the rising of the moon; and the latter flood in *f* will be less than the preceding flood in F. For the whole sea is divided into two hemispherical floods, one in the hemisphere KH*k* on the north side, the other in the opposite hemisphere K*hk*, which we may therefore call the northern and the southern floods. These floods, being always opposite the one to the other, come by turns to the meridians of all places, after an interval of twelve lunar hours. And as the northern countries partake more of the northern flood, and the southern countries more of the southern flood, thence arise tides, alternately greater and less in all places without the equator, in which the luminaries rise and set. But the greatest tide will happen when the moon declines towards the vertex of the place, about the third hour after the appulse of the moon to the meridian above the horizon; and when the moon changes its declination *to the other side of the equator*, that which was the greater tide will be changed into a lesser. And the greatest difference of the floods will fall out about the times of the solstices; especially if the ascending node of the moon is about the first of Aries. So it is found by experience that the morning tides in winter exceed those of the evening, and the evening tides in summer exceed those of the morning; at Plymouth by the height of one foot, but at Bristol by the height of fifteen inches, according to the observations of Colepress and Sturmy.

But the motions which we have been describing suffer some alteration from that force of reciprocation, which the waters, being once moved, retain a little while *by their inertia*. Whence it comes to pass that the tides may continue for some time, though the actions of the luminaries should cease. This power of retaining the impressed motion lessens the difference of the alternate tides, and makes those tides which immediately succeed after the syzygies greater, and those which follow next after the quadratures less. And hence it is that the alternate tides at Plymouth and Bristol do not differ much more from each other than by the height of a foot or fifteen inches, and that the greatest tides at those ports are not the first but the third after the syzygies. And, besides, all the motions are retarded in their passage through shallow channels, so that the greatest tides of all, in some straits and mouths of rivers, are the fourth or even the fifth after the syzygies.

Further, it may happen that the tide may be propagated from the ocean through different channels towards the same port, and may pass quicker through some channels than through others; in which case the same tide, divided into two or more succeeding one another, may compound new motions of different kinds. Let us suppose two equal tides flowing towards the same port from different places, one preceding the other by six hours; and suppose the first tide to happen at the third hour of the approach of the moon to the meridian of the port. If the moon at the time of the approach to the meridian was in the equator, every six hours alternately there would arise equal floods, which, meeting with as many equal ebbs, would so balance each other that for that day the water would stagnate and be quiet. If the moon then declined from the equator, the tides in the ocean would be alternately greater and less, as was said; and from thence two greater and two less tides would be alternately propagated towards that port. But the two greater floods would make the greatest height of the waters to fall out in the middle time between both; and the greater and less floods would make the waters to rise to a mean height in the middle time between them, and in the middle time between the two less floods the waters would rise to their least height. Thus in the space of twenty-four hours the waters would come, not twice, as commonly, but once only to their greatest, and once only to their least height; and their greatest height, if the moon declined towards the elevated pole, would happen at the sixth or thirtieth hour after the approach of the moon to the meridian; and when the moon changed its declination, this flood would be changed into an ebb. An example of this Dr. Halley has given us, from the observations of seamen in the port of Batshaw, in the kingdom of Tunquin, in the latitude of 20° 50′ north. In that port, on the day which follows after the passage of the moon over the equator, the waters stagnate: when the moon declines to the north, they begin to flow and ebb, not twice, as in other ports, but once only every day; and the flood happens at the setting, and the greatest ebb at the rising of the moon. This tide increases with the declination of the moon till the seventh or eighth day; then for the seven or eight days following it decreases at the same rate as it had increased, and ceases when the moon changes its declination, crossing over the equator to the south. After which the flood is immediately changed into an ebb; and thenceforth the ebb happens at the setting and the flood at the rising of the moon; till the moon, again passing the equator, changes its declination. There are two inlets to this port and the neighboring channels, one from the seas of China, between the continent and the island of Leuconia; the other from the Indian Sea, between the continent and the island of Borneo. But whether there be really two tides propagated through the said channels, one from the Indian Sea in the space of twelve hours, and one from the sea of China in the space of six hours, which therefore happening at the third and ninth lunar hours, by being compounded together, produce those motions; or whether there be any other circumstances in the state of those seas, I leave to be determined by observations on the neighboring shores.

Thus I have explained the causes of the motions of the moon and of the sea. Now it is fit to subjoin something concerning the amount of those motions.

PROPOSITION 25. PROBLEM 6

To find the forces with which the sun disturbs the motions of the moon.

Let S represent the sun, T the earth, P the moon, CADB the moon's orbit. In SP take SK equal to ST; and let SL be to SK as the square of SK to SP: draw LM parallel to PT; and if ST or SK is supposed to represent the accelerated force of gravity of the earth towards the sun, SL will represent the accelerative force of gravity of the moon towards the sun. But that force is

compounded of the parts SM and LM, of which the force LM, and that part
of SM which is represented by TM, disturb the motion of the moon, as we have
shown in Prop. 66, Book I, and its Corollaries. Forasmuch as the earth and
moon are revolved about their common centre of gravity, the motion of the
earth about that centre will be also disturbed by the like forces; but we may
consider the sums both of the forces
and of the motions as in the moon,
and represent the sum of the forces
by the lines TM and ML, which are
analogous to them both. The force
ML (in its mean amount) is to the
centripetal force by which the moon
may be retained in its orbit revolving about the earth at rest, at the

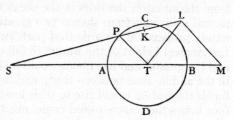

distance PT, as the square of the ratio of the periodic time of the moon about
the earth to the periodic time of the earth about the sun (by Cor. XVII, Prop.
66, Book I); that is, as the square of $27^d \cdot 7^h \cdot 43^m \cdot$ to $365^d \cdot 6^h \cdot 9^m \cdot$; or as 1000
to 178725; or as 1 to $178^{29}/_{40}$. But in Prop. 4 of this book we found that, if
both earth and moon were revolved about their common centre of gravity,
the mean distance of the one from the other would be nearly $60\frac{1}{2}$ mean semidiameters of the earth; and the force by which the moon may be kept revolving
in its orbit about the earth at rest at the distance PT of $60\frac{1}{2}$ semidiameters of
the earth, is to the force by which it may be revolved in the same time, at the
distance of 60 semidiameters, as $60\frac{1}{2}$ is to 60: and this force is to the force of
gravity with us very nearly as 1 is to $60 \cdot 60$. Therefore the mean force ML is
to the force of gravity on the surface of our earth as $1 \cdot 60\frac{1}{2}$ to $60 \cdot 60 \cdot 60 \cdot$
$178^{29}/_{40}$, or as 1 to 638092.6; hence, by the proportion of the lines TM, ML,
the force TM is also given; and these are the forces with which the sun disturbs
the motions of the moon.   Q.E.I.

PROPOSITION 26. PROBLEM 7

*To find the hourly increment of the area which the moon, by a radius drawn to
the earth, describes in a circular orbit.*

We have above shown that the area which the moon describes by a radius
drawn to the earth is proportional to the time of description, excepting so far
as the moon's motion is disturbed by the action of the sun; and here we propose
to investigate the inequality of the moment, or hourly increment *of that area or
motion so disturbed.* To render the calculus more easy, we shall suppose the
orbit of the moon to be circular, and neglect all inequalities but that only
which is now under consideration; and, because of the immense distance of the
sun, we shall further suppose that the lines SP and ST are parallel. By this
means, the force LM will be always reduced to its mean amount TP, as well as
the force TM to its mean amount 3PK. These forces (by Cor. II of the Laws of
Motion) compose the force TL; and this force, by letting fall the perpendicular
LE upon the radius TP, is resolved into the forces TE, EL; of which the force
TE, acting constantly in the direction of the radius TP, neither accelerates nor
retards the description of the area TPC made by that radius TP; but EL,
acting on the radius TP *in a perpendicular direction, accelerates or retards the
description of the area* in proportion as it accelerates or retards the moon. That

acceleration of the moon, in its passage from the quadrature C to the conjunction A, is in every moment of time as the *generating* accelerative force EL, that is, as $\dfrac{3\text{PK}\cdot\text{TK}}{\text{TP}}$. Let the time be represented by the mean motion of the moon, or (which comes to the same thing) by the angle CTP, or even by the arc CP. At right angles upon CT erect CG equal to CT; and, supposing the

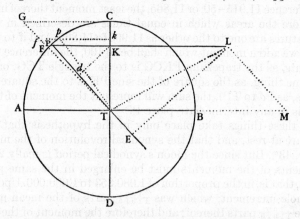

quadrantal arc AC to be divided into an infinite number of equal parts P*p*, &c., these *parts* may represent the like *infinite* number of the equal parts of time. Let fall *pk* perpendicular on CT, and draw TG meeting with KP, *kp* produced in F and *f*; then will FK be equal to TK, and K*k* be to PK as P*p* is to T*p*, that is, in a given proportion; and therefore FK·K*k*, or the area FK*kf*, will be as $\dfrac{3\text{PK}\cdot\text{TK}}{\text{TP}}$, that is, as EL; and, compounding, the whole area GCKF will vary as the sum of all the forces EL impressed upon the moon in the whole time CP; and therefore also as the velocity generated by that sum, that is, as the acceleration of the description of the area CTP, or as the increment of the moment *thereof*. The force by which the moon may in its periodic time CADB of 27^d. 7^h. 43^m. be retained revolving about the earth at rest at the distance TP, would cause a body falling in the time CT to describe the length ½CT, and at the same time to acquire a velocity equal to that with which the moon is moved in its orbit. This appears from Cor. ix, Prop. 4, Book i. But since K*d*, drawn perpendicular on TP, is *but* a third part of EL, and *equal* to the half of TP, or ML, in the octants, the force EL in the octants, where it is greatest, will exceed the force ML in the ratio of 3 to 2; and therefore will be to that force by which the moon in its periodic time may be retained revolving about the earth at rest as 100 is to ⅔·17872½, or 11915; and in the time CT will generate a velocity equal to $\tfrac{100}{11915}$ parts of the velocity of the moon; but in the time CPA will generate a greater velocity in the proportion of CA to CT or TP. Let the greatest EL force in the octants be represented by the area FK·K*k*, or by the rectangle ½TP·P*p*, which is equal thereto; and the velocity which that greatest force can generate in any time CP will be to the velocity which any other lesser force EL can generate in the same time as the rectangle ½TP·CP to the area KCGF; but the velocities generated in the whole time CPA will be one to the other as the rectangle ½TP·CA is to the triangle TCG, or as the quadrantal arc CA is to the radius TP; and therefore the latter velocity generated in the whole time will be $\frac{100}{11915}$ parts of the velocity of the moon. To this velocity of the moon, which is proportional to the mean moment of the area (supposing this mean moment to be represented by the number 11,915), we add and subtract the half of the other velocity; the sum 11,915+50, or 11,965, will represent the greatest moment of the area in the syzygy A; and the difference 11,915−50, or 11,865, the least moment thereof in the quadratures. Therefore the areas which in equal times are described in the syzygies and quadratures are one to the other as 11,965 to 11,865. And if to the least moment 11,865 we add a moment which shall be to 100, the difference of the two former moments, as the trapezium FKCG is to the triangle TCG, or, which comes to the same thing, as the square of the sine PK is to the square of the radius TP (that is, as Pd to TP), the sum will represent the moment of the area when the moon is in any intermediate place P.

But these things take place only in the hypothesis that the sun and the earth are at rest, and that the synodical revolution of the moon is finished in 27^d. 7^h. 43^m. But since the moon's synodical period is really 29^d. 12^h. 44^m., the increments of the moments must be enlarged in the same proportion as the time is, that is, in the proportion of 1,080,853 to 1,000,000. Upon which account, the whole increment, which was $\frac{100}{11915}$ parts of the mean moment, will now become $\frac{100}{11023}$ parts thereof; and therefore the moment of the area in the quadrature of the moon will be to the moment thereof in the syzygy as 11,023−50 to 11,023+50; or as 10,973 to 11,073; and to the moment thereof, when the moon is in any intermediate place P, as 10,973 to 10,973+Pd; that is, supposing TP = 100.

The area, therefore, which the moon, by a radius drawn to the earth, describes in the several little equal parts of time, is nearly as the sum of the number 219.46, and the versed sine of the double distance of the moon from the nearest quadrature, considered in a circle which hath unity for its radius. Thus it is when the variation in the octants is in its mean quantity. But if the variation there is greater or less, that versed sine must be augmented or diminished in the same proportion.

PROPOSITION 27. PROBLEM 8

From the hourly motion of the moon to find its distance from the earth.

The area which the moon, by a radius drawn to the earth, describes in every moment of time, is as the hourly motion of the moon and the square of the distance of the moon from the earth conjointly. And therefore the distance of the moon from the earth varies directly as the square root of the area and inversely as the square root of the hourly motion, taken jointly.   Q.E.I.

COR. I. Hence the apparent diameter of the moon is given; for it is inversely as the distance of the moon from the earth. Let astronomers try how accurately this rule agrees with the phenomena.

COR. II. Hence also the orbit of the moon may be more exactly defined from the phenomena than hitherto could be done.

PROPOSITION 28. PROBLEM 9

To find the diameters of the orbit, in which, without eccentricity, the moon would move.

The curvature of the orbit which a body describes, if attracted in lines perpendicular to the orbit, is directly as the force of attraction, and inversely as the square of the velocity. I estimate the curvatures of lines compared one with another according to the evanescent ratio of the sines or tangents of their angles of contact to equal radii, supposing those radii to be infinitely diminished. But the attraction of the moon towards the earth in the syzygies is the excess of its gravity towards the earth above the force of the sun 2PK (see Fig., Prop. 25), by which force the accelerative gravity of the moon towards the sun exceeds the accelerative gravity of the earth towards the sun or is exceeded by it. But in the quadratures that attraction is the sum of the gravity of the moon towards the earth, and the sun's force KT, by which the moon is attracted towards the earth. And these attractions, putting N for $\dfrac{AT+CT}{2}$,

are nearly as $\dfrac{178725}{AT^2} - \dfrac{2000}{CT \cdot N}$ and $\dfrac{178725}{CT^2} + \dfrac{1000}{AT \cdot N}$, or as $178{,}725N \cdot CT^2 - 2000AT^2 \cdot CT$, and $178{,}725N \cdot AT^2 + 1000CT^2 \cdot AT$. For if the accelerative gravity of the moon towards the earth be represented by the number 178,725, the mean force ML, which in the quadratures is PT or TK, and draws the moon towards the earth, will be 1000, and the mean force TM in the syzygies will be 3000; from which, if we subtract the mean force ML, there will remain 2000, the force by which the moon in the syzygies is drawn from the earth, and which we above called 2PK. But the velocity of the moon in the syzygies A and B is to its velocity in the quadratures C and D as CT is to AT, and as the moment of the area, which the moon by a radius drawn to the earth describes in the syzygies, is to the moment of that area *described* in the quadratures conjointly; that is, as 11,073CT is to 10,973AT. Take the square of this ratio inversely, and the former ratio directly, and the curvature of the moon's orbit in the syzygies will be to the curvature thereof in the quadratures as $120{,}406{,}729 \cdot 178{,}725AT^2 \cdot CT^2 \cdot N - 120{,}406{,}729 \cdot 2000AT^4 \cdot CT$ is to $122{,}611{,}329 \cdot 178{,}725AT^2 \cdot CT^2 \cdot N + 122{,}611{,}329 \cdot 1000CT^4 \cdot AT$, that is, as $2{,}151{,}969AT \cdot CT \cdot N - 24{,}081AT^3$ is to $2{,}191{,}371AT \cdot CT \cdot N + 12{,}261CT^3$.

Because the figure of the moon's orbit is unknown, let us, in its stead, assume the ellipse DBCA, in the centre of which we suppose the earth to be situated, and the greater axis DC to lie between the quadratures as the lesser AB between the syzygies. But since the plane of this ellipse is revolved about the

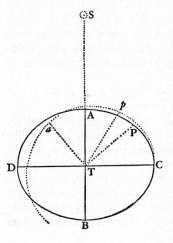

earth by an angular motion, and the orbit, whose curvature we now examine, should be described in a plane void of such motion, we are to consider the figure which the moon, while it is revolved in that ellipse, describes in this plane, that is to say, the figure C*pa*, the several points *p* of which are found by assuming any point P in the ellipse, which may represent the place of the moon, and drawing T*p* equal to TP in such manner that the angle PT*p* may be equal to the apparent motion of the sun from the time of the last quadrature in C; or (which comes to the same thing) that the angle CT*p* may be to the angle CTP as the time of the synodic revolution of the moon to the time of the periodic revolution thereof, or as 29^d. 12^h. 44^m. to 27^d.

$7^h.$ $43^m.$ If, therefore, in this proportion we take the angle CTa to the right angle CTA, and make Ta of equal length with TA, we shall have a the lower and C the upper apse of this orbit Cpa. But, by computation, I find that the difference between the curvature of this orbit Cpa at the vertex a, and the curvature of a circle described about the centre T with the interval TA, is to the difference between the curvature of the ellipse at the vertex A, and the curvature of the same circle, as the square of the ratio of the angle CTP to the angle CTp; and that the curvature of the ellipse in A is to the curvature of that circle as the square of the ratio of TA is to TC; and the curvature of that circle is to the curvature of a circle described about the centre T with the radius TC as TC is to TA; but that the curvature of this *last arch* is to the curvature of the ellipse in C as the square of the ratio of TA is to TC; and that the difference between the curvature of the ellipse in the vertex C, and the curvature of this last circle, is to the difference between the curvature of the figure Tpa, at the vertex C, and the curvature of this same *last* circle, as the square of the ratio of the angle CTp to the angle CTP. All these relations are easily derived from the sines of the angles of contact, and of the differences of those angles. But, by comparing those ratios, we find the curvature of the figure Cpa at a to be to its curvature at C as $AT^3 - \frac{16824}{100000} CT^2 \cdot AT$ is to $CT^3 + \frac{16824}{100000} AT^2 \cdot CT$; where the number $\frac{16824}{100000}$ represents the difference of the squares of the angles CTP and CTp, divided by the square of the lesser angle CTP; or (which is all one) the difference of the squares of the times $27^d.$ $7^h.$ $43^m.$ and $29^d.$ $12^h.$ $44^m.$ divided by the square of the time $27^d.$ $7^h.$ $43^m.$

Since, therefore, a represents the syzygy of the moon, and C its quadrature, the ratio now found must be the same as the ratio of the curvature of the moon's orb in the syzygies to the curvature thereof in the quadratures, which we found above. Therefore, in order to find the ratio of CT to AT, let us multiply the extremes and the means of the resulting proportion, and the terms which come out, divided by AT·CT, yield the following equation: $2062.79CT^4 - 2,151,969N \cdot CT^3 + 368,676N \cdot AT \cdot CT^2 + 36,342AT^2 \cdot CT^2 - 362,047N \cdot AT^2 \cdot CT + 2,191,371N \cdot AT^3 + 4051.4AT^4 = 0.$ Now if for the half sum N of the terms AT and CT we put 1, and x for their half difference, then CT will be $= 1+x$, and AT $= 1 - x$. And substituting those values in the equation, after resolving thereof, we shall find $x = 0.00719$; and from thence the semidiameter CT $= 1.00719$, and the semidiameter AT $= 0.99281$, which numbers are nearly as $70\frac{1}{24}$, and $69\frac{1}{24}$. Therefore the moon's distance from the earth in the syzygies is to its distance in the quadratures (setting aside the consideration of eccentricity) as $69\frac{1}{24}$ to $70\frac{1}{24}$; or, in round numbers, as 69 to 70.

PROPOSITION 29. PROBLEM 10

To find the variation of the moon.

This inequality is due partly to the elliptic figure of the moon's orbit, partly to the inequality of the moments of the area which the moon by a radius drawn to the earth describes. If the moon P revolved in the ellipse DBCA about the earth quiescent in the centre of the ellipse, and by the radius TP, drawn to the earth, described the area CTP, proportional to the time *of description;* and the greatest semidiameter CT of the ellipse was to the least TA as 70 to 69; the tangent of the angle CTP would be to the tangent of the angle of the mean motion, computed from the quadrature C, as the semidiameter

TA of the ellipse to its semidiameter TC, or as 69 to 70. But the description of the area CTP as the moon advances from the quadrature to the syzygy, ought to be in such manner accelerated, that the moment of the area in the moon's syzygy may be to the moment thereof in its quadrature as 11,073 to 10,973; and that the excess of the moment in any intermediate place P above the moment in the quadrature may be as the square of the sine of the angle CTP; which we may effect with accuracy enough, if we diminish the tangent of the angle CTP in the ratio obtained from the square root of the ratio of the number 10,973 to the number 11,073, that is, in the ratio of the number 68.6877 to the number 69. On this account the tangent of the angle CTP will now be to the tangent of the mean motion as 68.6877 is to 70; and the angle CTP in the octants, where the mean motion is 45°, will be found 44° 27′ 28″, which subtracted from 45°, the angle of the mean motion, leaves the greatest variation 32′ 32″. Thus it would be, if the moon, in passing from the quadrature to the syzygy, described an angle CTA of 90° only. But because of the motion of the earth, by which the sun is apparently transferred forwards, the moon, before it overtakes the sun, describes an angle CTa, greater than a right angle, in the ratio of the time of the synodic revolution of the moon to the time of its periodic revolution, that is, in the ratio of 29ᵈ. 12ʰ. 44ᵐ. to 27ᵈ. 7ʰ. 43ᵐ. Whence it comes to pass that all the angles about the centre T are dilated in the same ratio; and the greatest variation, which otherwise would be *but 32′ 32″*, now augmented in the said proportion, becomes 35′ 10″.

And this is its magnitude in the mean distance of the sun from the earth, neglecting the differences which may arise from the curvature of the great orbit, and the stronger action of the sun upon the moon when horned and new, than when gibbous and full. In other distances of the sun from the earth, the greatest variation is in a ratio compounded, directly of the square of the ratio of the time of the synodic revolution of the moon (the time of the year being given), and inversely as the cube of the ratio of the distance of the sun from the earth. And, therefore, in the apogee of the sun, the greatest variation is 33′ 14″, and in its perigee 37′ 11″, if the eccentricity of the sun is to the transverse semidiameter of the great orbit as $16^{15}/_{16}$ to 1000.

Hitherto we have investigated the variation in an orbit not eccentric, in which, to wit, the moon in its octants is always in its mean distance from the earth. If the moon, on account of its eccentricity, is more or less removed from the earth than if placed in this orbit, the variation may be something greater, or something less, than according to this rule. But I leave the excess or defect to the determination of astronomers from the phenomena.

PROPOSITION 30. PROBLEM 11

To find the hourly motion of the nodes of the moon in a circular orbit.

Let S represent the sun, T the earth, P the moon, NP*n* the orbit of the moon, N*pn* the orthographic projection of the orbit upon the plane of the ecliptic; N, *n* the nodes, *n*TN*m* the line of the nodes produced indefinitely; PI, PK perpendiculars upon the lines ST, Q*q*; P*p* a perpendicular upon the plane of the ecliptic; A, B the moon's syzygies in the plane of the ecliptic; AZ a perpendicular let fall upon N*n*, the line of the nodes; Q, *q* the quadratures of the moon in the plane of the ecliptic, and *p*K a perpendicular on the line Q*q* lying between the quadratures. The force of the sun to disturb the motion of the moon

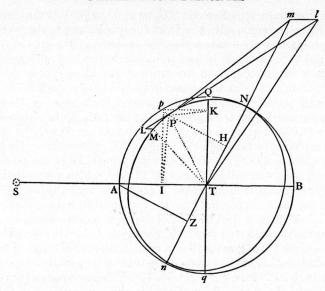

(by Prop. 25) is twofold, one proportional to the line LM, the other to the line MT, in the scheme of that Proposition; and the moon by the former force is drawn towards the earth, by the latter towards the sun, in a direction parallel to the right line ST joining the earth and the sun. The former force LM acts in the direction of the plane of the moon's orbit, and therefore makes no change upon the situation thereof, and is upon that account to be neglected; the latter force MT, by which the plane of the moon's orbit is disturbed, is the same with the force 3PK or 3IT. And this force (by Prop. 25) is to the force by which the moon may, in its periodic times, be uniformly revolved in a circle about the earth at rest, as 3IT to the radius of the circle multiplied by the number 178.725, or as IT to the radius thereof multiplied by 59.575. But in this calculus, and all that follows, I consider all the lines drawn from the moon to the sun as parallel to the line which joins the earth and the sun; because what inclination there is almost as much diminishes all effects in some cases as it augments them in others; and we are now inquiring after the mean motions of the nodes, neglecting such niceties as are of no moment and would only serve to render the calculus more complicated.

Now suppose PM to represent an arc which the moon describes in the least moment of time, and ML a little line, the half of which the moon, by the impulse of the said force 3IT, would describe in the same time; and joining PL, MP, let them be produced to m and l, where they cut the plane of the ecliptic, and upon Tm let fall the perpendicular PH. Now, since the right line ML is parallel to the plane of the ecliptic, and therefore can never meet with the right line ml which lies in that plane, and yet both those right lines lie in one common plane LMPml, they will be parallel, and upon that account the triangles LMP, lmP will be similar. And seeing MPm lies in the plane of the orbit, in which the moon did move while in the place P, the point m will fall upon the line Nn, which passes through the nodes N, n, of that orbit. And because the force by which the half of the little line LM is generated, if the whole had been together, and at once impressed in the point P, would have generated that whole line, and caused the moon to move in the arc whose chord is LP; that is to say, would have transferred the moon from the plane MPmT into the plane LPlT; therefore the angular motion of the nodes generated by that force will be equal to the angle mTl. But ml is to mP as ML to MP; and since MP, because of the time given, is also given, ml will be as the rectangle ML$\cdot m$P, that is, as the rectangle IT$\cdot m$P. And if Tml is a right angle, the angle mTl will be as $\dfrac{ml}{Tm}$, and therefore as $\dfrac{IT \cdot P m}{Tm}$, that is (because Tm and mP, TP and PH are proportional), as $\dfrac{IT \cdot PH}{TP}$; and, therefore, because TP is given, as IT$\cdot$PH. But if the angle Tml or STN is oblique, the angle mTl will be yet less, in proportion of the sine of the angle STN to the radius, or AZ to AT. And therefore the velocity of the nodes is as IT$\cdot$PH$\cdot$AZ, or as the product of the sines of the three angles TPI, PTN, and STN.

If these are right angles, as happens when the nodes are in the quadratures, and the moon in the syzygy, the little line ml will be removed to an infinite distance, and the angle mTl will become equal to the angle mPl. But in this case the angle mPl is to the angle PTM, which the moon in the same time by its apparent motion describes about the earth, as 1 to 59.575. For the angle mPl is equal to the angle LPM, that is, to the angle of the moon's deflection from a rectilinear path; which angle, if the gravity of the moon should have then ceased, the said force of the sun 3IT would by itself have generated in that given time; and the angle PTM is equal to the angle of the moon's deflection from a rectilinear path; which angle, if the force of the sun 3IT should have then ceased, the force alone by which the moon is retained in its orbit would have generated in the same time. And these forces (as we have above shown) are the one to the other as 1 to 59.575. Since, therefore, the mean hourly motion of the moon (in respect of the fixed stars) is 32^m 56^s 27th 12½^{iv} the hourly motion of the node in this case will be 33^s 10th 33^{iv} 12^v. But in other cases the hourly motion will be to 33^s 10th 33^{iv} 12^v as the product of the sines of the three angles TPI, PTN, and STN (or of the distances of the moon from the quadrature, of the moon from the node, and of the node from the sun) to the cube of the radius. And as often as the sine of any angle is changed from positive to negative, and from negative to positive, so often must the regressive be changed into a progressive, and the progressive into a regressive motion. Whence it comes to pass that the nodes are progressive as often as the moon happens to be placed between either quadrature, and the node nearest to that quadrature. In other cases they are regressive, and by the excess of the regress above the progress, they are monthly transferred backwards.

COR. I. Hence if from P and M, the extreme points of a least arc PM, on the line Qq joining the quadratures we let fall the perpendiculars PK, Mk, and produce the same till they cut the line of the nodes Nn in D and d, the hourly motion of the nodes will be as the area MPDd, and the square of the line AZ, conjointly. For let PK, PH, and AZ be the three said sines, viz., PK the sine of the distance of the moon from the quadrature, PH the sine of the distance of the moon from the node, and AZ the sine of the distance of the node from the sun; and the velocity of the node will be as the product PK$\cdot$PH$\cdot$AZ. But

PT is to PK as PM to Kk; and, therefore, because PT and PM are given, Kk will be as PK. Likewise AT is to PD as AZ is to PH, and therefore PH is as the rectangle PD·AZ; and, by compounding those proportions, PK·PH is as the solid content Kk·PD·AZ, and PK·PH·AZ as Kk·PD·AZ^2; that is, as the area PDdM and AZ^2 conjointly.   Q.E.D.

Cor. ii. In any given position of the nodes their mean hourly motion is half their hourly motion in the moon's syzygies; and therefore is to 16^s 35th 16^{iv} 36^v as the square of the sine of the distance of the nodes from the syzygies is to the square of the radius, or as AZ^2 to AT^2. For if the moon, by an uniform motion, describes the semicircle QAq, the sum of all the areas PDdM, during the time of the moon's passage from Q to M, will make up the area QMdE, terminating at the tangent QE of the circle; and by the time that the moon has arrived at the point n, that sum will make up the whole area EQAn described by the line PD: but when the moon proceeds from n to q, the line PD will fall without the circle, and describe the area nqe, terminating at the tangent qe of the circle, which area, because the nodes were before regressive, but are now progressive,

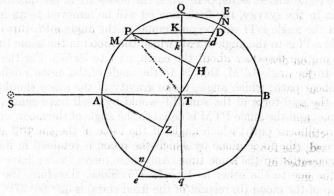

must be subtracted from the former area, and, being itself equal to the area QEN, will leave the semicircle NQAn. While, therefore, the moon describes a semicircle, the sum of all the areas PDdM will be the area of that semicircle; and while the moon describes a complete circle, the sum of those areas will be the area of the whole circle. But the area PDdM, when the moon is in the syzygies, is the rectangle of the arc PM into the radius PT; and the sum of all the areas, *every one* equal to this area, in the time that the moon describes a complete circle, is the rectangle of the whole circumference into the radius of the circle; and this rectangle, being double the area of the circle, will be double the former sum. If, therefore, the nodes went on with that velocity uniformly continued which they acquire in the moon's syzygies, they would describe a space double that which they describe in fact; and, therefore, the mean motion, by which, if uniformly continued, they would describe the same space with that which they do in fact describe by an unequal motion, is *but* one-half of that motion which they are possessed of in the moon's syzygies. Wherefore, since their greatest hourly motion, if the nodes are in the quadratures, is 33^s 10th 33^{iv} 12^v, their mean hourly motion in this case will be 16^s 35th 16^{iv} 36^v. And seeing the hourly motion of the nodes is everywhere as AZ^2 and the area PDdM conjointly, and, therefore, in the moon's syzygies, the hourly motion of the nodes is as AZ² and the area PD*d*M conjointly, that is (because the area PD*d*M described in the syzygies is given), as AZ², therefore the mean motion also will be as AZ²; and, therefore, when the nodes are without the quadratures, this motion will be to 16ˢ 35ᵗʰ 16ⁱᵛ 36ᵛ as AZ² to AT².　　Q.E.D.

PROPOSITION 31. PROBLEM 12

To find the hourly motion of the nodes of the moon in an elliptic orbit.

Let Q*pmaq* represent an ellipse described with the greater axis Q*q* and the less axis *ab*; QA*q*B a circle circumscribed; T the earth in the common centre of both; S the sun; *p* the moon moving in this ellipse; and *pm* an arc which it describes in the least moment of time; N and *n* the nodes joined by the line N*n*; *p*K and *mk* perpendiculars upon the axis Q*q*, produced both ways till they meet the circle in P and M, and the line of the nodes in D and *d*. And if the moon, by a radius drawn to the earth, describes an area proportional to the time *of description*, the hourly motion of the node in the ellipse will be as the area *p*D*dm* and AZ² conjointly.

For let PF touch the circle in P, and produced meet TN in F; and *pf* touch the ellipse in *p*, and produced meet the same TN in *f*, and both tangents concur in the axis TQ at Y; and let ML represent the space which the moon, by the impulse of the above-mentioned force 3IT or 3PK, would describe with a transverse motion, in the meantime while revolving in the circle it describes the arc PM; and *ml* denote the space which the moon revolving in the ellipse would describe in the same time by the impulse of the same force 3IT or 3PK; and let LP and *lp* be produced till they meet the plane of the ecliptic in G and *g*, and FG and *fg* be joined, of which FG produced may cut *pf*, *pg*, and TQ, in

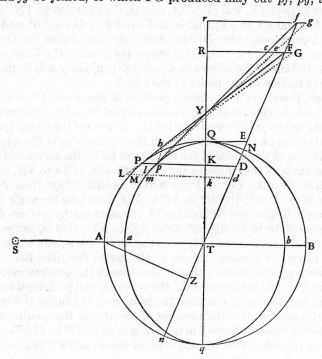

c, e, and R respectively; and fg produced may cut TQ in r. Because the force 3IT or 3PK in the circle is to the force 3IT or $3p$K in the ellipse as PK to pK, or as AT to aT, the space ML generated by the former force will be to the space ml generated by the latter as PK to pK; that is, because of the similar figures PYKp and FYRc, as FR to cR. But (because of the similar triangles PLM, PGF) ML is to FG as PL is to PG, that is (on account of the parallels Lk, PK, GR), as pl is to pe, that is (because of the similar triangles plm, cpe), as lm is to ce; and inversely as LM is to lm, or as FR is to cR, so is FG to ce. And therefore if fg was to ce as fy to cY, that is, as fr to cR (that is, as fr to FR and FR to cR conjointly, that is, as fT to FT, and FG to ce conjointly), because the ratio of FG to ce, expunged on both sides, leaves the ratios fg to FG and fT to FT, fg would be to FG as fT to FT; and, therefore, the angles which FG and fg would subtend at the earth T would be equal to each other. But these angles (by what we have shown in the preceding Proposition) are the motions of the nodes, while the moon describes in the circle the arc PM, in the ellipse the arc pm; and therefore the motions of the nodes in the circle and in the ellipse would be equal to each other. Thus, I say, it would be, if fg was to ce as fY to cY, that is, if fg was equal to $\dfrac{ce \cdot f\mathrm{Y}}{c\mathrm{Y}}$. But because of the similar triangles fgp, cep, fg is to ce as fp to cp; and therefore fg is equal to $\dfrac{ce \cdot fp}{cp}$; and therefore the angle which fg subtends in fact is to the former angle which FG subtends, that is to say, the motion of the nodes in the ellipse is to the motion of the same in the circle as this fg or $\dfrac{ce \cdot fp}{cp}$ to the former fg or $\dfrac{ce \cdot f\mathrm{Y}}{c\mathrm{Y}}$, that is, as $fp \cdot c$Y to fY$\cdot cp$, or as fp to fY, and cY to cp; that is, if ph parallel to TN meet FP in h, as Fh to FY and FY to FP; that is, as Fh to FP or Dp to DP, and therefore as the area Dpmd to the area DPMd. And, therefore, seeing (by Cor. I, Prop. 30) the latter area and AZ² conjointly are proportional to the hourly motion of the nodes in the circle, the former area and AZ² conjointly will be proportional to the hourly motion of the nodes in the ellipse.   Q.E.D.

COR. Since, therefore, in any given position of the nodes, the sum of all the areas pDdm, in the time while the moon is carried from the quadrature to any place m, is the area mpQEd terminated at the tangent of the ellipse QE; and the sum of all those areas, in one entire revolution, is the area of the whole ellipse; the mean motion of the nodes in the ellipse will be to the mean motion of the nodes in the circle as the ellipse to the circle; that is, as Ta to TA, or 69 to 70. And, therefore, since (by Cor. II, Prop. 30) the mean hourly motion of the nodes in the circle is to $16^s\ 35^{th}\ 16^{iv}\ 36^v$ as AZ² to AT², if we take the angle $16^s\ 21^{th}\ 3^{iv}$ 30^v to the angle $16^s\ 35^{th}\ 16^{iv}\ 36^v$ as 69 to 70, the mean hourly motion of the nodes in the ellipses will be to $16^s\ 21^{th}\ 3^{iv}\ 30^v$ as AZ² to AT²; that is, as the square of the sine of the distance of the node from the sun to the square of the radius.

But the moon, by a radius drawn to the earth, describes the area in the syzygies with a greater velocity than it does that in the quadratures, and upon that account the time is contracted in the syzygies, and prolonged in the quadratures; and together with the time the motion of the nodes is likewise augmented or diminished. But the moment of the area in the quadratures of the moon was to the moment thereof in the syzygies as 10,973 to 11,073; and therefore the mean moment in the octants is to the excess in the syzygies, and to the defect in the quadratures, as 11,023, the half-sum of those numbers, is to their half-difference 50. Wherefore, since the time of the moon in the several little equal parts of its orbit is inversely as its velocity, the mean time in the octants will be to the excess of the time in the quadratures, and to the defect *of the time* in the syzygies arising from this cause, nearly as 11,023 to 50. But, reckoning from the quadratures to the syzygies, I find that the excess of the moments of the area, in the several places above the least moment in the quadratures, is nearly as the square of the sine of the moon's distance from the quadratures; and therefore the difference between the moment in any place, and the mean moment in the octants, is as the difference between the square of the sine of the moon's distance from the quadratures, and the square of the sine of 45 degrees, or half the square of the radius; and the increment of the time in the several places between the octants and quadratures, and the decrement thereof between the octants and syzygies, is in the same proportion. But the motion of the nodes, while the moon describes the several little equal parts of its orbit, is accelerated or retarded as the square of the time; for that motion, while the moon describes PM, is (other things being equal) as ML, and ML varies as the square of the time. Wherefore, the motion of the nodes in the syzygies, in the time while the moon describes given little parts of its orbit, is diminished as the square of the ratio of the number 11,073 to the number 11,023; and the decrement is to the remaining motion as 100 to 10,973; but to the whole motion is as 100 to 11,073, nearly. But the decrement in the places between the octants and syzygies, and the increment in the places between the octants and quadratures, is to this decrement nearly as the whole motion in these places to the whole motion in the syzygies, and the difference between the square of the sine of the moon's distance from the quadrature, and the half-square of the radius, is to the half-square of the radius conjointly. Wherefore, if the nodes are in the quadratures, and we take two places, one on one side, one on the other, equally distant from the octant and other two distant by the same interval, one from the syzygy, the other from the quadrature, and from the decrements of the motions in the two places between the syzygy and octant we subtract the increments of the motions in the two other places between the octant and the quadrature, the remaining decrement will be equal to the decrement in the syzygy, as will easily appear by computation; and therefore the mean decrement, which ought to be subtracted from the mean motion of the nodes, is the fourth part of the decrement in the syzygy. The whole hourly motion of the nodes in the syzygies (when the moon by a radius drawn to the earth was supposed to describe an area proportional to the time) was $32^s\ 42^{th}\ 7^{iv}$. And we have shown that the decrement of the motion of the nodes, in the time while the moon, now moving with greater velocity, describes the same space, was to this motion as 100 to 11,073; and therefore this decrement is $17^{th}\ 43^{iv}\ 11^v$. The fourth part of which $4^{th}\ 25^{iv}\ 48^v$ subtracted from the mean hourly motion above found, $16^s\ 21^{th}\ 3^{iv}\ 30^v$, leaves $16^s\ 16^{th}\ 37^{iv}\ 42^v$, their correct mean hourly motion.

If the nodes are without the quadratures, and two places are considered, one on one side, one on the other, equally distant from the syzygies, the sum of the motions of the nodes, when the moon is in those places, will be to the sum of their motions, when the moon is in the same places and the nodes in the quadratures, as AZ^2 to AT^2. And the decrements of the motions arising from the causes but now explained will be mutually as the motions themselves, and therefore the remaining motions will be mutually between themselves as AZ^2 to AT^2; and the mean motions will be as the remaining motions. And, therefore, in any given position of the nodes, their correct mean hourly motion is to 16^s 16th 37^{iv} 42^v as AZ^2 to AT^2; that is, as the square of the sine of the distance of the nodes from the syzygies to the square of the radius.

Proposition 32. Problem 13

To find the mean motion of the nodes of the moon.

The yearly mean motion is the sum of all the mean hourly motions throughout the course of the year. Suppose that the node is in N, and that, after every hour is elapsed, it is drawn back again to its former place; so that, notwithstanding its proper motion, it may constantly remain in the same situation with respect to the fixed stars; while in the meantime the sun S, by the motion of the earth, is seen to leave the node, and to proceed till it completes its apparent annual course by an uniform motion. Let A*a* represent a given least arc, which the right line TS always drawn to the sun, by its intersection with the circle NA*n*, describes in the least given moment of time; and the mean hourly motion (from what we have above shown) will be as AZ^2, that is (because AZ and ZY are proportional), as the rectangle of AZ into ZY, that is, as the area AZY*a*; and the sum of all the mean hourly motions from the beginning will be as the sum of all the areas *a*YZA, that is, as the area NAZ. But the greatest AZY*a* is equal to the rectangle of the arc A*a* into the radius of the circle; and therefore the sum of all these rectangles in the whole circle will be to the like sum of all the greatest rectangles as the area of the whole circle to the rectangle of the whole circumference into the radius, that is, as 1 to 2. But the hourly motion corresponding to that greatest rectangle was 16^s 16th 37^{iv} 42^v and this motion in the complete course of the sidereal year, $365^d.$ $6^h.$ $9^s.$, amounts to $39°$ $38'$ $7''$ $50'''$; and therefore the half thereof, $19°$ $49'$ $3''$ $55'''$, is the mean motion of the nodes corresponding to the whole circle. And the motion of the nodes, in the time while the sun is carried from N to A, is to $19°$ $49'$ $3''$ $55'''$ as the area NAZ to the whole circle.

Thus it would be if the node was after every hour drawn back again to its former place, that so, after a complete revolution, the sun at the year's end would be found again in the same node which it had left when the year began. But, because of the motion of the node in the meantime, the sun must needs meet the node sooner; and now it remains that we compute the abbreviation of the time. Since, then, the sun, in the course of the year, travels 360 degrees, and the node in the same time by its greatest motion would be carried $39°$ $38'$ $7''$ $50'''$, or 39.6355 degrees; and the mean motion of the node in any place N is to its mean motion in its quadratures as AZ^2 to AT^2; the motion of the sun will be to the motion of the node in N as 360 AT^2 to $39.6355AZ^2$; that is, as $9.0827646AT^2$ to AZ^2. Therefore, if we suppose the circumference NA*n* of the whole circle to be divided into little equal parts, such as A*a*, the time in which the sun would describe the little arc A*a*, if the circle was quiescent, will be to the time in which it would describe the same arc, supposing the circle together with the nodes to be revolved about the centre T, inversely as $9.0827646AT^2$ to $9.0827646AT^2+AZ^2$; for the time is inversely as the velocity with which the little arc is described, and this velocity is the sum of the velocities of both sun and node. If, therefore, the sector NTA represent the time in which the sun by itself, without the motion of the node, would describe the arc NA, and the indefinitely small part ATa of the sector represent the little moment of the

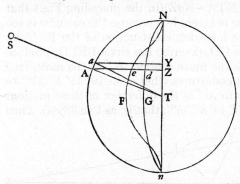

time in which it would describe the least arc Aa; and (letting fall aY perpendicular upon Nn) if in AZ we take dZ of such length that the rectangle of dZ into ZY may be to the least part ATa of the sector as AZ² to 9.0827646AT²+AZ²; that is to say, that dZ may be to ½AZ as AT² to 9.0827646AT²+AZ²; the rectangle of dZ into ZY will represent the decrement of the time arising from the motion of the node, while the arc Aa is described; and if the curve NdGn is the locus where the point d is always found, the curvilinear area NdZ will be as the whole decrement *of time* while the whole arc NA is described; and, therefore, the excess of the sector NAT above the area NdZ will be as the whole time. But because the motion of the node in a less time is less in proportion to the time, the area AaYZ must also be diminished in the same proportion; which may be done by taking in AZ the line eZ of such length, that it may be to the length of AZ as AZ² to 9.0827646AT²+AZ²; for so the rectangle of eZ into ZY will be to the area AZYa as the decrement of the time in which the arc Aa is described to the whole time in which it would have been described, if the node had been quiescent; and, therefore, that rectangle will be as the decrement of the motion of the node. And if the curve NeFn is the locus of the point e, the whole area NeZ, which is the sum of all the decrements *of that motion*, will be as the whole decrement *thereof* during the time in which the arc AN is described; and the remaining area NAe will be as the remaining motion, which is the true motion of the node, during the time in which the whole arc NA is described by the joint motions of both sun and node. Now the area of the semicircle is to the area of the figure NeFn found by the method of infinite series nearly as 793 to 60. But the motion corresponding *or proportional* to the whole circle was 19° 49′ 3″ 55‴; and therefore the motion corresponding to double the figure NeFn is 1° 29′ 58″ 2‴, which taken from the former motion leaves 18° 19′ 5″ 53‴, the whole motion of the node with respect to the fixed stars in the interval between two of its conjunctions with the sun; and this motion subtracted from the annual motion of the sun, 360°, leaves 341° 40′ 54″ 7‴, the motion of the sun in the interval between the same conjunctions. But as this motion is to the annual motion 360°, so is the motion of the node but just now found 18° 19′ 5″ 53‴ to its annual motion, which will therefore be 19° 18′ 1″ 23‴; and this is the mean motion of the nodes in the sidereal year. By astronomical tables, it is 19° 21′ 21″ 50‴. The difference is less than $\frac{1}{300}$ part of the whole motion, and seems to arise from the eccentricity of the moon's orbit, and its inclination to the plane of the ecliptic. By the eccentricity of this orbit the motion of the nodes is too much accelerated; and, on the other hand, by the inclination of the orbit, the motion of the nodes is somewhat retarded, and reduced to its just velocity.

PROPOSITION 33. PROBLEM 14

To find the true motion of the nodes of the moon.

In the time which is as the area NTA−NdZ (in the preceding Fig.) that motion is as the area NAe, and hence is given; but because the calculus is too difficult, it will be better to use the following construction of the Problem. About the centre C, with any radius CD, describe the circle BEFD; produce DC to A so as AB may be to AC as the mean motion to half the mean true motion when the nodes are in their quadratures (that is, as 19° 18′ 1″ 23‴ to 19° 49′ 3″ 55‴; and therefore BC is to AC as the difference of those motions 0° 31′ 2″ 32‴ to the latter motion 19° 49′ 3″ 55‴, that is, as 1 to 38³⁄₁₀). Then

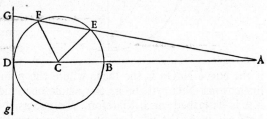

through the point D draw the indefinite line Gg, touching the circle in D; and if we take the angle BCE, or BCF, equal to the double distance of the sun from the place of the node, as found by the mean motion, and drawing AE or AF cutting the perpendicular DG in G, we take another angle which shall be to the whole motion of the node in the interval between its syzygies (that is, to 9° 11′ 3″) as the tangent DG to the whole circumference of the circle BED, and add this *last* angle (for which the angle DAG may be used) to the mean motion of the nodes, while they are passing from the quadratures to the syzygies, and subtract it from their mean motion while they are passing from the syzygies to the quadratures, we shall have their true motion; for the true motion so found will nearly agree with the true motion which comes out from assuming the times as the area NTA−NdZ, and the motion of the node as the area NAe; as anyone who chooses to examine and make the computations will find: and this is the semimenstrual equation of the motion of the nodes. But there is also a menstrual equation, but which is by no means necessary for finding of the moon's latitude; for since the variation of the inclination of the moon's orbit to the plane of the ecliptic is liable to a twofold inequality, the one semimenstrual, the other menstrual, the menstrual inequality *of this variation*, and the menstrual equation of the nodes, so moderate and correct each other, that in computing the latitude of the moon both may be neglected.

Cor. From this and the preceding Proposition it appears that the nodes are quiescent in their syzygies, but regressive in their quadratures, by an hourly motion of 16ˢ 19ᵗʰ 26ⁱᵛ; and that the equation of the motion of the nodes in the octants is 1° 30′; all of which exactly agree with the phenomena of the heavens.

SCHOLIUM

Mr. Machin, Professor Gresham, and Dr. Henry Pemberton, separately found out the motion of the nodes by a different method. Mention has been made of this method in another place. Their papers, which I have seen, contained two Propositions, and exactly agreed with each other in both of them. Mr. Machin's paper, coming first to my hands, I shall here insert.

THE MOTION OF THE MOON'S NODES

"PROPOSITION 1

"*The mean motion of the sun from the node is defined by a geometric mean proportional between the mean motion of the sun and that mean motion with which the sun recedes with the greatest swiftness from the node in the quadratures.*

"Let T be the earth's place, Nn the line of the moon's nodes at any given time, KTM a perpendicular thereto, TA a right line revolving about the centre with the same angular velocity with which the sun and the node recede from each other, in such sort that the angle between the quiescent right line Nn and the revolving line TA may be always equal to the distance of the places of the sun and node. Now if any right line TK be divided into parts TS and SK, and those parts be taken as the mean hourly motion of the sun to the mean hourly motion of the node in the quadratures, and there be taken the right line TH, a mean proportional between the part TS and the whole TK, this right line will be proportional to the sun's mean motion from the node.

"For let there be described the circle NK*n*M from the centre T and with the radius TK, and about the same centre, with the semiaxes TH and TN, let there be described an ellipse NH*n*L; and in the time in which the sun recedes from the node through the arc N*a*, if there be drawn the right line T*ba*, the area of the sector NT*a* will be the exponent of the sum of the motions of the sun and node in the same time. Let, therefore, the extremely small arc *a*A be that which the right line T*ba*, revolving according to the aforesaid law, will uniformly describe in a given interval of time, and the extremely small sector TA*a* will be as the sum of the velocities with which the sun and node are carried two different ways in that time. Now the sun's velocity is almost uniform, its inequality being so small as scarcely to produce the least inequality in the mean motion of the nodes. The other part of this sum, namely, the mean quantity of the velocity of the node, is increased in the recess from the syzygies in a squared ratio of the sine of its distance from the sun (by Cor., Prop. 31 of this book), and, being greatest in its quadratures with the sun in K, is in the same ratio to the sun's velocity as SK to TS, that is, as (the difference of the squares of TK and TH, or) the rectangle KHM to TH². But the ellipse NBH divides the sector AT*a*, the exponent of the sum of these two velocities, into two parts AB*ba* and BT*b*, proportional to the velocities. For, produce BT to the circle in β, and from the point B let fall upon the greater axis the perpendicular BG, which being produced both ways may meet the circle in the points F and *f*; and because the space AB*ba* is to the sector TB*b* as the rectangle ABβ is to BT² (that rectangle being equal to the difference of the squares of TA and TB, because the right line Aβ is equally cut in T, and unequally in B), therefore when the space AB*ba* is the greatest of all in K, this ratio will be the same as the ratio of the rectangle KHM to HT². But the greatest mean velocity of the node was shown above to be in that very ratio to the velocity of the sun; and therefore in

315

the quadratures the sector AT*a* is divided into parts proportional to the velocities. And because the rectangle KHM is to HT² as FB*f* to BG², and the rectangle ABβ is equal to the rectangle FB*f*, therefore the little area AB*ba*, where it is greatest, is to the remaining sector TB*b* as the rectangle ABβ is to BG². But the ratio of these little areas always was as the rectangle ABβ to BT²; and therefore the little area AB*ba* in the place A is less than its correspondent little area in the quadratures in the squared ratio of BG to BT, that is, in the squared

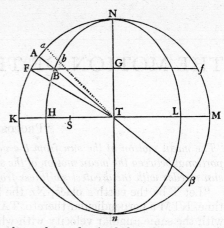

ratio of the sine of the sun's distance from the node. And therefore the sum of all the little areas AB*ba*, namely, the space ABN, will be as the motion of the node in the time in which the sun hath been going over the arc NA since he left the node; and the remaining space, namely, the elliptic sector NTB, will be as the sun's mean motion in the same time. And because the mean annual motion of the node is that motion which it performs in the time that the sun completes one period of its course, the mean motion of the node from the sun will be to the mean motion of the sun itself as the area of the circle is to the area of the ellipse; that is, as the right line TK to the right line TH, which is a mean proportional between TK and TS; or, which comes to the same, as the mean proportional TH to the right line TS.

"PROPOSITION 2

"The mean motion of the moon's nodes being given, to find their true motion.

"Let the angle A be the distance of the sun from the mean place of the node, or the sun's mean motion from the node. Then if we take the angle B, whose tangent is to the tangent of the angle A as TH to TK, that is, as the square root of the ratio of the mean hourly motion of the sun to the mean hourly motion of the sun from the node, when the node is in the quadrature, that angle B will be the distance of the sun from the node's true place. For join FT, and, by the demonstration of the last Proposition, the angle FTN will be the distance of the sun from the mean place of the node, and the angle ATN the distance from the true place, and the tangents of these angles are between themselves as TK to TH.

"Cor. Hence the angle FTA is the equation of the moon's nodes; and the sine of this angle, where it is greatest in the octants, is to the radius as KH is to TK+TH. But the sine of this equation in any other place A is to the greatest sine as the sine of the sums of the angles FTN+ATN is to the radius; that is, nearly as the sine of double the distance of the sun from the mean place of the node (namely, 2FTN) to the radius.

"SCHOLIUM

"If the mean hourly motion of the nodes in the quadratures be 16″ 16‴ 37^{iv} 42^{v}, that is, in a whole sidereal year, 39° 38′ 7″ 50‴, TH will be to TK as the square root of the ratio of the number 9.0827646 to the number 10.0827646, that is, as 18.6524761 to 19.6524761. And, therefore, TH is to HK as 18.6524761 to 1; that is, as the motion of the sun in a sidereal year to the mean motion of the node 19° 18′ 1″ 23⅔‴.

"But if the mean motion of the moon's nodes in 20 Julian years is 386° 50′ 16″, as is obtained from the observations made use of in the theory of the moon, the mean motion of the nodes in one sidereal year will be 19° 20′ 31″ 58‴ and TH will be to HK as 360° to 19° 20′ 31″ 58‴; that is, as 18.61214 to 1: and from hence the mean hourly motion of the nodes in the quadratures will come out 16″ 18‴ 48^{iv}. And the greatest equation of the nodes in the octants will be 1° 29′ 57″."

PROPOSITION 34. PROBLEM 15

To find the hourly variation of the inclination of the moon's orbit to the plane of the ecliptic.

Let A and *a* represent the syzygies; Q and *q* the quadratures; N and *n* the nodes; P the place of the moon in its orbit; *p* the orthographic projection of that place upon the plane of the ecliptic; and *mTl* the momentary motion of the nodes as above. If upon T*m* we let fall the perpendicular PG, and joining

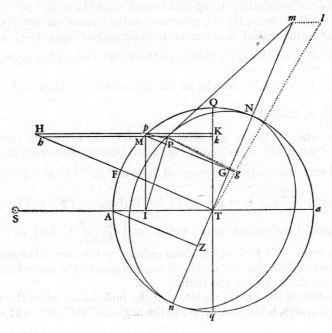

pG we produce it till it meet Tl in g, and join also Pg, the angle PGp will be the inclination of the moon's orbit to the plane of the ecliptic when the moon is in P; and the angle Pgp will be the inclination of the same after a small moment of time is elapsed; and therefore the angle GPg will be the momentary variation of the inclination. But this angle GPg is to the angle GTg as TG to PG and Pp to PG conjointly. And, therefore, if for the moment of time we assume an hour, since the angle GTg (by Prop. 30) is to the angle $33'' \ 10''' \ 33^{iv}$ as IT·PG·AZ to AT^3, the angle GPg (or the hourly variation of the inclination) will be to the angle $33'' \ 10''' \ 33^{iv}$ as IT·AZ·TG·$\dfrac{Pp}{PG}$ to AT^3.   Q.E.I.

And thus it would be if the moon were uniformly revolved in a circular orbit. But if the orbit is elliptical, the mean motion of the nodes will be diminished in proportion of the less axis to the greater, as we have shown above; and the variation of the inclination will be also diminished in the same proportion.

COR. I. Upon Nn erect the perpendicular TF, and let pM be the hourly motion of the moon in the plane of the ecliptic; upon QT let fall the perpendiculars pK, Mk, and produce them till they meet TF in H and h; then IT will be to AT as Kk to Mp; and TG to Hp as TZ to AT; and, therefore, IT·TG will be equal to $\dfrac{Kk \cdot Hp \cdot TZ}{Mp}$, that is, equal to the area HpMh multiplied into the ratio $\dfrac{TZ}{Mp}$: and therefore the hourly variation of the inclination will be to $33''$ $10''' \ 33^{iv}$ as the area HpMh multiplied into AZ·$\dfrac{TZ}{Mp}$·$\dfrac{Pp}{PG}$ is to AT^3.

COR. II. And, therefore, if the earth and nodes were after every hour drawn back from their new and instantly restored to their old places, so that their situation might continue given for a whole periodic month together, the whole variation of the inclination during that month would be to $33'' \ 10''' \ 33^{iv}$ as the aggregate of all the areas HpMh, generated in the time of one revolution of the point p (with due regard in summing to their proper signs $+ -$), multiplied into AZ·TZ·$\dfrac{Pp}{PG}$ to Mp·AT^3; that is, as the whole circle QAqa multiplied into AZ·TZ·$\dfrac{Pp}{PG}$ to Mp·AT^3, that is, as the circumference QAqa multiplied into AZ·TZ·$\dfrac{Pp}{PG}$ to 2Mp·AT^2.

COR. III. And, therefore, in a given position of the nodes, the mean hourly variation, from which, if uniformly continued through the whole month, that menstrual variation might be generated, is to $33'' \ 10''' \ 33^{iv}$ as AZ·TZ$\dfrac{Pp}{PG}$ is to 2AT^2, or as Pp·$\dfrac{AZ \cdot TZ}{\frac{1}{2}AT}$ is to PG·4AT; that is (because Pp is to PG as the sine of the aforesaid inclination to the radius, and $\dfrac{AZ \cdot TZ}{\frac{1}{2}AT}$ to 4AT as the sine of double the angle ATn to four times the radius), as the sine of the same inclination multiplied into the sine of double the distance of the nodes from the sun to four times the square of the radius.

COR. IV. Seeing the hourly variation of the inclination, when the nodes are in the quadratures, is (by this Prop.) to the angle $33'' \ 10''' \ 33^{iv}$ as IT·AZ·TG·

$\frac{Pp}{PG}$ is to AT³, that is, as $\frac{IT \cdot TG}{\frac{1}{2}AT} \cdot \frac{Pp}{PG}$ to 2AT, that is, as the sine of double the

distance of the moon from the quadratures multiplied into $\frac{Pp}{PG}$ is to twice the

radius, the sum of all the hourly variations during the time that the moon, in this situation of the nodes, passes from the quadrature to the syzygy (that is, in the space of 177⅙ hours) will be to the sum of as many angles 33″ 10‴ 33ⁱᵛ or 5878″, as the sum of all the sines of double the distance of the moon from the

quadratures multiplied into $\frac{Pp}{PG}$ is to the sum of as many diameters; that is, as

the diameter multiplied into $\frac{Pp}{PG}$ is to the circumference; that is, if the inclin-

ation be 5° 1′, as $7 \cdot \frac{874}{10000}$ is to 22, or as 278 to 10,000. And, therefore, the whole variation, composed out of the sum of all the hourly variations in the aforesaid time, is 163″, or 2′ 43″.

PROPOSITION 35. PROBLEM 16

To a given time to find the inclination of the moon's orbit to the plane of the ecliptic.

Let AD be the sine of the greatest inclination, and AB the sine of the least. Bisect BD in C; and round the centre C, with the radius BC, describe the circle

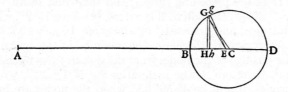

BGD. In AC take CE in the same proportion to EB as EB to twice BA. And if to the time given we set off the angle AEG equal to double the distance of the nodes from the quadratures, and upon AD let fall the perpendicular GH, AH will be the sine of the inclination required.

For GE² is equal to
$$GH^2 + HE^2 = BHD + HE^2 = HBD + HE^2 - BH^2 = HBD + BE^2 -$$
$$2BH \cdot BE = BE^2 + 2EC \cdot BH = 2EC \cdot AB + 2EC \cdot BH = 2EC \cdot AH;$$
wherefore, since 2EC is given, GE² will be as AH. Now let AE*g* represent double the distance of the nodes from the quadratures, in a given moment of time after, and the arc G*g*, on account of the given angle GE*g*, will be as the distance GE. But H*h* is to G*g* as GH to GC, and, therefore, H*h* is as the rec-

tangle GH · G*g*, or GH · GE, that is, as $\frac{GH}{GE} \cdot GE^2$, or $\frac{GH}{GE} \cdot AH$; that is, as AH and

the sine of the angle AEG conjointly. If, therefore, in any one case, AH be the sine of inclination, it will increase by the same increments as the sine of inclination doth (by Cor. III of the preceding Prop.), and therefore will always continue equal to that sine. But when the point G falls upon either point B or D, AH is equal to this sine, and therefore remains always equal thereto.   Q.E.D.

In this demonstration I have supposed that the angle BEG, representing double the distance of the nodes from the quadratures, increaseth uniformly; for I cannot descend to every minute circumstance of inequality. Now suppose that BEG is a right angle, and that G*g* is in this case the hourly increment of double the distance of the nodes from the sun; then (by Cor. III of the last Prop.) the hourly variation of the inclination in the same case will be to 33″ 10‴ 33^{iv} as the rectangle of AH, the sine of the inclination, into the sine of the right angle BEG, double the distance of the nodes from the sun, is to four times the square of the radius; that is, as AH, the sine of the mean inclination, is to four times the radius; that is, seeing the mean inclination is about 5° 8½′, as its sine 896 is to 40,000, the quadruple of the radius, or as 224 to 10,000. But the whole variation corresponding to BD, the difference of the sines, is to this hourly variation as the diameter BD is to the arc Gg, that is, conjointly as the diameter BD to the semicircumference BGD, and as the time of 2079^{7}⁄$_{10}$ hours, in which the node proceeds from the quadratures to the syzygies, is to one hour, that is, as 7 to 11, and 2079^{7}⁄$_{10}$ to 1. Therefore compounding all these proportions, we shall have the whole variation BD to 33″ 10‴ 33^{iv} as 224·7· 2079^{7}⁄$_{10}$ is to 110,000, that is, as 29,645 to 1000; and from thence that variation BD will come out 16′ 23½″.

And this is the greatest variation of the inclination, abstracting from the situation of the moon in its orbit; for, if the nodes are in the syzygies, the inclination suffers no change from the various positions of the moon. But if the nodes are in the quadratures, the inclination is less when the moon is in the syzygies than when it is in the quadratures by a difference of 2′ 43″, as we showed (Cor. IV of the preceding Prop.); and the whole mean variation BD, diminished by 1′ 21½″, the half of this excess, becomes 15′ 2″, when the moon is in the quadratures; and, increased by the same, becomes 17′ 45″ when the moon is in the syzygies. If, therefore, the moon be in the syzygies, the whole variation in the passage of the nodes from the quadratures to the syzygies will be 17′ 45″; and, therefore, if the inclination be 5° 17′ 20″, when the nodes are in the syzygies, it will be 4° 59′ 35″ when the nodes are in the quadratures and the moon in the syzygies. The truth of all this is confirmed by observations.

Now if the inclination of the orbit should be required when the moon is in the syzygies, and the nodes anywhere between them and the quadratures, let AB be to AD as the sine of 4° 59′ 35″ is to the sine of 5° 17′ 20″, and take the angle AEG equal to double the distance of the nodes from the quadratures; and AH will be the sine of the inclination desired. To this inclination of the orbit the inclination of the same is equal, when the moon is 90° distant from the nodes. In other situations of the moon, this menstrual inequality, to which the variation of the inclination is subject in the calculus of the moon's latitude, is balanced, and in a manner taken off, by the menstrual inequality of the motion of the nodes (as we said before), and therefore may be neglected in the computation of the said latitude.

SCHOLIUM

By these computations of the lunar motions I was desirous of showing that by the theory of gravity the motions of the moon could be calculated from their physical causes. By the same theory I moreover found that the annual equation of the mean motion of the moon arises from the varying dilatation which the orbit of the moon suffers from the action of the sun according to Cor. VI, Prop. 66, Book I. The force of this action is greater in the perigean sun, and dilates the moon's orbit; in the apogean sun it is less, and permits the orbit to be again contracted. The moon moves slower in the dilated and faster in the contracted orbit; and the annual equation, by which this inequality is regulated, vanishes in the apogee and perigee of the sun. In the mean distance of the sun from the earth it rises to about 11′ 50″; in other distances of the sun it is proportional to the equation of the sun's centre, and is added to the mean motion of the moon, while the earth is passing from its aphelion to its perhelion, and subtracted while the earth is in the opposite semicircle. Taking for the radius of the great orbit 1000, and $16\frac{7}{8}$ for the earth's eccentricity, this equation, when of the greatest magnitude, by the theory of gravity comes out 11′ 49″. But the eccentricity of the earth seems to be somewhat greater, and with the eccentricity this equation will be augmented in the same proportion. Suppose the eccentricity $16\frac{11}{12}$, and the greatest equation will be 11′ 51″.

Further, I found that the apogee and nodes of the moon move faster in the perihelion of the earth, where the force of the sun's action is greater, than in the aphelion thereof, and that inversely as the cube of the ratio of the earth's distance from the sun; and hence arise annual equations of those motions proportional to the equation of the sun's centre. Now the motion of the sun varies inversely as the square of the earth's distance from the sun; and the greatest equation of the centre which this inequality generates is 1° 56′ 20″, corresponding to the above-mentioned eccentricity of the sun, $16\frac{11}{12}$. But if the motion of the sun had been inversely as the cube of the distance, this inequality would have generated the greatest equation 2° 54′ 30″; and therefore the greatest equations which the inequalities of the motions of the moon's apogee and nodes do generate are to 2° 54′ 30″ as the mean diurnal motion of the moon's apogee and the mean diurnal motion of its nodes are to the mean diurnal motion of the sun. Hence the greatest equation of the mean motion of the apogee comes out 19′ 43″, and the greatest equation of the mean motion of the nodes 9′ 24″. The former equation is added, and the latter subtracted, while the earth is passing from its perihelion to its aphelion, and contrariwise when the earth is in the opposite semicircle.

By the theory of gravity I likewise found that the action of the sun upon the moon is somewhat greater when the transverse diameter of the moon's orbit passes through the sun than when the same is perpendicular upon the line which joins the earth and the sun; and therefore the moon's orbit is somewhat larger in the former than in the latter case. And hence arises another equation of the moon's mean motion, depending upon the situation of the moon's apogee in respect of the sun, which is greatest when the moon's apogee is in the octants of the sun, and vanishes when the apogee arrives at the quadratures or syzygies; and it is added to the mean motion while the moon's apogee is passing from the quadrature of the sun to the syzygy, and subtracted while the apogee is passing from the syzygy to the quadrature. This equation, which I shall call the semiannual, when greatest in the octants of the apogee, arises to about 3′ 45″, so far as I could determine from the phenomena: and this is its quantity in the mean distance of the sun from the earth. But it is increased and diminished inversely as the cube of the sun's distance, and therefore is nearly 3′ 34″ when that distance is greatest, and 3′ 56″ when least. But when the moon's apogee is without the octants, it becomes less, and is to its greatest amount as the sine of double the distance of the moon's apogee from the nearest syzygy or quadrature is to the radius.

By the same theory of gravity, the action of the sun upon the moon is somewhat greater when the line of the moon's nodes passes through the sun than when it is at right angles with the line which joins the sun and the earth; and hence arises another equation of the moon's mean motion, which I shall call the second semiannual; and this is greatest when the nodes are in the octants of the sun, and vanishes when they are in the syzygies or quadratures; and in other positions of the nodes is proportional to the sine of double the distance of either node from the nearest syzygy or quadrature. And it is added to the mean motion of the moon, if the sun is behind the node which is nearest to him, and is subtracted, if forward; and in the octants, where it is of the greatest magnitude, it arises to 47″ in the mean distance of the sun from the earth, as I find from the theory of gravity. In other distances of the sun, this equation, greatest in the octants of the nodes, is inversely as the cube of the sun's distance from the earth; and therefore in the sun's perigee it comes to about 49″, and in its apogee to about 45″.

By the same theory of gravity, the moon's apogee goes forwards at the greatest rate when it is either in conjunction with or in opposition to the sun, but in its quadratures with the sun it goes backwards; and the eccentricity comes, in the former case, to its greatest quantity; in the latter, to its least, by Cor. VII, VIII, and IX, Prop. 66, Book I. And those inequalities, by the Corollaries we have named, are very great, and generate the principle which I call the semiannual equation of the apogee; and this semiannual equation in its greatest quantity comes to about 12° 18′, as nearly as I could determine from the phenomena. Our countryman, Horrox, was the first who advanced the theory of the moon's moving in an ellipse about the earth placed in its lower focus. Dr. Halley improved the notion, by putting the centre of the ellipse in an epicycle whose centre is uniformly revolved about the earth; and from the motion in this epicycle the mentioned inequalities in the progress and regress of the apogee, and in the quantity of eccentricity, do arise. Suppose the mean distance of the moon from the earth to be divided into 100,000 parts, and let T represent the earth, and TC the moon's mean eccentricity of 5505 such parts. Produce TC to B, so as CB may be the sine of the greatest semiannual equation 12° 18′ to the radius TC; and the circle BDA described about the centre C, with the radius CB, will be the epicycle spoken of,
in which the centre of the moon's orbit is placed, and revolved according to the order of the letters BDA. Set off the angle BCD equal to twice the annual argument, or twice the distance of the sun's true place from the place of the moon's apogee once corrected, and CTD will be the semiannual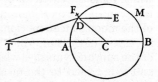
equation of the moon's apogee, and TD the eccentricity of its orbit, tending to the place of the apogee now twice corrected. But, having the moon's mean motion, the place of its apogee, and its eccentricity, as well as the longer axis of its orbit 200,000, from these data the true place of the moon in its orbit, together with its distance from the earth, may be determined by the methods commonly known.

In the perihelion of the earth, where the force of the sun is greatest, the centre of the moon's orbit moves faster about the centre C than in the aphelion, and that inversely as the cube of the sun's distance from the earth. But, because the equation of the sun's centre is included in the annual argument, the centre of the moon's orbit moves faster in its epicycle BDA, inversely as the square of the sun's distance from the earth. Therefore, that it may move yet faster, inversely as the distance, suppose that from D, the centre of the orbit, a right line DE is drawn, tending towards the moon's apogee once corrected, that is, parallel to TC; and set off the angle EDF equal to the excess of the aforesaid annual argument above the distance of the moon's apogee from the sun's perigee forwards; or, which comes to the same thing, take the angle CDF equal to the complement of the sun's true anomaly to 360°; and let DF be to DC as twice the eccentricity of the great orbit to the sun's mean distance from the earth, and the sun's mean diurnal motion from the moon's apogee to the sun's mean diurnal motion from its own apogee conjointly, that is, as 33⅞ to 1000, and 52′ 27″ 16‴ to 59′ 8″ 10‴ conjointly, or as 3 to 100; and imagine the centre of the moon's orbit placed in the point F to be revolved in an epicycle whose centre of the moon's orbit placed in the point F to be revolved in an epicycle whose centre is D, and radius DF, while the point D moves in the circumference of the circle DABD: for by this means the centre of the moon's orbit comes to describe a certain curved line about the centre C, with a velocity which will be almost inversely as the cube of the sun's distance from the earth, as it ought to be.

The calculus of this motion is difficult, but may be rendered easier by the following approximation. Assuming, as above, the moon's mean distance from the earth of 100,000 parts, and the eccentricity TC of 5505 such parts, the line CB or CD will be found 1172¾, and DF 35⅕ of those parts; and this line DF at the distance TC subtends the angle at the earth, which the removal of the centre of the orbit from the place D to the place F generates in the motion of this centre; and double this line DF in a parallel position, at the distance of the upper focus of the moon's orbit from the earth, subtends at the earth the same angle as DF did before, which that removal generates in the motion of this upper focus; but at the distance of the moon from the earth this double line 2DF at the upper focus, in a parallel position to the first line DF, subtends an angle at the moon, which the said removal generates in the motion of the moon, which angle may be therefore called the second equation of the moon's centre; and this equation, in the mean distance of the moon from the earth, is nearly as the sine of the angle which that line DF contains with the line drawn from the point F to the moon, and when greatest amounts to 2′ 25″. But the angle which the line DF contains with the line drawn from the point F to the moon is found either by subtracting the angle EDF from the mean anomaly of the moon, or by adding the distance of the moon from the sun to the distance of the moon's apogee from the apogee of the sun; and as the radius is to the sine of the angle thus found, so is 2′ 25″ to the second equation of the centre: to be added, if the fore-mentioned sum be less than a semi-circle; to be subtracted, if greater. And from the moon's place in its orbit thus corrected, its longitude may be found in the syzygies of the luminaries.

The atmosphere of the earth to the height of 35 or 40 miles refracts the sun's light. This refraction scatters and spreads the light over the earth's shadow; and the dissipated light near the limits of the shadow dilates the shadow. On this account, to the diameter of the shadow, as it comes out by the parallax, I add 1 or 1⅓ minutes in lunar eclipses.

But the theory of the moon ought to be examined and proved from the phenomena, first in the syzygies, then in the quadratures, and last of all in the octants; and whoever pleases to undertake the work will find it not amiss to assume the following mean motions of the sun and moon at the Royal Observatory of Greenwich, to the last day of December at noon, in the year 1700, o.s.: the mean motion of the sun ♏ 20° 43′ 40″, and of its apogee ♋ 7° 44′ 30″; the mean motion of the moon ♒ 15° 21′ 00″; of its apogee, ♓ 8° 20′ 00″; and of its ascending node ♌ 27° 24′ 20″; and the difference of meridians between the Observatory at Greenwich and the Royal Observatory at Paris, 0ʰ. 9ᵐ. 20ˢ.: but the mean motion of the moon and of its apogee are not yet obtained with sufficient accuracy.

PROPOSITION 36. PROBLEM 17

To find the force of the sun to move the sea.

The sun's force ML or PT to disturb the motions of the moon was (by Prop. 25), in the moon's quadratures, to the force of gravity with us, as 1 to 638092.6; and the force TM − LM or 2PK in the moon's syzygies is double that quantity. But, descending to the surface of the earth, these forces are diminished in proportion of the distances from the centre of the earth, that is, in the proportion of 60½ to 1; and therefore the former force on the earth's surface is to the force of gravity as 1 to 38,604,600; and by this force the sea is depressed in such places as are 90 degrees distant from the sun. But by the other force, which is twice as great, the sea is raised not only in the places directly under the sun, but in those also which are directly opposed to it; and the sum of these forces is to the force of gravity as 1 to 12,868,200. And because the same force excites the same motion, whether it depresses the waters in those places which are 90 degrees distant from the sun, or raises them in the places which are directly under and directly opposed to the sun, the aforesaid sum will be the total force of the sun to disturb the sea, and will have the same effect as if the whole was employed in raising the sea in the places directly under and directly opposed to the sun, and did not act at all in the places which are 90 degrees removed from the sun.

And this is the force of the sun to disturb the sea in any given place, where the sun is at the same time both vertical, and in its mean distance from the earth. In other positions of the sun, its force to raise the sea is directly as the versed sine of double its altitude above the horizon of the place, and inversely as the cube of the distance from the earth.

COR. Since the centrifugal force of the parts of the earth, arising from the earth's diurnal motion, which is to the force of gravity as 1 is to 289, raises the waters under the equator to a height exceeding that under the poles by 85,472 Paris feet, as above, in Prop. 19, the force of the sun, which we have now shown to be to the force of gravity as 1 is to 12,868,200, and therefore is to that centrifugal force as 289 to 12,868,200, or as 1 to 44,527, will be able to raise the waters in the places directly under and directly opposed to the sun to a height exceeding that in the places which are 90 degrees removed from the sun only by one Paris foot and 113¹⁄₃₀ inches; for this measure is to the measure of 85,472 feet as 1 to 44,527.

PROPOSITION 37. PROBLEM 18

To find the force of the moon to move the sea.

The force of the moon to move the sea is to be deduced from its ratio to the force of the sun, and this ratio is to be determined from the ratio of the motions of the sea, which are the effects of those forces. Before the mouth of the river Avon, three miles below Bristol, the height of the ascent of the water in the vernal and autumnal syzygies of the luminaries (by the observations of Samuel Sturmy) amounts to about 45 feet, but in the quadratures to 25 only. The former of those heights arises from the sum of the aforesaid forces, the latter from their difference. If, therefore, S and L are supposed to represent respectively the forces of the sun and moon while they are in the equator, as well as in their mean distances from the earth, we shall have $L+S$ to $L-S$ as 45 to 25, or as 9 to 5.

At Plymouth (by the observations of Samuel Colepress) the tide in its mean height rises to about 16 feet, and in the spring and autumn the height thereof in the syzygies may exceed that in the quadratures by more than 7 or 8 feet. Suppose the greatest difference of those heights to be 9 feet, and $L+S$ will be to $L-S$ as $20\frac{1}{2}$ to $11\frac{1}{2}$, or as 41 to 23; a proportion that agrees well enough with the former. But because of the great tide at Bristol, we are rather to depend upon the observations of Sturmy; and, therefore, till we procure something that is more certain, we shall use the proportion of 9 to 5.

But because of the reciprocal motions of the waters, the greatest tides do not happen at the times of the syzygies of the luminaries, but, as we have said before, are the third in order after the syzygies; or (reckoning from the syzygies) follow next after the third approach of the moon to the meridian of the place after the syzygies; or rather (as Sturmy observes) are the third after the day of the new or full moon, or rather nearly after the twelfth hour from the new or full moon, and therefore fall nearly upon the forty-third hour after the new or full moon. But in this port they come to pass about the seventh hour after the approach of the moon to the meridian of the place; and therefore follow next after the approach of the moon to the meridian, when the moon is distant from the sun, or from opposition with the sun by about 18 or 19 degrees forwards. So the summer and winter seasons come not to their height in the solstices themselves, but when the sun is advanced beyond the solstices by about a tenth part of its whole course, that is, by about 36 or 37 degrees. In like manner, the greatest tide is raised after the approach of the moon to the meridian of the place, when the moon has passed by the sun, *or the opposition thereof*, by about a tenth part of the whole motion from *one greatest* tide to *the next following greatest* tide. Suppose that distance about $18\frac{1}{2}$ degrees; and the sun's force in this distance of the moon from the syzygies and quadratures will be of less moment to augment and diminish that part of the motion of the sea which proceeds from the motion of the moon than in the syzygies and quadratures themselves in the proportion of the radius to the cosine of double this distance, or of an angle of 37 degrees; that is, in the ratio of 10,000,000 to 7,986,355; and, therefore, in the preceding analogy, in place of S we must put 0.7986355S.

But further, the force of the moon in the quadratures must be diminished, on account of its declination from the equator; for the moon in those quadratures, or rather in $18\frac{1}{2}$ degrees past the quadratures, declines from the equator by about 23° 13′; and the force of either luminary to move the sea is diminished as it declines from the equator nearly as the square of the cosine of the declination; and therefore the force of the moon in those quadratures is only 0.8570327L; hence we have $L+0.7986355S$ to $0.8570327L-0.7986355S$ as 9 to 5.

Further yet, the diameters of the orbit in which the moon should move, setting aside the consideration of eccentricity, are one to the other as 69 to 70; and therefore the moon's distance from the earth in the syzygies is to its distance in the quadratures, other things being equal, as 69 to 70; and its distances, when $18\frac{1}{2}$ degrees advanced beyond the syzygies, where the greatest tide was excited, and when $18\frac{1}{2}$ degrees passed by the quadratures, where the least tide was produced, are to its mean distance as 69.098747 and 69.897345 to $69\frac{1}{2}$. But the force of the moon to move the sea varies inversely as the cube of its distance; and therefore its forces, in the greatest and least of those distances, are to its force in its mean distance as 0.9830427 and 1.017522 is to 1. From this we have $1.017522L \cdot 0.7986355S$ to $0.9830427 \cdot 0.8570327L - 0.7986355S$ as 9 to 5; and S to L as 1 to 4.4815. Therefore, since the force of the sun is to the force of gravity as 1 to 12,868,200, the moon's force will be to the force of gravity as 1 to 2,871,400.

COR. I. Since the waters attracted by the sun's force rise to the height of 1 foot and $11\frac{1}{30}$ inches, the moon's force will raise the same to the height of 8 feet and $7\frac{5}{22}$ inches; and the joint forces of both will raise the same to the height of $10\frac{1}{2}$ feet; and when the moon is in its perigee to the height of $12\frac{1}{2}$ feet, and more, especially when the wind sets the same way as the tide. And a force of that amount is abundantly sufficient to produce all the motions of the sea, and agrees well with the ratio of those motions; for in such seas as lie free and open from east to west, as in the Pacific sea, and in those tracts of the Atlantic and Ethiopic seas which lie without the tropics, the waters commonly rise to 6, 9, 12, or 15 feet; but in the Pacific sea, which is of a greater depth, as well as of a larger extent, the tides are said to be greater than in the Atlantic and Ethiopic seas; for, to have a full tide raised, an extent of sea from east to west is required of no less than 90 degrees. In the Ethiopic sea, the waters rise to a less height within the tropics than in the temperate zones: because of the narrowness of the sea between Africa and the southern parts of America. In the middle of the open sea the waters cannot rise without falling together, and at the same time, upon both the eastern and western shores, when, notwithstanding, in our narrow seas, they ought to fall on those shores by alternate turns; upon this account there is commonly but a small flood and ebb in such islands as lie far distant from the continent. On the contrary, in some ports, where to fill and empty the bays alternately the waters are with great violence forced in and out through shallow channels, the flood and ebb must be greater than ordinary; as at Plymouth and Chepstow Bridge in England, at the mountains of St. Michael, and the town of Avranches, in Normandy, and at Cambaia and Pegu in the East Indies. In these places the sea is hurried in and out with such violence as sometimes to lay the shores under water, sometimes to leave them dry for many miles. Nor is this force of the influx and efflux to be stopped till it has raised and depressed the waters to 30, 40, or 50 feet and above. And a like account is to be given of long and shallow channels or straits, such as the Magellanic straits, and those channels which environ England. The tide in such ports and straits, by the violence of the influx and efflux, is augmented greatly. But on such shores as lie towards the deep and open sea with a steep descent, where the waters may freely rise and fall without that precipitation of influx and efflux, the ratio of the tides agrees with the forces of the sun and moon.

Cor. ii. Since the moon's force to move the sea is to the force of gravity as 1 to 2,871,400, it is evident that this force is inappreciable in statical or hydrostatical experiments, or even in those of pendulums. It is in the tides only that this force shows itself by any sensible effect.

Cor. iii. Because the force of the moon for moving the sea is to the like force of the sun as 4.4815 to 1, and those forces (by Cor. xiv, Prop. 66, Book i) are as the densities of the bodies of the sun and moon and the cubes of their apparent diameters conjointly, the density of the moon will be to the density of the sun directly as 4.4815 to 1, and inversely as the cube of the moon's diameter to the cube of the sun's diameter; that is (seeing the mean apparent diameters of the moon and sun are 31' 16½'', and 32' 12''), as 4891 to 1000. But the density of the sun was to the density of the earth as 1000 to 4000; and therefore the density of the moon is to the density of the earth as 4891 is to 4000, or as 11 to 9. Therefore the body of the moon is more dense and more earthly than the earth itself.

Cor. iv. And since the true diameter of the moon (from the observations of astronomers) is to the true diameter of the earth as 100 to 365, the mass of matter in the moon will be to the mass of matter in the earth as 1 to 39.788.

Cor. v. And the accelerative gravity on the surface of the moon will be about three times less than the accelerative gravity on the surface of the earth.

Cor. vi. And the distance of the moon's centre from the centre of the earth will be to the distance of the moon's centre from the common centre of gravity of the earth and moon as 40.788 to 39.788.

Cor. vii. And the mean distance of the centre of the moon from the centre of the earth will be (in the moon's octants) nearly $60\frac{2}{5}$ of the greatest semidiameters of the earth; for the greatest semidiameter of the earth was 19,658,600 Paris feet, and the mean distance of the centres of the earth and moon, consisting of $60\frac{2}{5}$ such semidiameters, is equal to 1,187,379,440 feet. And this distance (by the preceding Cor.) is to the distance of the moon's centre from the common centre of gravity of the earth and moon as 40.788 to 39.788; which latter distance, therefore, is 1,158,268,534 feet. And since the moon, in respect of the fixed stars, performs its revolution in $27^d. 7^h. 43\frac{4}{9}^m.$, the versed sine of that angle which the moon in a minute of time describes is 12,752,341 to the radius 1,000,000,000,000,000; and as the radius is to this versed sine, so are 1,158,268,534 feet to 14.7706353 feet. The moon, therefore, falling towards the earth by that force which retains it in its orbit, would in one minute of time describe 14.7706353 feet; and, if we augment this force in the proportion of $178^{29}/_{40}$ to $177^{29}/_{40}$, we shall have the total force of gravity at the orbit of the moon, by Cor., Prop. 3; and the moon falling by this force, in one minute of time would describe 14.8538067 feet. And at the 60th part of the distance of the moon from the earth's centre, that is, at the distance of 197,896,573 feet from the centre of the earth, a body falling by its weight, would, in one second of time, likewise describe 14.8538067 feet. And, therefore, at the distance of 19,615,800, which compose one mean semidiameter of the earth, a heavy body would describe in falling 15.11175, or 15 feet, 1 inch, and $4\frac{1}{11}$ lines, in the same time. This will be the descent of bodies in the latitude of 45 degrees. And by the foregoing table, to be found under Prop. 20, the descent in the latitude of Paris will be a little greater by an excess of about $\frac{2}{3}$ parts of a line. Therefore, by this computation, heavy bodies in the latitude of Paris falling in a vacuum will describe

15 Paris feet, 1 inch, $4^{25}\!/_{33}$ lines, very nearly, in one second of time. And if the gravity be diminished by taking away a quantity equal to the centrifugal force arising in that latitude from the earth's diurnal motion, heavy bodies falling there will describe in one second of time 15 feet, 1 inch, and $1\frac{1}{2}$ lines. And with this velocity heavy bodies do really fall in the latitude of Paris, as we have shown above in Props. 4 and 19.

COR. VIII. The mean distance of the centres of the earth and moon in the syzygies of the moon is equal to 60 of the greatest semidiameters of the earth, subtracting only about one 30th part of a semidiameter; and in the moon's quadratures the mean distance of the same centres is $60^{5}\!/_{6}$ such semidiameters of the earth; for these two distances are to the mean distance of the moon in the octants as 69 and 70 to $69\frac{1}{2}$, by Prop. 28.

COR. IX. The mean distance of the centres of the earth and moon in the syzygies of the moon is 60 mean semidiameters of the earth, and a 10th part of one semidiameter; and in the moon's quadratures the mean distance of the same centres is 61 mean semidiameters of the earth, subtracting one 30th part of one semidiameter.

COR. X. In the moon's syzygies its mean horizontal parallax in the latitudes of 0, 30, 38, 45, 52, 60, 90 degrees is 57′ 20″, 57′ 16″, 57′ 14″, 57′ 12″, 57′ 10″, 57′ 8″, 57′ 4″, respectively.

In these computations I do not consider the magnetic attraction of the earth, whose quantity is very small and unknown: if this quantity should ever be found out, and the measures of degrees upon the meridian, the lengths of isochronous pendulums in different parallels, the laws of the motions of the sea, and the moon's parallax, with the apparent diameters of the sun and moon, should be more exactly determined from phenomena: we should then be enabled to bring this calculation to a greater accuracy.

PROPOSITION 38. PROBLEM 19

To find the figure of the moon's body.

If the moon's body were fluid like our sea, the force of the earth to raise that fluid in the nearest and remotest parts would be to the force of the moon by which our sea is raised in the places under and opposite to the moon as the accelerative gravity of the moon towards the earth is to the accelerative gravity of the earth towards the moon, and the diameter of the moon is to the diameter of the earth conjointly; that is, as 39.788 to 1, and 100 to 365 conjointly, or as 1081 to 100. Therefore, since our sea, by the force of the moon, is raised to $8\frac{3}{5}$ feet, the lunar fluid would be raised by the force of the earth to 93 feet; and upon this account the figure of the moon would be a spheroid, whose greatest diameter produced would pass through the centre of the earth, and exceed the diameters perpendicular thereto by 186 feet. Such a figure, therefore, the moon possesses, and must have had from the beginning.   Q.E.I.

COR. Hence it is that the same face of the moon always is turned toward the earth; nor can the body of the moon possibly rest in any other position, but would return always by a libratory motion to this situation; but those librations, however, must be exceedingly slow, because of the weakness of the forces which excite them; so that the face of the moon, which should be always directed to the earth, may, for the reason assigned in Prop. 17, be turned towards the other focus of the moon's orbit, without being immediately drawn back, and turned again towards the earth.

LEMMA 1

If APEp represent the earth uniformly dense, marked with the centre C, the poles P, p, and the equator AE; and if about the centre C, with the radius CP, we suppose the sphere Pape to be described, and QR to denote the plane on which a right line, drawn from the centre of the sun to the centre of the earth, stands at right angles; and further suppose that the several particles of the whole exterior earth PapAPepE, without the height of the said sphere, endeavor to recede towards this side and that side from the plane QR, every particle by a force proportional to its distance from that plane; I say, in the first place, that the whole force and efficacy of all the particles that are situated in AE, the circle of the equator, and disposed uniformly without the globe, encompassing the same after the manner of a ring, to wheel the earth about its centre, is to the whole force and efficacy of as many particles in that point A of the equator which is at the greatest distance from the plane QR, to wheel the earth about its centre with a like circular motion as is 1 to 2. And that circular motion will be performed about an axis lying in the common section of the equator and the plane QR.

For let there be described from the centre K, with the diameter IL, the semicircle INL. Suppose the semicircumference INL to be divided into innumerable equal parts, and from the several parts N to the diameter IL let fall the sines NM. Then the sums of the squares of all the sines NM will be equal

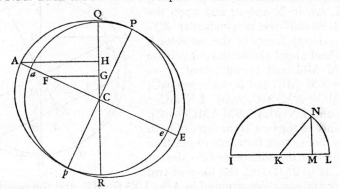

to the sums of the squares of the sines KM, and both sums together will be equal to the sums of the squares of as many semidiameters KN; and therefore the sum of the squares of all the sines NM will be but half so great as the sum of the squares of as many semidiameters KN.

Suppose now the circumference of the circle AE to be divided into the like number of little equal parts, and from every such part F a perpendicular FG to be let fall upon the plane QR, as well as the perpendicular AH from the point A. Then the force by which the particle F recedes from the plane QR will (by supposition) be as that perpendicular FG; and this force multiplied by the distance CG will represent the power of the particle F to turn the earth round its centre. And, therefore, the power of a particle in the place F will be to the power of a particle in the place A as FG·GC is to AH·HC; that is, as FC^2 to AC^2: and therefore the whole power of all the particles F, in their proper places

F, will be to the power of the like number of particles in the place A as the sum of all the FC² is to the sum of all the AC², that is (by what we have demonstrated before), as 1 to 2.   Q.E.D.

And because the action of those particles is exerted in the direction of lines perpendicularly receding from the plane QR, and that equally from each side of this plane, they will wheel about the circumference of the circle of the equator, together with the adherent body of the earth, round an axis which lies as well in the plane QR as in that of the equator.

LEMMA 2

The same things still supposed, I say, in the second place, that the total force or power of all the particles situated everywhere about the sphere to turn the earth about the said axis is to the whole force of the like number of particles, uniformly disposed round the whole circumference of the equator AE in the fashion of a ring, to turn the whole earth about with the like circular motion as is 2 to 5.

For let IK be any lesser circle parallel to the equator AE, and let L*l* be any two equal particles in this circle, situated without the sphere P*ape*; and if upon the plane QR, which is at right angles with a radius drawn to the sun, we let fall the perpendiculars LM, *lm*, the total forces by which these particles recede from the plane QR will be proportional to the perpendiculars LM, *lm*. Let the right line L*l* be drawn parallel to the plane P*ape*, and bisect the same in X; and

through the point X draw N*n* parallel to the plane QR, and meeting the perpendiculars LM, *lm*, in N and *n;* and upon the plane QR let fall the perpendicular XY. And the contrary forces of the particles L and *l* to wheel about the earth contrariwise are as LM·MC, and *lm·mC;* that is, as LN·MC+NM·MC, and *ln·mC−nm·mC;* or LN·MC+NM·MC, and LN·*m*C−NM·*m*C, and LN·M*m*−NM·(MC+*m*C), the difference of the two, is the force of both taken together to turn the earth round. The positive part of this difference LN·M*m*, or 2LN·NX, is to 2AH·HC, the force of two

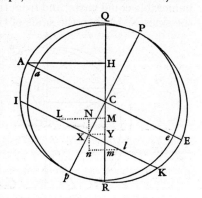

particles of the same size situated in A, as LX² to AC²; and the negative part NM·(MC+*m*C), or 2XY·CY, is to 2AH·HC, the force of the same two particles situated in A, as CX² to AC². And therefore the difference of the parts, that is, the force of the two particles L and *l*, taken together, to wheel the earth about, is to the force of two particles, equal to the former and situated in the place A, to turn in like manner the earth round, as LX²−CX² is to AC². But if the circumference IK of the circle IK is supposed to be divided into an infinite number of little equal parts L, all the LX² will be to the like number of IX² as 1 to 2 (by Lem. 1); and to the same number of AC² as IX² is to 2AC²; and the same number of CX² to as many AC² as 2CX² is to 2AC². Therefore the united forces of all the particles in the circumference of the circle IK are to the joint forces of as many particles in the place A as IX²−2CX² is to 2AC²; and therefore (by Lem. 1) to the united forces of as many particles in the circumference of the circle AE as IX²−2CX² is to AC².

Now if Pp, the diameter of the sphere, is conceived to be divided into an infinite number of equal parts, upon which a like number of circles IK are supposed to stand, the matter in the circumference of every circle IK will be as IX^2; and therefore the force of that matter to turn the earth about will be as IX^2 into IX^2 − 2CX^2; and the force of the same matter, if it was situated in the circumference of the circle AE, would be as IX^2 into AC^2. And therefore the force of all the particles of the whole matter situated without the sphere in the circumferences of all the circles is to the force of the like number of particles situated in the circumference of the greatest circle AE as all the IX^2 into IX^2 − 2CX^2 is to as many IX^2 into AC^2; that is, as all the AC^2 − CX^2 into AC^2 − 3CX^2 to as many AC^2 − CX^2 into AC^2; that is, as all the AC^4 − 4AC^2 · CX^2 + 3CX^4 to as many AC^4 − AC^2 · CX^2; that is, as the whole fluent quantity whose fluxion is AC^4 − 4AC^2 · CX^2 + 3CX^4, is to the whole fluent quantity, whose fluxion is AC^4 − AC^2 · CX^2; and, therefore, by the method of fluxions, as AC^4 · CX − $\frac{4}{3}$AC^2 · CX^3 + $\frac{3}{5}$CX^5 is to AC^4 · CX − $\frac{1}{3}$AC^2 · CX^3; that is, if for CX we write the whole Cp, or AC, as $\frac{4}{15}$AC^5 is to $\frac{2}{3}$AC^5; that is, as 2 is to 5. Q.E.D.

LEMMA 3

The same things still supposed, I say, in the third place, that the motion of the whole earth about the axis above named arising from the motions of all the particles, will be to the motion of the aforesaid ring about the same axis in a ratio compounded of the ratio of the matter in the earth to the matter in the ring; and the ratio of three squares of the quadrantal arc of any circle to two squares of its diameter, that is, in the ratio of the matter to the matter, and of the number 925,275 to the number 1,000,000.

For the motion of a cylinder revolved about its quiescent axis is to the motion of the inscribed sphere revolved together with it as any four equal squares are to three circles inscribed in three of those squares, and the motion of this cylinder is to the motion of an exceedingly thin ring surrounding both sphere and cylinder in their common contact as double the matter in the cylinder is to triple the matter in the ring; and this motion of the ring, uniformly continued about the axis of the cylinder, is to the uniform motion of the same about its own diameter performed in the same periodic time as is the circumference of a circle to double its diameter.

HYPOTHESIS II

IF THE OTHER PARTS OF THE EARTH WERE TAKEN AWAY, AND THE REMAINING RING WAS CARRIED ALONE ABOUT THE SUN IN THE ORBIT OF THE EARTH BY THE ANNUAL MOTION, WHILE BY THE DIURNAL MOTION IT WAS IN THE MEAN-TIME REVOLVED ABOUT ITS OWN AXIS INCLINED TO THE PLANE OF THE ECLIPTIC BY AN ANGLE OF 23$\frac{1}{2}$ DEGREES, THE MOTION OF THE EQUINOCTIAL POINTS WOULD BE THE SAME, WHETHER THE RING WERE FLUID, OR WHETHER IT CONSISTED OF A HARD AND RIGID MATTER.

PROPOSITION 39. PROBLEM 20

To find the precession of the equinoxes.

The middle hourly motion of the moon's nodes in a circular orbit, when the nodes are in the quadratures, was 16″ 35‴ 16^{iv} 36^v; the half of which, 8″ 17‴ 38^{iv} 18^v (for the reasons above explained), is the mean hourly motion of the nodes in such an orbit, which motion in a whole sidereal year becomes 20° 11′ 46″.

Since, therefore, ·the nodes of the moon in such an orbit would be yearly transferred 20° 11′ 46″ backwards, and, if there were more moons, the motion of the nodes of every one (by Cor. xvi, Prop. 66, Book i) would be as its periodic time, if upon the surface of the earth a moon was revolved in the time of a sidereal day, the annual motion of the nodes of this moon would be to 20° 11′ 46″ as 23$^{\rm h}$. 56$^{\rm m}$., the sidereal day, is to 27$^{\rm d}$. 7$^{\rm h}$. 43$^{\rm m}$., the periodic time of our moon, that is, as 1436 is to 39,343. And the same thing would happen to the nodes of a ring of moons encompassing the earth, whether these moons did not mutually touch each the other, or whether they were molten, and formed into a continued ring, or whether that ring should become rigid and inflexible.

Let us, then, suppose that this ring is in quantity of matter equal to the whole exterior earth PapAPepE, which lies without the sphere P$a$pe (see Fig., Lem. 2); and because this sphere is to that exterior earth as aC^2 is to AC$^2 - a$C^2, that is (seeing PC or aC the least semidiameter of the earth is to AC the greatest semidiameter of the same as 229 is to 230), as 52,441 is to 459; if this ring encompassed the earth round the equator, and both together were revolved about the diameter of the ring, the motion of the ring (by Lem. 3) would be to the motion of the inner sphere as 459 to 52,441 and 1,000,000 to 925,275 conjointly, that is, as 4590 to 485,223; and therefore the motion of the ring would be to the sum of the motions of both ring and sphere as 4590 is to 489,813. Therefore, if the ring adheres to the sphere, and communicates its motion to the sphere, by which its nodes or equinoctial points recede, the motion remaining in the ring will be to its former motion as 4590 is to 489,813; on account of which the motion of the equinoctial points will be diminished in the same ratio. Therefore, the annual motion of the equinoctial points of the body, composed of both ring and sphere, will be to the motion 20° 11′ 46″ as 1436 to 39,343 and 4590 to 489,813 conjointly, that is, as 100 to 292,369. But the forces by which the nodes of a number of moons (as we explained above), and therefore by which the equinoctial points of the ring recede (that is, the forces 3IT, in Fig., Prop. 30), are in the several particles as the distances of those particles from the plane QR; and by these forces the particles recede from that plane: and therefore (by Lem. 2) if the matter of the ring was spread all over the surface of the sphere, after the fashion of the figure PapAPepE, in order to make up that exterior part of the earth, the total force or power of all the particles to wheel about the earth round any diameter of the equator, and therefore to move the equinoctial points, would become less than before in the proportion of 2 to 5. Therefore the annual regress of the equinoxes now would be to 20° 11′ 46″ as 10 is to 73,092; that is, would be 9″ 56‴ 50$^{\rm iv}$.

But because the plane of the equator is inclined to that of the ecliptic, this motion is to be diminished in the ratio of the sine 91,706 (which is the cosine of 23½ degrees) to the radius 100,000; and the remaining motion will now be 9″ 7‴ 20$^{\rm iv}$, which is the annual precession of the equinoxes arising from the force of the sun.

But the force of the moon to move the sea was to the force of the sun nearly as 4.4815 to 1; and the force of the moon to move the equinoxes is to that of the sun in the same proportion. Whence the annual precession of the equinoxes proceeding from the force of the moon comes out 40″ 52‴ 52$^{\rm iv}$, and the total annual precession arising from the united forces of both will be 50″ 00‴ 12$^{\rm iv}$, the amount of which motion agrees with the phenomena; for the precession of the equinoxes, by astronomical observations, is about 50″ yearly.

If the height of the earth at the equator exceeds its height at the poles by more than $17\frac{1}{6}$ miles, the matter thereof will be more rare near the surface than at the centre; and the precession of the equinoxes will be augmented by the excess of height, and diminished by the greater rarity.

And now we have described the system of the sun, the earth, moon, and planets, it remains that we add something about the comets.

LEMMA 4

The comets are more remote than the moon, and are in the regions of the planets.

As the comets were placed by astronomers beyond the moon, because they were found to have no diurnal parallax, so their annual parallax is a convincing proof of their descending into the regions of the planets; for all the comets which move in a direct course according to the order of the signs, about the end of their appearance become more than ordinarily slow or retrograde, if the earth is between them and the sun; and more than ordinarily swift, if the earth is approaching to a heliocentric opposition with them; on the other hand, those which move against the order of the signs, towards the end of their appearance appear swifter than they ought to be, if the earth is between them and the sun; and slower, and perhaps retrograde, if the earth is in the other side of its orbit. And these appearances proceed chiefly from the diverse situations which the earth acquires in the course of its motion, after the same manner as it happens to the planets, which appear sometimes retrograde, sometimes more slowly, and sometimes more swiftly, progressive, according as the motion of the earth falls in with that of the planet, or is directed in the contrary way. If the earth move the same way with the comet, but, by an angular motion about the sun, so much swifter that right lines drawn from the earth to the comet converge towards the parts beyond the comet, the comet seen from the earth, because of its slower motion, will appear retrograde; and even if the earth is slower than the comet, the motion of the earth being subtracted, the motion of the comet will at least appear retarded; but if the earth tends the contrary way to that of the comet, the motion of the comet will from thence appear accelerated; and from this apparent acceleration, or retardation, or regressive motion, the distance of the comet may be inferred in this manner.

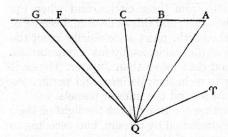

Let $\Upsilon QA, \Upsilon QB, \Upsilon QC$ be three observed longitudes of the comet about the time of its first appearing, and ΥQF its last observed longitude before its disappearing. Draw the right line ABC, whose parts AB, BC, intercepted between the right lines QA and QB, QB and QC, may be one to the other as the two times between the three first observations. Produce AC to G, so that AG may be to AB as the time between the first and last observations is to the time between the first and second; and join QG. Now if the comet did move uniformly in a right line, and the earth either stood still, or was likewise carried forwards in a right line by an uniform motion, the angle ΥQG would be the longitude of the comet at the time of the last observation. Therefore, the angle FQG, which is the difference of the longitude, proceeds from the inequality of the motions of the comet and the earth; and if the earth and comet move contrary ways, this angle is added to the angle ♈QG, and accelerates the apparent motion of the comet; but if the comet moves the same way with the earth, it is subtracted, and either retards the motion of the comet, or perhaps renders it retrograde, as we have just now explained. This angle, therefore, proceeding chiefly from the motion of the earth, is justly to be esteemed the parallax of the comet, there being neglected thereby some little increment or decrement that may arise from the unequal motion of the comet in its orbit. From this parallax we thus deduce the distance of the comet. Let S represent

the sun, *ac*T the great orbit, *a* the earth's place in the first observation, *c* the place of the earth in the third observation, T the place of the earth in the last observation, and T♈ a right line drawn to the beginning of Aries. Set off the angle ♈TV equal to the angle ♈QF, that is, equal to the longitude of the comet at the time when the earth is in T; join *ac*, and produce it to *g*, so that *ag* may be to *ac* as AG is to AC; and *g* will be the place at which the earth would have arrived in the time of the last observation, if it had continued to move uniformly in the right line *ac*. Therefore, if we draw *g*♈ parallel

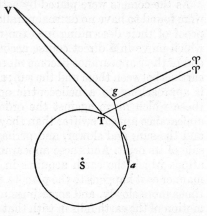

to T♈, and make the angle ♈*g*V equal to the angle ♈QG, this angle ♈*g*V will be equal to the longitude of the comet seen from the place *g*, and the angle TV*g* will be the parallax which arises from the earth's being transferred from the place *g* into the place T; and therefore V will be the place of the comet in the plane of the ecliptic. And this place V is commonly lower than the orbit of Jupiter.

The same thing may be deduced from the incurvation of the way of the comets; for these bodies move almost in great circles, while their velocity is great; but about the end of their course, when that part of their apparent motion which arises from the parallax bears a greater proportion to their whole apparent motion, they commonly deviate from those circles, and when the earth goes to one side, they deviate to the other; and this deflection, because of its corresponding with the motion of the earth, must arise chiefly from the parallax; and the quantity thereof is so considerable, as, by my computation, to place the disappearing comets a good deal lower than Jupiter. Hence it follows that when they approach nearer to us in their perigees and perihelions they often descend below the orbits of Mars and the inferior planets.

The near approach of the comets is further confirmed from the light of their heads; for the light of a celestial body, illuminated by the sun, and receding to remote parts, diminishes as the fourth power of the distance; namely, as the square, on account of the increase of the distance from the sun, and as another square, on account of the decrease of the apparent diameter. Therefore, if both the quantity of light and the apparent diameter of a comet are given, its distance will be given also, by taking the distance of the comet to the distance of a planet directly as their diameters and inversely as the square root of their lights. Thus, in the comet of the year 1682, Mr. Flamsteed observed with a telescope of 16 feet, and measured with a micrometer, the least diameter of its head, 2′ 00″; but the nucleus or star in the middle of the head scarcely amounted to the tenth part of this measure, and therefore its diameter was only 11″ or 12″; but in the light and splendor of its head it surpassed that of the comet in the year 1680, and might be compared with the stars of the first or second magnitude. Let us suppose that Saturn with its ring was about four times more lucid; and because the light of the ring was almost equal to the light of the globe within, and the apparent diameter of the globe is about 21″, and there-fore the united light of both globe and ring would be equal to the light of a globe whose diameter is 30″, it follows that the distance of the comet was to the distance of Saturn inversely as 1 to $\sqrt{4}$, and directly as 12″ to 30″; that is, as 24 to 30, or 4 to 5. Again; the comet in the month of April, 1665, as Hewelcke informs us, excelled almost all the fixed stars in splendor, and even Saturn itself, as being of a much more vivid color; for this comet was more lucid than that other which had appeared about the end of the preceding year, and had been compared to the stars of the first magnitude. The diameter of its head was about 6′; but the nucleus, compared with the planets by means of a tele-scope, was plainly less than Jupiter; and sometimes judged less, sometimes judged equal, to the globe of Saturn within the ring. Since, then, the diameters of the heads of the comets seldom exceed 8′ or 12′, and the diameter of the nucleus or central star is but about a tenth or perhaps fifteenth part of the diameter of the head, it appears that these stars are generally of about the same apparent magnitude with the planets. But since their light may be often compared with the light of Saturn, yea, and sometimes exceeds it, it is evident that all comets in their perihelions must either be placed below or not far above Saturn; and they are much mistaken who remove them almost as far as the fixed stars; for if it were so, the comets could receive no more light from our sun than our planets do from the fixed stars.

So far we have gone, without considering the obscuration which comets suffer from that plenty of thick smoke which encompasses their heads, and through which the heads always show dull, as through a cloud. But the more a body is obscured by this smoke, the nearer must it be allowed to come to the sun, that it may vie with the planets in the quantity of light which it reflects. Hence it is probable that the comets descend far below the orbit of Saturn, as we proved before from their parallax. But, above all, the thing is evinced from their tails, which must be due either to the sun's light reflected by a smoke arising from them, and dispersing itself through the ether, or to the light of their own heads. In the former case, we must shorten the distance of the comets, lest we be obliged to allow that the smoke arising from their heads is propagated through such a vast extent of space, and with such a velocity and expansion as will seem altogether incredible; in the latter case, the whole light of both head and tail is to be ascribed to the central nucleus. But, then, if we suppose all this light to be united and condensed within the disk of the nucleus, certainly the nucleus will by far exceed Jupiter itself in splendor, especially when it emits a very large and lucid tail. If, therefore, under a less apparent diameter, it reflects more light, it must be much more illuminated by the sun, and therefore much nearer to it; and the same argument will bring down the heads of comets sometimes within the orbit of Venus, viz., when, being hid under the sun's rays, they emit such huge and splendid tails, like beams of fire, as sometimes they do; for if all that light was supposed to be gathered together into one star, it would sometimes exceed not one Venus only, but a great many such united into one.

Lastly, the same thing is inferred from the light of the heads, which increases in the recess of the comets from the earth towards the sun, and decreases in their return from the sun towards the earth. Thus, the comet of the year 1665 (by the observations of Hewelcke), from the time that it was first seen, was always losing of its apparent motion, and therefore had already passed its perigee; but yet the splendor of its head was daily increasing, till, being hid under the sun's rays, the comet ceased to appear. The comet of the year 1683 (by the observations of the same Hewelcke), about the end of July, when it first appeared, moved at a very slow rate, advancing only about 40 or 45 minutes in its orbit in a day's time; but from that time its diurnal motion was continually upon the increase, till September 4, when it arose to about 5 degrees; and therefore, in all this interval of time, the comet was approaching to the earth. This is likewise proved from the diameter of its head, measured with a micrometer; for, on August 6, Hewelcke found it only 6′ 5″, including the coma, which, on September 2, he observed to be 9′ 7″; and therefore its head appeared far less about the beginning than towards the end of the motion, though about the beginning, because nearer to the sun, it appeared far more lucid than towards the end, as the same Hewelcke declares. Therefore in all this interval of time, on account of its recess from the sun, it decreased in splendor, notwithstanding its approach towards the earth. The comet of the year 1618, about the middle of December, and that of the year 1680, about the end of the same month, did both move with their greatest velocity, and were therefore then in their perigees, but the greatest splendor of their heads was seen two weeks before, when they had just got clear of the sun's rays, and the greatest splendor of their tails a little earlier, when yet nearer to the sun. The head of the former comet (according to the observations of Cysat), on December 1, appeared greater than the stars of the first magnitude; and, on December 16 (then in the perigee), it was diminished but little in magnitude, but much diminished in the splendor and brightness of its light. On January 7, Kepler, being uncertain about the head, left off observing. On December 12, the head of the latter comet was seen and observed by Mr. Flamsteed, when but 9 degrees distant from the sun, which is scarcely to be done in a star of the third magnitude. On December 15 and 17, it appeared as a star of the third magnitude, its luster being diminished by the brightness of the clouds near the setting sun. On December 26, when it moved with the greatest velocity, being almost in its perigee, it was less than the mouth of Pegasus, a star of the third magnitude. On January 3, it appeared as a star of the fourth. On January 9, as one of the fifth. On January 13, it was hid by the splendor of the moon, then in her increase. On January 25, it was scarcely equal to the stars of the seventh magnitude. If we compare equal intervals of time, taken on one side of the perigee and then on the other, we shall find that the head of the comet, which at both intervals of time was far, but yet equally removed from the earth, and should therefore have shone with equal splendor, appeared brightest on the side of the perigee towards the sun, and disappeared on the other. Therefore, from the great difference of light in the one situation and in the other, we conclude the great vicinity of the sun and comet in the former, for the light of comets tends to be regular, and to appear greatest when the heads move fastest, and are therefore in their perigees, except so far as it is increased by their nearness to the sun.

Cor. i. Therefore the comets shine by the sun's light, which they reflect.

Cor. ii. From what has been said, we may likewise understand why comets are so frequently seen in that region in which the sun is, and so seldom in the other. If they were visible in the regions far above Saturn, they would appear more frequently in the parts opposite to the sun; for such as were in those parts would be nearer to the earth, whereas the presence of the sun must obscure and hide those that appear in the region in which he is. Yet, looking over the history of comets, I find that four or five times more have been seen in the hemisphere towards the sun than in the opposite hemisphere; besides, without doubt, not a few, which have been hid by the light of the sun: for comets descending into our parts neither emit tails, nor are so well illuminated by the sun as to reveal themselves to our naked eyes, until they have come nearer to us than Jupiter. But the far greater part of that spherical space, which is described about the sun with so small a radius, lies on that side of the earth which faces the sun; and the comets in that greater part are commonly more strongly illuminated, for they are for the most part nearer to the sun.

Cor. iii. Hence also it is evident that the celestial spaces are void of resistance; for though the comets are carried in oblique paths, and sometimes contrary to the course of the planets, yet they move every way with the greatest freedom, and preserve their motions for an exceeding long time, even where contrary to the course of the planets. I am out in my judgment, if they are not a sort of planets revolving in orbits returning into themselves with a continual motion; for the opinion of some writers, that they are no other than meteors, an opinion based on the continual changes that happen to their heads, seems to have no foundation; for the heads of comets are encompassed with huge atmospheres, and the lowermost parts of these atmospheres must be the densest; and therefore it is in the clouds only, not in the bodies of the comets themselves, that these changes are seen. Thus the earth, if it were viewed from the planets, would, without all doubt, shine by the light of its clouds, and the solid body would scarcely appear through the surrounding clouds. Thus also the belts of Jupiter are formed in the clouds of that planet, for they change their position to each other, and the solid body of Jupiter is hardly to be seen through them; and much more must the bodies of comets be hid under their atmospheres, which are both deeper and thicker.

Proposition 40. Theorem 20

That the comets move in some of the conic sections, having their foci in the centre of the sun, and by radii drawn to the sun describe areas proportional to the times.

This Proposition appears from Cor. i, Prop. 13, Book i, compared with Props. 8, 12, and 13, Book iii.

Cor. i. Hence if comets revolve in orbits returning into themselves, the orbits will be ellipses; and their periodic times will be to the periodic times of the planets as the $\frac{3}{2}$th power of their principal axes. And therefore the comets, which for the most part of their course are more remote than the planets, and upon that account describe orbits with greater axes, will require a longer time to finish their revolutions. Thus if the axis of a comet's orbit was four times greater than the axis of the orbit of Saturn, the time of the revolution of the comet would be to the time of the revolution of Saturn, that is, to 30 years, as $4\sqrt{4}$ (or 8) is to 1, and would therefore be 240 years.

COR. II. But their orbits will be so near to parabolas, that parabolas may be used for them without sensible error.

COR. III. And, therefore, by Cor. VII, Prop. 16, Book I, the velocity of every comet will always be to the velocity of any planet, supposed to be revolved at the same distance in a circle about the sun, nearly as the square root of double the distance of the planet from the centre of the sun to the distance of the comet from the sun's centre. Let us suppose the radius of the great orbit, or the greatest semidiameter of the ellipse which the earth describes, to consist of 100,000,000 parts; and then the earth by its mean diurnal motion will describe 1,720,212 of those parts, and 71,675½ by its hourly motion. And therefore the comet, at the same mean distance of the earth from the sun, with a velocity which is to the velocity of the earth as $\sqrt{2}$ to 1, would by its diurnal motion describe 2,432,747 parts, and 101,364½ parts by its hourly motion. But at greater or less distances both the diurnal and hourly motion will be to this diurnal and hourly motion inversely as the square root of the distances, and is therefore given.

COR. IV. Therefore if the latus rectum of the parabola is four times the radius of the great orbit, and the square of that radius is supposed to consist of 100,000,000 parts, the area which the comet will daily describe by a radius drawn to the sun will be 1,216,373½ parts, and the hourly area will be 50,682¼ parts. But, if the latus rectum is greater or less in any ratio, the diurnal and hourly area will be less or greater inversely as the square root of that ratio.

LEMMA 5

To find a curved line of the parabolic kind which shall pass through any given number of points.

Let those points be A, B, C, D, E, F, &c., and from the same to any right line HN, given in position, let fall as many perpendiculars AH, BI, CK, DL, EM, FN, &c.

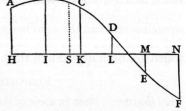

$$b \quad 2b \quad 3b \quad 4b \quad 5b$$
$$c \quad 2c \quad 3c \quad 4c$$
$$d \quad 2d \quad 3d$$
$$e \quad 2e$$
$$f$$

CASE 1. If HI, IK, KL, &c., the intervals of the points H, I, K, L, M, N, &c., are equal, take b, $2b$, $3b$, $4b$, $5b$, &c., the first differences of the perpendiculars AH, BI, CK, &c.; their second differences, c, $2c$, $3c$, $4c$, &c.; their third, d, $2d$, $3d$, &c., that is to say, so as AH$-$BI may be$=b$, BI$-$CK$=2b$, CK$-$DL$=3b$, DL$+$EM$=4b$, $-$EM$+$FN$=5b$, &c.; then $b-2b=c$, &c., and so on to the last difference, which is here f. Then, erecting any perpendicular RS, which may be considered as an ordinate of the curve required, in order to find the length of this ordinate, suppose the intervals HI, IK, KL, LM, &c., to be units, and let AH$=a$, $-$HS$=p$, ½p into$-$IS$=q$, ⅓q into $+$SK$=r$, ¼r into$+$SL$=s$, ⅕s nto$+$SM$=t$; proceeding in this manner, to ME, the last perpendicular but one, and prefixing negative signs before the terms HS, IS, &c., which lie from S towards A; and positive signs before the terms SK, SL, &c., which lie on the other side of the point S; and, observing well the signs, RS will be $=a+bp+cq+dr+es+ft,+\&c.$

CASE 2. But if HI, IK, &c., the intervals of the points H, I, K, L, &c., are unequal, take $b, 2b, 3b, 4b, 5b,$ &c., the first differences of the perpendiculars AH, BI, CK, &c., divided by the intervals between those perpendiculars; $c, 2c,$ $3c, 4c,$ &c., their second differences, divided by the intervals between every two; $d, 2d, 3d,$ &c., their third differences, divided by the intervals between every three; $e, 2e,$ &c., their fourth differences, divided by the intervals between every four; and so forth; that is, in such manner, that b may be $=\dfrac{AH-BI}{HI}$,

$$2b=\frac{BI-CK}{IK}, \quad 3b=\frac{CK-DL}{KL}, \quad \&c., \text{ then } c=\frac{b-2b}{HK}, \quad 2c=\frac{2b-3b}{IL}, \quad 3c=\frac{3b-4b}{KM}, \&c.,$$

then $d=\dfrac{c-2c}{HL}$, $2d=\dfrac{2c-3c}{IM}$, &c. And those differences being found, let AH be $=a$, $-HS=p$, p into $-IS=q$, q into $+SK=r$, r into $+SL=s$, s into $+SM=t$; proceeding in this manner to ME, the last perpendicular but one; and the ordinate RS will be$=a+bp+cq+dr+es+ft+\&c.$

COR. Hence the areas of all curves may be nearly found; for if some number of points of the curve to be squared are found, and a parabola be supposed to be drawn through those points, the area of this parabola will be nearly the same with the area of the curvilinear figure proposed to be squared: but the parabola can be always squared geometrically by methods generally known.

LEMMA 6

Certain observed places of a comet being given, to find the place of the same at any intermediate given time.

Let HI, IK, KL, LM (in the preceding Fig.) represent the times between the observations; HA, IB, KC, LD, ME, five observed longitudes of the comet; and HS the given time between the first observation and the longitude required. Then if a regular curve ABCDE is supposed to be drawn through the points A, B, C, D, E, and the ordinate RS is found out by the preceding Lemma, RS will be the longitude required.

By the same method, from five observed latitudes, we may find the latitude at a given time.

If the differences of the observed longitudes are small, let us say 4 or 5 degrees, then three or four observations will be sufficient to find a new longitude and latitude; but if the differences are greater, as of 10 or 20 degrees, five observations ought to be used.

LEMMA 7

Through a given point P to drawn a right line BC, whose parts PB, PC, cut off by two right lines AB, AC, given in position, may be one to the other in a given ratio.

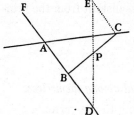

From the given point P suppose any right line PD to be drawn to either of the right lines given, as AB; and produce the same towards AC, the other given right line, as far as E, so as PE may be to PD in the given ratio. Let EC be parallel to AD. Draw CPB, and PC will be to PB as PE to PD.

Q.E.F.

Let ABC be a parabola, having its focus in S. By the chord AC bisected in I cut off the segment ABCI, whose diameter is Iμ and vertex μ. In Iμ produced take μO equal to one-half of Iμ. Join OS, and produce it to ξ, so that Sξ may be equal to 2SO. Now, supposing a comet to revolve in the arc CBA, draw ξB, cutting AC in E: I say, the point E will cut off from the chord AC the segment AE, nearly proportional to the time.

For if we join EO, cutting the parabolic arc ABC in Y, and draw μX touching the same arc in the vertex μ, and meeting EO in X, the curvilinear area AEXμA will be to the curvilinear area ACYμA as AE to AC; and, therefore,

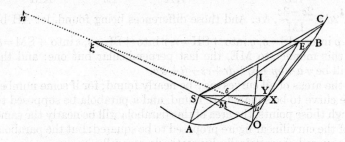

since the triangle ASE is to the triangle ASC in the same ratio, the whole area ASEXμA will be to the whole area ASCYμA as AE is to AC. But, because ξO is to SO as 3 to 1, and EO to XO in the same ratio, SX will be parallel to EB; and, therefore, joining BX, the triangle SEB will be equal to the triangle XEB. Therefore, if to the area ASEXμA we add the triangle EXB, and from the sum subtract the triangle SEB, there will remain the area ASBXμA, equal to the area ASEXμA, and therefore in the ratio to the area ASCYμA as AE to AC. But the area ASBYμA is nearly equal to the area ASBXμA; and this area ASBYμA is to the area ASCYμA as the time of description of the arc AB is to the time of description of the whole arc AC; and, therefore, AE is to AC nearly in the proportion of the times.   Q.E.D.

COR. When the point B falls upon the vertex μ of the parabola, AE is to AC accurately in the proportion of the times.

If we join μξ cutting AC in δ, and in it take ξn in proportion to μB as 27MI to 16 Mμ, and draw Bn, this Bn will cut the chord AC, in the ratio of the times, more accurately than before; but the point n is to be taken beyond or on this side the point ξ, according as the point B is more or less distant from the principal vertex of the parabola than the point μ.

The right lines Iμ and μM, and the length $\frac{AI^2}{4Sμ}$, are equal among themselves.

For 4Sμ is the latus rectum of the parabola belonging to the vertex μ.

Lemma 10

Produce Sμ *to* N *and* P, *so that* μN *may be one-third of* μI, *and* SP *may be to* SN *as* SN *to* Sμ; *and in the time that a comet would describe the arc* AμC, *if it was supposed to move always forwards with the velocity which it has in a height equal to* SP, *it would describe a length equal to the chord* AC.

For if the comet with the velocity which it hath in μ was in the said time supposed to move uniformly forwards in the right line which touches the parabola in μ, the area which it would describe by a radius drawn to the point S

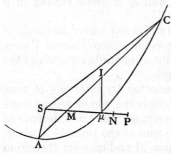

would be equal to the parabolic area ASCμA; and therefore the space contained under the length described in the tangent and the length Sμ would be to the space contained under the lengths AC and SM as the area ASCμA is to the triangle ASC, that is, as SN to SM. Therefore AC is to the length described in the tangent as Sμ to SN. But since the velocity of the comet in the height SP (by Cor. vi, Prop. 16, Book i) is to the velocity of the same in the height Sμ, inversely as the square root of SP

to Sμ, that is, in the ratio of Sμ to SN, it follows that the length described with this velocity will be to the length in the same time described in the tangent, as Sμ to SN. Therefore, since AC, and the length described with this new velocity, are in the same proportion to the length described in the tangent, they must be equal between themselves. Q.E.D.

Cor. Therefore a comet, with that velocity which it hath in the height S$\mu + \frac{2}{3}$Iμ, would in the same time nearly describe the chord AC.

Lemma 11

If a comet void of all motion was let fall from the height SN, *or* S$\mu + \frac{1}{3}$Iμ, *towards the sun, and was still impelled to the sun by the same force uniformly continued by which it was impelled at first, the same, in one-half of that time in which it might describe the arc* AC *in its own orbit, would in descending describe a space equal to the length* Iμ.

For in the same time that the comet would require to describe the parabolic arc AC, it would (by the last Lemma), with that velocity which it hath in the height SP, describe the chord AC; and, therefore (by Cor. vii, Prop. 16, Book i), if it was in the same time supposed to revolve by the force of its own gravity in a circle whose semidiameter was SP, it would describe an arc of that circle, the length of which would be to the chord of the parabolic arc AC in the ratio of 1 to $\sqrt{2}$. Therefore, if with that weight, which in the height SP it hath towards the sun, it should fall from that height towards the sun, it would (by Cor. ix, Prop. 16, Book

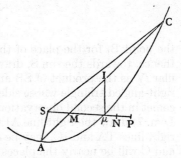

i) in half the said time describe a space equal to the square of half the said chord, divided by four times the height SP, that is, it would describe the space

$\dfrac{\text{AI}^2}{4\text{SP}}$. But since the weight of the comet towards the sun in the height SN is to the weight of the same towards the sun in the height SP as SP to Sμ, the comet, by the weight which it hath in the height SN, in falling from that height towards the sun, would in the same time describe the space $\dfrac{\text{AI}^2}{4\text{S}\mu}$; that is, a space equal to the length Iμ or μM.   Q.E.D.

Proposition 41. Problem 21

From three given observations to determine the orbit of a comet moving in a parabola.

This being a Problem of very great difficulty, I tried many methods of resolving it; and several of those Problems, the composition whereof I have given in the first book, tended to this purpose. But afterwards I contrived the following solution, which is somewhat more simple.

Select three observations distant one from another by intervals of time nearly equal; but let that interval of time in which the comet moves more slowly be somewhat greater than the other; namely, so that the difference of the times may be to the sum of the times as the sum of the times is to about 600 days; or that the point E may fall nearly upon M and may err therefrom rather towards I than towards A. If such direct observations are not at hand, a new place of the comet must be found, by Lemma 6.

Let S represent the sun; T, t, τ three places of the earth in the earth's orbit; TA, tB, τC three observed longitudes of the comet; V the time between the first observation and the second; W the time between the second and the third; X the length which in the whole time V+W the comet might describe with that velocity which it has in the mean distance of the earth from the sun, which length is to be found by Cor. III, Prop. XL, Book III; and tV a perpendicular upon the chord Tτ. In the mean observed longitude tB take at pleasure

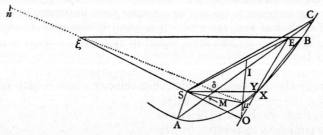

the point B, for the place of the comet in the plane of the ecliptic; and from thence, towards the sun S, draw the line BE, which may be to the perpendicular tV as the product of SB and St^2 is to the cube of the hypothenuse of the right-angled triangle whose sides are SB and the tangent of the latitude of the comet in the second observation to the radius tB. And through the point E (by Lem. 7) draw the right line AEC, whose parts AE and EC, terminating in the right lines TA and τC, may be one to the other as the times V and W: then A and C will be nearly the places of the comet in the plane of the ecliptic in the first and third observations, if B was its place rightly assumed in the second.

Upon AC, bisected in I, erect the perpendicular Ii. Through B imagine the

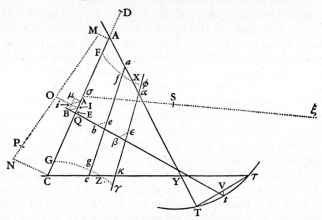

line B*i* drawn parallel to AC. Imagine the line S*i* drawn, cutting AC in λ, and complete the parallelogram *i*Iλμ. Take Iσ equal to 3Iλ; and through the sun S imagine the line σξ drawn equal to 3Sσ+3*i*λ. Then, canceling the letters A, E, C, I, from the point B towards the point ξ, imagine the new line BE drawn, which may be to the former BE as the square of the ratio of the distance BS to the quantity Sμ+⅓*i*λ. And through the point E draw again the right line AEC by the same rule as before; that is, so that its parts AE and EC may be one to the other as the times V and W between the observations. Thus A and C will be the places of the comet more accurately.

Upon AC, bisected in I, erect the perpendiculars AM, CN, IO, of which AM and CN may be the tangents of the latitudes in the first and third observations, to the radii TA and τC. Join MN, cutting IO and O. Draw the rectangular parallelogram *i*Iλμ, as before. In IA produced take ID equal to Sμ+⅔*i*λ. Then in MN, towards N, take MP, which may be to the above-found length X as the square root of the ratio of the mean distance of the earth from the sun (or of the semidiameter of the earth's orbit) to the distance OD. If the point P fall upon the point N; A, B, and C will be three places of the comet, through which its orbit is to be described in the plane of the ecliptic. But if the point P falls not upon the point N, in the right line AC take CG equal to NP, so that the points G and P may lie on the same side of the line NC.

By the same method as the points E, A, C, G were found from the assumed point B, from other points *b* and β assumed at pleasure, find out the new points *e*, *a*, *c*, *g*; and ε, α, κ, γ. Then through G, *g*, and γ draw the circumference of a circle G*g*γ, cutting the right line τC in Z: and Z will be one place of the comet in the plane of the ecliptic. And in AC, *ac*, *ak*, taking AF, *af*, αφ, equal respectively to CG, *cg*, κγ; through the points F, *f*, and φ, draw the circumference of a circle F*f*φ, cutting the right line AT in X; and the point X will be another place of the comet in the plane of the ecliptic. And at the points X and Z, erecting the tangents of the latitudes of the comet to the radii TX and τZ, two places of the comet in its own orbit will be determined. Lastly, if (by Prop. 19, Book I) to the focus S a parabola is described passing through those two places, this parabola will be the orbit of the comet.   Q.E.I.

The demonstration of this construction follows from the preceding Lemmas, because the right line AC is cut in E in the proportion of the times, by Lemma

7, as it ought to be by Lemma 8; and BE, by Lemma 11, is a portion of the right line BS or Bξ in the plane of the ecliptic, intercepted between the arc ABC and the chord AEC; and MP (by Cor., Lem. 10) is the length of the chord of that arc, which the comet should describe in its proper orbit between the first and third observations, and therefore is equal to MN, providing B is a true place of the comet in the plane of the ecliptic.

But it will be convenient to assume the points B, b, β, not at random, but nearly true. If the angle AQt, at which the projection of the orbit in the plane of the ecliptic cuts the right line tB, is roughly known, at that angle with Bt draw the line AC, which may be to $\frac{4}{3}$Tτ as the square root of the ratio of SQ to St; and, drawing the right line SEB so as its part EB may be equal to the length Vt, the point B will be determined, which we are to use for the first time. Then, canceling the right line AC and drawing anew AC according to the preceding construction, and, moreover, finding the length MP, in tB take the point b, by this rule, that, if TA and τC intersect each other in Y, the distance Yb may be to the distance YB in a ratio compounded of the ratio of MP to MN, and the square root of the ratio of SB to Sb. And by the same method you may find the third point β, if you please to repeat the operation the third time; but if this method is followed, two operations generally will be sufficient; for if the distance Bb happens to be very small, after the points F, f, and G, g, are found, draw the right lines Ff and Gg, and they will cut TA and τC in the points required, X and Z.

EXAMPLE

Let the comet of the year 1680 be proposed. The following table shows the motion thereof, as observed by Flamsteed, and calculated afterwards by him from his observations, and corrected by Dr. Halley from the same observations.

	Time		Sun's longitude	Comet's	
	Apparent	True		Longitude	Latitude north
	h m	h m s	° ′ ″	° ′ ″	° ′ ″
1680, Dec. 12	4.46	4.46. 0	♑ 1.51.23	♑ 6.32.30	8.28. 0
21	6.32½	6.36.59	11.06.44	♒ 5.08.12	21.42.13
24	6.12	6.17.52	14.09.26	18.49.23	25.23. 5
26	5.14	5.20.44	16.09.22	28.24.13	27.00.52
29	7.55	8.03.02	19.19.43	♓13.10.41	28.09.58
30	8.02	8.10.26	20.21.09	17.38.20	28.11.53
1681, Jan. 5	5.51	6.01.38	26.22.18	♈ 8.48.53	26.15. 7
9	6.49	7.00.53	♒ 0.29.02	18.44.04	24.11.56
10	5.54	6.06.10	1.27.43	20.40.50	23.43.52
13	6.56	7.08.55	4.33.20	25.59.48	22.17.28
25	7.44	7.58.42	16.45.36	♉ 9.35. 0	17.56.30
30	8.07	8.21.53	21.49.58	13.19.51	16.42.18
Feb. 2	6.20	6.34.51	24.46.59	15.13.53	16.04. 1
5	6.50	7.04.41	27.49.51	16.59.06	15.27. 3

To these you may add some observations of mine.

These observations were made by a telescope of 7 feet, with a micrometer and threads placed in the focus of the telescope; by these instruments we determined the positions both of the fixed stars among themselves, and of the

	Apparent time	Comet's	
		Longitude	Latitude north
	h m	° ′ ″	° ′ ″
1681, Feb. 25	8.30	♉26.18.35	12.46.46
27	8.15	27.04.30	12.36.12
Mar. 1	11. 0	27.52.42	12.23.40
2	8. 0	28.12.48	12.19.38
5	11.30	29.18. 0	12.03.16
7	9.30	♊ 0. 4. 0	11.57. 0
9	8.30	0.43. 4	11.45.52

comet in respect of the fixed stars. Let A represent the star of the fourth magnitude in the left heel of Perseus (Bayer's *o*), B the following star of the third magnitude in the left foot (Bayer's ζ), C a star of the sixth magnitude (Bayer's

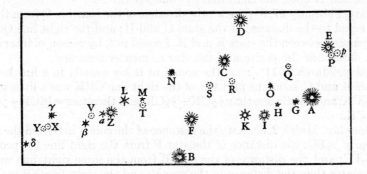

n) in the heel of the same foot, and D, E, F, G, H, I, K, L, M, N, O, Z, *a*, *β*, *γ*, *δ* other smaller stars in the same foot; and let *p*, P, Q, R, S, T, V, X represent the places of the comet in the observations above set down; and, reckoning the distance AB of $80^7/_{12}$ parts, AC was $52^1/_4$ of those parts; BC, $58^5/_6$; AD, $57^5/_{12}$; BD, $82^6/_{11}$; CD, $23^2/_3$; AE, $29^4/_7$; CE, $57^1/_2$; DE, $49^{11}/_{12}$; AI, $27^7/_{12}$; BI, $52^1/_6$; CI, $36^7/_{12}$; DI, $53^5/_{11}$; AK, $38^2/_3$; BK, 43; CK, $31^5/_9$; FK, 29; FB, 23; FC, $36^1/_4$; AH, $18^6/_7$; DH, $50^7/_8$; BN, $46^5/_{12}$; CN, $31^1/_3$; BL, $45^5/_{12}$; NL, $31^5/_7$. HO was to HI as 7 to 6, and, produced, did pass between the stars D and E, so as the distance of the star D from this right line was $^1/_6$CD. LM was to LN as 2 to 9, and, produced, did pass through the star H. Thus were the positions of the fixed stars determined in respect to one another.

The fixed stars	Their longitudes	Latitude north	The fixed stars	Their longitudes	Latitude north
	° ′ ″	° ′ ″		° ′ ″	° ′ ″
A	♉26.41.50	12. 8.36	L	♉29.33.34	12. 7.48
B	28.40.23	11.17.54	M	29.18.54	12. 7.20
C	27.58.30	12.40.25	N	28.48.29	12.31. 9
E	26.27.17	12.52. 7	Z	29.44.48	11.57.13
F	28.28.37	11.52.22	*a*	29.52. 3	11.55.48
G	26.56. 8	12. 4.58	*β*	♊ 0. 8.23	11.48.56
H	27.11.45	12. 2. 1	*γ*	0.40.10	11.55.18
I	27.25. 2	11.53.11	*δ*	1. 3.20	11.30.42
K	27.42. 7	11.53.26			

Mr. Pound has since observed a second time the positions of these fixed stars amongst themselves, and obtained their longitudes and latitudes according to the preceding table.

The positions of the comet to these fixed stars were observed to be as follows:

Friday, February 25, o.s., at $8\frac{1}{2}^h$. p.m., the distance of the comet in p from the star E was less than $\frac{3}{13}$ AE, and greater than $\frac{1}{5}$AE, and therefore nearly equal to $\frac{3}{14}$AE; and the angle ApE was a little obtuse, but almost right. For from A, letting fall a perpendicular on pE, the distance of the comet from that perpendicular was $\frac{1}{5}p$E.

The same night, at $9\frac{1}{2}^h$., the distance of the comet in P from the star E was greater than $\frac{1}{4\frac{1}{6}}$AE, and less than $\frac{1}{5\frac{1}{4}}$AE, and therefore nearly equal to $\frac{1}{4\frac{7}{8}}$ of AE, or $\frac{8}{39}$ AE. But the distance of the comet from the perpendicular let fall from the star A upon the right line PE was $\frac{4}{5}$PE.

Sunday, February 27, $8\frac{1}{4}^h$. p.m., the distance of the comet in Q from the star O was equal to the distance of the stars O and H; and the right line QO produced passed between the stars K and B. I could not, by reason of intervening clouds, determine the position of the star to greater accuracy.

Tuesday, March 1, 11^h. p.m., the comet in R lay exactly in a line between the stars K and C, so as the part CR of the right line CRK was a little greater than $\frac{1}{3}$CK, and a little less than $\frac{1}{3}$CK$+\frac{1}{8}$CR, and therefore $=\frac{1}{3}$CK$+\frac{1}{16}$CR, or $\frac{16}{45}$CK.

Wednesday, March 2, 8^h. p.m., the distance of the comet in S from the star C was nearly $\frac{4}{9}$FC; the distance of the star F from the right line CS produced was $\frac{1}{24}$FC; and the distance of the star B from the same right line was five times greater than the distance of the star F; and the right line NS produced passed between the stars H and I five or six times nearer to the star H than to the star I.

Saturday, March 5, $11\frac{1}{2}^h$. p.m., when the comet was in T, the right line MT was equal to $\frac{1}{2}$ML, and the right line LT produced passed between B and F four or five times nearer to F than to B, cutting off from BF a fifth or sixth part thereof towards F; and MT produced passed on the outside of the space BF towards the star B four times nearer to the star B than to the star F. M was a very small star, scarcely to be seen by the telescope; but the star L was greater, and of about the eighth magnitude.

Monday, March 7, $9\frac{1}{2}^h$. p.m., the comet being in V, the right line Va produced did pass between B and F, cutting off, from BF towards F, $\frac{1}{10}$ of BF, and was to the right line $V\beta$ as 5 to 4. And the distance of the comet from the right line $a\beta$ was $\frac{1}{2}V\beta$.

Wednesday, March 9, $8\frac{1}{2}^h$. p.m., the comet being in X, the right line γX was equal to $\frac{1}{4}\gamma\delta$; and the perpendicular let fall from the star δ upon the right line γX was $\frac{2}{5}$ of $\gamma\delta$.

The same night, at 12^h., the comet being in Y, the right line γY was equal to $\frac{1}{3}$ of $\gamma\delta$, or a little less, as perhaps $\frac{5}{16}$ of $\gamma\delta$; and a perpendicular let fall from the star δ on the right line γY was equal to about $\frac{1}{6}$ or $\frac{1}{7}\gamma\delta$. But the comet, being then extremely near the horizon, was scarcely discernible, and therefore its place could not be determined with the same certainty as in the foregoing observations.

From these observations, by constructions of figures and calculations, I deduced the longitudes and latitudes of the comet; and Mr. Pound, by correcting the places of the fixed stars, has determined more correctly the places of the comet, which correct places are set down above. Though my micrometer was none of the best, yet the errors in longitude and latitude (as derived from my observations) scarcely exceed one minute. The comet (according to my observations), about the end of its motion, began to decline sensibly towards the north, from the parallel which it described about the end of February.

Now, in order to determine the orbit of the comet from the observations above described, I selected those three which Flamsteed made (Dec. 21, Jan. 5, and Jan. 25); from which I found St of 9842.1 parts, and Vt of 455, supposing the semidiameter of the earth's orbit contains 10,000. Then, for the first observation, assuming tB of 5657 of those parts, I found SB 9747, BE for the first time 412, Sμ 9503, $i\lambda$413, BE for the second time 421, OD 10,186, X 8528.4, PM 8450, MN 8475, NP 25; from this, by the second operation, I obtained the distance tb 5640; and by this operation I at last deduced the distances TX 4775 and τZ 11,322. From these values, determining the orbit, I found its descending node in ♋, and ascending node in ♑ 1° 53′; the inclination of its plane to the plane of the ecliptic 61° 20⅓′, the vertex thereof (or the perihelion of the comet) distant from the node 8° 38′, and in ♐ 27° 43′, with latitude 7° 34′ south; its latus rectum 236.8; and the diurnal area described by a radius drawn to the sun 93,585, supposing the square of the semidiameter of the earth's orbit 100,000,000; that the comet in this orbit moved directly according to the order of the signs, and on Dec. 8^d. 00^h. 04^m. P.M. was in the vertex or perihelion of its orbit. All this I determined by scale and compass, and the chords of angles, taken from the table of natural sines, in a pretty large figure, in which, to wit, the radius of the earth's orbit (consisting of 10,000 parts) was equal to 16⅓ inches of an English foot.

Lastly, in order to discover whether the comet did truly move in the orbit so determined, I investigated its places in this orbit partly by arithmetical operations, and partly by scale and compass, to the times of some of the observations, as may be seen in the following table:

	The Comet's						
	Distance from sun	*Longitude computed*	*Latitude computed*	*Longitude observed*	*Latitude observed*	*Difference longitude*	*Difference latitude*
Dec. 12	2792	♑ 6° 32′	8° 18½	♑ 6° 31½	8° 26	+1	− 7½
29	8403	♓13.13⅔	28.00	♓13.11¾	28.10$\frac{1}{12}$	+2	−10$\frac{1}{12}$
Feb. 5	16669	♉17.00	15.29⅔	♉16.59⅞	15.27⅖	+0	+ 2¼
Mar. 5	21737	29.19¾	12. 4	29.20$\frac{6}{7}$	12. 3½	−1	+ ½

But afterwards Dr. Halley did determine the orbit to a greater accuracy by an arithmetical calculus than could be done by graphic operations; and, retaining the place of the nodes in ♋ and ♑ 1° 53′, and the inclination of the plane of the orbit to the ecliptic 61° 20⅓′, as well as the time of the comet's being in perihelion, Dec. 8^d. 00^h. 04^m. he found the distance of the perihelion from the ascending node measured in the comet's orbit 9° 20′, and the latus rectum of the parabola 2430 parts, supposing the mean distance of the sun from the earth to be 100,000 parts; and from these data by an accurate arithmetical calculus, he computed the places of the comet to the times of the observations as given in the table on page 348.

This comet also appeared in the November before, and at Coburg, in Saxony, was observed by Mr. Gottfried Kirch, on the 4th of that month, on the 6th and 11th, o.s.; from its positions to the nearest fixed stars observed with sufficient accuracy, sometimes with a two-foot, and sometimes with a ten-foot telescope; from the difference of longitudes of Coburg and London, 11°; and from the places of the fixed stars observed by Mr. Pound, Dr. Halley has determined the places of the comet as follows:

Nov. 3, 17ʰ. 2ᵐ., apparent time at London, the comet was in ♌ 29° 51′, with 1° 17′ 45″ latitude north.

Nov. 5, 15ʰ. 58ᵐ., the comet was in ♍ 3° 23′, with 1° 6′ latitude north.

Nov. 10, 16ʰ. 31ᵐ., the comet was equally distant from two stars in ♌, which are designated σ and τ in Bayer; but it had not quite touched the right line that joins them, but was very little distant from it. In Flamsteed's cat-

True time			The Comet's			Errors in	
		Distance from the sun	Longitude computed	Latitude computed		Longitude	Latitude
	d h m		° ′ ″	° ′ ″		′ ″	′ ″
Dec.	12. 4.46.	28028	♑ 6.29.25	8.26. 0 bor.		−3. 5	−2. 0
	21. 6.37.	61076	♒ 5. 6.30	21.43.20		−1.42	+1. 7
	24. 6.18.	70008	18.48.20	25.22.40		−1. 3	−0.25
	26. 5.20.	75576	28.22.45	27. 1.36		−1.28	+0.44
	29. 8. 3.	84021	♓13.12.40	28.10.10		+1.59	+0.12
	30. 8.10.	86661	17.40. 5	28.11.20		+1.45	−0.33
Jan.	5. 6. 1.½	101440	♈ 8.49.49	26.15.15		+0.56	+0. 8
	9. 7. 0.	110959	18.44.36	24.12.54		+0.32	+0.58
	10. 6. 6.	113162	20.41. 0	23.44.10		+0.10	+0.18
	13. 7. 9.	120000	26. 0.21	22.17.30		+0.33	+0. 2
	25. 7.59.	145370	♉ 9.33.40	17.57.55		−1.20	+1.25
	30. 8.22.	155303	13.17.41	16.42. 7		−2.10	−0.11
Feb.	2. 6.35.	160951	15.11.11	16. 4.15		−2.42	+0.14
	5. 7. 4.½	166686	16.58.55	15.29.13		−0.41	+2. 0
	25. 8.41.	202570	26.15.46	12.48. 0		−2.49	+1.10
Mar.	5.11.39.	216205	29.18.35	12. 5.40		+0.35	+2.14

alogue this star σ was then in ♍ 14° 15′, with 1° 41′ latitude north nearly, and τ in ♍17° 3½′ with 0° 34′ latitude south; and the middle point between those stars was ♍ 15° 39¼′, with 0° 33½′ latitude north. Let the distance of the comet from that right line be about 10′ or 12′; and the difference of the longitude of the comet and that middle point will be 7′; and the difference of the latitude nearly 7½′; and thence it follows that the comet was in ♍ 15° 32′, with about 26′ latitude north.

The first observation from the position of the comet with respect to certain small fixed stars had all the exactness that could be desired; the second also was accurate enough. In the third observation, which was the least accurate, there might be an error of 6′ or 7′, but hardly greater. The longitude of the comet, as found in the first and most accurate observation, being computed in the aforesaid parabolic orbit, comes out ♌ 29° 30′ 32″, its latitude north 1° 25′ 7″, and its distance from the sun 115,546.

Moreover, Dr. Halley, observing that a remarkable comet had appeared four times at equal intervals of 575 years (that is, in the month of September after Julius Caesar was killed; [in A.D.] 531, in the consulate of Lampadius and Orestes; [in] 1106, in the month of February: and at the end of the year 1680; and that with a long and remarkable tail, except when it was seen after Caesar's death, at which time, by reason of the inconvenient situation of the earth, the tail was not so conspicuous), set himself to find out an elliptic orbit whose greater axis should be 1,382,957 parts, the mean distance of the earth from the sun containing 10,000 such; in this orbit a comet might revolve in 575 years; and, placing the ascending node in ♋ 2° 2′, the inclination of the plane of the orbit to the plane of the ecliptic in an angle of 61° 6′ 48″, the perihelion of the comet in this plane in ♐ 22° 44′ 25″, the equal time of the perihelion Dec. 7ᵈ. 23ʰ. 9ᵐ., the distance of the perihelion from the ascending node in the

True time	Longitude observed	Latitude N observed	Longitude computed	Latitude computed	Errors in longitude	Errors in latitude
d h m	° ′ ″	° ′ ″	° ′ ″	° ′ ″	′ ″	′ ″
Nov. 3.16.47	♌29.51. 0	1.17.45	♌29.51.22	1.17.32 N	+0.22	−0.13
5.15.37	♍ 3.23. 0	1. 6. 0	♍ 3.24.32	1. 6. 9	+1.32	+0. 9
10.16.18	15.32. 0	0.27. 0	15.33. 2	0.25. 7	+1. 2	−1.53
16.17.00			♎ 8.16.45	0.53. 7 S		
18.21.34			18.52.15	1.26.54		
20.17. 0			28.10.36	1.53.35		
23.17. 5			♏13.22.42	2.29. 0		
Dec. 12. 4.46	♑ 6.32.30	8.28. 0	♑ 6.31.20	8.29 .6 N	−1.10	+1. 6
21. 6.37	♒ 5. 8.12	21.42.13	♒ 5. 6.14	21.44.42	−1.58	+2.29
24. 6.18	18.49.23	25.23. 5	18.47.30	25.23.35	−1.53	+0.30
26. 5.21	28.24.13	27. 0.52	28.21.42	27. 2. 1	−2.31	+1. 9
29. 8. 3	♓13.10.41	28. 9.58	♓13.11.14	28.10.38	+0.33	+0.40
30. 8.10	17.38. 0	28.11.53	17.38.27	28.11.37	+0. 7	−0.16
Jan. 5. 6. 1½	♈ 8.48.53	26.15. 7	♈ 8.48.51	26.14.57	−0. 2	−0.10
9. 7. 1	18.44. 4	24.11.56	18.43.51	24.12.17	−0.13	+0.21
10. 6. 6	20.40.50	23.43.32	20.40.23	23.43.25	−0.27	−0. 7
13. 7. 9	25.59.48	22.17.28	26. 0. 8	22.16.32	+0.20	−0.56
25. 7.59	♉ 9.35. 0	17.56.30	♉ 9.34.11	17.56. 6	−0.49	−0.24
30. 8.22	13.19.51	16.42.18	13.18.28	16.40. 5	−1.23	−2.13
Feb. 2. 6.35	15.13.53	16. 4. 1	15.11.59	16. 2.17	−1.54	−1.54
5. 7. 4½	16.59. 6	15.27. 3	16.59.17	15.27. 0	+0.11	−0. 3
25. 8.41	26.18.35	12.46.46	26.16.59	12.45.22	−1.36	−1.24
Mar. 1.11.10	27.52.42	12.23.40	27.51.47	12.22.28	−0.55	−1.12
5.11.39	29.18. 0	12. 3.16	29.20.11	12. 2.50	+2.11	−0.26
9. 8.38	♊ 0.43. 4	11.45.52	♊ 0.42.43	11.45.35	−0.21	−0.17

plane of the ecliptic 9° 17′ 35″, and its conjugate axis 18,481.2, he computed the motions of the comet in this elliptic orbit. The places of the comet, as deduced from the observations, and as arising from computation made in this orbit, may be seen in the preceding table.

The observations of this comet from the beginning to the end agree as perfectly with the motion of the comet in the orbit just now described as the motions of the planets do with the theories from whence they are calculated, and by this agreement plainly evince that it was one and the same comet that appeared all that time, and also that the orbit of that comet is here rightly defined.

In the foregoing table we have omitted the observations of Nov. 16, 18, 20, and 23, as not sufficiently accurate, for at those times several persons had observed the comet. Nov. 17, o.s., Ponthio and his companions, at 6ʰ. in the morning at Rome (that is, 5^h. 10^m. at London), by threads directed to the fixed stars, observed the comet in $\simeq 8°$ 30', with latitude 0° 40' south. Their observations may be seen in a treatise which Ponthio published concerning this comet. Cellio, who was present, and communicated his observations in a letter to Cassini, saw the comet at the same hour in $\simeq 8°$ 30', with latitude 0° 30' south. It was likewise seen by Gallet at the same hour at Avignon (that is, at 5^h. 42^m. morning at London) in $\simeq 8°$ without latitude. But by the theory the comet was at that time in $\simeq 8°$ 16' 45'', and its latitude was 0° 53' 7'' south.

Nov.18, at 6^h. 30^m. in the morning at Rome (that is, at $5^h.40^m$. at London), Ponthio observed the comet in $\simeq 13°$ 30', with latitude 1° 20' south; and Cellio in $\simeq 13°$ 30', with latitude 1° 00' south. But at 5^h. 30^m. in the morning at Avignon, Gallet saw it in $\simeq 13°$ 00', with latitude 1° 00' south. In the University of La Fleche, in France, at 5^h. in the morning (that is, at 5^h. 9^m. at London), it was seen by Ango, in the middle between two small stars, one of which is the middle of the three which lie in a right line in the southern hand of Virgo, Bayer's Ψ; and the other is the outmost of the wing, Bayer's θ. Hence, the comet was then in $\simeq 12°$ 46' with latitude 50' south. And I was informed by Dr. Halley, that on the same day at Boston in New England, in the latitude of $42\frac{1}{2}°$, at 5^h. in the morning (that is, at 9^h. 44^m. in the morning at London) the comet was seen near $\simeq 14°$, with latitude 1° 30' south.

Nov. 19, at $4\frac{1}{2}^h$. at Cambridge, the comet (by the observation of a young man) was distant from Spica $\text{m}\hspace{-2pt}\gamma$ about 2° towards the northwest. Now the Spike was at that time in $\simeq 19°$ 23' 47'', with latitude 2° 1' 59'' south. The same day, at 5^h. in the morning, at Boston in New England, the comet was distant from Spica $\text{m}\hspace{-2pt}\gamma$ 1°, with the difference of 40' in latitude. The same day, in the island of Jamaica, it was about 1° distant from Spica $\text{m}\hspace{-2pt}\gamma$. The same day, Mr. Arthur Storer, at the river Patuxent, near Hunting Creek, in Maryland, in the confines of Virginia in latitude $38\frac{1}{2}°$, at 5^h. in the morning (that is, at 10^h. at London), saw the comet above Spica $\text{m}\hspace{-2pt}\gamma$, and very nearly joined with it, the distance between them being about $\frac{3}{4}$ of one degree. And from these observations compared, I conclude, that at 9^h. 44^m. at London the comet was in $\simeq 18°$ 50', with about 1° 25' latitude south. Now by the theory the comet was at that time in $\simeq 18°$ 52' 15'', with 1° 26' 54'' latitude south.

Nov. 20, Montenari, Professor of Astronomy at Padua, at 6^h. in the morning at Venice (that is, 5^h. 10^m. at London), saw the comet in $\simeq 23°$, with latitude 1° 30' south. The same day, at Boston, it was distant from Spica $\text{m}\hspace{-2pt}\gamma$ by about 4° of longitude east, and therefore was in $\simeq 23°$ 24', nearly.

Nov. 21, Ponthio and his companions, at $7\frac{1}{4}^h$. in the morning, observed the comet in $\simeq 27°$ 50', with latitude 1° 16' south; Cellio, in $\simeq 28°$; Ango at 5^h. in the morning, in $\simeq 27°$ 45'; Montenari in $\simeq 27°$ 51'. The same day, in the island of Jamaica, it was seen near the beginning of m, and of about the same latitude with Spica $\text{m}\hspace{-2pt}\gamma$, that is, 2° 2'. The same day, at 5^h. morning, at Ballasore, in the East Indies (that is, at 11^h. 20^m. of the night preceding at London), the distance of the comet from Spica $\text{m}\hspace{-2pt}\gamma$ was taken 7° 35' to the east. It was in a right line between the Spike and the Balance, and therefore was then in $\simeq 26°$ 58', with about 1° 11' latitude south; and after 5^h. 40^m. (that is, at 5^h. in the morning at London), it was in $\simeq 28°$ 12' with 1° 16' latitude south. Now by the theory the comet was then in $\simeq 28°$ 10' 36'', with 1° 53' 35'' latitude south.

Nov. 22, the comet was seen by Montenari in ♏ 2° 33′; but at Boston in New England it was found in about ♏ 3°, and with almost the same latitude as before, that is, 1° 30′. The same day, at 5ʰ. morning at Ballasore, the comet was observed in ♏ 1° 50′; and therefore at 5ʰ. morning at London, the comet was in ♏ 3° 5′, nearly. The same day at 6½ʰ. in the morning at London, Dr. Hooke observed it in about ♏ 3° 30′, and that in the right line which passeth through Spica ♍ and Cor Leonis; not, indeed, exactly, but deviating a little from that line towards the north. Montenari likewise observed, that this day, and some days after, a right line drawn from the comet through Spica passed by the south side of Cor Leonis at a very small distance therefrom. The right line through Cor Leonis and Spica ♍ did cut the ecliptic in ♍ 3° 46′ at an angle of 2° 51′; and, if the comet had been in this line and in ♏ 3°, its latitude would have been 2° 26′; but since Hooke and Montenari agree that the comet was at some small distance from this line towards the north, its latitude must have been somewhat less. On the 20th, by the observation of Montenari, its latitude was almost the same with that of Spica ♍, that is, about 1° 30′. But by the agreement of Hooke, Montenari, and Ango, the latitude was continually increasing, and therefore must now, on the 22d, be sensibly greater than 1° 30′; and, taking a mean between the extreme limits but now stated, 2° 26′ and 1° 30′, the latitude will be about 1° 58′. Hooke and Montenari agree that the tail of the comet was directed towards Spica ♍, declining a little from that star towards the south according to Hooke, but towards the north according to Montenari; and, therefore, that declination was scarcely sensible; and the tail, lying nearly parallel to the equator, deviated a little from the opposition of the sun towards the north.

Nov. 23, o.s., at 5ʰ. morning, at Nuremberg (that is, at 4½ʰ. at London), Mr. Zimmerman saw the comet in ♏ 8° 8′, with 2° 31′ south latitude, its place being obtained by taking its distances from fixed stars.

Nov. 24, before sunrise, the comet was seen by Montenari in ♏ 12° 52′ on the north side of the right line through Cor Leonis and Spica ♍, and therefore its latitude was somewhat less than 2° 38′; and since the latitude, as we said, by the concurring observations of Montenari, Ango, and Hooke, was continually increasing, therefore, it was now, on the 24th, somewhat greater than 1° 58′; and, taking the mean quantity, may be reckoned 2° 18′, without any considerable error. Ponthio and Gallet will have it that the latitude was now decreasing; and Cellio, and the observer in New England, that it continued the same, viz., of about 1°, or 1½°. The observations of Ponthio and Cellio are rougher, especially those which were made by taking the azimuths and altitudes; as are also the observations of Gallet. Those are better which were made by taking the position of the comet to the fixed stars by Montenari, Hooke, Ango, and the observer in New England, and sometimes by Ponthio and Cellio. The same day, at 5ʰ. morning, at Ballasore, the comet was observed in ♏ 11° 45′; and, therefore, at 5ʰ. morning at London, was in ♏ 13°, nearly. And, by the theory, the comet was at that time in ♏ 13° 22′ 42″.

Nov. 25, before sunrise, Montenari observed the comet in ♏ 17¾°, nearly; and Cellio observed at the same time that the comet was in a right line between the bright star in the right thigh of Virgo and the southern scale of Libra; and this right line cuts the comet's way in ♏ 18° 36′. And, by the theory, the comet was in ♏ 18⅓°, nearly.

From all this it is plain that these observations agree with the theory, so far as they agree with one another; and by this agreement it is made clear that it was one and the same comet that appeared all the time from Nov. 4 to Mar. 9. The path of this comet did twice cut the plane of the ecliptic, and therefore was not a right line. It did cut the ecliptic not in opposite parts of the heavens, but in the end of Virgo and beginning of Capricorn, including an arc of about 98°; and therefore the way of the comet did very much deviate from the path of a great circle; for in the month of Nov. it declined at least 3° from the ecliptic towards the south; and in the month of Dec. following it declined 29° from the ecliptic towards the north; the two parts of the orbit in which the comet descended towards the sun, and ascended again from the sun, declining one from the other by an apparent angle of above 30°, as observed by Montenari. This comet traveled over nine signs, namely, from the last degree of ♌ to the beginning of ♓, beside the sign of ♌, through which it passed before it began to be seen; and there is no other theory by which a comet can go over so great a part of the heavens with a regular motion. The motion of this comet was very unequable; for about the 20th of Nov. it described about 5° a day. Then its motion being retarded between Nov. 26 and Dec. 12, to wit, in the space of 15½ days, it described only 40°. But the motion thereof being afterwards accelerated, it described near 5° a day, till its motion began to be again retarded. And the theory which justly corresponds with a motion so unequable, and through so great a part of the heavens, which observes the same laws with the theory of the planets, and which accurately agrees with accurate astronomical observations, cannot be otherwise than true.

And, thinking it would not be improper, I have given in the annexed figure, plotted in the plane of the curve, a true representation of the orbit which this comet described, and of the tail which it emitted in several places. In this drawing ABC represents the orbit of the comet, D the sun, DE the axis of the orbit, DF the line of the nodes, GH the intersection of the sphere of the earth's

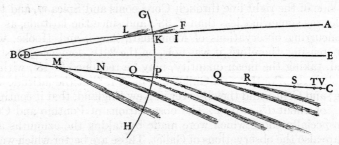

orbit with the plane of the comet's orbit, I the place of the comet Nov. 4, 1680; K the place of the same Nov. 11; L the place of the same Nov. 19; M its place Dec. 12; N its place Dec. 21; O its place Dec. 29; P its place Jan. 5 following; Q its place Jan. 25; R its place Feb. 5; S its place Feb. 25; T its place March 5; and V its place March 9. In determining the length of the tail, I made the following observations:

Nov. 4 and 6, the tail did not appear; Nov. 11, the tail just began to show itself, but did not appear above ½ degree long through a 10-foot telescope; Nov. 17, the tail was seen by Ponthio more than 15° long; Nov. 18, in New England, the tail appeared 30° long, and directly opposite to the sun, extending itself to the planet Mars, which was then in ♏, 9° 54′; Nov. 19, in Maryland, the tail was found 15° or 20° long; Dec. 10 (by the observation of Mr. Flamsteed), the tail passed through the middle of the distance intercepted between the tail of the serpent of Ophiuchus and the star δ in the south wing of Aquila, and did terminate near the stars A, ω, b in Bayer's tables. Therefore the end of the tail was in ♑ 19½°, with latitude about 34¼° north; Dec. 11, it ascended to the head of Sagitta (Bayer's α, β), terminating in ♑ 26° 43′, with latitude 38° 34′ north; Dec. 12, it passed through the middle of Sagitta, nor did it reach much farther; terminating in ♒ 4°, with latitude 42½° north, nearly. But these things are to be understood of the length of the brighter part of the tail; for, with a more faint light, observed, too, perhaps, in a serener sky, at Rome, Dec. 12, 5ʰ. 40ᵐ., by the observation of Ponthio, the tail arose to 10° above the rump of the Swan, and the side thereof towards the west and towards the north was 45′ distant from this star. But about that time the tail was 3° broad towards the upper end; and therefore the middle thereof was 2° 15′ distant from that star towards the south, and the upper end was in ♓ 22°, with latitude 61° north; and thence the tail was about 70° long; Dec. 21, it extended almost to Cassiopeia's Chair, equally distant from β and from Schedir, so as its distance from either of the two was equal to the distance of the one from the other, and therefore did terminate in ♈ 24°, with latitude 47½°; Dec. 29, it reached to a contact with Scheat on its left, and exactly filled up the space between the two stars in the northern foot of Andromeda, being 54° in length; and therefore terminated in ♉ 19°, with 35° of latitude; Jan. 5, it touched the star π in the breast of Andromeda on its right side, and the star μ of the girdle on its left; and, according to our observations, was 40° long; but it was curved, and the convex side thereof lay to the south; and near the head of the comet it made an angle of 4° with the circle which passed through the sun and the comet's head; but towards the other end it was inclined to that circle in an angle of about 10° or 11°; and the chord of the tail contained with that circle an angle of 8°. Jan. 13, the tail terminated between Alamech and Algol, with a light that was sensible enough; but with a faint light it ended over against the star κ in Perseus' side. The distance of the end of the tail from the circle passing through the sun and the comet was 3° 50′; and the inclination of the chord of the tail to that circle was 8½°. Jan. 25 and 26, it shone with a faint light to the length of 6° or 7°; and, for a night or two after, when there was a very clear sky, it extended to the length of 12°, or somewhat more, with a light that was very faint and very hardly to be seen; but the axis thereof was exactly directed to the bright star in the eastern shoulder of Auriga, and therefore deviated from the opposition of the sun towards the north by an angle of 10°. Lastly, Feb. 10, with a telescope I observed the tail 2° long; for that fainter light which I spoke of did not appear through the glasses. But Ponthio writes that, on Feb. 7, he saw the tail 12° long. Feb. 25, the comet was without a tail, and so continued till it disappeared.

Now if one reflects upon the orbit described, and duly considers the other appearances of this comet, he will be easily satisfied that the bodies of comets are solid, compact, fixed, and durable, like the bodies of the planets; for if they were nothing else but the vapors or exhalations of the earth, of the sun, and other planets, this comet, in its passage by the neighborhood of the sun, would have been immediately dissipated; for the heat of the sun is as the density of its rays, that is, inversely as the square of the distance of the places from the sun. Therefore, since on Dec. 8, when the comet was in its perihelion, the distance thereof from the centre of the sun was to the distance of the earth from the same as about 6 to 1000, the sun's heat on the comet was at that time to the heat of the summer-sun with us as 1,000,000 to 36, or as 28,000 to 1. But the heat of boiling water is about three times greater than the heat which dry earth acquires from the summer-sun, as I have tried; and the heat of red-hot iron (if my conjecture is right) is about three or four times greater than the heat of boiling water. And therefore the heat which dry earth on the comet, while in its perihelion, might have received from the rays of the sun, was about 2000 times greater than the heat of red-hot iron. But by so fierce a heat, vapors and exhalations, and every volatile matter, must have been immediately consumed and dissipated.

This comet, therefore, must have received an immense heat from the sun, and retained that heat for an exceeding long time; for a globe of iron of an inch in diameter, exposed red-hot to the open air, will scarcely lose all its heat in an hour's time; but a greater globe would retain its heat longer in the ratio of its diameter, because the surface (in proportion to which it is cooled by the contact of the ambient air) is in that ratio less in respect of the quantity of the included hot matter; and therefore a globe of red-hot iron equal to our earth, that is, about 40,000,000 feet in diameter, would scarcely cool in an equal number of days, or in above 50,000 years. But I suspect that the duration of heat may, on account of some latent causes, increase in a yet less ratio than that of the diameter; and I should be glad that the true ratio was investigated by experiments.

It is further to be observed, that the comet in the month of December, just after it had been heated by the sun, did emit a much longer tail, and much more splendid, than in the month of November before, when it had not yet arrived at its perihelion; and, universally, the greatest and most fulgent tails always arise from comets immediately after their passing by the neighborhood of the sun. Therefore the heat received by the comet conduces to the greatness of the tail: from this, I think I may infer, that the tail is nothing else but a very fine vapor, which the head or nucleus of the comet emits by its heat.

But we have had three several opinions about the tails of comets: for some will have it that they are nothing else but the beams of the sun's light transmitted through the comets' heads, which they suppose to be transparent; others, that they proceed from the refraction which light suffers in passing from the comet's head to the earth; and, lastly, others, that they are a sort of cloud or vapor constantly rising from the comets' heads, and tending towards the parts opposite to the sun. The first is the opinion of such as are yet unacquainted with optics; for the beams of the sun are seen in a darkened room only in consequence of the light that is reflected from them by the little particles of dust and smoke which are always flying about in the air; and, for that reason, in air impregnated with thick smoke, those beams appear with great brightness, and impress the eye more strongly; in a yet finer air they appear more faint, and are less easily discerned; but in the heavens, where there is no matter to reflect the light, they can never be seen at all. Light is not seen as it is in the beam, but as it is thence reflected to our eyes; for vision can be produced in no other way than by rays falling upon the eyes; and, therefore, there must be some reflecting matter in those parts where the tails of the comets are seen: for otherwise, since all the celestial spaces are equally illuminated by the sun's light, no part of the heavens could appear with more splendor than another. The second opinion is liable to many difficulties. The tails of comets are never seen variegated with those colors which commonly are inseparable from refraction; and the distinct transmission of the light of the fixed stars and planets to us is a demonstration that the ether or celestial medium is not endowed with any refractive power: for, as to what is alleged, that the fixed stars have been sometimes seen by the Egyptians environed with a coma, because that has but rarely happened, it is rather to be ascribed to a casual refraction of clouds; and so the radiation and scintillation of the fixed stars to the refractions both of the eyes and air; for, upon laying a telescope to the eye, those radiations and scintillations immediately disappear. By the tremulous agitation of the air and ascending vapors, it happens that the rays of light are alternately turned aside from the narrow space of the pupil of the eye; but no such thing can have place in the much wider aperture of the object glass of a telescope; and hence it is that a scintillation is occasioned in the former case, which ceases in the latter; and this cessation in the latter case is a demonstration of the regular transmission of light through the heavens, without any perceptible refraction. But, to obviate an objection that may be made from the appearing of no tail in such comets as shine but with a faint light, as if the secondary rays were then too weak to affect the eyes, and for that reason it is that the tails of the fixed stars do not appear, we are to consider, that by the means of telescopes the light of the fixed stars may be augmented above an hundredfold, and yet no tails are seen; that the light of the planets is yet more copious without any tail; but that comets are seen sometimes with huge tails, when the light of their heads is but faint and dull. For so it happened in the comet of the year 1680, when in the month of December it was scarcely equal in light to the stars of the second magnitude, and yet emitted a notable tail, extending to the length of 40°, 50°, 60°, or 70°, and upwards; and afterwards, on the 27th and 28th of January, when the head appeared but as a star of the 7th magnitude, yet the tail (as we said above), with a light that was clearly perceptible, though faint, was stretched out to 6° or 7° in length, and with a languishing light that was more difficult to see, even to 12°, and upwards. But on the 9th and 10th of February, when to the naked eye the head appeared no more, through a telescope I viewed the tail of 2° in length. But further: if the tail was due to the crumbling of the celestial matter, and did deviate from the opposition of the sun, according to the figure of the heavens, that deviation in the same places of the heavens should be always directed towards the same parts. But the comet of the year 1680, December 28^{d}. 8½^{h}. P.M. at London, was seen in ♓ 8° 41', with latitude north 28° 6'; while the sun was in ♑ 18° 26'. And the comet of the year 1577, December 29^{d}., was in ♓ 8° 41', with latitude north 28° 40', and the sun, as before, in about ♑ 18° 26'. In both cases the situation of the earth was the same, and the comet appeared in the same place of the heavens; yet in the former case the tail of the comet (as well by my observations as by the observations of others) deviated from the opposition of the sun towards the north by an angle of 4½ degrees; whereas in the latter there was (according to the observations of Tycho) a deviation of 21 degrees towards the south. The crumbling, therefore, of the heavens being thus disproved, it remains that the phenomena of the tails of comets must be derived from some reflecting matter.

And that the tails of comets do arise from their heads, and tend towards the parts opposite to the sun, is further confirmed from the laws which the tails observe: As that, lying in the planes of the comets' orbits which pass through the sun, they constantly deviate from the opposition of the sun towards the parts which the comets' heads in their progress along these orbits have left. That to a spectator, placed in those planes, they appear in the parts directly opposite to the sun; but, as the spectator recedes from those planes, their deviation begins to appear, and daily becomes greater. That the deviation, other things being equal, appears less when the tail is more oblique to the orbit of the comet, as well as when the head of the comet approaches nearer to the sun, especially if the angle of deviation is estimated near the head of the comet. That the tails which have no deviation appear straight, but the tails which deviate are likewise bended into a certain curvature. That this curvature is greater when the deviation is greater; and is more sensible when the tail, other things being equal, is longer; for in the shorter tails the curvature is hardly to be perceived. That the angle of deviation is less near the comet's head, but greater towards the other end of the tail; and that because the convex side of the tail regards the parts from which the deviation is made, and which lie in a right line drawn out infinitely from the sun through the comet's head. And that the tails that are long and broad, and shine with a stronger light, appear more resplendent and more exactly defined on the convex than on the concave side. Upon these accounts it is plain that the phenomena of the tails of comets depend upon the motions of their heads, and by no means upon the places of the heavens in which their heads are seen; and that, therefore, the tails of comets do not proceed from the refraction of the heavens, but from their own heads, which furnish the matter that forms the tail. For, as in our air, the smoke of a heated body ascends either perpendicularly if the body is at rest, or obliquely if the body is moved obliquely, so in the heavens, where all bodies gravitate towards the sun, smoke and vapor must (as we have already said) ascend from the sun, and either rise perpendicularly if the smoking body is at rest, or obliquely if the body, in all the progress of its motion, is always leaving those places from which the upper or higher parts of the vapor had risen before; and that obliquity will be least where the vapor ascends with most velocity, namely, near the smoking body, when that is near the sun. But, because the obliquity varies, the column of vapor will be incurvated; and because the vapor in the preceding side is something more recent, *that is, has ascended something more late from the body*, it will therefore be somewhat more dense on that side, and must on that account reflect more light, as well as be better defined. I add nothing concerning the sudden uncertain agitation of the tails of comets, and their irregular figures, which authors sometimes describe, because they may arise from the mutations of our air, and the motions of our clouds, in part obscuring those tails; or, perhaps, from parts of the Milky Way which might have been confounded with and mistaken for parts of the tails of the comets as they passed by.

But that the atmospheres of comets may furnish a supply of vapor great enough to fill so immense spaces, we may easily understand from the rarity of our own air; for the air near the surface of our earth possesses a space 850 times greater than water of the same weight; and therefore a cylinder of air 850 feet high is of equal weight with a cylinder of water of the same breadth, and but one foot high. But a cylinder of air reaching to the top of the atmosphere is of equal weight with a cylinder of water about 33 feet high: and, therefore, if from the whole cylinder of air the lower part of 850 feet high is taken away, the remaining upper part will be of equal weight with a cylinder of water 32 feet high: and from thence (and by the hypothesis, confirmed by many experiments, that the compression of air is as the weight of the incumbent atmosphere, and that the force of gravity is inversely as the square of the distance from the centre of the earth) proceeding by calculation, by Cor., Prop. 22, Book II, I found, that, at the height of one semidiameter of the earth, reckoned from the earth's surface, the air is more rare than with us in a far greater ratio than that of the whole space within the orbit of Saturn to a spherical space one inch in diameter; and therefore, if a sphere of our air of but one inch in thickness was equally rarefied with the air at the height of one semidiameter of the earth from the earth's surface, it would fill all the regions of the planets to the orb of Saturn, and far beyond it. Therefore, since the air at greater distances is immensely rarefied, and the coma or atmosphere of comets is ordinarily about ten times higher, reckoning from their centres, than the surface of the nucleus, and the tails rise yet higher, they must therefore be exceedingly rare; and though, on account of the much thicker atmospheres of comets, and the great gravitation of their bodies towards the sun, as well as of the particles of their air and vapors towards each other, it may happen that the air in the celestial spaces and in the tails of comets is not so vastly rarefied, yet from this computation it is plain that a very small quantity of air and vapor is abundantly sufficient to produce all the appearances of the tails of comets; for that they are, indeed, of a very notable rarity appears from the shining of the stars through them. The atmosphere of the earth, illuminated by the sun's light, though but of a few miles in thickness, quite obscures and extinguishes the light not only of all the stars, but even of the moon itself; whereas the smallest stars are seen to shine through the immense thickness of the tails of comets, likewise illuminated by the sun, without the least diminution of their splendor. Nor is the brightness of the tails of most comets ordinarily greater than that of our air, an inch or two in thickness, reflecting in a darkened room the light of the sunbeams let in by a hole of the window shutter.

And we may pretty nearly determine the time spent during the ascent of the vapor from the comet's head to the extremity of the tail, by drawing a right line from the extremity of the tail to the sun, and marking the place where that right line intersects the comet's orbit; for the vapor that is now in the extremity of the tail, if it has ascended in a right line from the sun, must have begun to rise from the head at the time when the head was in the point of intersection. It is true, the vapor does not rise in a right line from the sun, but, retaining the motion which it had from the comet before its ascent, and compounding that motion with its motion of ascent, arises obliquely; and, therefore, the solution of the Problem will be more exact, if we draw the line which intersects the orbit parallel to the length of the tail; or rather (because of the curvilinear motion of the comet) diverging a little from the line or length of the tail. And by means of this principle I found that the vapor which, January 25, was in the extremity of the tail, had begun to rise from the head before

December 11, and therefore had spent in its whole ascent 45 days; but that the whole tail which appeared on December 10 had finished its ascent in the space of the two days then elapsed from the time of the comet's being in its perihelion. The vapor, therefore, about the beginning and in the neighborhood of the sun rose with the greatest velocity, and afterwards continued to ascend with a motion constantly retarded by its own gravity; and the higher it ascended, the more it added to the length of the tail; and while the tail continued to be seen, it was made up of almost all that vapor which had risen since the time of the comet's being in its perihelion; nor did that part of the vapor which had risen first, and which formed the extremity of the tail, cease to appear, till its too great distance, as well from the sun, from which it received its light, as from our eyes, rendered it invisible. Whence also it is that the tails of other comets which are short do not rise from their heads with a swift and continued motion, and soon after disappear, but are permanent and lasting columns of vapors and exhalations, which, ascending from the heads with a slow motion of many days, and partaking of the motion of the heads which they had from the beginning, continue to go along together with them through the heavens. From this again we have another argument proving the celestial spaces to be free, and without resistance, since in them not only the solid bodies of the planets and comets, but also the extremely rare vapors of comets' tails, maintain their rapid motions with great freedom, and for an exceeding long time.

Kepler ascribes the ascent of the tails of the comets to the atmospheres of their heads; and their direction towards the parts opposite to the sun to the action of the rays of light carrying along with them the matter of the comets' tails; and without any great incongruity we may suppose that, in so free spaces, so fine a matter as that of the ether may yield to the action of the rays of the sun's light, though those rays are not able sensibly to move the gross substances in our parts, which are clogged with so palpable a resistance. Another author thinks that there may be a sort of particles of matter endowed with a principle of levity, as well as others are with a power of gravity; that the matter of the tails of comets may be of the former sort, and that its ascent from the sun may be owing to its levity; but, considering that the gravity of terrestrial bodies is as the matter of the bodies, and therefore can be neither more nor less in the same quantity of matter, I am inclined to believe that this ascent may rather proceed from the rarefaction of the matter of the comets' tails. The ascent of smoke in a chimney is due to the impulse of the air with which it is entangled. The air rarefied by heat ascends, because its specific gravity is diminished, and in its ascent carries along with it the smoke which floats in it; and why may not the tail of a comet rise from the sun after the same manner? For the sun's rays do not act upon the mediums which they pervade otherwise than by reflection and refraction; and those reflecting particles heated by this action, heat the matter of the ether which is involved with them. That matter is rarefied by the heat which it acquires, and because, by this rarefaction, the specific gravity with which it tended towards the sun before is diminished, it will ascend therefrom, and carry along with it the reflecting particles of which the tail of the comet is composed. But the ascent of the vapors is further promoted by their circumgyration about the sun; in consequence thereof they endeavor to recede from the sun, while the sun's atmos-

phere and the other matter of the heavens are either altogether quiescent, or
are only moved with a slower circumgyration derived from the rotation of the
sun. And these are the causes of the ascent of the tails of the comets in the
neighborhood of the sun, where their orbits are bent into a greater curvature,
and the comets themselves are plunged into the denser and therefore heavier
parts of the sun's atmosphere: upon which account they do then emit tails of
an huge length; for the tails which then arise, retaining their own proper motion, and in the meantime gravitating towards the sun, must be revolved in
ellipses about the sun in like manner as the heads are, and by that motion
must always accompany the heads, and freely adhere to them. For the gravitation of the vapors towards the sun can no more force the tails to abandon
the heads, and descend to the sun, than the gravitation of the heads can oblige
them to fall from the tails. They must by their common gravity either fall
together towards the sun, or be retarded together in their common ascent
therefrom; and, therefore (whether from the causes already described, or from
any others), the tails and heads of comets may easily acquire and freely retain
any position one to the other, without disturbance or impediment from that
common gravitation.

The tails, therefore, that rise in the perihelian positions of the comets will
go along with their heads into far remote parts, and together with the heads
will either return again from thence to us, after a long course of years, or rather
will be there rarefied, and by degrees quite vanish away; for afterwards, in the
descent of the heads towards the sun, new short tails will be emitted from the
heads with a slow motion; and those tails by degrees will be augmented immensely, especially in such comets as in their perihelian distances descend as
low as the sun's atmosphere; for all vapor in those free spaces is in a perpetual
state of rarefaction and dilatation; and from hence it is that the tails of all
comets are broader at their upper extremity than near their heads. And it is
not unlikely but that the vapor, thus continually rarefied and dilated, may be
at last dissipated and scattered through the whole heavens, and by little and
little be attracted towards the planets by its gravity, and mixed with their
atmosphere; for as the seas are absolutely necessary to the constitution of our
earth, that from them, the sun, by its heat, may exhale a sufficient quantity of
vapors, which, being gathered together into clouds, may drop down in rain,
for watering of the earth, and for the production and nourishment of vegetables; or, being condensed with cold on the tops of mountains (as some philosophers with reason judge), may run down in springs and rivers; so for the
conservation of the seas, and fluids of the planets, comets seem to be required,
that, from their exhalations and vapors condensed, the wastes of the planetary
fluids spent upon vegetation and putrefaction, and converted into dry earth,
may be continually supplied and made up; for all vegetables entirely derive
their growths from fluids, and afterwards, in great measure, are turned into
dry earth by putrefaction; and a sort of slime is always found to settle at the
bottom of putrefied fluids; and hence it is that the bulk of the solid earth is
continually increased; and the fluids, if they are not supplied from without,
must be in a continual decrease, and quite fail at last. I suspect, moreover, that
it is chiefly from the comets that spirit comes, which is indeed the smallest but
the most subtle and useful part of our air, and so much required to sustain the
life of all things with us.

The atmospheres of comets, in their descent towards the sun, by running out into the tails, are spent and diminished, and become narrower, at least on that side which regards the sun; and in receding from the sun, when they less run out into the tails, they are again enlarged, if Hewelcke has justly marked their appearances. But they are seen least of all just after they have been most heated by the sun, and on that account then emit the longest and most resplendent tails; and, perhaps, at the same time, the nuclei are environed with a denser and blacker smoke in the lowermost parts of their atmosphere; for smoke that is raised by a great and intense heat is commonly the denser and blacker. Thus the head of that comet which we have been describing, at equal distances both from the sun and from the earth, appeared darker after it had passed by its perihelion than it did before; for in the month of December it was commonly compared with the stars of the third magnitude, but in November with those of the first or second; and such as saw both appearances have described the first as of another and greater comet than the second. For, November 19, this comet appeared to a young man at Cambridge, though with a pale and dull light, yet equal to Spica Virginis; and at that time it shone with greater brightness than it did afterwards. And Montenari, November 20, o.s., observed it larger than the stars of the first magnitude, its tail being then 2 degrees long. And Mr. Storer (by letters which have come into my hands) writes that in the month of December, when the tail appeared of the greatest bulk and splendor, the head was but small, and far less than that which was seen in the month of November before sun rising; and, conjecturing at the cause of the appearance, he judged it to proceed from the existence of a greater quantity of matter in the head at first, which was afterwards gradually spent.

And, for the same reason, I find, that the heads of other comets, which did put forth tails of the greatest bulk and splendor, have appeared but obscure and small. For in Brazil, March 5, 1668, N.S., 7ʰ. P.M., Valentin Estancel saw a comet near the horizon, and towards the southwest, with a head so small as scarcely to be discerned, but with a tail above measure splendid, so that the reflection thereof from the sea was easily seen by those who stood on the shore; it looked like a fiery beam extended 23 degrees in length from the west to south, almost parallel to the horizon. But this excessive splendor continued only three days, decreasing apace afterwards; and while the splendor was decreasing, the bulk of the tail increased: also in Portugal it is said to have taken up one-quarter of the heavens, that is, 45 degrees, extending from west to east with a very notable splendor, though the whole tail was not seen in those parts, because the head was always hid under the horizon: and from the increase of the bulk and decrease of the splendor of the tail, it appears that the head was then in its recess from the sun, and had been very near to it in its perihelion, as the comet of 1680 was. And we read, in the *Saxon Chronicle*, of a like comet appearing in the year 1106, *the star whereof was small and obscure* (as that of 1680), *but the splendor of its tail was very bright, and like a huge fiery beam stretched out in a direction between the east and north,* as Hewelcke has it also from Simeon, the monk of Durham. This comet appeared in the beginning of February, about the evening, and towards the southwest part of heaven; from this, and from the position of the tail, we infer that the head was near the sun. Matthew Paris says, *It was distant from the sun by about a cubit, from three o'clock* (rather six) *till nine, putting forth a long tail.* Such also was that resplendent comet described by Aristotle, *Meteorology*, i, 6. *The head whereof could not be seen, because it had set before the sun, or at least was hid under the sun's rays; but next day it was seen as well as might be; for, having left the sun but a very little way, it set immediately after it. And the scattered light of the head, obscured by the too great splendor* (of the tail) *did not yet appear. But afterwards* (as Aristotle says) *when the splendor* (of the tail) *had diminished,* (the head of) *the comet recovered its native brightness; and the splendor* (of its tail) *reached now to a third part of the heavens* (that is, to 60°). *This appearance was in the winter season* (the fourth year of the 101st Olympiad), *and, rising to Orion's girdle, it there vanished away.* It is true that the comet of 1618, which came out directly from under the sun's rays with a very large tail, seemed to equal, if not to exceed, the stars of the first magnitude; but then, abundance of other comets have appeared yet greater than this, that put forth shorter tails; some of which are said to have appeared as big as Jupiter, others as big as Venus, or even as the moon.

We have said that comets are a sort of planets revolved in very eccentric orbits about the sun; and as, in the planets which are without tails, those are commonly less which are revolved in lesser orbits, and nearer to the sun, so in comets it is probable that those which in their perihelion approach nearer to the sun are generally of less magnitude, that they may not agitate the sun too much by their attractions. But as to the transverse diameters of their orbits, and the periodic times of their revolutions, I leave them to be determined by comparing comets together which after long intervals of time return again in the same orbit. In the meantime, the following Proposition may give some light in that inquiry.

PROPOSITION 42. PROBLEM 22

To correct a comet's orbit found as above.

OPERATION 1. Assume that position of the plane of the orbit which was determined according to the preceding Proposition; and select three places of the comet, deduced from very accurate observations, and at great distances one from the other. Then suppose A to represent the time between the first observation and the second, and B the time between the second and the third; but it will be convenient that in one of those times the comet be in its perigee, or at least not far from it. From those apparent places find, by trigonometric operations, the three true places of the comet in that assumed plane of the orbit; then through the places found, and about the centre of the sun as the focus, describe a conic section by arithmetical operations, according to Prop. 21, Book I. Let the areas of this figure which are terminated by radii drawn from the sun to the places found be D and E; namely, D the area between the first observation and the second, and E the area between the second and third; and let T represent the whole time in which the whole area D+E should be described with the velocity of the comet found by Prop. 16, Book I.

OPER. 2. Retaining the inclination of the plane of the orbit to the plane of the ecliptic, let the longitude of the nodes of the plane of the orbit be increased by the addition of 20' or 30', which call P. Then from the aforesaid three observed places of the comet let the three true places be found (as before) in this new plane; as also the orbit passing through those places, and the two areas of the same described between the two observations, which call d and e; and let t be the whole time in which the whole area d+e should be described.

OPER. 3. Retaining the longitude of the nodes in the first operation, let the inclination of the plane of the orbit to the plane of the ecliptic be increased by adding thereto 20′ or 30′, which call Q. Then from the aforesaid three observed apparent places of the comet let the three true places be found in this new plane, as well as the orbit passing through them, and the two areas of the same described between the observation, which call δ and ε; and let τ be the whole time in which the whole area δ+ε should be described.

Then taking C to 1 as A to B; and G to 1 as D to E; and g to 1 as d to e; and γ to 1 as δ to ε; let S be the true time between the first observation and the third; and, observing well the signs + and −, let such numbers m and n be found out as will make $2G-2C=mG-mg+nG-n\gamma$; and $2T-2S=mT-mt +nT-n\tau$. And if, in the first operation, I represents the inclination of the plane of the orbit to the plane of the ecliptic, and K the longitude of either node, then $I+nQ$ will be the true inclination of the plane of the orbit to the plane of the ecliptic, and $K+mP$ the true longitude of the node. And, lastly, if in the first, second, and third operations, the quantities R, r, and ρ, represent the parameters of the orbit, and the quantities $\frac{1}{L}, \frac{1}{l}, \frac{1}{\gamma}$, the transverse diameters of the same, then $R+mr-mR+n\rho-nR$ will be the true parameter, and $\frac{1}{L+ml-mL+n\lambda-nL}$ will be the true transverse diameter of the orbit which the comet describes; and from the transverse diameter given the periodic time of the comet is also given. Q.E.I. But the periodic times of the revolutions of comets, and the transverse diameters of their orbits, cannot be accurately enough determined but by comparing comets together which appear at different times. If, after equal intervals of time, several comets are found to have described the same orbit, we may thence conclude that they are all but one and the same comet revolved in the same orbit; and then from the times of their revolutions the transverse diameters of their orbits will be given, and from those diameters the elliptic orbits themselves will be determined.

To this purpose the orbits of many comets ought to be computed, supposing those orbits to be parabolic; for such orbits will always nearly agree with the phenomena, as appears not only from the parabolic orbit of the comet of the year 1680, which I compared above with the observations, but likewise from that of the notable comet which appeared in the year 1664 and 1665, and was observed by Hewelcke, who, from his own observations, calculated the longitudes and latitudes thereof, though with little accuracy. But from the same observations Dr. Halley did again compute its places; and from those new places determined its orbit, finding its ascending node in ♋ 21° 13′ 55″; the inclination of the orbit to the plane of the ecliptic 21° 18′ 40″; the distance of its perihelion from the node, estimated in the comet's orbit, 49° 27′ 30″, its perihelion in ♌ 8° 40′ 30″, with heliocentric latitude south 16° 01′ 45″; the comet to have been in its perihelion November 24$^{\rm d}$. 11$^{\rm h}$. 52$^{\rm m}$. P.M. equal time at London, or 13$^{\rm h}$. 8$^{\rm m}$. at Danzig, O.S.; and that the latus rectum of the parabola was 410,286 of such parts as the sun's mean distance from the earth is supposed to contain 100,000. And how nearly the places of the comet computed in this orbit agree with the observations, will appear from the table calculated by Dr. Halley (p 364).

In February, the beginning of the year 1665, the first star of Aries, which I shall hereafter call γ, was in Υ 28° 30′ 15″, with 7° 8′ 58″ north latitude; the second star of Aries was in Υ 29° 17′ 18″, with 8° 28′ 16″ north latitude; another star of the seventh magnitude, which I call A, was in Υ 28° 24′ 45″, with 8° 28′ 33″ north latitude. The comet Feb. 7^d. 7^h. 30^m. at Paris (that is, Feb. 7^d. 8^h. 37^m. at Danzig), o.s., made a triangle with those stars γ and A, which was right-angled in γ; and the distance of the comet from the star γ was equal to the distance of the stars γ and A, that is, 1° 19′ 46″ of a great circle; and therefore in the parallel of the latitude of the star γ it was 1° 20′ 26″. Therefore if from the longitude of the star γ there be subtracted the longitude 1° 20′ 26″, there will remain the longitude of the comet Υ 27° 9′ 49″. M. Auzout, from this observation of his, placed the comet in Υ 27° 0′, nearly; and, by the drawing in which Dr. Hooke delineated its motion, it was then in Υ 26° 59′ 24″. I place it in Υ 27° 4′ 46″, taking the middle between the two extremes.

From the same observations, M. Auzout made the latitude of the comet at that time 7° and 4′ or 5′ to the north; but he had done better to have made it 7° 3′ 29″, the difference of the latitudes of the comet and the star γ being equal to the difference of the longitude of the stars γ and A.

February 22^d. 7^h. 30^m. at London, that is, February 22^d. 8^h. 46^m. at Danzig, the distance of the comet from the star A, according to Dr. Hooke's observation, as was delineated by himself in a scheme, and also by the observations of M. Auzout, delineated in like manner by M. Petit, was a fifth part of the distance between the star A and the first star of Aries, or 15′ 57″; and the distance of the comet from a right line joining the star A and the first of Aries was a fourth part of the same fifth part, that is, 4′; and therefore the comet was in Υ 28° 29′ 46″, with 8° 12′ 36″ north latitude.

March 1, 7^h. 0^m. at London, that is, March 1, 8^h. 16^m. at Danzig, the comet was observed near the second star in Aries, the distance between them being to the distance between the first and second stars in Aries, that is, to 1° 33′, as 4 to 45 according to Dr. Hooke, or as 2 to 23 according to M. Gottignies. And, therefore, the distance of the comet from the second star in Aries was 8′ 16″ according to Dr. Hooke, or 8′ 5″ according to M. Gottignies; or, taking a mean between both, 8′ 10″. But, according to M. Gottignies, the comet had gone beyond the second star of Aries about a fourth or a fifth part of the space that it commonly went over in a day, to wit, about 1′ 35″ (in which he agrees very well with M. Auzout); or, according to Dr. Hooke, not quite so much, as perhaps only 1′. Therefore if to the longitude of the first star in Aries we add 1′, and 8′ 10″ to its latitude, we shall have the longitude of the comet Υ 29° 18′, with 8° 36′ 26″ north latitude.

March 7, 7^h. 30^m. at Paris, that is, March 7, 7^h. 37^m. at Danzig, from the observations of M. Auzout, the distance of the comet from the second star in Aries was equal to the distance of that star from the star A, that is, 52′ 29″; and the difference of the longitude of the comet and the second star in Aries was 45′ or 46′, or, taking a mean quantity, 45′ 30″; and therefore the comet was in Υ 0° 2′ 48″. From the drawing constructed by M. Petit, based on the observations of M. Auzout, Hewelcke determined the latitude of the comet 8° 54′. But the engraver did not rightly trace the curvature of the comet's way towards the end of the motion; and Hevelius, in the drawing of M. Auzout's observations which he constructed himself, corrected this irregular curvature,

Apparent time at Danzig	The observed distances of the comet from		The observed places		The places computed in the orbit
December		° ′ ″		° ′ ″	° ′ ″
d h m	The Lion's heart	46.24.20	Long. ♎ 7.01.00		♎ 7. 1.29
3.18.29½	The Virgin's spike	22.52.10	Lat. S. 21.39. 0		21.38.50
4.18. 1½	The Lion's heart	46. 2.45	Long. ♎ 6.15. 0		♎ 6.16. 5
	The Virgin's spike	23.52.40	Lat. S. 22.24. 0		22.24. 0
7.17.48	The Lion's heart	44.48. 0	Long. ♎ 3. 6. 0		♎ 3. 7.33
	The Virgin's spike	27.56.40	Lat. S. 25.22. 0		25.21.40
17.14.43	The Lion's heart	53.15.15	Long. ♌ 2.56. 0		♌ 2.56. 0
	Orion's right shoulder	45.43.30	Lat. S. 49.25. 0		49.25. 0
19. 9.25	Procyon	35.13.50	Long. ♊ 28.40.30		♊ 28.43. 0
	Bright star of Whale's jaw	52.56. 0	Lat. S. 45.48. 0		45.46. 0
20. 9.53½	Procyon	40.49. 0	Long. ♊ 13.03. 0		♊ 13. 5. 0
	Bright star of Whale's jaw	40.04. 0	Lat. S. 39.54. 0		39.53. 0
21. 9. 9½	Orion's right shoulder	26.21.25	Long. ♊ 2.16. 0		♊ 2.18.30
	Bright star of Whale's jaw	29.28. 0	Lat. S. 33.41. 0		33.39.40
22. 9. 0	Orion's right shoulder	29.47. 0	Long. ♉ 24.24. 0		♉ 24.27. 0
	Bright star of Whale's jaw	20.29.30	Lat. S. 27.45. 0		27.46. 0
26. 7.58	The bright star of Aries	23.20. 0	Long. ♉ 9. 0. 0		♉ 9. 2.28
	Aldebaran	26.44. 0	Lat. S. 12.36. 0		12.34.13
27. 6.45	The bright star of Aries	20.45. 0	Long. ♉ 7. 5.40		♉ 7. 8.45
	Aldebaran	28.10. 0	Lat. S. 10.23. 0		10.23.13
28. 7.39	The bright star of Aries	18.29. 0	Long. ♉ 5.24.45		♉ 5.27.52
	Palilicium	29.37. 0	Lat. S. 8.22.50		8.23.37
31. 6.45	Andromeda's girdle	30.48.10	Long. ♉ 2. 7.40		♉ 2. 8.20
	Palilicium	32.53.30	Lat. S. 4.13. 0		4.16.25
Jan. 1665	Andromeda's girdle	25.11. 0	Long. ♈ 28.24.47		♈ 28.24. 0
7. 7.37½	Palilicium	37.12.25	Lat. N. 0.54. 0		0.53. 0
13. 7. 0	Andromeda's head	28. 7.10	Long. ♈ 27. 6.54		♈ 27. 6.39
	Palilicium	38.55.20	Lat. N. 3. 6.50		3. 7.40
24. 7.29	Andromeda's girdle	20.32.15	Long. ♈ 26.29.15		♈ 26.28.50
	Palilicium	40. 5. 0	Lat. N. 5.25.50		5.26. 0
February			Long. ♈ 27. 4.46		♈ 27.24.55
7. 8.37			Lat. N. 7. 3.29		7. 3.15
22. 8.46			Long. ♈ 28.29.46		♈ 28.29.58
			Lat. N. 8.12.36		8.10.25
March			Long. ♈ 29.18.15		♈ 29.18.20
1. 8.16			Lat. N. 8.36.26		8.36.12
7. 8.37			Long. ♉ 0. 2.48		♉ 0. 2.42
			Lat. N. 8.56.30		8.56.56

and so made the latitude of the comet 8° 55′ 30″. And, by further correcting this irregularity, the latitude may become 8° 56′, or 8° 57′.

This comet was also seen March 9, and at that time its place must have been in ♉ 0° 18′, with 9° 3½′ north latitude, nearly.

This comet appeared for three months, in which space of time it traveled over almost six signs, and in one of the days described almost 20 degrees. Its course did very much deviate from a great circle, bending towards the north, and its motion towards the end from retrograde became direct; and, notwithstanding that its course was so uncommon, yet by the table it appears that the theory, from beginning to end, agrees with the observations no less accurately than the theories of the planets usually do with the observations of them; but we are to subtract about 2′ when the comet was swiftest, which we may effect by taking off 12″ from the angle between the ascending node and the perihelion, or by making that angle 49° 27′ 18″. The annual parallax of both these comets (this and the preceding) was very conspicuous, and by its quantity demonstrates the annual motion of the earth in the earth's orbit.

This theory is likewise confirmed by the motion of that comet, which in the year 1683 appeared retrograde, in an orbit whose plane contained almost a right angle with the plane of the ecliptic, and whose ascending node (by the computation of Dr. Halley) was in ♍ 23° 23′; the inclination of its orbit to the ecliptic 83° 11′; its perihelion in ♊ 25° 29′ 30″; its perihelian distance from the sun 56,020 of such parts as the radius of the earth's orbit contains 100,000; and the time of its perihelion was July 2ᵈ. 3ʰ. 50ᵐ. And the places thereof, computed by Dr. Halley in this orbit, are compared with the places observed by Mr. Flamsteed, in the following table.

This theory is yet further confirmed by the motion of that retrograde comet which appeared in the year 1682. The ascending node of this (by Dr. Halley's

1683 Equatorial time	Sun's place	Comet's longitude computed	Latitude north computed	Comet's longitude observed	Latitude north observed	Difference longitude	Difference latitude
d h m	° ′ ″	° ′ ″	° ′ ″	° ′ ″	° ′ ″	′ ″	′ ″
July 13.12.55	♌ 1.02.30	♋ 13.05.42	29.28.13	♋ 13. 6.42	29.28.20	+1.00	+0.07
15.11.15	2.53.12	11.37.48	29.34. 0	11.39.43	29.34.50	+1.55	+0.50
17.10.20	4.45.45	10. 7. 6	29.33.30	10. 8.40	29.34. 0	+1.34	+0.30
23.13.40	10.38.21	5.10.27	28.51.42	5.11.30	28.50.28	+1.03	−1.14
25.14. 5	12.35.28	3.27.53	24.24.47	3.27. 0	28.23.40	−0.53	−1. 7
31. 9.42	18.09.22	♊27.55. 3	26.22.52	♊27.54.24	26.22.25	−0.39	−0.27
31.14.55	18.21.53	27.41. 7	26.16.57	27.41. 8	26.14.50	+0. 1	−2. 7
Aug. 2.14.56	20.17.16	25.29.32	25.16.19	25.28.46	25.17.28	−0.46	+1. 9
4.10.49	22.02.50	23.18.20	24.10.49	23.16.55	24.12.19	−1.25	+1.30
6.10. 9	23.56.45	20.42.23	22.47. 5	20.40.32	22.49. 5	−1.51	+2. 0
9.10.26	26.50.52	16. 7.57	20. 6.37	16. 5.55	20. 6.10	−2. 2	−0.27
15.14. 1	♍ 2.47.13	3.30.48	11.37.33	3.26.18	11.32. 1	−4.30	−5.32
16.15.10	3.48. 2	0.43. 7	9.34.16	0.41.55	9.34.13	−1.12	−0. 3
18.15.44	5.45.33	♉24.52.53	5.11.15	♉24.49. 5	5. 9.11	−3.48	−2. 4
			South		South		
22.14.44	9.35.49	11. 7.14	5.16.58	11.07.12	5.16.58	−0. 2	−0. 3
23.15.52	10.36.48	7. 2.18	8.17. 9	7. 1.17	8.16.41	−1. 1	−0.28
26.16. 2	13.31.10	♈24.45.31	16.38. 0	♈24.44.00	16.38.20	−1.31	+0.20

computation) was in ♉ 21° 16′ 30″; the inclination of its orbit to the plane of the ecliptic 17° 56′ 00″; its perihelion in ♒ 2° 52′ 50″; its perihelian distance from the sun 58,328 parts, of which the radius of the earth's orbit contains 100,000; the equal time of the comet's being in its perihelion September 4ᵈ. 7ʰ. 39ᵐ. And its places determined from Mr. Flamsteed's observations, are compared with its places computed from our theory in the following table:

1682 App. time	Sun's place	Comet's longitude computed	Latitude north computed	Comet's longitude observed	Latitude north observed	Difference longitude	Difference latitude
d h m	° ′ ″	° ′ ″	° ′ ″	° ′ ″	° ′ ″	′ ″	′ ″
Aug. 19.16.38	♍ 7. 0. 7	♌ 18.14.28	25.50. 7	♌ 18.14.40	25.49.55	−0.12	+0.12
20.15.38	7.55.52	24.46.23	26.14.42	24.46.22	26.12.52	+0. 1	+1.50
21. 8.21	8.36.14	29.37.15	26.20. 3	29.38.02	26.17.37	−0.47	+2.26
22. 8. 8	9.33.55	♍ 6.29.53	26. 8.42	♍ 6.30. 3	26. 7.12	−0.10	+1.30
29.08.20	16.22.40	♎ 12.37.54	18.37.47	♎ 12.37.49	18.34. 5	+0. 5	+3.42
30. 7.45	17.19.41	15.36. 1	17.26.43	15.35.18	17.27.17	+0.43	−0.34
Sept. 1. 7.33	19.16. 9	20.30.53	15.13. 0	20.27. 4	15. 9.49	+3.49	+3.11
4. 7.22	22.11.28	25.42. 0	12.23.48	25.40.58	12.22. 0	+1. 2	+1.48
5. 7.32	23.10.29	27. 0.46	11.33.08	26.59.24	11.33.51	+1.22	−0.43
8. 7.16	26. 5.58	29.58.44	9.26.46	29.58.45	9.26.43	−0. 1	+0. 3
9. 7.26	27. 5. 9	♏ 0.44.10	8.49.10	♏ 0.44. 4	8.48.25	+0. 6	+0.45

This theory is also confirmed by the retrograde motion of the comet that appeared in the year 1723. The ascending node of this comet (according to the computation of Mr. Bradley, Savilian Professor of Astronomy at Oxford) was in ♈ 14° 16′, the inclination of the orbit to the plane of the ecliptic 49° 59′. Its perihelion was in ♉ 12° 15′ 20″, its perihelian distance from the sun 998,651 parts, of which the radius of the earth's orbit contains 1,000,000, and the equal time of its perihelion September 16ᵈ. 16ʰ. 10ᵐ. The places of this comet computed in this orbit by Mr. Bradley, and compared with the places observed by himself, his uncle Mr. Pound, and Dr. Halley, may be seen in the following table.

1723 Equatorial time	Comet's longitude observed	Latitude north observed	Comet's longitude computed	Latitude north computed	Difference longitude	Difference latitude
d h m	° ′ ″	° ′ ″	° ′ ″	° ′ ″	″	″
Oct. 9.8. 5	♒ 7.22.15	5. 2. 0	♒ 7.21.26	5. 2.47	+49	−47
10.6.21	6.41.12	7.44.13	6.41.42	7.43.18	−50	+55
12.7.22	5.39.58	11.55. 0	5.40.19	11.54.55	−21	+ 5
14.8.57	4.59.49	14.43.50	5. 0.37	14.44. 1	−48	−11
15.6.35	4.47.41	15.40.51	4.47.45	15.40.55	− 4	− 4
21.6.22	4. 2.32	19.41.49	4. 2.21	19.42. 3	+11	−14
22.6.24	3.59. 2	20. 8.12	3.59.10	20. 8.17	− 8	− 5
24.8. 2	3.55.29	20.55.18	3.55.11	20.55. 9	+18	+ 9
29.8.56	3.56.17	22.20.27	3.56.42	22.20.10	−25	+17
30.6.20	3.58. 9	22.32.28	3.58.17	22.32.12	− 8	+16
Nov. 5.5.53	4.16.30	23.38.33	4.16.23	23.38. 7	+ 7	+26
8.7. 6	4.29.36	24. 4.30	4.29.54	24. 4.40	−18	−10
14.6.20	5. 2.16	24.48.46	5. 2.51	24.48.16	−35	+30
20.7.45	5.42.20	25.24.45	5.43.13	25.25.17	−53	−32
Dec. 7.6.45	8. 4.13	26.54.18	8. 3.55	26.53.42	+18	+36

From these examples it is abundantly evident that the motions of comets are no less accurately represented by our theory than the motions of the planets commonly are by the theories of them; and, therefore, by means of this theory, we may enumerate the orbits of comets, and so discover the periodic time of a comet's revolution in any orbit; hence, at last, we shall have the transverse diameters of their elliptic orbits and their aphelian distances.

That retrograde comet which appeared in the year 1607 described an orbit whose ascending node (according to Dr. Halley's computation) was in ♉ 20° 21′; and the inclination of the plane of the orbit to the plane of the ecliptic 17° 2′, whose perihelion was in ♒ 2° 16′; and its perihelian distance from the sun 58,680 of such parts as the radius of the earth's orbit contains 100,000; and the comet was in its perihelion October 16ᵈ. 3ʰ. 50ᵐ.; which orbit agrees very nearly with the orbit of the comet which was seen in 1682. If these were not two different comets, but one and the same, that comet will finish one revolution in the space of 75 years; and the greater axis of its orbit will be to the greater axis of the earth's orbit as $\sqrt[3]{75^2}$ to 1, or as 1778 to 100, nearly. And the aphelian distance of this comet from the sun will be to the mean distance of the earth from the sun as about 35 to 1; from these data it will be no hard matter to determine the elliptic orbit of this comet. But these things are to be supposed on condition that, after the space of 75 years, the same comet shall return again in the same orbit. The other comets seem to ascend to greater heights, and to require a longer time to perform their revolutions.

But, because of the great number of comets, of the great distance of their aphelions from the sun, and of the slowness of their motions in the aphelions, they will, by their mutual gravitations, disturb each other; so that their eccentricities and the times of their revolutions will be sometimes a little increased, and sometimes diminished. Therefore, we are not to expect that the same comet will return exactly in the same orbit, and in the same periodic times: it will be sufficient if we find the changes no greater than may arise from the causes just spoken of.

And hence a reason may be assigned why comets are not comprehended within the limits of a zodiac, as the planets are; but, being confined to no bounds, are with various motions dispersed all over the heavens; namely, to this purpose, that in their aphelions, where their motions are exceedingly slow, receding to greater distances one from another, they may suffer less disturbance from their mutual gravitations: and hence it is that the comets which descend the lowest, and therefore move the slowest in their aphelions, ought also to ascend the highest.

The comet which appeared in the year 1680 was in its perihelion less distant from the sun than by a sixth part of the sun's diameter; and because of its extreme velocity in that proximity to the sun, and some density of the sun's atmosphere, it must have suffered some resistance and retardation; and therefore, being attracted somewhat nearer to the sun in every revolution, will at last fall down upon the body of the sun. Nay, in its aphelion, where it moves the slowest, it may sometimes happen to be yet further retarded by the attractions of other comets, and in consequence of this retardation descend to the sun. So fixed stars, that have been gradually wasted by the light and vapors emitted from them for a long time, may be recruited by comets that fall upon them; and from this fresh supply of new fuel those old stars, acquiring new splendor, may pass for new stars. Of this kind are such fixed stars as appear on a sudden, and shine with a wonderful brightness at first, and afterwards vanish by little and little. Such was that star which appeared in Cassiopeia's Chair; which Cornelis Gemma did not see upon the 8th of November, 1572, though he was observing that part of the heavens upon that very night, and the sky was perfectly serene; but the next night (November 9) he saw it shining much brighter than any of the fixed stars, and scarcely inferior to Venus in splendor. Tycho Brahe saw it upon the 11th of the same month, when it shone with the greatest lustre; and from that time he observed it to decay by little and little; and in 16 months' time it entirely disappeared. In the month of November, when it first appeared, its light was equal to that of Venus. In the month of December, its light was a little diminished, and was now become equal to that of Jupiter. In January, 1573, it was less than Jupiter, and greater than Sirius, and about the end of February and the beginning of March became equal to that star. In the months of April and May it was equal to a star of the second magnitude; in June, July, and August, to a star of the third magnitude; in September, October, and November, to those of the fourth magnitude; in December and January, 1574, to those of the fifth; in February to those of the sixth magnitude; and in March it entirely vanished. Its color at the beginning was clear, bright, and inclining to white; afterwards it turned a little yellow; and in March, 1573, it became ruddy, like Mars or Aldebaran; in May it turned to a kind of dusky whiteness, like that we observe in Saturn; and that color it retained ever after, but growing always more and more obscure. Such also was the star in the right foot of Serpentarius, which Kepler's scholars first observed September 30, o.s., 1604, with a light exceeding that of Jupiter, though the night before it was not to be seen; and from that time it decreased by little and little, and in 15 or 16 months entirely disappeared. Such a new star appearing with an unusual splendor is said to have moved Hipparchus to observe, and make a catalogue of, the fixed stars. As to those fixed stars that appear and disappear by turns, and increase slowly and by degrees, and scarcely ever exceed the stars of the third magnitude, they seem to be of another kind, which revolve about their axes, and, having a light and a dark side, show those two different sides by turns. The vapors which arise from the sun, the fixed stars, and the tails of the comets, may meet at last with, and fall into, the atmospheres of the planets by their gravity, and there be condensed and turned into water and humid spirits; and from thence, by a slow heat, pass gradually into the form of salts, and sulphurs, and tinctures, and mud, and clay, and sand, and stones, and coral, and other terrestrial substances.

GENERAL SCHOLIUM

THE hypothesis of vortices is pressed with many difficulties. That every planet by a radius drawn to the sun may describe areas proportional to the times of description, the periodic times of the several parts of the vortices should observe the square of their distances from the sun; but that the periodic times of the planets may obtain the $\frac{3}{2}$th power of their distances from the sun, the periodic times of the parts of the vortex ought to be as the $\frac{3}{2}$th power of their distances. That the smaller vortices may maintain their lesser revolutions about Saturn, Jupiter, and other planets, and swim quietly and undisturbed in the greater vortex of the sun, the periodic times of the parts of the sun's vortex should be equal; but the rotation of the sun and planets about their axes, which ought to correspond with the motions of their vortices, recede far from all these proportions. The motions of the comets are exceedingly regular, are governed by the same laws with the motions of the planets, and can by no means be accounted for by the hypothesis of vortices; for comets are carried with very eccentric motions through all parts of the heavens indifferently, with a freedom that is incompatible with the notion of a vortex.

Bodies projected in our air suffer no resistance but from the air. Withdraw the air, as is done in Mr. Boyle's vacuum, and the resistance ceases; for in this void a bit of fine down and a piece of solid gold descend with equal velocity. And the same argument must apply to the celestial spaces above the earth's atmosphere; in these spaces, where there is no air to resist their motions, all bodies will move with the greatest freedom; and the planets and comets will constantly pursue their revolutions in orbits given in kind and position, according to the laws above explained; but though these bodies may, indeed, continue in their orbits by the mere laws of gravity, yet they could by no means have at first derived the regular position of the orbits themselves from those laws.

The six primary planets are revolved about the sun in circles concentric with the sun, and with motions directed towards the same parts, and almost in the same plane. Ten moons are revolved about the earth, Jupiter, and Saturn, in circles concentric with them, with the same direction of motion, and nearly in the planes of the orbits of those planets; but it is not to be conceived that mere mechanical causes could give birth to so many regular motions, since the comets range over all parts of the heavens in very eccentric orbits; for by that kind of motion they pass easily through the orbs of the planets, and with great rapidity; and in their aphelions, where they move the slowest, and are detained the longest, they recede to the greatest distances from each other, and hence suffer the least disturbance from their mutual attractions. This most beautiful system of the sun, planets, and comets, could only proceed from the counsel and dominion of an intelligent and powerful Being. And if the fixed stars are the centres of other like systems, these, being formed by the like wise counsel, must be all subject to the dominion of One; especially since the light of the fixed stars is of the same nature with the light of the sun, and from every system light passes into all the other systems: and lest the systems of the fixed stars should, by their gravity, fall on each other, he hath placed those systems at immense distances from one another.

This Being governs all things, not as the soul of the world, but as Lord over all; and on account of his dominion he is wont to be called *Lord God* παντοκρά-τωρ, or *Universal Ruler;* for *God* is a relative word, and has a respect to servants; and *Deity* is the dominion of God not over his own body, as those imagine who fancy God to be the soul of the world, but over servants. The Supreme God is a Being eternal, infinite, absolutely perfect; but a being, however perfect, without dominion, cannot be said to be Lord God; for we say, my God, your God, the God of Israel, the God of Gods, and Lord of Lords; but we do not say, my Eternal, your Eternal, the Eternal of Israel, the Eternal of Gods; we do not say, my Infinite, or my Perfect: these are titles which have no respect to servants. The word *God*[1] usually signifies *Lord;* but every lord is not a God. It is the dominion of a spiritual being which constitutes a God: a true, supreme, or imaginary dominion makes a true, supreme, or imaginary God. And from his true dominion it follows that the true God is a living, intelligent, and powerful Being; and, from his other perfections, that he is supreme, or most perfect. He is eternal and infinite, omnipotent and omniscient; that is, his duration reaches from eternity to eternity; his presence from infinity to infinity; he governs all things, and knows all things that are or can be done. He is not eternity and infinity, but eternal and infinite; he is not duration or space, but he endures and is present. He endures forever, and is everywhere present; and, by existing always and everywhere, he constitutes duration and space. Since every particle of space is *always*, and every indivisible moment of duration is *everywhere*, certainly the Maker and Lord of all things cannot be *never* and *nowhere*. Every soul that has perception is, though in different times and in different organs of sense and motion, still the same indivisible person. There are given successive parts in duration, coexistent parts in space, but neither the one nor the other in the person of a man, or his thinking principle; and much less can they be found in the thinking substance of God. Every man, so far as he is a thing that has perception, is one and the same man during his whole life, in all and each of his organs of sense. God is the same God, always and everywhere. He is omnipresent not *virtually* only, but also *substantially;* for virtue cannot subsist without substance. In him[2] are all things contained and moved; yet neither affects the other: God suffers nothing from the motion of bodies; bodies find no resistance from the omnipresence of God. It is allowed by all that the Supreme God exists necessarily; and by the same necessity he

---

[1]Dr. Pocock derives the Latin word *Deus* from the Arabic *du* (in the oblique case *di*), which signifies *Lord*. And in this sense princes are called *gods*, Psalms, 82.6; and John, 10.35. And Moses is called a *god* to his brother Aaron, and a *god* to Pharaoh, Exodus, 4.16; and 7.1. And in the same sense the souls of dead princes were formerly, by the heathens, called *gods*, but falsely, because of their want of dominion.

[2]This was the opinion of the ancients. So Pythagoras, in Cicero *De natura deorum* i. Thales, Anaxagoras, Virgil, in *Georgics* iv. 220; and *Aeneid* vi. 721. Philo, *Allegories*, at the beginning of Book I. Aratus, in his *Phænomena*, at the beginning. So also the sacred writers: as St. Paul, in Acts, 17.27, 28. St. John's Gospel, 14.2. Moses, in Deuteronomy, 4.39; and 10.14. David, in Psalms, 139.7,8,9. Solomon, in I Kings, 8.27. Job, 22.12,13,14. Jeremiah, 23.23,24. The idolaters supposed the sun, moon, and stars, the souls of men, and other parts of the world, to be parts of the Supreme God, and therefore to be worshipped; but erroneously.

exists *always* and *everywhere*. Whence also he is all similar, all eye, all ear, all brain, all arm, all power to perceive, to understand, and to act; but in a manner not at all human, in a manner not at all corporeal, in a manner utterly unknown to us. As a blind man has no idea of colors, so have we no idea of the manner by which the all-wise God perceives and understands all things. He is utterly void of all body and bodily figure, and can therefore neither be seen, nor heard, nor touched; nor ought he to be worshiped under the representation of any corporeal thing. We have ideas of his attributes, but what the real substance of anything is we know not. In bodies, we see only their figures and colors, we hear only the sounds, we touch only their outward surfaces, we smell only the smells, and taste the savors; but their inward substances are not to be known either by our senses, or by any reflex act of our minds: much less, than, have we any idea of the substance of God. We know him only by his most wise and excellent contrivances of things, and final causes; we admire him for his perfections; but we reverence and adore him on account of his dominion: for we adore him as his servants; and a god without dominion, providence, and final causes, is nothing else but Fate and Nature. Blind metaphysical necessity, which is certainly the same always and everywhere, could produce no variety of things. All that diversity of natural things which we find suited to different times and places could arise from nothing but the ideas and will of a Being necessarily existing. But, by way of allegory, God is said to see, to speak, to laugh, to love, to hate, to desire, to give, to receive, to rejoice, to be angry, to fight, to frame, to work, to build; for all our notions of God are taken from the ways of mankind by a certain similitude, which, though not perfect, has some likeness, however. And thus much concerning God; to discourse of whom from the appearances of things, does certainly belong to natural philosophy.

Hitherto we have explained the phenomena of the heavens and of our sea by the power of gravity, but have not yet assigned the cause of this power. This is certain, that it must proceed from a cause that penetrates to the very centres of the sun and planets, without suffering the least diminution of its force; that operates not according to the quantity of the surfaces of the particles upon which it acts (as mechanical causes used to do), but according to the quantity of the solid matter which they contain, and propagates its virtue on all sides to immense distances, decreasing always as the inverse square of the distances. Gravitation towards the sun is made up out of the gravitations towards the several particles of which the body of the sun is composed; and in receding from the sun decreases accurately as the inverse square of the distances as far as the orbit of Saturn, as evidently appears from the quiescence of the aphelion of the planets; nay, and even to the remotest aphelion of the comets, if those aphelions are also quiescent. But hitherto I have not been able to discover the cause of those properties of gravity from phenomena, and I frame no hypotheses; for whatever is not deduced from the phenomena is to be called an hypothesis; and hypotheses, whether metaphysical or physical, whether of occult qualities or mechanical, have no place in experimental philosophy. In this philosophy particular propositions are inferred from the phenomena, and afterwards rendered general by induction. Thus it was that the impenetrability, the mobility, and the impulsive force of bodies, and the laws of motion and of gravitation, were discovered. And to us it is enough that gravity does really exist, and act according to the laws which we have explained, and abundantly serves to account for all the motions of the celestial bodies, and of our sea.

And now we might add something concerning a certain most subtle spirit which pervades and lies hid in all gross bodies; by the force and action of which spirit the particles of bodies attract one another at near distances, and cohere, if contiguous; and electric bodies operate to greater distances, as well repelling as attracting the neighboring corpuscles; and light is emitted, reflected, refracted, inflected, and heats bodies; and all sensation is excited, and the members of animal bodies move at the command of the will, namely, by the vibrations of this spirit, mutually propagated along the solid filaments of the nerves, from the outward organs of sense to the brain, and from the brain into the muscles. But these are things that cannot be explained in few words, nor are we furnished with that sufficiency of experiments which is required to an accurate determination and demonstration of the laws by which this electric and elastic spirit operates.

OPTICS

CONTENTS

ADVERTISEMENT TO FIRST EDITION

PART of the ensuing discourse about light was written at the desire of some gentlemen of the Royal Society, in the year 1675, and then sent to their Secretary, and read at their meetings, and the rest was added about twelve years after to complete the theory; except the third book, and the last proposition of the second, which were since put together out of scattered papers. To avoid being engaged in disputes about these matters, I have hitherto delayed the printing, and should still have delayed it, had not the importunity of friends prevailed upon me. If any other papers writ on this subject are got out of my hands they are imperfect, and were perhaps written before I had tried all the experiments here set down, and fully satisfied myself about the laws of refractions and composition of colours. I have here published what I think proper to come abroad, wishing that it may not be translated into another language without my consent.

The crowns of colours, which sometimes appear about the Sun and Moon, I have endeavoured to give an account of; but for want of sufficient observations leave that matter to be further examined. The subject of the third book I have also left imperfect, not having tried all the experiments which I intended when I was about these matters, nor repeated some of those which I did try, until I had satisfied myself about all their circumstances. To communicate what I have tried, and leave the rest to others for further enquiry, is all my design in publishing these papers.

In a letter written to Mr. Leibnitz in the year 1679, and published by Dr. Wallis, I mentioned a method by which I had found some general theorems about squaring curvilinear figures, or comparing them with the conic sections, or other the simplest figures with which they may be compared. And some years ago I lent out a manuscript containing such theorems, and having since met with some things copied out of it, I have on this occasion made it public, prefixing to it an Introduction, and subjoining a Scholium concerning that method. And I have joined with it another small tract concerning the curvilinear figures of the second kind, which was also written many years ago, and made known to some friends, who have solicited the making it public.

I. N.

April 1, 1704.

ADVERTISEMENT TO SECOND EDITION

In this Second Edition of these *Optics* I have omitted the mathematical tracts published at the end of the former edition, as not belonging to the subject. And at the end of the third book I have added some questions. And to shew that I do not take gravity for an essential property of bodies, I have added one question concerning its cause, choosing to propose it by way of a question, because I am not yet satisfied about it for want of experiments.

I. N.

July 16, 1717.

BOOK ONE

Part I

My design in this book is not to explain the properties of light by hypotheses, but to propose and prove them by reason and experiments: in order to which I shall premise the following definitions and axioms.

DEFINITIONS

DEFINITION I

By the rays of light I understand its least parts, and those as well successive in the same lines, as contemporary in several lines.

For it is manifest that light consists of parts, both successive and contemporary; because in the same place you may stop that which comes one moment, and let pass that which comes presently after; and in the same time you may stop it in any one place, and let it pass in any other. For that part of light which is stopped cannot be the same with that which is let pass. The least light or part of light, which may be stopped alone without the rest of the light, or propagated alone, or do or suffer any thing alone, which the rest of the light doth not or suffers not, I call a *ray* of light.

DEFINITION II

Refrangibility of the rays of light, is their disposition to be refracted or turned out of their way in passing out of one transparent body or medium into another. And a greater or less refrangibility of rays is their disposition to be turned more or less out of their way in like incidences on the same medium.

Mathematicians usually consider the rays of light to be lines reaching from the luminous body to the body illuminated, and the refraction of those rays to be the bending or breaking of those lines in their passing out of one medium into another. And thus may rays and refractions be considered, if light be propagated in an instant. But by an argument taken from the equations of the times of the eclipses of Jupiter's satellites, it seems that light is propagated in time, spending in its passage from the Sun to us about seven minutes of time: and, therefore, I have chosen to define rays and refractions in such general terms as may agree to light in both cases.

DEFINITION III

Reflexibility of rays is their disposition to be reflected or turned back into the same medium from any other medium upon whose surface they fall. And rays are more or less reflexible which are turned back more or less easily.

As if light pass out of a glass into air, and by being inclined more and more to the common surface of the glass and air, begins at length to be totally reflected by that surface; those sorts of rays which at like incidences are reflected most copiously, or by inclining the rays begin soonest to be totally reflected, are most reflexible.

DEFINITION IV

The angle of incidence is that angle which the line described by the incident ray contains with the perpendicular to the reflecting or refracting surface at the point of incidence.

DEFINITION V

The angle of reflexion or refraction is the angle which the line described by the reflected or refracted ray containeth with the perpendicular to the reflecting or refracting surface at the point of incidence.

DEFINITION VI

The sines of incidence, reflexion, and refraction are the sines of the angles of incidence, reflexion, and refraction.

DEFINITION VII

The light whose rays are all alike refrangible I call Simple, Homogeneal and Similar; and that whose rays are some more refrangible than others I call compound, heterogeneal *and* dissimilar.

The former light I call homogeneal, not because I would affirm it so in all respects, but because the rays which agree in refrangibility agree at least in all those their other properties which I consider in the following discourse.

DEFINITION VIII

The colours of homogeneal lights I call primary, homogeneal *and* simple; *and those of heterogeneal lights,* heterogeneal *and* compound.

For these are always compounded of the colours of homogeneal lights; as will appear in the following discourse.

AXIOMS

AXIOM I

The angles of reflexion and refraction lie in one and the same plane with the angle of incidence.

AXIOM II

The angle of reflexion is equal to the angle of incidence.

AXIOM III

If the refracted ray be returned directly back to the point of incidence, it shall be refracted into the line before described by the incident ray.

AXIOM IV

Refraction out of the rarer medium into the denser is made towards the perpendicular; that is, so that the angle of refraction be less than the angle of incidence.

AXIOM V

The sine of incidence is either accurately or very nearly in a given ratio to the sine of refraction.

Whence if that proportion be known in any one inclination of the incident ray, 'tis known in all the inclinations, and thereby the refraction in all cases of incidence on the same refracting body may be determined. Thus, if the refraction be made out of air into water, the sine of incidence of the red light is to the sine of its refraction as 4 to 3. If out of air into glass, the sines are as 17 to 11. In light of other colours the sines have other proportions: but the difference is so little that it need seldom be considered.

Suppose, therefore, that RS [Fig. 1] represents the surface of stagnating water, and that C is the point of incidence in which any ray coming in the air from A in the line AC is reflected

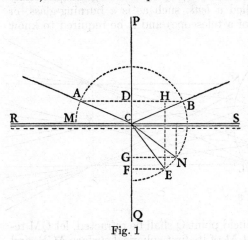

Fig. 1

or refracted, and I would know whither this ray shall go after reflexion or refraction: I erect upon the surface of the water from the point of incidence the perpendicular CP and produce it downwards to Q, and conclude by the first Axiom that the ray after reflexion and refraction shall be found somewhere in the plane of the angle of incidence ACP produced. I let fall, therefore, upon the perpendicular CP the sine of incidence AD; and if the reflected ray be desired, I produce AD to B so that DB be equal to AD, and draw CB. For this line CB shall be the reflected ray; the angle of reflexion BCP and its sine BD being equal to the angle and sine of incidence, as they ought to be by the second Axiom. But if the refracted ray be desired, I produce AD to H, so that DH may be to AD as the sine of refraction to the sine of incidence, that is (if the light be red) as 3 to 4; and about the centre C and in the plane ACP, with the radius CA describing a circle ABE, I draw a parallel to the perpendicular CPQ, the line HE cutting the circumference in E and joining CE; this line CE shall be the line of the refracted ray. For if EF be let fall perpendicularly on the line PQ, this line EF shall be the sine of refraction of the ray CE, the angle of refraction being ECQ; and this sine EF is equal to DH, and consequently in proportion to the sine of incidence AD as 3 to 4.

In like manner, if there be a prism of glass (that is, a glass bounded with two equal and parallel triangular ends, and three plain and well polished sides, which meet in three parallel lines running from the three angles of one end to the

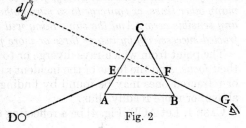

Fig. 2

three angles of the other end) and if the refraction of the light in passing cross this prism be desired: let ACB [Fig. 2] represent a plane cutting this prism transversely to its three parallel lines or edges there where the light passeth through it, and let DE be the ray incident upon the first side of the prism AC where the light goes into the glass; and by putting the proportion of the sine of incidence to the sine of refraction as 17 to 11 find EF the first refracted ray. Then, taking this ray for the incident ray upon the second side of the glass BC where the light goes out, find the next refracted ray FG by putting the proportion of the sine of incidence to the sine of refraction as 11 to 17. For if the sine of incidence out of air into glass be to the sine of refraction as 17 to 11, the sine of incidence out of glass into air must on the contrary be to the sine of refraction as 11 to 17, by the third Axiom.

Much after the same manner, if ACBD [Fig. 3] represent a glass spherically convex on both sides (usually called a *lens*, such as is a burning-glass, or spectacle-glass, or an object-glass of a telescope) and it be required to know

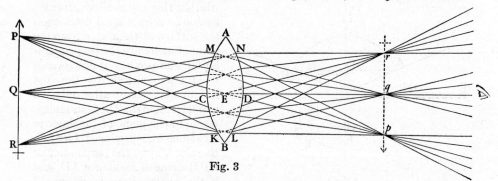

Fig. 3

how light falling upon it from any lucid point Q shall be refracted, let QM represent a ray falling upon any point M of its first spherical surface ACB, and by erecting a perpendicular to the glass at the point M, find the first refracted ray MN by the proportion of the sines 17 to 11. Let that ray in going out of the glass be incident upon N, and then find the second refracted ray Nq by the proportion of the sines 11 to 17. And after the same manner may the refraction be found when the lens is convex on one side and plane or concave on the other, or concave on both sides.

AXIOM VI

Homogeneal rays which flow from several points of any object, and fall perpendicularly or almost perpendicularly on any reflecting or refracting plane or spherical surface, shall afterwards diverge from so many other points, or be parallel to so many other lines, or converge to so many other points, either accurately or without any sensible error. And the same thing will happen if the rays be reflected or refracted successively by two or three or more plane or spherical surfaces.

The point from which rays diverge or to which they converge may be called their *focus*. And the focus of the incident rays being given, that of the reflected or refracted ones may be found by finding the refraction of any two rays, as above; or more readily thus:

CASE 1. Let ACB [Fig. 4] be a reflecting or refracting plane, and Q the focus

of the incident rays, and Qq C a perpendicular to that plane. And if this perpendicular be produced to q, so that qC be equal to QC, the point q shall be the
focus of the reflected rays; or if qC be taken on the same side of the plane with

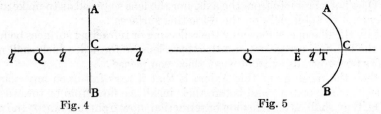

Fig. 4   Fig. 5

QC, and in proportion to QC as the sine of incidence to the sine of refraction,
the point q shall be the focus of the refracted rays.

CASE 2. Let ACB [Fig. 5] be the reflecting surface of any sphere whose centre
is E. Bisect any radius thereof, (suppose EC) in T, and if in that radius on the
same side the point T you take the points Q and q, so that TQ, TE, and Tq be
continual proportionals, and the point Q be the focus of the incident rays, the
point q shall be the focus of the reflected ones.

CASE 3. Let ACB [Fig. 6] be the refracting surface of any sphere whose centre
is E. In any radius thereof EC produced both ways take ET and Ct equal to
one another and severally in such proportion to that radius as the lesser of the

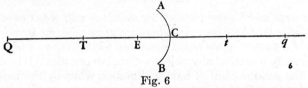

Fig. 6

sines of incidence and refraction hath to the difference of those sines. And then
if in the same line you find any two points Q and q, so that TQ be to ET as Et
to tq, taking tq the contrary way from t which TQ lieth from T, and if the point
Q be the focus of any incident rays, the point q shall be the focus of the refracted
ones.

And by the same means the focus of the rays after two or more reflexions or
refractions may be found.

CASE 4. Let ACBD [Fig. 7] be any refracting lens, spherically convex or
concave or plane on either side, and let CD be its axis (that is, the line which

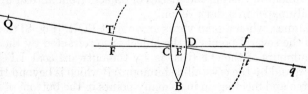

Fig. 7

cuts both its surfaces perpendicularly, and passes through the centres of the
spheres), and in this axis produced let F and f be the foci of the refracted rays
found as above, when the incident rays on both sides the lens are parallel to the
same axis; and upon the diameter Ff bisected in E, describe a circle. Suppose
now that any point Q be the focus of any incident rays. Draw QE cutting the

said circle in T and *t*, and therein take *tq* in such proportion to *t*E as *t*E or TE hath to TQ. Let *tq* lie the contrary way from *t* which TQ doth from T, and *q* shall be the focus of the refracted rays without any sensible error, provided the point Q be not so remote from the axis, nor the lens so broad as to make any of the rays fall too obliquely on the refracting surfaces.

And by the like operations may the reflecting or refracting surfaces be found when the two foci are given, and thereby a lens be formed, which shall make the rays flow towards or from what place you please.

So then the meaning of this Axiom is that if rays fall upon any plane or spherical surface or lens, and before their incidence flow from or towards any point Q, they shall, after reflexion or refraction, flow from or towards the point *q* found by the foregoing rules. And if the incident rays flow from or towards several points Q, the reflected or refracted rays shall flow from or towards so many other points *q* found by the same rules. Whether the reflected and refracted rays flow from or towards the point *q* is easily known by the situation of that point. For if that point be on the same side of the reflecting or refracting surface or lens with the point Q, and the incident rays flow from the point Q, the reflected flow towards the point *q* and the refracted from it; and if the incident rays flow towards Q, the reflected flow from *q*, and the refracted towards it. And the contrary happens when *q* is on the other side of the surface.

AXIOM VII

Wherever the rays which come from all the points of any object meet again in so many points after they have been made to converge by reflection or refraction, there they will make a picture of the object upon any white body on which they fall.

So if PR [Fig. 3] represent any object without doors, and AB be a lens placed at a hole in the window-shut of a dark chamber, whereby the rays that come from any point Q of that object are made to converge and meet again in the point *q*; and if a sheet of white paper be held at *q* for the light there to fall upon it, the picture of that object PR will appear upon the paper in its proper shape and colours. For as the light which comes from the point Q goes to the point *q*, so the light which comes from other points P and R of the object will go to so many other correspondent points *p* and *r* (as is manifest by the sixth Axiom); so that every point of the object shall illuminate a correspondent point of the picture, and thereby make a picture like the object in shape and colour, this only excepted, that the picture shall be inverted. And this is the reason of that vulgar experiment of casting the species of objects from abroad upon a wall or sheet of white paper in a dark room.

In like manner, when a man views any object PQR, [Fig. 8] the light which comes from the several points of the object is so refracted by the transparent skins and humours of the eye (that is, by the outward coat EFG, called the *tunica cornea*, and by the crystalline humour AB which is beyond the pupil *mk*) as to converge and meet again in so many points in the bottom of the eye, and there to paint the picture of the object upon that skin (called the *tunica retina*) with which the bottom of the eye is covered. For anatomists, when they have taken off from the bottom of the eye that outward and most thick coat called the *dura mater*, can then see through the thinner coats the pictures of objects lively painted thereon. And these pictures, propagated by motion along the fibres of the optic nerves into the brain, are the cause of vision. For accordingly

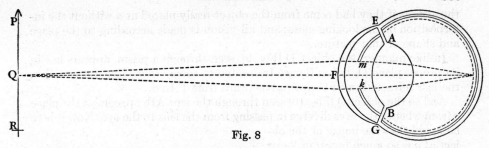

Fig. 8

as these pictures are perfect or imperfect, the object is seen perfectly or imperfectly. If the eye be tinged with any colour (as in the disease of the jaundice) so as to tinge the pictures in the bottom of the eye with that colour, then all objects appear tinged with the same colour. If the humours of the eye by old age decay, so as by shrinking to make the cornea and coat of the crystalline humour grow flatter than before, the light will not be refracted enough, and for want of a sufficient refraction will not converge to the bottom of the eye but to some place beyond it, and by consequence paint in the bottom of the eye a confused picture, and according to the indistinctness of this picture the object will appear confused. This is the reason of the decay of sight in old men, and shews why their sight is mended by spectacles. For those convex glasses supply the defect of plumpness in the eye, and by increasing the refraction make the rays converge sooner, so as to convene distinctly at the bottom of the eye if the glass have a due degree of convexity. And the contrary happens in short-sighted men whose eyes are too plump. For the refraction being now too great, the rays converge and convene in the eyes before they come at the bottom; and therefore the picture made in the bottom and the vision caused thereby will not be distinct, unless the object be brought so near the eye as that the place where the converging rays convene may be removed to the bottom, or that the plumpness of the eye be taken off and the refractions diminished by a concave-glass of a due degree of concavity, or lastly that by age the eye grow flatter till it come to a due figure: For short-sighted men see remote objects best in old age, and therefore they are accounted to have the most lasting eyes.

AXIOM VIII

An object seen by reflexion or refraction appears in that place from whence the rays after their last reflexion or refraction diverge in falling on the spectator's eye.

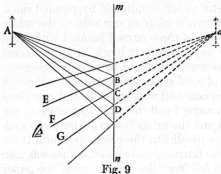

Fig. 9

If the object A [Fig. 9] be seen by reflexion of a looking-glass *mn*, it shall appear, not in its proper place A, but behind the glass at *a*, from whence any rays AB, AC, AD, which flow from one and the same point of the object, do, after their reflexion made in the points B, C, D, diverge in going from the glass to E, F, G, where they are incident on the spectator's eyes. For these rays do make the same picture in the bottom of the eyes as if they had come from the object really placed at *a* without the interposition of the looking-glass; and all vision is made according to the place and shape of that picture.

In like manner, the object D [Fig. 2], seen through a prism, appears not in its proper place D, but is thence translated to some other place *d* situated in the last refracted ray FG drawn backward from F to *d*.

And so the object Q [Fig. 10] seen through the lens AB, appears at the place *q* from whence the rays diverge in passing from the lens to the eye. Now it is to be noted that the image of the object at *q* is so much bigger or lesser than the object itself at Q, as the distance of the image at *q* from the lens AB is bigger or less than the distance of the object at Q from the same lens. And if the object be seen through two or more such convex or concave glasses, every glass shall

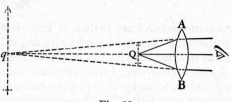

Fig. 10

make a new image, and the object shall appear in the place of the bigness of the last image. Which consideration unfolds the theory of microscopes and telescopes. For that theory consists in almost nothing else than the describing such glasses as shall make the last image of any object as distinct and large and luminous as it can conveniently be made.

I have now given in Axioms and their explications the sum of what hath hitherto been treated of in Optics. For what hath been generally agreed on I content myself to assume under the notion of Principles, in order to what I have further to write. And this may suffice for an Introduction to readers of quick wit and good understanding not yet versed in Optics: although those who are already acquainted with this science, and have handled glasses, will more readily apprehend what followeth.

PROPOSITIONS

Proposition 1. Theorem 1

Lights which differ in colour, differ also in degrees of refrangibility.

The Proof by Experiments

Experiment 1. I took a black oblong stiff paper terminated by parallel sides, and, with a perpendicular right line drawn cross from one side to the other, distinguished it into two equal parts. One of these parts I painted with a red colour and the other with a blue. The paper was very black, and the colours intense and thickly laid on, that the phenomenon might be more conspicuous. This paper I viewed through a prism of solid glass, whose two sides through which the light passed to the eye were plane and well polished, and contained an angle of about sixty degrees; which angle I call the refracting angle of the prism. And whilst I viewed it, I held it and the prism before a window in such manner that the sides of the paper were parallel to the prism, and both those sides and the prism were parallel to the horizon, and the cross line was also parallel to it: and that the light which fell from the window upon the paper made an angle with the paper equal to that angle which was made with the same paper by the light reflected from it to the eye. Beyond the prism was the wall of the chamber under the window covered over with black cloth, and the cloth was involved in darkness that no light might be reflected from thence, which in passing by the edges of the paper to the eye, might mingle itself with the light of the paper, and obscure the phenomenon thereof. These things being thus ordered, I found that if the refracting angle of the prism be turned upwards, so that the paper may seem to be lifted upwards by the refraction, its blue half will be lifted higher by the refraction than its red half. But if the refracting angle of the prism be turned downward, so that the paper may seem to be carried lower by the refraction, its blue half will be carried something lower thereby than its red half. Wherefore in both cases the light which comes from the blue half of the paper through the prism to the eye does in like circumstances suffer a greater refraction than the light which comes from the red half, and by consequence is more refrangible.

ILLUSTRATION. In the eleventh Figure, MN represents the window, and DE the paper terminated with parallel sides DJ and HE, and by the transverse line FG distinguished into two halves,

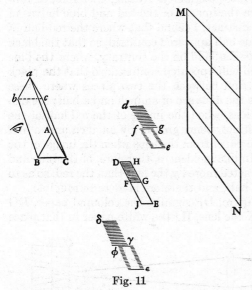

Fig. 11

the one DG of an intensely blue colour, the other FE of an intensely red. And BAC*cab* represents the prism whose refracting planes AB*ba* and AC*ca* meet in the edge of the refracting angle A*a*. This edge A*a*, being upward, is parallel both to the horizon and to the parallel edges of the paper DJ and HE, and the transverse line FG is perpendicular to the plane of the window. And *de* represents the image of the paper seen by refraction upwards in such manner that the blue half DG is carried higher to *dg* than the red half FE is to *fe*, and therefore suffers a greater refraction. If the edge of the refracting angle be turned downward, the image of the paper will be refracted downward; suppose to δε, and the blue half will be refracted lower to δγ than the red half is to φε.

EXPER. 2. About the aforesaid paper, whose two halves were painted over with red and blue, and which was stiff like thin pasteboard, I lapped several times a slender thread of very black silk, in such manner that the several parts of the thread might appear upon the colours like so many black lines drawn over them, or like long and slender dark shadows cast upon them. I might have drawn black lines with a pen, but the threads were smaller and better defined. This paper thus coloured and lined I set against a wall perpendicularly to the horizon, so that one of the colours might stand to the right hand, and the other to the left. Close before the paper, at the confine of the colours below, I placed a candle to illuminate the paper strongly: for the experiment was tried in the night. The flame of the candle reached up to the lower edge of the paper, or a very little higher. Then at the distance of six feet, and one or two inches from the paper upon the floor I erected a glass lens four inches and a quarter broad, which might collect the rays coming from the several points of the paper, and make them converge towards so many other points at the same distance of six feet, and one or two inches on the other side of the lens, and so form the image of the coloured paper upon a white paper placed there, after the same manner that a lens at a hole in a window casts the images of objects abroad upon a sheet of white paper in a dark room. The aforesaid white paper, erected perpendicular to the horizon and to the rays which fell upon it from the lens, I moved sometimes towards the lens, sometimes from it, to find the places where the images of the blue and red parts of the coloured paper appeared most distinct. Those places I easily knew by the images of the black lines which I had made by winding the silk about the paper. For the images of those fine and slender lines (which by reason of their blackness were like shadows on the colours) were confused and scarce visible, unless when the colours on either side of each line were terminated most distinctly. Noting, therefore, as diligently as I could, the places where the images of the red and blue halves of the coloured paper appeared most distinct, I found that where the red half of the paper appeared distinct, the blue half appeared confused, so that the black lines drawn upon it could scarce be seen; and on the contrary, where the blue half appeared most distinct, the red half appeared confused, so that the black lines upon it were scarce visible. And between the two places where these images appeared distinct there was the distance of an inch and a half; the distance of the white paper from the lens, when the image of the red half of the coloured paper appeared most distinct, being greater by an inch and a half than the distance of the same white paper from the lens, when the image of the blue half appeared most distinct. In like incidences, therefore, of the blue and red upon the lens, the blue was refracted more by the lens than the red, so as to converge sooner by an inch and a half, and therefore is more refrangible.

ILLUSTRATION. In the twelfth Figure, DE signifies the coloured paper, DG the blue half, FE the red half, MN the lens, HJ the white paper in that place

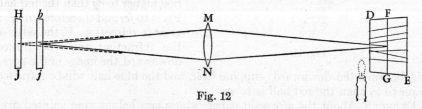

Fig. 12

where the red half with its black lines appeared distinct, and *hj* the same paper in that place where the blue half appeared distinct. The place *hj* was nearer to the lens MN than the place HJ by an inch and a half.

SCHOLIUM. The same things succeed, notwithstanding that some of the circumstances be varied; as in the first experiment when the prism and paper are any ways inclined to the horizon, and in both when coloured lines are drawn upon very black paper. But in the description of these experiments, I have set down such circumstances, by which either the phenomenon might be rendered more conspicuous, or a novice might more easily try them, or by which I did try them only. The same thing I have often done in the following experiments; concerning all which, this one admonition may suffice: now, from these experiments it follows not that all the light of the blue is more refrangible than all the light of the red; for both lights are mixed of rays differently refrangible, so that in the red there are some rays not less refrangible than those of the blue, and in the blue there are some rays not more refrangible than those of the red; but these rays, in proportion to the whole light, are but few, and serve to diminish the event of the experiment, but are not able to destroy it. For, if the red and blue colours were more dilute and weak, the distance of the images would be less than an inch and a half; and if they were more intense and full, that distance would be greater, as will appear hereafter. These experiments may suffice for the colours of natural bodies. For in the colours made by the refraction of prisms, this Proposition will appear by the experiments which are now to follow in the next Proposition.

PROPOSITION 2. THEOREM 2

The light of the Sun consists of rays differently refrangible.

The Proof by Experiments

EXPER. 3. In a very dark chamber, at a round hole, about one-third part of an inch broad, made in the shut of a window, I placed a glass prism, whereby the beam of the Sun's light, which came in at that hole, might be refracted upwards toward the opposite wall of the chamber, and there form a coloured image of the Sun. The axis of the prism (that is, the line passing through the middle of the prism from one end of it to the other end parallel to the edge of the refracting angle) was in this and the following experiments perpendicular to the incident rays. About this axis I turned the prism slowly, and saw the refracted light on the wall, or coloured image of the Sun, first to descend, and then to ascend. Between the descent and ascent, when the image seemed stationary, I stopped the prism, and fixed it in that posture, that it should be moved no more. For in that posture the refractions of the light at the two sides of the refracting angle, that is, at the entrance of the rays into the prism, and at their going out of it, were equal to one another. So also in other experiments, as often as I would have the refractions on both sides the prism to be equal to one another, I noted the place where the image of the Sun formed by the refracted light stood still between its two contrary motions, in the common period of its progress and regress; and when the image fell upon that place, I made fast the prism. And in this posture, as the most convenient, it is to be understood that all the prisms are placed in the following experiments, unless where some other posture is described. The prism, therefore, being placed in this posture, I let the refracted light fall perpendicularly upon a sheet of white paper at the opposite wall of the chamber, and observed the figure and dimensions of the solar image formed on the paper by that light. This image was oblong and not oval, but terminated with two rectilinear and parallel sides, and two semicircular ends. On its sides it was bounded pretty distinctly, but on its ends very confusedly and indistinctly, the light there decaying and vanishing by degrees. The breadth of this image answered to the Sun's diameter, and was about two inches and the eighth part of an inch, including the penumbra. For the image was eighteen feet and a half distant from the prism, and at this distance that breadth, if diminished by the diameter of the hole in the window-shut (that is, by a quarter of an inch), subtended an angle at the prism of about half a degree, which is the Sun's apparent diameter. But the length of the image was about ten inches and a quarter, and the length of the rectilinear sides about eight inches; and the refracting angle of the prism, whereby so great a length was made, was 64 degrees. With a less angle the length of the image was less, the breadth remaining the same. If the prism was turned about its axis that way which made the rays emerge more obliquely out of the second refracting surface of the prism, the image soon became an inch or two longer, or more; and if the prism was turned about the contrary way, so as to make the rays fall more obliquely on the first refracting surface, the image soon became an inch or two shorter. And, therefore, in trying this experiment, I was as curious as I could be in placing the prism, by the above-mentioned rule, exactly in such a posture that the refractions of the rays at their emergence out of the prism might be equal to that at their incidence on it. This prism had some veins running along within the glass from one end to the other, which scattered some of the sun's light irregularly, but had no sensible effect in increasing the length of the coloured spectrum. For I tried the same experiment with other prisms with the same success. And particularly with a prism which seemed free from such veins, and whose refracting angle was $62\frac{1}{2}$ degrees, I found the length of the image $9\frac{3}{4}$ or 10 inches at the distance of $18\frac{1}{2}$ feet from the prism, the breadth of the hole in the window-shut being one-quarter of an inch, as before. And because it is easy to commit a mistake in placing the prism in its due posture, I repeated the experiment four or five times, and always found the length of the image that which is set down above. With another prism of clearer glass and better polish, which seemed free from veins, and whose refracting angle was $63\frac{1}{2}$ degrees, the length of this image at the same distance of $18\frac{1}{2}$ feet was also about 10 inches, or $10\frac{1}{8}$. Beyond these measures for about $\frac{1}{4}$ or $\frac{1}{3}$ of an inch at either end of the spectrum the light of the clouds seemed to be a little tinged with red and violet, but so very faintly, that I suspected that tincture might either wholly, or in great measure, arise from some rays of the spectrum scattered irregularly by some inequalities in the substance and polish of the glass, and, therefore, I did not include it in these measures. Now, the different magnitude of the hole in the window-shut, and different thickness of the prism where the rays passed through it, and different inclinations of the prism to the horizon, made no sensible changes in the length of the image. Neither did the different matter of the prisms make any: for in a vessel made of polished plates of glass cemented together in the shape of a prism and filled with water, there is the like success of the experiment according to the quantity of the refraction. It is further to be observed, that the rays went on in right lines from the prism to the image, and, therefore, at their very going out of the prism, had all that inclination to one another from which the length of the image proceeded, that is, the inclination of more than two degrees and a half. And yet, according to the laws of Optics vulgarly received, they could not possibly be so much inclined to one another. For let EG [Fig. 13] represent the window-shut, F the hole made therein through which a beam of the Sun's light was transmitted into the darkened chamber, and ABC a triangular imaginary plane whereby the prism is feigned to be cut transversely through the middle of the light. Or if you please, let ABC represent the prism itself, looking directly towards the spectator's eye with its nearer end: and let XY be the Sun, MN the paper upon which the solar image or spectrum is cast, and PT the image itself whose sides towards v and w are rectilinear and parallel, and ends towards P and T semi-circular. YKHP and XLJT are two rays, the first of which comes from the lower part of the Sun to the higher part of the image, and is refracted in the prism at K and H, and the latter comes from the higher part of the Sun to the lower part of the image, and is refracted at L and J. Since the refractions on

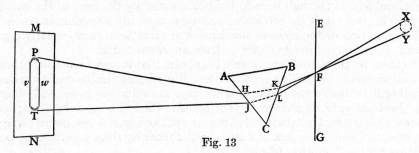

Fig. 13

both sides the prism are equal to one another, that is, the refraction at K equal to the refraction at J, and the refraction at L equal to the refraction at H, so that the refractions of the incident rays at K and L, taken together, are equal to the refractions of the emergent rays at H and J taken together: it follows, by adding equal things to equal things, that the refractions at K and H taken together are equal to the refractions at J and L taken together, and, therefore, the two rays being equally refracted, have the same inclination to one another after refraction which they had before; that is, the inclination of half a degree answering to the Sun's diameter. For so great was the inclination of the rays to one another before refraction. So then, the length of the image PT would by the rules of vulgar Optics subtend an angle of half a degree at the prism, and by consequence be equal to the breadth vw; and, therefore, the image would be round. Thus it would be were the two rays XLJT and YKHP, and all the rest which form the image PwTv, alike refrangible. And, therefore, seeing by experience it is found that the image is not round, but about five times longer than broad, the rays which, going to the upper end P of the image, suffer the greatest refraction must be more refrangible than those which go to the lower end T, unless the inequality of refraction be casual.

This image or spectrum PT was coloured, being red at its least refracted end T, and violet at its most refracted end P, and yellow, green and blue in the intermediate spaces. Which agrees with the first Proposition, that lights which differ in colour do also differ in refrangibility. The length of the image in the foregoing experiments I measured from the faintest and outmost red at one end, to the faintest and outmost blue at the other end, excepting only a little penumbra, whose breadth scarce exceeded a quarter of an inch, as was said above.

EXPER. 4. In the Sun's beam which was propagated into the room through the hole in the window-shut, at the distance of some feet from the hole, I held the prism in such a posture, that its axis might be perpendicular to that beam. Then I looked through the prism upon the hole, and turning the prism to and fro about its axis to make the image of the hole ascend and descend, when between its two contrary motions it seemed stationary, I stopped the prism, that the refractions of both sides of the refracting angle might be equal to each other, as in the former experiment. In this situation of the prism, viewing through it the said hole, I observed the length of its refracted image to be many times greater than its breadth, and that the most refracted part thereof appeared violet, the least refracted red, the middle parts blue, green and yellow in order. The same thing happened when I removed the prism out of the Sun's light, and looked through it upon the hole shining by the light of the clouds beyond it. And yet, if the refraction were done regularly according to one certain proportion of the sines of incidence and refraction, as is vulgarly supposed, the refracted image ought to have appeared round.

So then, by these two experiments it appears that in equal incidences there is a considerable inequality of refractions. But whence this inequality arises, whether it be that some of the incident rays are refracted more, and others less, constantly, or by chance, or that one and the same ray is by refraction disturbed, shattered, dilated, and as it were split and spread into many diverging rays, as Grimaldi supposes, does not yet appear by these experiments, but will appear by those that follow.

EXPER. 5. Considering, therefore, that if in the third experiment the image of the Sun should be drawn out into an oblong form, either by a dilatation of every ray, or by any other casual inequality of the refractions, the same oblong image would by a second refraction made sideways be drawn out as much in breadth by the like dilatation of the rays, or other casual inequality of the refractions sideways, I tried what would be the effects of such a second refraction. For this end I ordered all things as in the third experiment, and then placed a second prism immediately after the first in a cross position to it, that it might again refract the beam of the Sun's light which came to it through the first prism. In the first prism this beam was refracted upwards, and in the second sideways. And I found that by the refraction of the second prism, the breadth of the image was not increased, but its superior part, which in the first prism suffered the greater refraction, and appeared violet and blue, did again in the second prism suffer a greater refraction than its inferior part, which appeared red and yellow, and this without any dilatation of the image in breadth.

ILLUSTRATION. Let S [Figs. 14, 15] represent the Sun, F the hole in the window, ABC the first prism, DH the second prism, Y the round image of the Sun made by a direct beam of light when the prisms are taken away, PT the oblong image of the Sun made by that beam passing through the first prism alone, when the second prism is taken away, and pt the image made by the cross refractions of both prisms together. Now, if the rays which tend towards the several points of the round image Y were dilated and spread by the refraction of the first prism, so that they should not any longer go in single lines to single points, but that every ray being split, shattered, and changed from a linear ray to a superficies of rays diverging from the point of refraction, and lying in the plane of the angles of incidence and refraction, they should go in those planes to so many lines reaching almost from one end of the image PT to the other, and if that image should thence become oblong, those rays and their several parts tending towards the several points of the image PT ought to be again

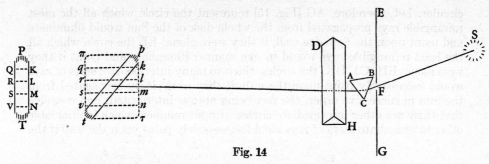

Fig. 14

dilated and spread sideways by the transverse refraction of the second prism, so as to compose a four square image, such as is represented at $\pi\tau$. For the better understanding of which, let the image PT be distinguished into five equal parts PQK, KQRL, LRSM, MSVN, NVT. And by the same irregularity that the orbicular light Y is by the refraction of the first prism dilated and drawn out into a long image PT, the light PQK which takes up a space of the same length and breadth with the light Y ought to be by the refraction of the second prism dilated and drawn out into the long image πqkp, and the light KQRL into the long image $kqrl$, and the lights LRSM, MSVN, NVT, into so many other long images $lrsm$, $msvn$, $nvt\tau$; and all these long images would compose the four square images $\pi\tau$. Thus it ought to be were every ray dilated by refraction, and spread into a triangular superficies of rays diverging from the point of refraction. For the second refraction would spread the rays one way as much as the first doth another, and so dilate the image in breadth as much as the first doth in length. And the same thing ought to happen were some rays casually refracted more than others. But the event is otherwise. The image PT was not made broader by the refraction of the second prism, but only became oblique, as 'tis represented at pt, its upper end P being by the refraction translated to a greater distance than its lower end T. So then the light which went towards the upper end P of the image was (at equal incidences) more refracted in the second prism than the light which tended towards the lower end T, that is, the blue and violet, than the red and yellow; and therefore was more refrangible. The same light was by the refraction of the first prism translated farther from the place Y to which it tended before refraction; and, therefore, suffered as well in the first prism as in the second a greater refraction than the rest of the light, and by consequence was more refrangible than the rest, even before its incidence on the first prism.

Sometimes I placed a third prism after the second, and sometimes also a fourth after the third, by all which the image might be often refracted sideways: but the rays which were more refracted than the rest in the first prism were also more refracted in all the rest, and that without any dilatation of the image sideways: and, therefore, those rays for their constancy of a greater refraction are deservedly reputed more refrangible.

But that the meaning of this experiment may more clearly appear, it is to be considered that the rays which are equally refrangible do fall upon a circle answering to the Sun's disk. For this was proved in the third experiment. By a circle I understand not here a perfect geometrical circle, but any orbicular figure whose length is equal to its breadth, and which, as to sense, may seem circular. Let, therefore, AG [Fig. 15] represent the circle which all the most refrangible rays propagated from the whole disk of the Sun would illuminate and paint upon the opposite wall, if they were alone; EL the circle which all the least refrangible rays would in like manner illuminate and paint if they were alone; BH, CJ, DK, the circles which so many intermediate sorts of rays would successively paint upon the wall, if they were singly propagated from the Sun in successive order, the rest being always intercepted; and conceive that there are other intermediate circles without number, which innumerable other intermediate sorts of rays would successively paint upon the wall if the

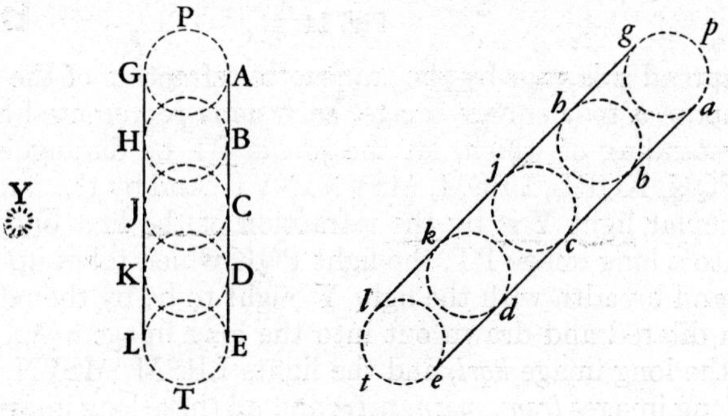

Fig. 15

Sun should successively emit every sort apart. And seeing the Sun emits all these sorts at once, they must all together illuminate and paint innumerable equal circles, of all which, being according to their degrees of refrangibility placed in order in a continual series, that oblong spectrum PT is composed which I described in the third experiment. Now, if the Sun's circular image Y [Fig. 15] which is made by an unrefracted beam of light was by any dilation of the single rays, or by any other irregularity in the refraction of the first prism, converted into the oblong spectrum, PT: then ought every circle AG, BH, CJ, &c. in that spectrum, by the cross refraction of the second prism again dilating or otherwise scattering the rays as before, to be in like manner drawn out and transformed into an oblong figure, and thereby the breadth of the image PT would be now as much augmented as the length of the image Y was before by the refraction of the first prism; and thus by the refractions of both prisms together would be formed a four square figure $p\pi t\tau$, as I described above. Wherefore, since the breadth of the spectrum PT is not increased by the refraction sideways, it is certain that the rays are not split or dilated, or otherways irregularly scattered by that refraction, but that every circle is by a regular and uniform refraction translated entire into another place, as the circle AG by the greatest refraction into the place ag, the circle BH by a less refraction into the place bh, the circle CJ by a refraction still less into the place cj, and so of the rest; by which means a new spectrum pt inclined to the former PT is in like manner composed of circles lying in a right line; and these circles must be of the same bigness with the former, because the breadths of all the spectrums Y, PT, and pt at equal distances from the prisms are equal.

I considered, further, that by the breadth of the hole F through which the light enters into the dark chamber, there is a penumbra made in the circuit of the spectrum Y, and that penumbra remains in the rectilinear sides of the spectrums PT and *pt*. I placed, therefore, at that hole a lens or object-glass of a telescope which might cast the image of the Sun distinctly on Y without any penumbra at all, and found that the penumbra of the rectilinear sides of the oblong spectrums PT and *pt* was also thereby taken away, so that those sides appeared as distinctly defined as did the circumference of the first image Y. Thus it happens if the glass of the prisms be free from veins, and their sides be accurately plane and well polished without those numberless waves or curls which usually arise from sand-holes a little smoothed in polishing with putty. If the glass be only well polished and free from veins, and the sides not accurately plane, but a little convex or concave, as it frequently happens; yet may the three spectrums Y, PT, and *pt* want penumbras, but not in equal distances from the prisms. Now, from this want of penumbras I knew more certainly that every one of the circles was refracted according to some most regular, uniform, and constant law. For if there were any irregularity in the refraction, the right lines AE and GL, which all the circles in the spectrum PT do touch, could not by that refraction be translated into the lines *ae* and *gl* as distinct and straight as they were before, but there would arise in those translated lines some penumbra or crookedness or undulation, or other sensible perturbation contrary to what is found by experience. Whatsoever penumbra or perturbation should be made in the circles by the cross refraction of the second prism, all that penumbra or perturbation would be conspicuous in the right lines *ae* and *gl* which touch those circles. And, therefore, since there is no such penumbra or perturbation in those right lines, there must be none in the circles. Since the distance between those tangents or breadth of the spectrum is not increased by the refractions, the diameters of the circles are not increased thereby. Since those tangents continue to be right lines, every circle which in the first prism is more or less refracted is exactly in the same proportion more or less refracted in the second. And seeing all these things continue to succeed after the same manner when the rays are again in a third prism, and again in a fourth refracted sideways, it is evident that the rays of one and the same circle, as to their degree of refrangibility, continue always uniform and homogeneal to one another, and that those of several circles do differ in degree of refrangibility, and that in some certain and constant proportion. Which is the thing I was to prove.

There is yet another circumstance or two of this experiment by which it becomes still more plain and convincing. Let the second prism DH [Fig. 16] be placed not immediately after the first, but at some distance from it; suppose

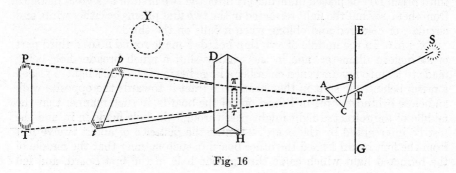

Fig. 16

in the mid-way between it and the wall on which the oblong spectrum PT is cast, so that the light from the first prism may fall upon it in the form of an oblong spectrum ππ parallel to this second prism, and be refracted sideways to form the oblong spectrum pt upon the wall. And you will find, as before, that this spectrum pt is inclined to that spectrum PT, which the first prism forms alone without the second; the blue ends P and p being farther distant from one another than the red ones T and t, and by consequence that the rays which go to the blue end π of the image ππ, and which therefore suffer the greatest refraction in the first prism, are again in the second prism more refracted than the rest.

The same thing I tried also by letting the Sun's light into a dark room through two little round holes F and φ [Fig. 17] made in the window, and with two parallel prisms ABC and αβγ placed at those holes (one at each) refracting

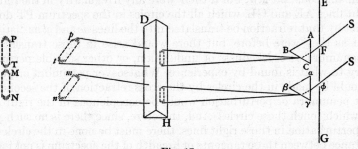

Fig. 17

those two beams of light to the opposite wall of the chamber, in such manner that the two coloured images PT and MN which they there painted were joined end to end and lay in one straight line, the red end T of the one touching the blue end M of the other. For if these two refracted beams were again by a third prism DH placed cross to the two first, refracted sideways, and the spectrums thereby translated to some other part of the wall of the chamber, suppose the spectrum PT to pt and the spectrum MN to mn, these translated spectrums pt and mn would not lie in one straight line with their ends contiguous as before, but be broken off from one another and become parallel, the blue end m of the image mn being by a greater refraction translated farther from its former place MT, than the red end t of the other image pt from the same place MT; which puts the Proposition past dispute. And this happens whether the third prism DH be placed immediately after the two first, or at a great distance from them, so that the light refracted in the two first prisms be either white and circular, or coloured and oblong when it falls on the third.

EXPER. 6. In the middle of two thin boards I made round holes a third part of an inch in diameter, and in the window-shut a much broader hole being made to let into my darkened chamber a large beam of the Sun's light, I placed a prism behind the shut in that beam to refract it towards the opposite wall, and close behind the prism I fixed one of the boards, in such manner that the middle of the refracted light might pass through the hole made in it, and the rest be intercepted by the board. Then at the distance of about twelve feet from the first board I fixed the other board in such manner that the middle of the refracted light which came through the hole in the first board, and fell upon the opposite wall, might pass through the hole in this other board, and the rest being intercepted by the board might paint upon it the coloured spectrum of the Sun. And close behind this board I fixed another prism to refract the light which came through the hole. Then I returned speedily to the first prism, and by turning it slowly to and fro about its axis, I caused the image which fell upon the second board to move up and down upon that board, that all its parts might successively pass through the hole in that board and fall upon the prism behind it. And in the meantime I noted the places on the opposite wall to which that light after its refraction in the second prism did pass; and by the difference of the places I found that the light which being most refracted in the first prism did go the the blue end of the image, was again more refracted in the second prism than the light which went to the red end of that image, which proves as well the first Proposition as the second. And this happened whether the axis of the two prisms were parallel, or inclined to one another, and to the horizon in any given angles.

ILLUSTRATION. Let F [Fig. 18] be the wide hole in the window-shut, through which the Sun shines upon the first prism ABC, and let the refracted light fall

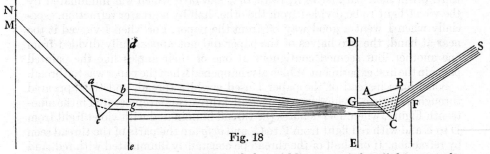

Fig. 18

upon the middle of the board DE, and the middle part of that light upon the hole G made in the middle part of that board. Let this trajected part of that light fall again upon the middle of the second board de, and there paint such an oblong coloured image of the Sun as was described in the third experiment. By turning the prism ABC slowly to and fro about its axis, this image will be made to move up and down the board de, and by this means all its parts from one end to the other may be made to pass successively through the hole g which is made in the middle of that board. In the meanwhile, another prism abc is to be fixed next after that hole g, to refract the trajected light a second time. And these things being thus ordered, I marked the places M and N of the opposite wall upon which the refracted light fell, and found that whilst the two boards and second prism remained unmoved, those places, by turning the first prism about its axis, were changed perpetually. For when the lower part of the light which fell upon the second board de was cast through the hole g, it went to a lower place M on the wall, and when the higher part of that light was cast through the same hole g, it went to a higher place N on the wall, and when any intermediate part of the light was cast through that hole, it went to some place on the wall between M and N. The unchanged position of the holes in the boards made the incidence of the rays upon the second prism to be the same in all cases. And yet in that common incidence some of the rays were more refracted, and others less. And those were more refracted in this prism, which by a greater refraction in the first prism were more turned out of the way, and, therefore, for their constancy of being more refracted are deservedly called more refrangible.

EXPER. 7. At two holes made near one another in my window-shut I placed two prisms, one at each, which might cast upon the opposite wall (after the manner of the third experiment) two oblong coloured images of the Sun. And at a little distance from the wall I placed a long slender paper with straight and parallel edges, and ordered the prisms and paper so that the red colour of one image might fall directly upon one half of the paper, and the violet colour of the other image upon the other half of the same paper; so that the paper appeared of two colours, red and violet, much after the manner of the painted paper in the first and second experiments. Then with a black cloth I covered the wall behind the paper, that no light might be reflected from it to disturb the experiment, and viewing the paper through a third prism held parallel to it, I saw that half of it which was illuminated by the violet light to be divided from the other half by a greater refraction, especially when I went a good way off from the paper. For when I viewed it too near at hand, the two halves of the paper did not appear fully divided from one another, but seemed contiguous at one of their angles like the painted paper in the first experiment. Which also happened when the paper was too broad.

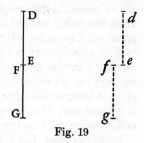

Fig. 19

Sometimes instead of the paper I used a white thread, and this appeared through the prism divided into two parallel threads as is represented in the nineteenth Figure, where DG denotes the thread illuminated with violet light from D to E and with red light from F to G, and *defg* are the parts of the thread seen by refraction. If one half of the thread be constantly illuminated with red, and the other half be illuminated with all the colours successively (which may be done by causing one of the prisms to be turned about its axis whilst the other remains unmoved), this other half, in viewing the thread through the prism, will appear in a continual right line with the first half when illuminated with red, and begin to be a little divided from it when illuminated with orange, and remove farther from it when illuminated with yellow, and still farther when with green, and farther when with blue, and go yet farther off when illuminated with indigo, and farthest when with deep violet. Which plainly shews that the lights of several colours are more and more refrangible one than another, in this order of their colours: red, orange, yellow, green, blue, indigo, deep violet; and so proves as well the first Proposition as the second.

I caused also the coloured spectrums PT [Fig. 17] and MN made in a dark chamber by the refractions of two prisms to lie in a right line end to end, as was described above in the fifth experiment, and viewing them through a third prism held parallel to their length, they appeared no longer in a right line, but became broken from one another, as they are represented at *pt* and *mn*, the violet end *m* of the spectrum *mn* being by a greater refraction translated farther from its former place MT than the red end *t* of the other spectrum *pt*.

I further caused those two spectrums PT [Fig. 20] and MN to become coincident in an inverted order of their colours, the red end of each falling on the violet end of the other, as they are represented in the oblong figure PTMN;

and then viewing them through a prism DH held parallel to their length, they
appeared not co-incident, as when viewed with the naked eye, but in the form

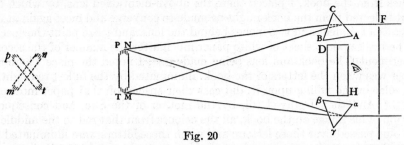

Fig. 20

of two distinct spectrums *pt* and *mn* crossing one another in the middle after
the manner of the letter X. Which shews that the red of the one spectrum and
violet of the other, which were co-incident at PN and MT, being parted from
one another by a greater refraction of the violet to *p* and *m* than of the red to
n and *t*, do differ in degrees of refrangibility.

I illuminated also a little circular piece of white paper all over with the
lights of both prisms intermixed, and when it was illuminated with the red of
one spectrum, and deep violet of the other, so as by the mixture of those
colours to appear all over purple, I viewed the paper, first at a less distance,
and then at a greater, through a third prism; and as I went from the paper, the
refracted image thereof became more and more divided by the unequal refraction of the two mixed colours, and at length parted into two distinct images,
a red one and a violet one, whereof the violet was farthest from the paper, and
therefore suffered the greatest refraction. And when that prism at the window,
which cast the violet on the paper, was taken away, the violet image disappeared; but when the other prism was taken away the red vanished; which
shews that these two images were nothing else than the lights of the two prisms,
which had been intermixed on the purple paper, but were parted again by their
unequal refractions made in the third prism, through which the paper was
viewed. This also was observable, that if one of the prisms at the window
(suppose that which cast the violet on the paper) was turned about its axis to
make all the colours, in this order: violet, indigo, blue, green, yellow, orange,
red, fall successively on the paper from that prism, the violet image changed
colour accordingly, turning successively to indigo, blue, green, yellow and red,
and in changing colour came nearer and nearer to the red image made by the
other prism, until when it was also red both images became fully co-incident.

I placed also two paper circles very near one another, the one in the red light
of one prism, and the other in the violet light of the other. The circles were
each of them an inch in diameter, and behind them the wall was dark, that the
experiment might not be disturbed by any light coming from thence. These
circles thus illuminated, I viewed through a prism so held that the refraction
might be made towards the red circle, and as I went from them they came
nearer and nearer together, and at length became co-incident; and afterwards
when I went still farther off, they parted again in a contrary order, the violet
by a greater refraction being carried beyond the red.

EXPER. 8. In summer, when the Sun's light uses to be strongest, I placed a
prism at the hole of the window-shut, as in the third experiment, yet so that

its axis might be parallel to the axis of the world, and at the opposite wall in the Sun's refracted light, I placed an open book. Then going six feet and two inches from the book, I placed there the above-mentioned lens, by which the light reflected from the book might be made to converge and meet again at the distance of six feet and two inches behind the lens, and there paint the species of the book upon a sheet of white paper much after the manner of the second experiment. The book and lens being made fast, I noted the place where the paper was when the letters of the book, illuminated by the fullest red light of the solar image falling upon it, did cast their species on that paper most distinctly. And then I stayed till, by the motion of the Sun, and consequent motion of his image on the book, all the colours from that red to the middle of the blue passed over those letters; and when those letters were illuminated by that blue, I noted again the place of the paper when they cast their species most distinctly upon it: And I found that this last place of the paper was nearer to the lens than its former place by about two inches and a half, or two and three quarters. So much sooner, therefore, did the light in the violet end of the image by a greater refraction converge and meet, than the light in the red end. But in trying this, the chamber was as dark as I could make it. For, if these colours be diluted and weakened by the mixture of any adventitious light, the distance between the places of the paper will not be so great. This distance in the second experiment, where the colours of natural bodies were made use of, was but an inch and a half, by reason of the imperfection of those colours. Here in the colours of the prism, which are manifestly more full, intense, and lively than those of natural bodies, the distance is two inches and three quarters. And were the colours still more full, I question not but that the distance would be considerably greater. For the coloured light of the prism, by the interfering of the circles described in the second figure of the fifth experiment [Fig. 15], and also by the light of the very bright clouds next the Sun's body intermixing with these colours, and by the light scattered by the inequalities in the polish of the prism, was so very much compounded, that the species which those faint and dark colours, the indigo and violet, cast upon the paper were not distinct enough to be well observed.

EXPER. 9. A prism, whose two angles at its base were equal to one another, and half right ones, and the third a right one, I placed in a beam of the Sun's light let into a dark chamber through a hole in the window-shut, as in the third experiment. And turning the prism slowly about its axis, until all the light which went through one of its angles, and was refracted by it began to be reflected by its base, at which till then it went out of the glass, I observed that those rays which had suffered the greatest refraction were sooner reflected than the rest. I conceived, therefore, that those rays of the reflected light, which were most refrangible, did first of all by a total reflexion become more copious in that light than the rest, and that afterwards the rest also, by a total reflexion, became as copious as these. To try this, I made the reflected light pass through another prism, and being refracted by it to fall afterwards upon a sheet of white paper placed at some distance behind it, and there by that refraction to paint the usual colours of the prism. And then causing the first prism to be turned about its axis as above, I observed that when those rays, which in this prism had suffered the greatest refraction, and appeared of a blue and violet colour, began to be totally reflected, the blue and violet light on the paper, which was most refracted in the second prism, received a sensible increase above that of the red and yellow, which was least refracted; and afterwards, when the rest of the light which was green, yellow, and red, began to be totally reflected in the first prism, the light of those colours on the paper received as great an increase as the violet and blue had done before. Whence 'tis manifest that the beam of light reflected by the base of the prism, being augmented first by the more refrangible rays, and afterwards by the less refrangible ones, is compounded of rays differently refrangible. And that all such reflected light is of the same nature with the Sun's light before its incidence on the base of the prism, no man ever doubted; it being generally allowed that light by such reflexions suffers no alteration in its modifications and properties. I do not here take notice of any refractions made in the sides of the first prism, because the light enters it perpendicularly at the first side, and goes out perpendicularly at the second side, and therefore suffers none. So then, the Sun's incident light being of the same temper and constitution with his emergent light, and the last being compounded of rays differently refrangible, the first must be in like manner compounded.

ILLUSTRATION. In the twenty-first Figure, ABC is the first prism, BC its base, B and C its equal angles at the base, each of 45 degrees, A its rectangular

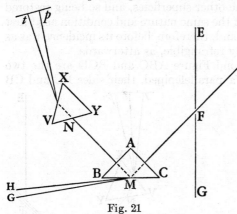

Fig. 21

vertex, FM a beam of the Sun's light let into a dark room through a hole F one third part of an inch broad, M its incidence on the base of the prism, MG a less refracted ray, MH a more refracted ray, MN the beam of light reflected from the base, VXY the second prism by which this beam in passing through it is refracted, Nt the less refracted light of this beam, and Np the more refracted part thereof. When the first prism ABC is turned about its axis according to the order of the letters ABC,

the rays MH emerge more and more obliquely out of that prism, and at length after their most oblique emergence are reflected towards N, and going on to p do increase the number of the rays Np. Afterwards, by continuing the motion of the first prism, the rays MG are also reflected to N and increase the number of the rays Nt. And, therefore, the light MN admits into its composition, first the more refrangible rays, and then the less refrangible rays, and yet after this composition is of the same nature with the Sun's immediate light FM, the reflexion of the specular base BC causing no alteration therein.

EXPER. 10. Two prisms, which were alike in shape, I tied so together that, their axis and opposite sides being parallel, they composed a parallelepiped. And, the Sun shining into my dark chamber through a little hole in the window-shut, I placed that parallelepiped in his beam at some distance from the hole, in such a posture that the axes of the prisms might be perpendicular to the incident rays, and that those rays, being incident upon the first side of one prism, might go on through the two contiguous sides of both prisms, and emerge out of the last side of the second prism. This side, being parallel to the first side of the first prism, caused the emerging light to be parallel to the incident. Then, beyond these two prisms I placed a third, which might refract that emergent light, and by that refraction cast the usual colours of the prism upon the opposite wall, or upon a sheet of white paper held at a convenient distance behind the prism for that refracted light to fall upon it. After this I turned the parallelopiped about its axis, and found that when the contiguous sides of the two prisms became so oblique to the incident rays that those rays began all of them to be reflected, those rays which in the third prism had suffered the greatest refraction, and painted the paper with violet and blue, were first of all by a total reflexion taken out of the transmitted light, the rest remaining and on the paper painting their colours of green, yellow, orange and red, as before; and afterwards by continuing the motion of the two prisms, the rest of the rays also by a total reflexion vanished in order, according to their degrees of refrangibility. The light, therefore, which emerged out of the two prisms is compounded of rays differently refrangible, seeing the more refrangible rays may be taken out of it, while the less refrangible remain. But this light being trajected only through the parallel superficies of the two prisms, if it suffered any change by the refraction of one superficies it lost that impression by the contrary refraction of the other superficies, and so being restored to its pristine constitution, became of the same nature and condition as at first before its incidence on those prisms; and, therefore, before its incidence was as much compounded of rays differently refrangible, as afterwards.

ILLUSTRATION. In the twenty-second Figure ABC and BCD are the two prisms tied together in the form of a parallelepiped, their sides BC and CB being contiguous, and their sides AB and CD parallel. And HJK is the third prism, by which the Sun's light propagated through the hole F into the dark chamber, and there passing through those sides of the prisms AB, BC, CB and CD, is refracted at O to the white paper PT, falling there partly upon P by a greater refraction, partly upon T by a less refraction, and partly upon R and other intermediate places by intermediate refractions. By turning the parallelepiped ACBD about its axis, according to the order of the letters A, C, D, B, at length when the contiguous planes BC and CB become sufficiently oblique

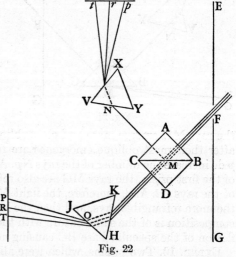

Fig. 22

to the rays FM, which are incident upon them at M, there will vanish totally out of the refracted light OPT, first of all the most refracted rays OP (the rest OR and OT remaining as before), then the rays OR and other intermediate ones, and, lastly, the least refracted rays OT. For when the plane BC becomes sufficiently oblique to the rays incident upon it, those rays will begin to be totally reflected by it towards N; and first the most refrangible rays will be totally reflected (as was explained in the preceding experiment) and by consequence must first disappear at P, and afterwards the rest as they are in order totally reflected to N, they must disappear in the same order at R and T. So then the rays, which at O suffer the greatest refraction, may be taken out of the light MO whilst the rest of the rays remain in it, and therefore that light MO is compounded of rays differently refrangible. And because the planes AB and CD are parallel, and, therefore, by equal and contrary refractions destroy one another's effects, the incident light FM must be of the same kind and nature with the emergent light MO, and therefore doth also consist of rays differently refrangible. These two lights FM and MO, before the most refrangible rays are separated out of the emergent light MO, agree in colour and in all other properties so far as my observation reaches, and, therefore, are deservedly reputed of the same nature and constitution, and by consequence the one is compounded as well as the other. But after the most refrangible rays begin to be totally reflected, and thereby separated out of the emergent light MO, that light changes its colour from white to a dilute and faint yellow, a pretty good orange, a very full red successively, and then totally vanishes. For after the most refrangible rays, which paint the paper at P with a purple colour, are by a total reflexion taken out of the beam of light MO, the rest of the colours which appear on the paper at R and T being mixed in the light MO compound there a faint yellow, and after the blue and part of the green which appear on the paper between P and R are taken away, the rest which appear between R and T (that is, the yellow, orange, red and a little green) being mixed in the beam MO compound there an orange; and when all the rays are by reflexion taken out of the beam MO, except the least refrangible, which at T appear of a full red, their colour is the same in that beam MO as afterwards at T, the refraction of the prism HJK serving only to separate the differently refrangible rays, without making any alteration in their colours, as shall be more fully proved hereafter. All which confirms as well the first Proposition as the second.

Scholium. If this experiment and the former be conjoined and made one by applying a fourth prism VXY [Fig. 22] to refract the reflected beam MN towards *tp*, the conclusion will be clearer. For then the light N*p*, which in the fourth prism is more refracted, will become fuller and stronger when the light OP, which in the third prism HJK is more refracted, vanishes at P; and afterwards when the less refracted light OT vanishes at T, the less refracted light N*t* will become increased whilst the more refracted light at *p* receives no further increase. And as the trajected beam MO in vanishing is always of such a colour as ought to result from the mixture of the colours which fall upon the paper PT, so is the reflected beam MN always of such a colour as ought to result from the mixture of the colours which fall upon the paper *pt*. For when the most refrangible rays are by a total reflexion taken out of the beam MO, and leave that beam of an orange colour, the excess of those rays in the reflected light does not only make the violet, indigo and blue at *p* more full, but also makes the beam MN change from the yellowish colour of the Sun's light to a pale white inclining to blue, and afterward recover its yellowish colour again, so soon as all the rest of the transmitted light MOT is reflected.

Now, seeing that in all this variety of experiments, whether the trial be made in light reflected, and that either from natural bodies, as in the first and second experiment, or specular, as in the ninth; or in light refracted, and that either before the unequally refracted rays are by diverging separated from one another, and losing their whiteness which they have altogether, appear severally of several colours, as in the fifth experiment; or after they are separated from one another, and appear coloured as in the sixth, seventh, and eighth experiments; or in light trajected through parallel superficies, destroying each other's effects, as in the tenth experiment; there are always found rays, which at equal incidences on the same medium suffer unequal refractions, and that without any splitting or dilating of single rays, or contingence in the inequality of the refractions, as is proved in the fifth and sixth experiments. And seeing the rays which differ in refrangibility may be parted and sorted from one another, and that either by refraction as in the third experiment, or by reflexion as in the tenth, and then the several sorts apart at equal incidences suffer unequal refractions, and those sorts are more refracted than others after separation, which were more refracted before it, as in the sixth and following experiments, and if the Sun's light be trajected through three or more cross prisms successively, those rays which in the first prism are refracted more than others are in all the following prisms refracted more than others in the same rate and proportion, as appears by the fifth experiment; it's manifest that the Sun's light is an heterogeneous mixture of rays, some of which are constantly more refrangible than others, as was proposed.

PROPOSITION 3. THEOREM 3

The Sun's light consists of rays differing in reflexibility, and those rays are more reflexible than others which are more refrangible.

This is manifest by the ninth and tenth experiments: for in the ninth experiment, by turning the prism about its axis until the rays within it, which in going out into the air were refracted by its base, became so oblique to that base as to begin to be totally reflected thereby; those rays became first of all totally reflected, which before at equal incidences with the rest had suffered the greatest refraction. And the same thing happens in the reflexion made by the common base of the two prisms in the tenth experiment.

PROPOSITION 4. PROBLEM 1

To separate from one another the heterogeneous rays of compound light.

The heterogeneous rays are in some measure separated from one another by the refraction of the prism in the third experiment, and in the fifth experiment, by taking away the penumbra from the rectilinear sides of the coloured image, that separation in those very rectilinear sides or straight edges of the image becomes perfect. But in all places between those rectilinear edges, those innumerable circles there described, which are severally illuminated by homogeneal rays, by interfering with one another, and being everywhere commixed, do render the light sufficiently compound. But if these circles, whilst their centres keep their distances and positions, could be made less in diameter, their interfering one with another, and by consequence the mixture of the heterogeneous rays would be proportionally diminished. In the twenty-third Figure let AG, BH, CJ, DK, EL, FM be the circles which so many sorts of rays, flowing from the same disk of the Sun, do in the third experiment illuminate; of all which and innumerable other intermediate ones lying in a continual series between the two rectilinear and parallel edges of the Sun's oblong image

PT, that image is composed, as was explained in the fifth experiment. And let *ag, bh, cj, dk, el, fm* be so many less circles lying in a like continual series between two parallel right lines *af* and *gm* with the same distances between their centres, and illuminated by the same sorts of rays, that is, the circle *ag* with the same sort by which the corresponding circle AG was illuminated, and the

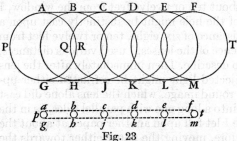

Fig. 23

circle *bh* with the same sort by which the corresponding circle BH was illuminated, and the rest of the circles *cj, dk, el, fm* respectively, with the same sorts of rays by which the several corresponding circles CJ, DK, EL, FM were illuminated. In the figure PT composed of the greater circles, three of those circles AG, BH, CJ, are so

expanded into one another that the three sorts of rays by which those circles are illuminated, together with other innumerable sorts of intermediate rays, are mixed at QR in the middle of the circle BH. And the like mixture happens throughout almost the whole length of the figure PT. But in the figure *pt* composed of the less circles, the three less circles *ag, bh, cj*, which answer to those three greater, do not extend into one another; nor are there anywhere mingled so much as any two of the three sorts of rays by which those circles are illuminated, and which in the figure PT are all of them intermingled at BH.

Now, he that shall thus consider it will easily understand that the mixture is diminished in the same proportion with the diameters of the circles. If the diameters of the circles, whilst their centres remain the same, be made three times less than before, the mixture will be also three times less; if ten times less, the mixture will be ten times less, and so of other proportions. That is, the mixture of the rays in the greater figure PT will be to their mixture in the less *pt* as the latitude of the greater figure is to the latitude of the less. For the latitudes of these figures are equal to the diameters of their circles. And hence it easily follows that the mixture of the rays in the refracted spectrum *pt* is to the mixture of the rays in the direct and immediate light of the Sun as the breadth of that spectrum is to the difference between the length and breadth of the same spectrum.

So, then, if we would diminish the mixture of the rays, we are to diminish the diameters of the circles. Now, these would be diminished if the Sun's diameter to which they answer could be made less than it is, or (which comes to the same purpose) if without doors, at a great distance from the prism towards the sun, some opaque body were placed, with a round hole in the middle of it, to intercept all the Sun's light, excepting so much as coming from the middle of his body could pass through that hole to the prism. For so the circles AG, BH, and the rest would not any longer answer to the whole disk of the Sun, but only to that part of it which could be seen from the prism through that hole, that it is to the apparent magnitude of that hole viewed from the prism. But that these circles may answer more distinctly to that hole, a lens is to be placed by the prism to cast the image of the hole (that is, every one of the circles AG, BH, &c.) distinctly upon the paper at PT, after such a manner, as by a lens placed at a window, the species of objects abroad are cast distinctly upon a paper within the room, and the rectilinear sides of the oblong solar image in the fifth experiment became distinct without any penumbra. If this be done, it will not be necessary to place that hole very far off; no, not beyond the window. And, therefore, instead of that hole, I used the hole in the window-shut, as follows:

EXPER. 11. In the Sun's light let into my darkened chamber through a small round hole in my window-shut, at about ten or twelve feet from the window, I placed a lens, by which the image of the hole might be distinctly cast upon a sheet of white paper, placed at the distance of six, eight, ten or twelve feet from the lens. For, according to the difference of the lenses, I used various distances, which I think not worth the while to describe. Then immediately after the lens I placed a prism, by which the trajected light might be refracted either upwards or sideways, and thereby the round image, which the lens alone did cast upon the paper might be drawn out into a long one with parallel sides, as in the third experiment. This oblong image I let fall upon another paper at about the same distance from the prism as before, moving the paper either towards the prism or from it, until I found the just distance where the rectilinear sides of the image became most distinct. For in this case, the circular images of the hole, which compose that image after the same manner that the circles *ag*, *bh*, *cj*, &c. do the figure *pt* [Fig. 23] were terminated most distinctly without any penumbra, and therefore extended into one another the least that they could, and by consequence the mixture of the heterogeneous rays was now the least of all. By this means I used to form an oblong image (such as is *pt*) [Fig. 23 and 24] of circular images of the hole (such as are *ag*, *bh*, *cj*, &c.), and by using a greater or less hole in the window-shut I made the circular images *ag*, *bh*, *cj*, &c. of which it was formed to become greater or less at pleasure, and thereby the mixture of the rays in the image *pt* to be as much, or as little, as I desired.

ILLUSTRATION. In the twenty-fourth Figure, F represents the circular hole in the window-shut, MN the lens, whereby the image or species of that hole is

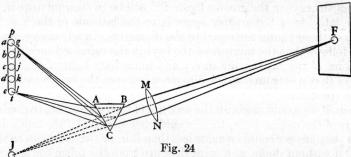

Fig. 24

cast distinctly upon a paper at J, ABC the prism, whereby the rays are at their emerging out of the lens refracted from J towards another paper at *pt*, and the round image at J is turned into an oblong image *pt* falling on that other paper. This image *pt* consists of circles placed one after another in a rectilinear order, as was sufficiently explained in the fifth experiment; and these circles are equal to the circle J, and consequently answer in magnitude to the hole F; and, therefore, by diminishing that hole they may be at pleasure diminished, whilst their centres remain in their places. By this means I made the breadth of the image *pt* to be forty times, and sometimes sixty or seventy times, less than its length. As, for instance, if the breadth of the hole F be one tenth of an inch, and MF

the distance of the lens from the hole be 12 feet; and if pB or pM the distance
of the image pt from the prism or lens be 10 feet, and the refracting angle of the
prism be 62 degrees, the breadth of the image pt will be one-twelfth of an inch,
and the length about six inches, and therefore the length to the breadth as 72
to 1, and by consequence the light of this image 71 times less compound than
the Sun's direct light. And light thus far simple and homogeneal is sufficient for
trying all the experiments in this book about simple light. For the composition
of heterogeneal rays is in this light so little that it is scarce to be discovered and
perceived by sense, except perhaps in the indigo and violet. For these being
dark colours do easily suffer a sensible allay by that little scattering light which
uses to be refracted irregularly by the inequalities of the prism.

Yet instead of the circular hole F, 'tis better to substitute an oblong hole
shaped like a long parallelogram with its length parallel to the prism ABC. For
if this hole be an inch or two long, and but a tenth or twentieth part of an inch
broad, or narrower, the light of the image pt will be as simple as before, or
simpler, and the image will become much broader, and therefore more fit to
have experiments tried in its light than before.

Instead of this parallelogram hole may be substituted a triangular one of
equal sides, whose base, for instance, is about the tenth part of an inch, and its
height an inch or more. For by this means, if the axis of the prism be parallel to
the perpendicular of the triangle, the image pt [Fig. 25] will now be formed of
equicrural triangles ag, bh, cj, dk, el, fm, &c. and innumerable other intermediate ones answering to the triangular hole in shape and bigness, and lying
one after another in a continual series between two parallel lines af and gm.

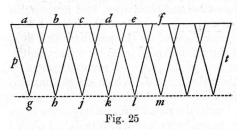

Fig. 25

These triangles are a little intermingled at their bases, but not at their
vertices; and, therefore, the light on
the brighter side af of the image,
where the bases of the triangles are,
is a little compounded, but on the
darker side gm is altogether uncompounded, and in all places between
the sides the composition is propor-
tional to the distances of the places from that obscurer side gm. And having
a spectrum pt of such a composition, we may try experiments either in its
stronger and less simple light near the side af, or in its weaker and simpler light
near the other side gm, as it shall seem most convenient.

But in making experiments of this kind the chamber ought to be made as
dark as can be, lest any foreign light mingle itself with the light of the spectrum
pt, and render it compound; especially if we would try experiments in the more
simple light next the side gm of the spectrum; which being fainter, will have a
less proportion to the foreign light; and so by the mixture of that light be more
troubled, and made more compound. The lens also ought to be good, such as
may serve for optical uses, and the prism ought to have a large angle, suppose
of 65 or 70 degrees, and to be well wrought, being made of glass free from
bubbles and veins, with its sides not a little convex or concave, as usually
happens, but truly plane, and its polish elaborate, as in working optic-glasses,
and not such as is usually wrought with putty, whereby the edges of the sand-
holes being worn away, there are left all over the glass a numberless company

of very little convex polite risings like waves. The edges also of the prism and lens, so far as they may make any irregular refraction, must be covered with a black paper glued on. And all the light of the Sun's beam let into the chamber, which is useless and unprofitable to the experiment, ought to be intercepted with black paper, or other black obstacles. For otherwise the useless light, being reflected every way in the chamber, will mix with the oblong spectrum, and help to disturb it. In trying these things, so much diligence is not altogether necessary, but it will promote the success of the experiments, and by a very scrupulous examiner of things deserves to be applied. It's difficult to get glass prisms fit for this purpose, and, therefore, I used sometimes prismatic vessels made with pieces of broken looking-glasses, and filled with rain water. And to increase the refraction, I sometimes impregnated the water strongly with *saccharum saturni*.

PROPOSITION 5. THEOREM 4

Homogeneal light is refracted regularly without any dilatation splitting or shattering of the rays, and the confused vision of objects seen through refracting bodies by heterogeneal light arises from the different refrangibility of several sorts of rays

The first part of this Proposition has been already sufficiently proved in the fifth experiment, and will further appear by the experiments which follow.

EXPER. 12. In the middle of a black paper I made a round hole about a fifth or sixth part of an inch in diameter. Upon this paper I caused the spectrum of homogeneal light, described in the former Proposition, so to fall that some part of the light might pass through the hole of the paper. This transmitted part of the light I refracted with a prism placed behind the paper, and letting this refracted light fall perpendicularly upon a white paper two or three feet distant from the prism, I found that the spectrum formed on the paper by this light was not oblong, as when 'tis made (in the third experiment) by refracting the Sun's compound light, but was (so far as I could judge by my eye) perfectly circular, the length being no greater than the breadth. Which shews that this light is refracted regularly without any dilatation of the rays.

EXPER. 13. In the homogeneal light I placed a paper circle of a quarter of an inch in diameter, and in the Sun's unrefracted heterogeneal white light I placed another paper circle of the same bigness. And going from the papers to the distance of some feet, I viewed both circles through a prism. The circle illuminated by the Sun's heterogeneal light appeared very oblong, as in the fourth experiment, the length being many times greater than the breadth; but the other circle, illuminated with homogeneal light, appeared circular and distinctly defined, as when 'tis viewed with the naked eye. Which proves the whole Proposition.

EXPER. 14. In the homogeneal light I placed flies, and such-like minute objects, and viewing them through a prism, I saw their parts as distinctly defined as if I had viewed them with the naked eye. The same objects placed in the Sun's unrefracted heterogeneal light, which was white, I viewed also through a prism, and saw them most confusedly defined, so that I could not distinguish their smaller parts from one another. I placed also the letters of a small print, one while in the homogeneal light, and then in the heterogeneal, and viewing them through a prism, they appeared in the latter case so confused and indistinct that I could not read them; but, in the former, they appeared so distinct that I could read readily, and thought I saw them as distinct, as when I viewed them with my naked eye. In both cases I viewed the same objects through the same prism at the same distance from me, and in the same situation. There was no difference but in the light by which the objects were illuminated, and which in one case was simple, and in the other compound; and, therefore, the distinct vision in the former case, and confused in the latter, could arise from nothing else than from that difference of the lights. Which proves the whole Proposition.

And in these three experiments it is further very remarkable that the colour of homogeneal light was never changed by the refraction.

PROPOSITION 6. THEOREM 5

The sine of incidence of every ray considered apart, is to its sine of refraction in a given ratio.

That every ray, considered apart, is constant to itself in some degree of refrangibility is sufficiently manifest out of what has been said. Those rays, which in the first refraction are at equal incidences most refracted, are also in the following refractions at equal incidences most refracted; and so of the least refrangible, and the rest which have any mean degree of refrangibility, as is manifest by the fifth, sixth, seventh, eighth, and ninth experiments. And those which the first time at like incidences are equally refracted, are again at like incidences equally and uniformly refracted, and that whether they be refracted before they be separated from one another, as in the fifth experiment, or whether they be refracted apart, as in the twelfth, thirteenth and fourteenth experiments. The refraction, therefore, of every ray apart is regular, and what rule that refraction observes we are now to shew.

The late writers in Optics teach that the sines of incidence are in a given proportion to the sines of refraction, as was explained in the fifth Axiom; and some by instruments fitted for measuring of refractions, or otherwise experimentally examining this proportion, do acquaint us that they have found it accurate. But whilst they, not understanding the different refrangibility of several rays, conceived them all to be refracted according to one and the same proportion, 'tis to be presumed that they adapted their measures only to the middle of the refracted light; so that from their measures we may conclude only that the rays which have a mean degree of refrangibility (that is, those which when separated from the rest appear green) are refracted according to a given proportion of their sines. And, therefore, we are now to shew that the like given proportions obtain in all the rest. That it should be so is very reasonable, Nature being ever conformable to herself; but an experimental proof is desired. And such a proof will be had if we can shew that the sines of refraction of rays differently refrangible are one to another in a given proportion when their sines of incidence are equal. For, if the sines of refraction of all the rays are in given proportions to the sine of refractions of a ray which has a mean degree of refrangibility, and this sine is in a given proportion to the equal sines of incidence, those other sines of refraction will also be in given proportions to the equal sines of incidence. Now, when the sines of incidence are equal, it will appear by the following experiment that the sines of refraction are in a given proportion to one another.

EXPER. 15. The Sun shining into a dark chamber through a little round hole in the window-shut; let S [Fig. 26] represent his round white image painted on the opposite wall by his direct light, PT his oblong coloured image made by refracting that light with a prism placed at the window; and *pt*, or *2p 2t*, *3p 3t*, his oblong coloured image made by refracting again the same light sideways with a second prism placed immediately after the first in a cross position to it, as was explained in the fifth experiment; that is to say, *pt* when the refraction of the second prism is small, *2p 2t* when its refraction is greater, and *3p 3t* when it is greatest. For such will be the diversity of the refractions, if the refracting angle of the second prism be of various magnitudes; suppose of fifteen or twenty degrees to make the image *pt*, of thirty or forty to make the image *2p 2t*, and of sixty to make the image *3p 3t*. But, for want of solid glass prisms with angles of convenient bignesses, there may be vessels made of polished plates of glass cemented together in the form of prisms and filled with water. These things being thus ordered, I observed that all the solar images or coloured spectrums PT, *pt*, *2p 2t*, *3p 3t* did very nearly converge to the place S on which

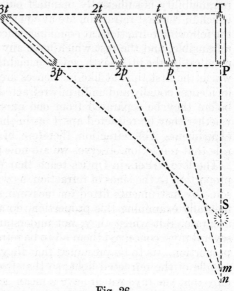

the direct light of the Sun fell and painted his white round image when the prisms were taken away. The axis of the spectrum PT (that is, the line drawn through the middle of it parallel to its rectilinear sides) did, when produced, pass exactly through the middle of that white round image S. And when the refraction of the second prism was equal to the refraction of the first, the refracting angles of them both being about 60 degrees, the axis of the spectrum *3p 3t* made by that refraction, did when produced pass also through the middle of the same white round image S. But when the refraction of the second prism was less than that of the first, the produced axes of the spectrums *tp* or *2t 2p*

Fig. 26

made by that refraction did cut the produced axis of the spectrum TP in the points *m* and *n*, a little beyond the centre of that white round image S. Whence the proportion of the line *3t*T to the line *3p*P was a little greater than the proportion of *2t*T or *2p*P, and this proportion a little greater than that of *t*T to *p*P. Now, when the light of the spectrum PT falls perpendicularly upon the wall, those lines *3t*T, *3p*P, and *2t*T, *2p*P, and *t*T, *p*P, are the tangents of the refractions, and, therefore, by this experiment the proportions of the tangents of the refractions are obtained, from whence the proportions of the sines being derived, they come out equal, so far as by viewing the spectrums, and using some mathematical reasoning, I could estimate. For I did not make an accurate computation. So then the proposition holds true in every ray apart, so far as appears by experiment. And that it is accurately true may be demonstrated upon this supposition: *That bodies refract light by acting upon its rays in lines* *perpendicular to their surfaces.* But in order to this demonstration, I must distinguish the motion of every ray into two motions, the one perpendicular to the refracting surface, the other parallel to it, and concerning the perpendicular motion lay down the following Proposition:

If any motion or moving thing whatsoever be incident with any velocity on any broad and thin space terminated on both sides by two parallel planes, and in its passage through that space be urged perpendicularly towards the farther plane by any force which at given distances from the plane is of given quantities, the perpendicular velocity of that motion or thing, at its emerging out of that space, shall be always equal to the square root of the sum of the square of the perpendicular velocity of that motion or thing at its incidence on that space; and of the square of the perpendicular velocity which that motion or thing would have at its emergence, if at its incidence its perpendicular velocity was infinitely little.

And the same proposition holds true of any motion or thing perpendicularly retarded in its passage through that space, if instead of the sum of the two squares you take their difference. The demonstration mathematicians will easily find out, and therefore I shall not trouble the reader with it.

Suppose now that a ray coming most obliquely in the line MC [Fig. 1] be refracted at C by the plane RS into the line CN, and if it be required to find the line CE, into which any other ray AC shall be refracted; let MC, AD, be the sines of incidence of the two rays, and NG, EF, their sines of refraction, and let the equal motions of the incident rays be represented by the equal lines MC and AC, and the motion MC being considered as parallel to the refracting plane, let the other motion AC be distinguished into two motions AD and DC, one of which AD is parallel, and the other DC perpendicular to the refracting surface. In like manner, let the motions of the emerging rays be distinguished into two, whereof the perpendicular ones are $\dfrac{MC}{NG}$ CG and $\dfrac{AD}{EF}$ CF. And if the force of the refracting plane begins to act upon the rays either in that plane or at a certain distance from it on the one side, and ends at a certain distance from it on the other side, and in all places between those two limits acts upon the rays in lines perpendicular to that refracting plane, and the actions upon the rays at equal distances from the refracting plane be equal, and at unequal ones either equal or unequal according to any rate whatever; that motion of the ray which is parallel to the refracting plane, will suffer no alteration by that force; and that motion which is perpendicular to it will be altered according to the rule of the foregoing proposition. If, therefore, for the perpendicular velocity of the emerging ray CN you write $\dfrac{MC}{NG}$ CG as above, then the perpendicular velocity of any other emerging ray CE which was $\dfrac{AD}{EF}$ CF, will be equal to the square root of $CDq + \dfrac{MCq}{NGq}$ CGq. And by squaring these equals, and adding to them the equals ADq and MCq − CDq, and dividing the sums by the equals CFq + EFq and CGq + NGq, you will have $\dfrac{MCq}{NGq}$ equal to $\dfrac{MCq}{NGq}$. Whence AD, the sine of incidence, is to EF the sine of refraction, as MC to NG, that is, in a given ratio. And this demonstration being general, without determining what light is, or by what kind of force it is refracted, or assuming any thing further than that the refracting body acts upon the rays in lines perpendicular to its surface; I take it to be a very convincing argument of the full truth of this Proposition.

So then, if the ratio of the sines of incidence and refraction of any sort of rays be found in any one case, 'tis given in all cases; and this may be readily found by the method in the following Proposition.

PROPOSITION 7. THEOREM 6

The perfection of telescopes is impeded by the different refrangibility of the rays of light.

The imperfection of telescopes is vulgarly attributed to the spherical figures of the glasses, and, therefore, mathematicians have propounded to figure them by the conical sections. To shew that they are mistaken, I have inserted this proposition; the truth of which will appear by the measure of the refractions of the several sorts of rays; and these measures I thus determine.

In the third experiment of this first part, where the refracting angle of the prism was 62½ degrees, the half of that angle 31 degrees 15 minutes is the angle of incidence of the rays at their going out of the glass into the air; and the sine of this angle is 5,188, the radius being 10,000. When the axis of this prism was parallel to the horizon, and the refraction of the rays at their incidence on this prism equal to that at their emergence out of it, I observed with a quadrant the angle which the mean refrangible rays, (that is, those which went to the middle of the Sun's coloured image) made with the horizon, and by this angle and the Sun's altitude observed at the same time, I found the angle which the emergent rays contained with the incident to be 44 degrees and 40 minutes and the half of this angle added to the angle of incidence 31 degrees 15 minutes makes the angle of refraction, which is, therefore, 53 degrees 35 minutes and its sine 8,047. These are the sines of incidence and refraction of the mean refrangible rays, and their proportion in round numbers is 20 to 31. This glass was of a colour inclining to green. The last of the prisms mentioned in the third experiment was of clear white glass; its refracting angle 63½ degrees; the angle which the emergent rays contained, with the incident 45 degrees 50 minutes; the sine of half the first angle 5,262; the sine of half the sum of the angles 8,157; and their proportion in round numbers 20 to 31, as before.

From the length of the image, which was about 9¾ or 10 inches, subduct its breadth, which was 2⅛ inches, and the remainder 7¾ inches would be the length of the image were the Sun but a point, and therefore subtends the angle which the most and least refrangible rays, when incident on the prism in the same lines, do contain with one another after their emergence. Whence this angle is 2 degrees 0′ 7″. For the distance between the image and the prism where this angle is made was 18½ feet, and at that distance the chord 7¾ inches subtends an angle of 2 degrees 0′ 7″. Now, half this angle is the angle which these emergent rays contain with the emergent mean refrangible rays, and a quarter thereof (that is, 30′ 2″) may be accounted the angle which they would contain with the same emergent mean refrangible rays, were they coincident to them within the glass, and suffered no other refraction than that at their emergence. For, if two equal refractions, the one at the incidence of the rays on the prism, the other at their emergence, make half the angle 2 degrees

0′ 7″, then one of those refractions will make about a quarter of that angle, and this quarter added to and subducted from the angle of refraction of the mean refrangible rays, which was 53 degrees 35′, gives the angles of refraction of the most and least refrangible rays 54 degrees 5′ 2″, and 53 degrees 4′ 58″, whose sines are 8,099 and 7,995, the common angle of incidence being 31 degrees 15′, and its sine 5,188; and these sines in the least round numbers are in proportion to one another, as 78 and 77 to 50.

Now, if you subduct the common sine of incidence 50 from the sines of refraction 77 and 78, the remainders 27 and 28 shew that in small refractions the refraction of the least refrangible rays is to the refraction of the most refrangible ones as 27 to 28 very nearly, and that the difference of the refractions of the least refrangible and most refrangible rays is about the $27\frac{1}{2}$th part of the whole refraction of the mean refrangible rays.

Whence they that are skilled in Optics will easily understand, that the breadth of the least circular space into which object-glasses of telescopes can collect all sorts of parallel rays, is about the $27\frac{1}{2}$th part of half the aperture of the glass, or 55th part of the whole aperture; and that the focus of the most refrangible rays is nearer to the object-glass than the focus of the least refrangible ones, by about the $27\frac{1}{2}$th part of the distance between the object-glass and the focus of the mean refrangible ones.

And if rays of all sorts, flowing from any one lucid point in the axis of any convex lens, be made by the refraction of the lens to converge to points not too remote from the lens, the focus of the most refrangible rays shall be nearer to the lens than the focus of the least refrangible ones, by a distance which is to the $27\frac{1}{2}$th part of the distance of the focus of the mean refrangible rays from the lens, as the distance between that focus and the lucid point, from whence the rays flow, is to the distance between that lucid point and the lens very nearly.

Now, to examine whether the difference between the refractions, which the most refrangible and the least refrangible rays flowing from the same point suffer in the object-glasses of telescopes and suchlike glasses, be so great as is here described, I contrived the following experiment:

EXPER. 16. The lens which I used in the second and eighth Experiments, being placed six feet and an inch distant from any object, collected the species of that object by the mean refrangible rays at the distance of six feet and an inch from the lens on the other side. And, therefore, by the foregoing rule, it ought to collect the species of that object by the least refrangible rays at the distance of six feet and $3\frac{2}{3}$ inches from the lens, and by the most refrangible ones at the distance of five feet and $10\frac{1}{3}$ inches from it: So that between the two places, where these least and most refrangible rays collect the species, there may be the distance of about $5\frac{1}{3}$ inches. For by that rule, as six feet and an inch (the distance of the lens from the lucid object) is to twelve feet and two inches (the distance of the lucid object from the focus of the mean refrangible rays) that is, as one is to two; so is the $27\frac{1}{2}$th part of six feet and an inch (the distance between the lens and the same focus) to the distance between the focus of the most refrangible rays and the focus of the least refrangible ones, which is, therefore, $5\frac{17}{55}$ inches; that is, very nearly $5\frac{1}{3}$ inches. Now, to know whether this measure was true, I repeated the second and eighth experiment with coloured light, which was less compounded than that I there made use of.

For I now separated the heterogeneous rays from one another by the method I described in the eleventh experiment, so as to make a coloured spectrum about twelve or fifteen times longer than broad. This spectrum I cast on a printed book, and placing the above-mentioned lens at the distance of six feet and an inch from this spectrum to collect the species of the illuminated letters at the same distance on the other side, I found that the species of the letters illuminated with blue were nearer to the lens than those illuminated with deep red by about three inches, or three and a quarter; but the species of the letters illuminated with indigo and violet appeared so confused and indistinct that I could not read them; whereupon, viewing the prism, I found it was full of veins running from one end of the glass to the other; so that the refraction could not be regular. I took another prism, therefore, which was free from veins, and instead of the letters I used two or three parallel black lines a little broader than the strokes of the letters, and casting the colours upon these lines in such manner that the lines ran along the colours from one end of the spectrum to the other, I found that the focus where the indigo, or confine of this colour and violet, cast the species of the black lines most distinctly, to be about four inches, or $4\frac{1}{4}$ nearer to the lens than the focus, where the deepest red cast the species of the same black lines most distinctly. The violet was so faint and dark that I could not discern the species of the lines distinctly by that colour; and, therefore, considering that the prism was made of a dark-coloured glass inclining to green, I took another prism of clear white glass; but the spectrum of colours which this prism made had long white streams of faint light shooting out from both ends of the colours, which made me conclude that something was amiss; and viewing the prism, I found two or three little bubbles in the glass, which refracted the light irregularly. Wherefore I covered that part of the glass with black paper, and letting the light pass through another part of it which was free from such bubbles, the spectrum of colours became free from those irregular streams of light, and was now such as I desired. But still I found the violet so dark and faint that I could scarce see the species of the lines by the violet, and not at all by the deepest part of it, which was next the end of the spectrum. I suspected, therefore, that this faint and dark colour might be allayed by that scattering light which was refracted, and reflected irregularly, partly by some very small bubbles in the glasses, and partly by the inequalities of their polish; which light, tho' it was but little, yet it being of a white colour, might suffice to affect the sense so strongly as to disturb the phenomena of that weak and dark colour, the violet; and, therefore, I tried (as in the 12th, 13th, and 14th experiments) whether the light of this colour did not consist of a sensible mixture of heterogeneous rays, but found it did not. Nor did the refractions cause any other sensible colour than violet to emerge out of this light, as they would have done out of white light, and by consequence out of this violet light had it been sensibly compounded with white light. And, therefore, I concluded that the reason why I could not see the species of the lines distinctly by this colour was only the darkness of this colour and thinness of its light, and its distance from the axis of the lens; I divided, therefore, those parallel black lines into equal parts, by which I might readily know the distances of the colours in the spectrum from one another, and noted the distances of the lens from the foci of such colours, as cast the species of the lines distinctly, and then considered whether the difference of those distances bear such proportion to

$5\frac{1}{3}$ inches, the greatest difference of the distances, which the foci of the deepest red and violet ought to have from the lens, as the distance of the observed colours from one another in the spectrum bear to the greatest distance of the deepest red and violet measured in the rectilinear sides of the spectrum, (that is, to the length of those sides) or excess of the length of the spectrum above its breadth. And my observations were as follows:

When I observed and compared the deepest sensible red, and the colour in the confine of green and blue, which at the rectilinear sides of the spectrum was distant from it half the length of those sides, the focus where the confine of green and blue cast the species of the lines distinctly on the paper was nearer to the lens than the focus, where the red cast those lines distinctly on it by about $2\frac{1}{2}$ or $2\frac{3}{4}$ inches. For sometimes the measures were a little greater, sometimes a little less, but seldom varied from one another above one-third of an inch. For it was very difficult to define the places of the foci, without some little errors. Now, if the colours distant half the length of the image (measured at its rectilinear sides) give $2\frac{1}{2}$ or $2\frac{3}{4}$ difference of the distances of their foci from the lens, then the colours distant the whole length ought to give 5 or $5\frac{1}{2}$ inches difference of those distances.

But here it's to be noted that I could not see the red to the full end of the spectrum, but only to the centre of the semicircle which bounded that end, or a little farther; and, therefore, I compared this red, not with that colour which was exactly in the middle of the spectrum, or confine of green and blue, but with that which verged a little more to the blue than to the green. And as I reckoned the whole length of the colours not to be the whole length of the spectrum, but the length of its rectilinear sides, so completing the semicircular ends into circles, when either of the observed colours fell within those circles, I measured the distance of that colour from the semicircular end of the spectrum, and subducting half this distance from the measured distance of the two colours I took the remainder for their corrected distance; and in these observations set down this corrected distance for the difference of the distances of their foci from the lens. For, as the length of the rectilinear sides of the spectrum would be the whole length of all the colours, were the circles of which (as we shewed) that spectrum consists contracted and reduced to physical points, so in that case this corrected distance would be the real distance of the two observed colours.

When, therefore, I further observed the deepest sensible red, and that blue whose corrected distance from it was $\frac{7}{12}$ parts of the length of the rectilinear sides of the spectrum, the difference of the distances of their foci from the lens was about $3\frac{1}{4}$ inches; and as 7 to 12, so is $3\frac{1}{4}$ to $5\frac{4}{7}$.

When I observed the deepest sensible red, and that indigo whose corrected distance was $\frac{8}{12}$ or $\frac{2}{3}$ of the length of the rectilinear sides of the spectrum, the difference of the distances of their foci from the lens was about $3\frac{2}{3}$ inches; and as 2 to 3, so is $3\frac{2}{3}$ to $5\frac{1}{2}$.

When I observed the deepest sensible red, and that deep indigo whose corrected distance from one another was $\frac{9}{12}$ or $\frac{3}{4}$ of the length of the rectilinear sides of the spectrum, the difference of the distances of their foci from the lens was about 4 inches; and as 3 to 4, so is 4 to $5\frac{1}{3}$.

When I observed the deepest sensible red, and that part of the violet next the indigo, whose corrected distance from the red was $\frac{10}{12}$ or $\frac{5}{6}$ of the length of the rectilinear sides of the spectrum, the difference of the distances of their foci from the lens was about $4\frac{1}{2}$ inches; and as 5 to 6, so is $4\frac{1}{2}$ to $5\frac{2}{5}$. For sometimes, when the lens was advantageously placed, so that its axis respected the blue, and all things else were well ordered, and the Sun shone clear, and I held my eye very near to the paper on which the lens cast the species of the lines, I could see pretty distinctly the species of those lines by that part of the violet which was next the indigo; and sometimes I could see them by above half the violet. For in making these experiments I had observed that the species of those colours only appear distinct which were in or near the axis of the lens; so that if the blue or indigo were in the axis, I could see their species distinctly; and then the red appeared much less distinct than before. Wherefore I contrived to make the spectrum of colours shorter than before, so that both its ends might be nearer to the axis of the lens. And now its length was about $2\frac{1}{2}$ inches, and breadth about $\frac{1}{5}$ or $\frac{1}{6}$ of an inch. Also, instead of the black lines on which the spectrum was cast, I made one black line broader than those, that I might see its species more easily; and this line I divided by short cross lines into equal parts, for measuring the distances of the observed colours. And now I could sometimes see the species of this line with its divisions almost as far as the centre of the semicircular violet end of the spectrum, and made these farther observations:

When I observed the deepest sensible red, and that part of the violet, whose corrected distance from it was about $\frac{8}{9}$ parts of the rectilinear sides of the spectrum, the difference of the distances of the foci of those colours from the lens was one time $4\frac{2}{3}$, another time $4\frac{3}{4}$, another time $4\frac{7}{8}$ inches; and as 8 to 9, so are $4\frac{2}{3}$, $4\frac{3}{4}$, $4\frac{7}{8}$, to $5\frac{1}{4}$, $5\frac{11}{32}$, $5\frac{31}{64}$, respectively.

When I observed the deepest sensible red, and deepest sensible violet, (the corrected distance of which colours, when all things were ordered to the best advantage, and the Sun shone very clear, was about $\frac{11}{12}$ or $\frac{15}{16}$ parts of the length of the rectilinear sides of the coloured spectrum) I found the difference of the distances of their foci from the lens sometimes $4\frac{3}{4}$ sometimes $5\frac{1}{4}$, and for the most part 5 inches or thereabouts; and as 11 to 12, or 15 to 16, so is five inches to $5\frac{5}{11}$ or $5\frac{1}{3}$ inches.

And by this progression of experiments I satisfied myself that, had the light at the very ends of the spectrum been strong enough to make the species of the black lines appear plainly on the paper, the focus of the deepest violet would have been found nearer to the lens, than the focus of the deepest red, by about $5\frac{1}{3}$ inches at least. And this is a further evidence that the sines of incidence and refraction of the several sorts of rays hold the same proportion to one another in the smallest refractions which they do in the greatest.

My progress in making this nice and troublesome experiment I have set down more at large, that they that shall try it after me may be aware of the circumspection requisite to make it succeed well. And if they cannot make it succeed so well as I did, they may notwithstanding collect by the proportion of the distance of the colours of the spectrum, to the difference of the distances of their foci from the lens, what would be the success in the more distant colours by a better trial. And yet, if they use a broader lens than I did, and fix it to a long strait staff, by means of which it may be readily and truly directed to the colour whose focus is desired, I question not but the experiment will succeed better with them than it did with me. For I directed the axis as nearly as I could to the middle of the colours, and then the faint ends of the spectrum being remote from the axis, cast their species less distinctly on the paper than they would have done had the axis been successively directed to them.

Now, by what has been said, it's certain that the rays which differ in refrangibility do not converge to the same focus; but if they flow from a lucid point, as far from the lens on one side as their foci are on the other, the focus of the most refrangible rays shall be nearer to the lens than that of the least refrangible, by above the fourteenth part of the whole distance; and if they flow from a lucid point, so very remote from the lens that before their incidence they may be accounted parallel, the focus of the most refrangible rays shall be nearer to the lens than the focus of the least refrangible by about the 27th or 28th part of their whole distance from it. And the diameter of the circle in the middle space between those two foci which they illuminate, when they fall there on any plane, perpendicular to the axis (which circle is the least into which they can all be gathered) is about the 55th part of the diameter of the aperture of the glass. So that 'tis a wonder that telescopes represent objects so distinct as they do. But were all the rays of light equally refrangible, the error arising only from the sphericalness of the figures of glasses would be many hundred times less. For, if the object-glass of a telescope be plano-convex, and the plane side be turned towards the object, and the diameter of the sphere, whereof this glass is a segment, be called D, and the semidiameter of the aperture of the glass be called S, and the sine of incidence out of glass into air be to the sine of refraction as I to R; the rays which come parallel to the axis of the glass, shall in the place where the image of the object is most distinctly made be scattered all over a little circle, whose diameter is $\dfrac{Rq \times S\ cub.}{Iq \times D\ quad.}$ very nearly, as I gather by computing the errors of the rays by the method of infinite series, and rejecting the terms whose quantities are inconsiderable. As for instance, if the sine of incidence I be to the sine of refraction R as 20 to 31, and if D the diameter of the sphere, to which the convex-side of the glass is ground, be 100 feet of 1200 inches, and S the semidiameter of the aperture be two inches, the diameter of the little circle, $\left(\text{that is } \dfrac{Rq \times S\ cub.}{Iq \times D\ quad.}\right)$ will be $\dfrac{31 \times 31 \times 8}{20 \times 20 \times 1200 \times 1200}$ (or $\frac{961}{72{,}000{,}000}$) parts of an inch. But the diameter of the little circle, through which these rays are scattered by unequal refrangibility, will be about the 55th part of the aperture of the object-glass, which here is four inches. And, therefore, the error arising from the spherical figure of the glass is to the error arising from the different refrangibility of the Rays as $\frac{961}{72{,}000{,}000}$ to $\frac{4}{55}$; that is, as 1 to 5449; and, therefore, being in comparison so very little, deserves not to be considered.

But you will say, if the errors caused by the different refrangibility be so very great, how comes it to pass that objects appear through telescopes so distinct as they do? I answer, 'tis because the erring rays are not scattered uniformly over all that circular space, but collected infinitely more densely in the centre than in any other part of the circle, and in the way from the centre to the circumference, grow continually rarer and rarer, so as at the circumference to become infinitely rare; and by reason of their rarity are not strong

enough to be visible unless in the centre and very near it. Let ADE [Fig. 27]
represent one of those circles described with the centre C, and semidiameter
AC, and let BFG be a smaller circle concentric to the former, cutting with its
circumference the diameter AC in B, and bisect AC in
N; and by my reckoning the density of the light in
any place B will be to its density in N as AB to BC;
and the whole light within the lesser circle BFG
will be to the whole light within the greater AED as
the excess of the square of AC above the square of
AB is to the square of AC. As if BC be the fifth part
of AC, the light will be four times denser in B than
in N, and the whole light within the less circle will be
to the whole light within the greater as nine to
twenty-five. Whence it's evident that the light within the less circle must strike the sense much more
strongly than that faint and dilated light round about between it and the
circumference of the greater.

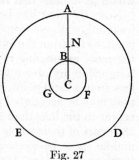

Fig. 27

But it's further to be noted that the most luminous of the prismatic colours
are the yellow and orange. These affect the senses more strongly than all the
rest together, and next to these in strength are the red and green. The blue
compared with these is a faint and dark colour, and the indigo and violet are
much darker and fainter, so that these compared with the stronger colours are
little to be regarded. The images of objects are therefore to be placed, not in
the focus of the mean refrangible rays, which are in the confine of green and
blue, but in the focus of those rays which are in the middle of the orange and
yellow; there where the colour is most luminous and fulgent (that is, in the
brightest yellow, that yellow which inclines more to orange than to green). And
by the refraction of these rays (whose sines of incidence and refraction in glass
are as 17 and 11) the refraction of glass and crystal for optical uses is to be
measured. Let us, therefore, place the image of the object in the focus of these
rays, and all the yellow and orange will fall within a circle whose diameter is
about the 250th part of the diameter of the aperture of the glass. And if you
add the brighter half of the red (that half which is next the orange) and the
brighter half of the green (that half which is next the yellow), about three fifth
parts of the light of these two colours will fall within the same circle, and two-
fifth parts will fall without it round about; and that which falls without will be
spread through almost as much more space as that which falls within, and so in
the gross be almost three times rarer. Of the other half of the red and green,
(that is, of the deep dark red and willow green), about one-quarter will fall
within this circle, and three-quarters without, and that which falls without will
be spread through about four or five times more space than that which falls
within; and so in the gross be rarer, and if compared with the whole light within
it, will be about 25 times rarer than all that taken in the gross; or rather more
than 30 or 40 times rarer, because the deep red in the end of the spectrum of
colours made by a prism is very thin and rare, and the willow green is something
rarer than the orange and yellow. The light of these colours, therefore, being so
very much rarer than that within the circle, will scarce affect the sense, especially since the deep red and willow green of this light are much darker
colours than the rest. And for the same reason the blue and violet being much

darker colours than these, and much more rarefied, may be neglected. For the dense and bright light of the circle will obscure the rare and weak light of these dark colours round about it, and render them almost insensible. The sensible image of a lucid point is, therefore, scarce broader than a circle, whose diameter is the 250th part of the diameter of the aperture of the object-glass of a good telescope, or not much broader, if you except a faint and dark misty light round about it, which a spectator will scarce regard. And, therefore, in a telescope whose aperture is four inches, and length an hundred feet, it exceeds not $2''\ 45'''$, or $3''$. And in a telescope whose aperture is two inches, and length 20 or 30 feet, it may be $5''$ or $6''$, and scarce above. And this answers well to experience: for some astronomers have found the diameters of the fixed stars, in telescopes of between 20 and 60 feet in length, to be about $5''$ or $6''$, or at most 8 or 10 seconds. But if the eye-glass be tinted faintly with the smoke of a lamp or torch, to obscure the light of the star, the fainter light in the circumference of the star ceases to be visible, and the star (if the glass be sufficiently soiled with smoke) appears something more like a mathematical point. And, for the same reason, the enormous part of the light in the circumference of every lucid point ought to be less discernible in shorter telescopes than in longer, because the shorter transmit less light to the eye.

Now, that the fixed stars, by reason of their immense distance, appear like points, unless so far as their light is dilated by refraction, may appear from hence; that when the moon passes over them and eclipses them, their light vanishes, not gradually like that of the planets, but all at once; and in the end of the eclipse it returns into sight all at once, or certainly in less time than the second of a minute; the refraction of the moon's atmosphere a little protracting the time in which the light of the star first vanishes, and afterwards returns into sight.

Now, if we suppose the sensible image of a lucid point to be even 250 times narrower than the aperture of the glass, yet this image would be still much greater than if it were only from the spherical figure of the glass. For were it not for the different refrangibility of the rays, its breadth in a 100-foot telescope, whose aperture is 4 inches, would be but $\frac{961}{72,000,000}$ parts of an inch, as is manifest by the foregoing computation. And, therefore, in this case, the greatest errors arising from the spherical figure of the glass would be to the greatest sensible errors arising from the different refrangibility of the rays as $\frac{961}{72,000,000}$ to $\frac{4}{250}$ at most; that is, only as 1 to 1200. And this sufficiently shews that it is not the spherical figures of glasses, but the different refrangibility of the rays, which hinders the perfection of telescopes.

There is another argument by which it may appear that the different refrangibility of rays is the true cause of the imperfection of telescopes. For the errors of the rays, arising from the spherical figures of object-glasses are as the cubes of the apertures of the object-glasses; and thence to make telescopes of various lengths magnify with equal distinctness, the apertures of the object-glasses, and the charges or magnifying powers, ought to be as the cubes of the square roots of their lengths; which doth not answer to experience. But the errors of the rays, arising from the different refrangibility, are as the apertures of the object-glasses; and thence to make telescopes of various lengths magnify with equal distinctness, their apertures and charges ought to be as the square roots of their lengths; and this answers to experience, as is well known. For instance, a telescope of 64 feet in length, with an aperture of 2⅔ inches, magnifies about 120 times, with as much distinctness as one of a foot in length, with ⅓ of an inch aperture, magnifies 15 times.

Now, were it not for this different refrangibility of rays, telescopes might be brought to a greater perfection than we have yet described, by composing the object-glass of two glasses with water between them. Let ADFC [Fig. 28] represent the object-glass composed of two glasses ABED and BEFC, alike convex on the outsides AGD and CHF, and alike concave on the insides BME, BNE, with water in the concavity BMEN. Let the sine of incidence out of glass into air be as I to R, and out of water into air, as K to R, and by consequence out of glass into water, as I to K: and let the diameter of the sphere to which the convex sides AGD and CHF are ground be D, and the diameter of the sphere to which the concave sides BME and BNE are ground be to D as the cube root of KK—KI to the cube root of RK—RI: and the refractions on the concave sides of the glasses will very much correct the errors of the refractions on the convex sides, so far as they arise from the sphericalness of the figure. And by this means might telescopes be brought to sufficient perfection, were it not for the different refrangibility of several sorts of rays. But by reason of this different refrangibility, I do not yet see any other means of improving telescopes by refractions alone, than that of increasing their lengths, for which end the late contrivance of Huygens seems well accommodated. For very long tubes are cumbersome, and scarce to be readily managed, and by reason of their length are very apt to bend, and shake by bending, so as to cause a continual trembling in the objects, whereby it becomes difficult to see them distinctly; whereas by his contrivance the glasses are readily manageable, and the object-glass being fixed upon a strong upright pole becomes more steady.

Fig. 28

Seeing, therefore, the improvement of telescopes of given lengths by refractions is desperate, I contrived heretofore a perspective by reflexion, using instead of an object-glass a concave metal. The diameter of the sphere to which the metal was ground concave was about 25 English inches, and by consequence the length of the instrument about six inches and a quarter. The eye-glass was plano-convex, and the diameter of the sphere to which the convex side was ground was about ⅕ of an inch, or a little less, and by consequence it magnified between 30 and 40 times. By another way of measuring I found that it magnified about 35 times. The concave metal bore an aperture of an inch and a third part; but the aperture was limited, not by an opaque circle covering the limb of the metal round about, but by an opaque circle placed between the eye-glass and the eye, and perforated in the middle with a little round hole for the rays to pass through to the eye. For this circle by being placed here, stopped much of the erroneous light which otherwise would have disturbed the vision. By comparing it with a pretty good perspective of four feet in length, made with a concave eye-glass, I could read at a greater distance with my own instrument than with the glass. Yet objects appeared much darker in it than in the glass, and that partly because more light was lost by reflexion in the metal, than by refraction in the glass, and partly because my instrument was overcharged. Had it magnified but 30 or 25 times, it would have made the object appear more brisk and pleasant. Two of these I made about 16 years ago, and have one of them still by me, by which I can prove the truth of what I write. Yet it is not so good as at the first. For the concave has been divers times tarnished and cleared again, by rubbing it with very soft leather. When I made these an artist in London undertook to imitate it; but using another way of polishing them than I did, he fell much short of what I had attained to, as I afterwards understood by discoursing the under-workman he had employed. The polish I used was in this manner: I had two round copper plates, each six inches in diameter, the one convex, the other concave, ground very true to one another. On the convex I ground the object-metal or concave which was to be polished, till it had taken the figure of the convex and was ready for a polish. Then I pitched over the convex very thinly, by dropping melted pitch upon it, and warming it to keep the pitch soft, whilst I ground it with the concave copper wetted to make it spread evenly all over the convex. Thus by working it well I made it as thin as a groat, and after the convex was cold I ground it again to give it as true a figure as I could. Then I took putty which I had made very fine by washing it from all its grosser particles, and laying a little of this upon the pitch, I ground it upon the pitch with the concave copper, till it had done making a noise; and then upon the pitch I ground the object-metal with a brisk motion for about two or three minutes of time, leaning hard upon it. Then I put fresh putty upon the pitch, and ground it again till it had done making a noise, and afterwards ground the object-metal upon it as before. And this work I repeated till the metal was polished, grinding it the last time with all my strength for a good while together, and frequently breathing upon the pitch, to keep it moist without laying on any more fresh putty. The object-metal was two inches broad, and about one-third part of an inch thick, to keep it from bending. I had two of these metals, and when I had polished them both I tried which was best, and ground the other again, to see if I could make it better than that which I kept. And thus by many trials I learned the way of polishing, till I made those two reflecting perspectives I spake of above. For this art of polishing will be better learned by repeated practice than by my description. Before I ground the object-metal on the pitch, I always ground the putty on it with the concave copper, till it had done making a noise, because if the particles of the putty were not by this means made to stick fast in the pitch, they would by rolling up and down grate and fret the object-metal and fill it full of little holes.

But because metal is more difficult to polish than glass, and is afterwards very apt to be spoiled by tarnishing, and reflects not so much light as glass quick-silvered over does, I would propound to use instead of the metal a glass ground concave on the foreside, and as much convex on the backside, and quick-silvered over on the convex side. The glass must be everywhere of the same thickness exactly. Otherwise it will make objects look coloured and indistinct. By such a glass I tried about five or six years ago to make a reflecting telescope of four feet in length to magnify about 150 times, and I satisfied myself that there wants nothing but a good artist to bring the design to perfection. For the glass being wrought by one of our London artists after such a manner as they grind glasses for telescopes, though it seemed as well wrought as the object-glasses use to be, yet when it was quick-silvered, the reflexion discovered innumerable inequalities all over the glass. And by reason of these inequalities, objects appeared indistinct in this instrument. For the errors of reflected rays caused by any inequality of the glass are about six times greater than the errors of refracted rays caused by the like inequalities. Yet by this experiment I satisfied myself that the reflexion on the concave side of the glass, which I feared would disturb the vision, did no sensible prejudice to it, and by consequence that nothing is wanting to perfect these telescopes, but good workmen who can grind and polish glasses truly spherical. An object-glass of a fourteen foot telescope, made by an artificer at London, I once mended considerably by grinding it on pitch with putty, and leaning very easily on it in the grinding, lest the putty should scratch it. Whether this way may not do well enough for polishing these reflecting glasses, I have not yet tried. But he that shall try either this or any other way of polishing which he may think better, may do well to make his glasses ready for polishing by grinding them without that violence, wherewith our London workmen press their glasses in grinding. For by such violent pressure, glasses are apt to bend a little in the grinding, and such bending will certainly spoil their figure. To recommend, therefore, the consideration of these reflecting glasses to such artists as are curious in figuring glasses, I shall describe this optical instrument in the following Proposition.

Proposition 8. Problem 2

To shorten telescopes.

Let ABCD [Fig. 29] represent a glass spherically concave on the foreside AB, and as much convex on the backside CD, so that it be everywhere of an equal thickness. Let it not be thicker on one side than on the other, lest it make objects appear coloured and indistinct, and let it be very truly wrought and quick-silvered over on the backside, and set in the tube VXYZ which must be very black within. Let EFG represent a prism of glass or crystal placed near the other end of the tube, in the middle of it, by means of a handle of brass or iron FGK, to the end of which made flat it is cemented. Let this prism be rectangular at E, and let the other two angles at F and G be accurately equal to each other, and by consequence equal to half right ones, and let the plane sides FE and GE be square, and by consequence the third side FG a rectangular parallelogram, whose length is to its breadth in a subduplicate proportion of two to one. Let it be so placed in the tube that the axis of the speculum may pass through the middle of the square side EF perpendicularly, and by consequence through the middle of the side FG at an angle of 45 degrees, and let the side EF be turned towards the speculum, and the dis-

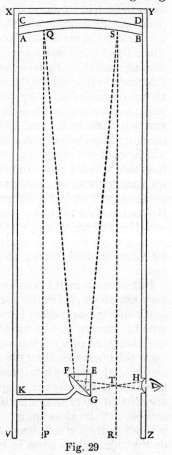

Fig. 29

tance of this prism from the speculum be such that the rays of the light PQ, RS, &c. which are incident upon the speculum in lines parallel to the axis thereof, may enter the prism at the side EF, and be reflected by the side FG, and thence go out of it through the side GE, to the point T, which must be the common focus of the speculum ABDC, and of a plano-convex eye-glass H, through which those rays must pass to the eye. And let the rays at their coming out of the glass pass through a small round hole, or aperture made in a little plate of lead, brass, or silver, wherewith the glass is to be covered, which hole must be no bigger than is necessary for light enough to pass through. For so it will render the object distinct, the plate in which 'tis made intercepting all the erroneous part of the light which comes from the verges of the speculum AB. Such an instrument well made, if it be six feet long (reckoning the length from the speculum to the prism, and thence to the focus T), will bear an aperture of six inches at the speculum, and magnify between two and three hundred times. But the hole H here limits the aperture with more advantage than if the aperture was placed at the speculum. If the instrument be made longer or shorter, the aperture must be in proportion as the cube of the square-square root of the length, and the magnifying as the aperture. But it's convenient that the speculum be an inch or two broader than the aperture at the least, and that the glass of the speculum be thick, that it bend not in the working. The prism EFG must be no bigger than is necessary, and its back-side FG must not be quick-silvered over. For, without quick-silver it will reflect all the light incident on it from the speculum.

In this instrument the object will be inverted, but may be erected by making the square sides FF and EG of the prism EFG not plane but spherically convex, that the rays may cross as well before they come at it as afterwards between it and the eye-glass. If it be desired that the instrument bear a larger aperture, that may be also done by composing the speculum of two glasses with water between them.

If the theory of making telescopes could at length be fully brought into practice, yet there would be certain bounds beyond which telescopes could not perform. For the air through which we look upon the stars is in a perpetual tremor; as may be seen by the tremulous motion of shadows cast from high towers, and by the twinkling of the fixed stars. But these stars do not twinkle when viewed through telescopes which have large apertures. For the rays of light, which pass through divers parts of the aperture, tremble each of them apart, and by means of their various and sometimes contrary tremors fall at one and the same time upon different points in the bottom of the eye, and their trembling motions are too quick and confused to be perceived severally. And all these illuminated points constitute one broad lucid point, composed of those many trembling points confusedly and insensibly mixed with one another by very short and swift tremors, and thereby cause the star to appear broader than it is and without any trembling of the whole. Long telescopes may cause objects to appear brighter and larger than short ones can do, but they cannot be so formed as to take away the confusion of the rays which arises from the tremors of the atmosphere. The only remedy is a most serene and quiet air, such as may perhaps be found on the tops of the highest mountains above the grosser clouds.

Part II

Proposition 1. Theorem 1

The phenomena of colours in refracted or reflected light are not caused by new modifications of the light variously impressed, according to the various terminations of the light and shadow.

The Proof by Experiments

Experiment 1. For if the Sun shine into a very dark chamber through an oblong hole F, [Fig. 1] whose breadth is the sixth or eighth part of an inch, or something less; and his beam FH do afterwards pass first through a very large prism ABC, distant about 20 feet from the hole, and parallel to it, and then (with its white part) through an oblong hole H, whose breadth is about the fortieth or sixtieth part of an inch, and which is made in a black opaque body GI, and placed at the distance of two or three feet from the prism, in a parallel situation both to the prism and to the former hole; and if this white light thus transmitted through the hole H fall afterwards upon a white paper pt, placed after that hole H at the distance of three or four feet from it, and there paint the

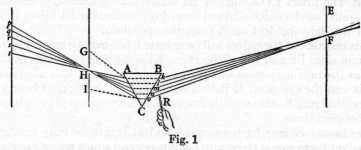

Fig. 1

usual colours of the prism, (suppose red at t, yellow at s, green at r, blue at q, and violet at p) you may with an iron wire, or any such like slender opaque body, whose breadth is about the tenth part of an inch, by intercepting the rays at k, l, m, n or o, take away any one of the colours at t, s, r, q or p, whilst the other colours remain upon the paper as before; or with an obstacle something bigger you may take away any two, or three, or four colours together, the rest remaining: So that any one of the colours as well as violet may become outmost in the confine of the shadow towards p, and any one of them as well as red may become outmost in the confine of the shadow towards t, and any one of them may also border upon the shadow made within the colours by the obstacle R intercepting some intermediate part of the light; and, lastly, any one of them by being left alone may border upon the shadow on either hand. All the colours have themselves indifferently to any confines of shadow, and therefore the differences of these colours from one another do not arise from the different confines of shadow, whereby light is variously modified, as has hitherto been the opinion of philosophers. In trying these things 'tis to be observed that by how much the holes F and H are narrower, and the intervals between them and the prism greater, and the chamber darker, by so much the better doth the experiment succeed; provided the light be not so far diminished but that the colours at *pt* be sufficiently visible. To procure a prism of solid glass large enough for this experiment will be difficult, and therefore a prismatic vessel must be made of polished glass plates cemented together, and filled with salt water or clear oil.

EXPER. 2. The Sun's light let into a dark chamber through the round hole F, [Fig. 2] half an inch wide, passed first through the prism ABC placed at the hole, and then through a lens PT something more than four inches broad, and about eight feet distant from the prism, and thence converged to O the focus of the lens distant from it about three feet, and there fell upon a white paper DE. If that paper was perpendicular to that light incident upon it, as 'tis

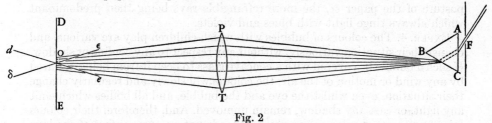

Fig. 2

represented in the posture DE, all the colours upon it at O appeared white. But if the paper being turned about an axis parallel to the prism, became very much inclined to the light, as 'tis represented in the positions *de* and *δε*, the same light in the one case appeared yellow and red, in the other blue. Here one and the same part of the light in one and the same place, according to the various inclinations of the paper, appeared in one case white, in another yellow or red, in a third blue, whilst the confine of light and shadow, and the refractions of the prism in all these cases remained the same.

EXPER. 3. Such another experiment may be more easily tried as follows: Let a broad beam of the Sun's light coming into a dark chamber through a hole in the window-shut be refracted by a large prism ABC, [Fig. 3] whose refracting angle C is more than 60 degrees, and so soon as it comes out of the prism, let it fall upon the white paper DE glued upon a stiff plane; and this light, when the paper is perpendicular to it, as 'tis represented in DE, will appear perfectly white upon the paper; but when the paper is very much inclined to it in such a manner as to keep always parallel to the axis of the prism, the whiteness of the

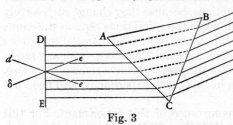

Fig. 3

whole light upon the paper will, according to the inclination of the paper this way or that way, change either into yellow and red, as in the posture *de*, or into blue and violet, as in the posture *δε*. And if the light before it fall upon the paper be twice refracted the same way by two parallel prisms, these colours will become the more conspicuous. Here all the middle parts of the broad beam of white light which fell upon the paper did, without any confine of shadow to modify it, become coloured all over with one uniform colour, the colour being always the same in the middle of the paper as at the edges, and this colour changed according to the various obliquity of the reflecting paper, without any change in the refractions or shadow, or in the light which fell upon the paper. And, therefore, these colours are to be derived from some other cause than the new modifications of light by refractions and shadows.

If it be asked, What then is their cause? I answer, That the paper in the posture *de*, being more oblique to the more refrangible rays than to the less refrangible ones, is more strongly illuminated by the latter than by the former, and, therefore, the less refrangible rays are predominant in the reflected light. And wherever they are predominant in any light, they tinge it with red or yellow, as may in some measure appear by the first Proposition of the first part of this book, and will more fully appear hereafter. And the contrary happens in the posture of the paper δε, the more refrangible rays being then predominant which always tinge light with blues and violets.

EXPER. 4. The colours of bubbles with which children play are various, and change their situation variously, without any respect to any confine or shadow. If such a bubble be covered with a concave glass to keep it from being agitated by any wind or motion of the air, the colours will slowly and regularly change their situation, even whilst the eye and the bubble, and all bodies which emit any light, or cast any shadow, remain unmoved. And, therefore, their colours arise from some regular cause which depends not on any confine of shadow. What this cause is will be shewed in the next book.

To these experiments may be added the tenth experiment of the first part of this first book, where the Sun's light in a dark room being trajected through the parallel superficies of two prisms tied together in the form of a parallelepiped, became totally of one uniform yellow or red colour, at its emerging out of the prisms. Here, in the production of these colours, the confine of shadow can have nothing to do. For the light changes from white to yellow, orange and red successively, without any alteration of the confine of shadow. And at both edges of the emerging light where the contrary confines of shadow ought to produce different effects, the colour is one and the same, whether it be white, yellow, orange or red. And in the middle of the emerging light, where there is no confine of shadow at all, the colour is the very same as at the edges, the whole light at its very first emergence being of one uniform colour, whether white, yellow, orange or red, and going on thence perpetually without any change of colour, such as the confine of shadow is vulgarly supposed to work in refracted light after its emergence. Neither can these colours arise from any new modifications of the light by refractions, because they change successively from white to yellow, orange and red, while the refractions remain the same, and also because the refractions are made contrary ways by parallel superficies which destroy one another's effects. They arise not, therefore, from any modifications of light made by refractions and shadows, but have some other cause. What that cause is we shewed above in this tenth experiment, and need not here repeat it.

There is yet another material circumstance of this experiment. For this emerging light being by a third prism HIK [Fig. 22 Part I.] refracted towards the paper PT, and there painting the usual colours of the prism, red, yellow, green, blue, violet: If these colours arose from the refractions of that prism modifying the light, they would not be in the light before its incidence on that prism. And yet in that experiment we found that when, by turning the two first prisms about their common axis all the colours were made to vanish but the red, the light, which makes that red being left alone, appeared of the very same red colour before its incidence on the third prism. And, in general, we find by other experiments that when the rays which differ in refrangibility are separated from one another, and any one sort of them is considered apart, the colour of the light which they compose cannot be changed by any refraction or reflexion whatever, as it ought to be were colours nothing else than modifications of light caused by refractions, and reflexions, and shadows. This unchangeableness of colour I am now to describe in the following Proposition.

PROPOSITION 2. THEOREM 2

All homogeneal light has its proper colour answering to its degree of refrangibility, and that colour cannot be changed by reflexions and refractions.

In the experiments of the fourth Proposition of the first part of this first book, when I had separated the heterogeneous rays from one another, the spectrum *pt* formed by the separated rays did in the progress from its end *p*, on which the most refrangible rays fell, unto its other end *t*, on which the least refrangible rays fell, appear tinged with this series of colours: violet, indigo, blue, green, yellow, orange, red, together with all their intermediate degrees in a continual succession perpetually varying. So that there appeared as many degrees of colours, as there were sorts of rays differing in refrangibility.

EXPER. 5. Now, that these colours could not be changed by refraction I knew by refracting with a prism sometimes one very little part of this light, sometimes another very little part, as is described in the twelfth experiment of the first part of this book. For by this refraction the colour of the light was never changed in the least. If any part of the red light was refracted, it remained totally of the same red colour as before. No orange, no yellow, no green or blue, no other new colour was produced by that refraction. Neither did the colour any way change by repeated refractions, but continued always the same red entirely as at first. The like constancy and immutability I found also in the blue, green, and other colours. So also, if I looked through a prism upon any body illuminated with any part of this homogeneal light, as in the fourteenth experiment of the first part of this book is described; I could not perceive any new colour generated this way. All bodies illuminated with compound light appear through prisms confused (as was said above) and tinged with various new colours, but those illuminated with homogeneal light appeared through prisms neither less distinct, nor otherwise coloured, than when viewed with the naked eyes. Their colours were not in the least changed by the refraction of the interposed prism. I speak here of a sensible change of colour: for the light which I here call homogeneal, being not absolutely homogeneal, there ought to arise some little change of colour from its heterogeneity. But, if that heterogeneity was so little as it might be made by the said experiments of the fourth Proposition, that change was not sensible, and therefore in experiments, where sense is judge, ought to be accounted none at all.

EXPER. 6. And as these colours were not changeable by refractions, so neither were they by reflexions. For all white, grey, red, yellow, green, blue, violet bodies, as paper, ashes, red lead, orpiment, indigo bice, gold, silver, copper, grass, blue flowers, violets, bubbles of water tinged with various colours, peacock's feathers, the tincture of *lignum nephriticum*, and such-like, in red homogeneal light appeared totally red, in blue light totally blue, in green light totally green, and so of other colours. In the homogeneal light of any colour they all appeared totally of that same colour, with this only difference: that some of them reflected that light more strongly, others more faintly. I never yet found any body, which by reflecting homogeneal light could sensibly change its colour.

From all which it is manifest that if the Sun's light consisted of but one sort of rays, there would be but one colour in the whole world, nor would it be possible to produce any new colour by reflexions and refractions, and, by consequence, that the variety of colours depends upon the composition of light.

DEFINITION

The homogeneal light and rays which appear red, or rather make objects appear so, I call rubrific or red-making; those which make objects appear yellow, green, blue, and violet, I call yellow-making, green-making, blue-making, violet-making, and so of the rest. And if at any time I speak of light and rays as coloured or endued with colours, I would be understood to speak not philosophically and properly, but grossly, and accordingly to such conceptions as vulgar people in seeing all these experiments would be apt to frame. For the rays, to speak properly, are not coloured. In them there is nothing else than a certain power and disposition to stir up a sensation of this or that colour. For as sound in a bell or musical string, or other sounding body, is nothing but a trembling motion, and in the air nothing but that motion propagated from the object, and in the sensorium 'tis a sense of that motion under the form of sound; so colours in the object are nothing but a disposition to reflect this or that sort of rays more copiously than the rest; in the rays they are nothing but their dispositions to propagate this or that motion into the sensorium, and in the sensorium they are sensations of those motions under the forms of colours.

PROPOSITION 3. PROBLEM 1

To define the refrangibility of the several sorts of homogeneal light answering to the several colours.

For determining this Problem I made the following experiment.

EXPER. 7. When I had caused the rectilinear sides AF, GM, [Fig. 4] of the spectrum of colours made by the prism to be distinctly defined, as in the fifth experiment of the first part of this book is described, there were found in it all

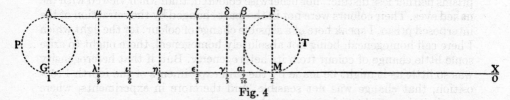

Fig. 4

the homogeneal colours in the same order and situation one among another as in the spectrum of simple light, described in the fourth Proposition of that part. For the circles of which the spectrum of compound light PT is composed, and which in the middle parts of the spectrum interfere, and are intermixed with one another, are not intermixed in their outmost parts where they touch those rectilinear sides AF and GM. And, therefore, in those rectilinear sides when distinctly defined, there is no new colour generated by refraction. I observed, also, that if anywhere between the two outmost circles TMF and PGA a right line, as $\gamma\delta$, was cross to the spectrum, so as both ends to fall perpendicularly upon its rectilinear sides, there appeared one and the same colour, and degree of colour from one end of this line to the other. I delineated, therefore, in a paper the perimeter of the spectrum FAP GMT, and, in trying the third experiment of the first part of this book, I held the paper so that the spectrum might fall upon this delineated figure, and agree with it exactly, whilst an assistant, whose eyes for distinguishing colours were more critical than mine, did by right lines $a\beta$, $\gamma\delta$, $\epsilon\zeta$, &c. drawn cross the spectrum, note the confines of the colours (that is, of the red $Ma\beta F$, of the orange $a\gamma\delta\beta$, of the yellow $\gamma\epsilon\zeta\delta$, of the green $\epsilon\eta\theta\zeta$, of the blue $\eta\iota\kappa\theta$, of the indigo $\iota\lambda\mu\kappa$, and of the violet $\lambda GA\mu$). And this operation being divers times repeated both in the same and in several papers, I found that the observations agreed well enough with one another, and that the rectilinear sides MG and FA were by the said cross lines divided after the manner of a musical chord. Let GM be produced to X, that MX may be equal to GM, and conceive GX, λX, ιX, ηX, ϵX, γX, aX, MX, to be in proportion to one another, as the numbers, $1, \frac{8}{9}, \frac{5}{6}, \frac{3}{4}, \frac{2}{3}, \frac{3}{5}, \frac{9}{16}, \frac{1}{2}$, and so to represent the chords of the key, and of a tone, a third minor, a fourth, a fifth, a sixth major, a seventh and an eighth above that key. And the intervals Ma, $a\gamma$, $\gamma\epsilon$, $\epsilon\eta$, $\eta\iota$, $\iota\lambda$, and λG, will be the spaces which the several colours (red, orange, yellow, green, blue, indigo, violet) take up.

Now, these intervals or spaces subtending the differences of the refractions of the rays going to the limits of those colours (that is, to the Points M, a, γ, ϵ, η, ι, λ, G) may without any sensible error be accounted proportional to the differences of the sines of refraction of those rays having one common sine of incidence; and, therefore, since the common sine of incidence of the most and least refrangible rays out of glass into air was (by a method described above) found in proportion to their sines of refraction as 50 to 77 and 78, divide the difference between the sines of refraction 77 and 78, as the line GM is divided by those intervals, and you will have $77, 77\frac{1}{8}, 77\frac{1}{5}, 77\frac{1}{3}, 77\frac{1}{2}, 77\frac{2}{3}, 77\frac{7}{9}, 78$, the sines of refraction of those rays out of glass into air, their common sine of incidence being 50. So, then, the sines of the incidences of all the red-making rays out of glass into air were to the sines of their refractions not greater than 50 to 77, nor less than 50 to $77\frac{1}{8}$, but they varied from one another according to all intermediate proportions. And the sines of the incidences of the green-making rays were to the sines of their refractions in all proportions from that of 50 to $77\frac{1}{3}$, unto that of 50 to $77\frac{1}{2}$. And by the like limits above-mentioned were the refractions of the rays belonging to the rest of the colours defined, the sines of the red-making rays extending from 77 to $77\frac{1}{8}$, those of the orange-making from $77\frac{1}{8}$ to $77\frac{1}{5}$, those of the yellow-making from $77\frac{1}{5}$ to $77\frac{1}{3}$, those of the green-making from $77\frac{1}{3}$ to $77\frac{1}{2}$, those of the blue-making from $77\frac{1}{2}$ to $77\frac{2}{3}$, those of the indigo-making from $67\frac{2}{3}$ to $77\frac{7}{9}$, and those of the violet from $77\frac{7}{9}$ to 78.

These are the laws of the refractions made out of glass into air, and thence, by the third Axiom of the first part of this book, the laws of the refractions made out of air into glass are easily derived.

Exper. 8. I found, moreover, that when light goes out of air through several contiguous refracting mediums as through water and glass, and thence goes out again into air, whether the refracting superficies be parallel or inclined to one another, that light as often as by contrary refractions 'tis so corrected, that it emergeth in lines parallel to those in which it was incident, continues ever after to be white. But if the emergent rays be inclined to the incident, the whiteness of the emerging light will by degrees in passing on from the place of emergence, become tinged in its edges with colours. This I tried by refracting light with prisms of glass placed within a prismatic vessel of water. Now, those colours argue a diverging and separation of the heterogeneous rays from one another by means of their unequal refractions, as in what follows will more fully appear. And, on the contrary, the permanent whiteness argues that in like incidences of the rays there is no such separation of the emerging rays, and by consequence no inequality of their whole refractions. Whence I seem to gather the two following theorems:

1. The excesses of the sines of refraction of several sorts of rays above their common sine of incidence when the refractions are made out of divers denser mediums immediately into one and the same rarer medium (suppose of air) are to one another in a given proportion.

2. The proportion of the sine of incidence to the sine of refraction of one and the same sort of rays out of one medium into another, is composed of the proportion of the sine of incidence to the sine of refraction out of the first medium into any third medium, and of the proportion of the sine of incidence to the sine of refraction out of that third medium into the second medium.

By the first theorem, the refractions of the rays of every sort made out of any medium into air are known by having the refraction of the rays of any one sort. As, for instance, if the refractions of the rays of every sort out of rain-water into air be desired, let the common sine of incidence out of glass into air be subducted from the sines of refraction, and the excesses will be 27, $27\frac{1}{8}$, $27\frac{1}{5}$, $27\frac{1}{3}$, $27\frac{1}{2}$, $27\frac{2}{3}$, $27\frac{7}{9}$, 28. Suppose, now, that the sine of incidence of the least refrangible rays be to their sine of refraction out of rain-water into air as 3 to 4, and say as 1 the difference of those sines is to 3 the sine of incidence, so is 27 the least of the excesses above-mentioned to a fourth number 81; and 81 will be the common sine of incidence out of rain-water into air, to which sine (if you add all the above-mentioned excesses) you will have the desired sines of the refractions 108, $108\frac{1}{8}$, $108\frac{1}{5}$, $108\frac{1}{3}$, $108\frac{1}{2}$, $108\frac{2}{3}$, $108\frac{7}{9}$, 109.

By the latter theorem, the refraction out of one medium into another is gathered as often as you have the refractions out of them both into any third medium. As if the sine of incidence of any ray out of glass into air be to its sine of refraction as 20 to 31, and the sine of incidence of the same ray out of air into water be to its sine of refraction as 4 to 3; the sine of incidence of that ray out of glass into water will be to its sine of refraction as 20 to 31 and 4 to 3 jointly; that is, as the factum of 20 and 4 to the factum of 31 and 3, or as 80 to 93.

And these theorems being admitted into Optics, there would be scope enough of handling that science voluminously after a new manner, not only by teaching those things which tend to the perfection of vision, but also by determining mathematically all kinds of phenomena of colours which could be produced by refractions. For to do this, there is nothing else requisite than to find out the separations of heterogeneous rays, and their various mixtures and proportions in every mixture. By this way of arguing I invented almost all the phenomena described in these books, beside some others less necessary to the argument;

and by the successes I met with in the trials, I dare promise that to him who shall argue truly, and then try all things with good glasses and sufficient circumspection, the expected event will not be wanting. But he is first to know what colours will arise from any others mixed in any assigned proportion.

PROPOSITION 4. THEOREM 3

Colours may be produced by composition which shall be like to the colours of homogeneal light as to the appearance of colour, but not as to the immutability of colour and constitution of light. And those colours by how much they are more compounded by so much are they less full and intense, and by too much composition they may be diluted and weakened till they cease, and the mixture becomes white or grey. There may be also colours produced by composition, which are not fully like any of the colours of homogeneal light.

For a mixture of homogeneal red and yellow compounds an orange, like in appearance of colour to that orange which in the series of unmixed prismatic colours lies between them; but the light of one orange is homogeneal as to refrangibility, and that of the other is heterogeneal, and the colour of the one, if viewed through a prism, remains unchanged, that of the other is changed and resolved into its component colours, red and yellow. And after the same manner other neighbouring homogeneal colours may compound new colours, like the intermediate homogeneal ones, as yellow and green, the colour between them both; and afterwards, if blue be added, there will be made a green the middle colour of the three which enter the composition. For the yellow and blue on either hand, if they are equal in quantity they draw the intermediate green equally towards themselves in composition, and so keep it as it were in equilibrium, that it verge not more to the yellow on the one hand, and to the blue on the other, but by their mixed actions remain still a middle colour. To this mixed green there may be further added some red and violet, and yet the green will not presently cease, but only grow less full and vivid, and by increasing the red and violet, it will grow more and more dilute until, by the prevalence of the added colours, it be overcome and turned into whiteness or some other colour. So if to the colour of any homogeneal light the Sun's white light composed of all sorts of rays be added, that colour will not vanish or change its species, but be diluted; and by adding more and more white it will be diluted more and more, perpetually. Lastly, if red and violet be mingled, there will be generated according to their various proportions various purples, such as are not like in appearance to the colour of any homogeneal light, and of these purples mixed with yellow and blue may be made other new colours.

PROPOSITION 5. THEOREM 4

Whiteness, and all grey colours between white and black, may be compounded of colours, and the whiteness of the Sun's light is compounded of all the primary colours mixed in a due proportion.

The Proof by Experiments

EXPERIMENT 9. The Sun shining into a dark chamber through a little round hole in the window-shut, and his light being there refracted by a prism to cast his coloured image PT [Fig. 5] upon the opposite wall, I held a white paper V to that image in such manner that it might be illuminated by the coloured light reflected from thence, and yet not intercept any part of that light in its passage from the prism to the spectrum. And I found that when the paper was held nearer to any colour than to the rest, it appeared of that colour to which it approached nearest; but when it was equally or almost equally distant from all the colours, so that it might be equally illuminated by them all, it appeared white. And in this last situation of the paper, if some colours were intercepted the paper lost its white colour, and appeared of the colour of the rest of the light which was not intercepted. So, then, the paper was illuminated with lights of various colours (namely, red, yellow, green, blue and violet) and every part

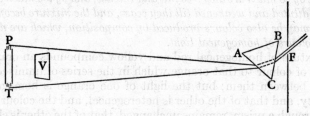

Fig. 5

of the light retained its proper colour until it was incident on the paper, and became reflected thence to the eye; so that if it had been either alone (the rest of the light being intercepted) or if it had abounded most, and been predominant in the light reflected from the paper, it would have tinged the paper with its own colour; and yet, being mixed with the rest of the colours in a due proportion, it made the paper look white, and therefore by a composition with the rest produced that colour. The several parts of the coloured light reflected from the spectrum, whilst they are propagated from thence through the air, do perpetually retain their proper colours, because wherever they fall upon the eyes of any spectator they make the several parts of the spectrum to appear under their proper colours. They retain, therefore, their proper colours when they fall upon the Paper V, and so by the confusion and perfect mixture of those colours compound the whiteness of the light reflected from thence.

EXPER. 10. Let that spectrum or solar image PT [Fig. 6] fall now upon the lens MN above four inches broad, and about six feet distant from the prism ABC and so figured that it may cause the coloured light which divergeth from the prism to converge and meet again at its focus G, about six or eight feet distant from the lens, and there to fall perpendicularly upon a white paper DE. And if you move this paper to and fro, you will perceive that near the lens, as at *de*, the whole solar image (suppose at *pt*) will appear upon it intensely

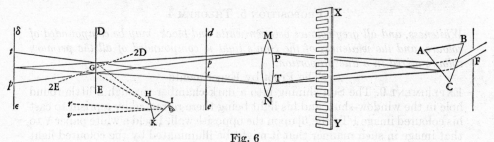

Fig. 6

coloured after the manner above-explained; and that by receding from the lens those colours will perpetually come towards one another, and, by mixing more and more, dilute one another continually until at length the paper come to the focus G, where by a perfect mixture they will wholly vanish and be converted into whiteness, the whole light appearing now upon the paper like a little white circle. And afterwards by receding farther from the lens, the rays which before converged will now cross one another in the focus G, and diverge from thence, and thereby make the colours to appear again, but yet in a contrary order; suppose at $\delta\epsilon$, where the red t is now above which before was below, and the violet p is below which before was above.

Let us now stop the paper at the focus G, where the light appears totally white and circular, and let us consider its whiteness. I say, that this is composed of the converging colours. For if any of those colours be intercepted at the lens, the whiteness will cease and degenerate into that colour which ariseth from the composition of the other colours which are not intercepted. And then if the intercepted colours be let pass and fall upon that compound colour, they mix with it, and by their mixture restore the whiteness. So if the violet, blue and green be intercepted, the remaining yellow, orange and red will compound upon the paper an orange, and then if the intercepted colours be let pass, they will fall upon this compounded orange, and together with it decompound a white. So also if the red and violet be intercepted, the remaining yellow, green and blue will compound a green upon the paper, and then the red and violet being let pass will fall upon this green, and together with it decompound a white. And that in this composition of white the several rays do not suffer any change in their colorific qualities by acting upon one another, but are only mixed, and by a mixture of their colours produce white, may further appear by these arguments.

If the paper be placed beyond the focus G, suppose at $\delta\epsilon$, and then the red colour at the lens be alternately intercepted, and let pass again, the violet colour on the paper will not suffer any change thereby, as it ought to do if the several sorts of rays acted upon one another in the focus G, where they cross. Neither will the red upon the paper be changed by any alternate stopping, and letting pass the violet which crosseth it.

And if the paper be placed at the focus G, and the white round image at G be viewed through the prism HIK, and by the refraction of that prism be translated to the place rv, and there appear tinged with various colours (namely, the violet at v and red at r, and others between) and then the red colours at the lens be often stopped and let pass by turns, the red at r will accordingly disappear, and return as often, but the violet at v will not thereby suffer any change. And so, by stopping and letting pass alternately the blue at the lens, the blue at v will accordingly disappear and return, without any change made in the red at r. The red, therefore, depends on one sort of rays, and the blue on another sort, which in the focus G, where they are commixed, do not act on one another. And there is the same reason of the other colours.

I considered, further, that when the most refrangible rays Pp, and the least refrangible ones Tt, are by converging inclined to one another, the paper, if held very oblique to those rays in the focus G, might reflect one sort of them more copiously than the other sort, and by that means the reflected light would be tinged in that focus with the colour of the predominant rays, provided those rays severally retained their colours, or colorific qualities in the composition of white made by them in that focus. But if they did not retain them in that white, but became all of them severally endued there with a disposition to strike the sense with the perception of white, then they could never lose their whiteness by such reflexions. I inclined, therefore, the paper to the rays very obliquely, as in the second experiment of this second part of the first book, that the most refrangible rays might be more copiously reflected than the rest, and the whiteness at length changed successively into blue, indigo, and violet. Then I inclined it the contrary way, that the least refrangible rays might be more copious in the reflected light than the rest, and the whiteness turned successively to yellow, orange, and red.

Lastly, I made an instrument XY in fashion of a comb whose teeth, being in number sixteen, were about an inch and a half broad, and the intervals of the teeth about two inches wide. Then by interposing successively the teeth of this instrument near the lens, I intercepted part of the colours by the interposed tooth, whilst the rest of them went on through the interval of the teeth to the paper DE, and there painted a round solar image. But the paper I had first placed so that the image might appear white as often as the comb was taken away; and then the Comb being as was said interposed, the whiteness by reason of the intercepted part of the colours at the lens did always change into the colour compounded of those colours which were not intercepted, and that colour was by the motion of the comb perpetually varied so that in the passing of every tooth over the lens all these colours (red, yellow, green, blue, and purple) did always succeed one another. I caused, therefore, all the teeth to pass successively over the lens, and when the motion was slow there appeared a perpetual succession of the colours upon the paper; but if I so much accelerated the motion that the colours by reason of their quick succession could not be distinguished from one another, the appearance of the single colours ceased. There was no red, no yellow, no green, no blue, nor purple to be seen any longer, but from a confusion of them all there arose one uniform white colour. Of the light which now by the mixture of all the colours appeared white, there was no part really white. One part was red, another yellow, a third green, a fourth blue, a fifth purple, and every part retains its proper colour till it strikes the sensorium. If the impressions follow one another slowly, so that they may be severally perceived, there is made a distinct sensation of all the colours one after another in a continual succession. But if the impressions follow one another so quickly that they cannot be severally perceived, there ariseth out of them all one common sensation, which is neither of this colour alone nor of that alone, but hath itself indifferently to them all, and this is a sensation of whiteness. By the quickness of the successions, the impressions of the several colours are confounded in the sensorium, and out of that confusion ariseth a mixed sensation. If a burning coal be nimbly moved round in a circle with gyrations continually repeated, the whole circle will apear like fire; the reason of which is that the sensation of the coal in the several places of that circle remains impressed on the sensorium until the coal return again to the same place. And so in a quick consecution of the colours the impression of every colour remains in the sensorium, until a revolution of all the colours be completed, and that first colour return again. The impressions, therefore, of all the successive colours are at once in the sensorium, and jointly stir up a sensation of them all; and so it is manifest by this experiment that the commixed impressions of all the colours do stir up and beget a sensation of white, that is, that whiteness is compounded of all the colours.

And if the comb be now taken away, that all the colours may at once pass from the lens to the paper, and be there intermixed, and together reflected thence to the spectator's eyes, their impressions on the sensorium being now more subtly and perfectly commixed there, ought much more to stir up a sensation of whiteness.

You may instead of the lens use two prisms HIK and LMN which, by refracting the coloured light the contrary way to that of the first refraction, may make the diverging rays converge and meet again in G, as you see represented in the seventh Figure. For where they meet and mix, they will compose a white light, as when a lens is used.

EXPER. 11. Let the Sun's coloured image PT [Fig. 8] fall upon the wall of a dark chamber, as in the third experiment of the first book, and let the same be viewed through a prism *abc*, held parallel to the prism ABC, by whose refraction that image was made, and let it now appear lower than before, suppose in the place S over against the red colour T. And if you go near to the image PT,

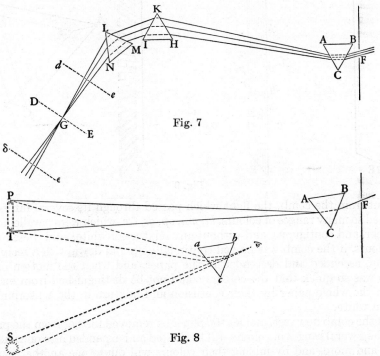

Fig. 7

Fig. 8

the spectrum S will appear oblong and coloured like the image PT; but if you recede from it the colours of the spectrum S will be contracted more and more, and at length vanish, that spectrum S becoming perfectly round and white; and if you recede yet farther, the colours will emerge again, but in a contrary order. Now that spectrum S appears white in that case, when the rays of several sorts which converge from the several parts of the image PT, to the prism *abc*, are so refracted unequally by it that in their passage from the prism to the eye they may diverge from one and the same point of the spectrum S, and so fall afterwards upon one and the same point in the bottom of the eye, and there be mingled.

And, further, if the comb be here made use of, by whose teeth the colours at the image PT may be successively intercepted, the spectrum S, when the comb is moved slowly, will be perpetually tinged with successive colours. But when, by accelerating the motion of the comb, the succession of the colours is so quick that they cannot be severally seen, that spectrum S, by a confused and mixed sensation of them all, will appear white.

EXPER. 12. The Sun shining through a large prism ABC [Fig. 9] upon a comb XY, placed immediately behind the prism, his light which passed through the interstices of the teeth fell upon a white paper DE. The breadths of the teeth were equal to their interstices, and seven teeth together with their interstices took up an inch in breadth. Now, when the paper was about two or three inches

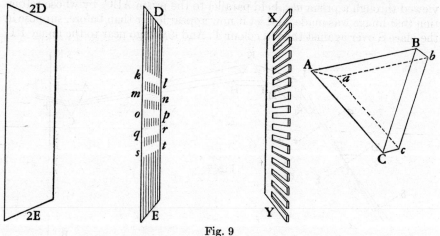

Fig. 9

distant from the comb, the light which passed through its several interstices painted so many ranges of colours, kl, mn, op, qr, &c. which were parallel to one another, and contiguous, and without any mixture of white. And these ranges of colours, if the comb was moved continually up and down with a reciprocal motion, ascended and descended in the paper, and when the motion of the comb was so quick that the colours could not be distinguished from one another, the whole paper by their confusion and mixture in the sensorium appeared white.

Let the comb now rest, and let the paper be removed farther from the prism, and the several ranges of colours will be dilated and expanded into one another more and more, and by mixing their colours will dilute one another, and at length, when the distance of the paper from the comb is about a foot, or a little more (suppose in the place 2D 2E) they will so far dilute one another as to become white.

With any obstacle, let all the light be now stopped which passes through any one interval of the teeth, so that the range of colours which comes from thence may be taken away, and you will see the light of the rest of the ranges to be expanded into the place of the range taken away, and there to be coloured. Let the intercepted range pass on as before, and its colours falling upon the colours of the other ranges, and mixing with them, will restore the whiteness.

Let the paper 2D 2E be now very much inclined to the rays, so that the most refrangible rays may be more copiously reflected than the rest, and the white colour of the paper through the excess of those rays will be changed into blue and violet. Let the paper be as much inclined the contrary way, that the least refrangible rays may be now more copiously reflected than the rest, and by their excess the whiteness will be changed into yellow and red. The several rays, therefore, in that white light do retain their colorific qualities, by which those of any sort, whenever they become more copious than the rest, do by their excess and predominance cause their proper colour to appear.

And by the same way of arguing, applied to the third experiment of this second part of the first book, it may be concluded that the white colour of all refracted light at its very first emergence, where it appears as white as before its incidence, is compounded of various colours.

EXPER. 13. In the foregoing experiment the several intervals of the teeth of the comb do the office of so many prisms, every interval producing the phenomenon of one prism. Whence instead of those intervals using several prisms, I tried to compound whiteness by mixing their colours, and did it by using only three prisms, as also by using only two as follows: Let two prisms ABC and abc, [Fig. 10] whose refracting angles B and b are equal, be so placed parallel to one

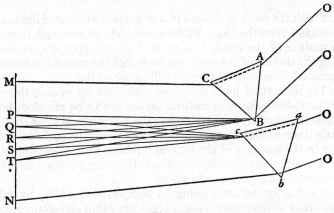

Fig. 10

another that the refracting angle B of the one may touch the angle c at the base of the other, and their planes CB and cb, at which the rays emerge, may lie in directum. Then let the light trajected through them fall upon the paper MN, distant about 8 or 12 inches from the prisms. And the colours generated by the interior limits B and c of the two prisms will be mingled at PT, and there compound white. For if either prism be taken away, the colours made by the other will appear in that place PT, and when the prism is restored to its place again, so that its colours may there fall upon the colours of the other, the mixture of them both will restore the whiteness.

This experiment succeeds also, as I have tried, when the angle b of the lower prism is a little greater than the angle B of the upper, and between the interior angles B and *c* there intercedes some space B*c*, as is represented in the figure, and the refracting planes BC and *bc* are neither in directum nor parallel to one another. For there is nothing more requisite to the success of this experiment than that the rays of all sorts may be uniformly mixed upon the paper in the place PT. If the most refrangible rays coming from the superior prism take up all the space from M to P, the rays of the same sort which come from the inferior prism ought to begin at P, and take up all the rest of the space from thence towards N. If the least refrangible rays coming from the superior prism take up the space MT, the rays of the same kind which come from the other prism ought to begin at T, and take up the remaining space TN. If one sort of the rays, which have intermediate degrees of refrangibility and come from the superior prism, be extended through the space MQ, and another sort of those rays through the space MR, and a third sort of them through the space MS, the same sorts of rays coming from the lower prism ought to illuminate the remaining spaces QN, RN, SN, respectively. And the same is to be understood of all the other sorts of rays. For thus the rays of every sort will be scattered uniformly and evenly through the whole space MN, and so, being everywhere mixed in the same proportion, they must everywhere produce the same colour. And, therefore, since by this mixture they produce white in the exterior spaces MP and TN, they must also produce white in the interior space PT. This is the reason of the composition by which whiteness was produced in this experiment, and by what other way soever I made the like composition, the result was whiteness.

Lastly, if with the teeth of a comb of a due size the coloured lights of the two prisms which fall upon the space PT be alternately intercepted, that space PT, when the motion of the comb is slow, will always appear coloured, but by accelerating the motion of the comb so much that the successive colours cannot be distinguished from one another, it will apear white.

EXPER. 14. Hitherto I have produced whiteness by mixing the colours of prisms. If, now, the colours of natural bodies are to be mingled, let water a little thickened with soap be agitated to raise a froth, and after that froth has stood a little there will appear to one that shall view it intently various colours everywhere in the surfaces of the several bubbles; but to one that shall go so far off that he cannot distinguish the colours from one another, the whole froth will grow white with a perfect whiteness.

EXPER. 15. Lastly, in attempting to compound a white, by mixing the coloured powders which painters use, I considered that all coloured powders do suppress and stop in them a very considerable part of the light by which they are illuminated. For they become coloured by reflecting the light of their own colours more copiously, and that of all other colours more sparingly, and yet they do not reflect the light of their own colours so copiously as white bodies do. If red lead, for instance, and a white paper be placed in the red light of the coloured spectrum made in a dark chamber by the refraction of a prism, as is described in the third experiment of the first part of this book, the paper will appear more lucid than the red lead, and therefore reflects the red-making rays more copiously than red lead doth. And if they be held in the light of any other colour, the light reflected by the paper will exceed the light reflected by the red lead in a much greater proportion. And the like happens in powders of other colours. And, therefore, by mixing such powders we are not to expect a strong and full white, such as is that of paper, but some dusky obscure one, such as might arise from a mixture of light and darkness, or from white and black; that is, a grey, or dun, or russet brown, such as are the colours of a man's nail, of a mouse, of ashes, of ordinary stones, of mortar, of dust and dirt in highways, and the like. And such a dark white I have often produced by mixing coloured powders. For thus one part of red lead, and five parts of *viride æris* composed a dun colour like that of a mouse. For these two colours were severally so compounded of others that in both together were a mixture of all colours; and there was less red lead used than *viride æris*, because of the fulness of its colour. Again, one part of red lead and four parts of blue bice composed a dun colour verging a little to purple, and by adding to this a certain mixture of orpiment and *viride æris* in a due proportion, the mixture lost its purple tincture and became perfectly dun. But the experiment succeeded best without minium thus: To orpiment I added by little and little a certain full bright purple, which painters use, until the orpiment ceased to be yellow, and became of a pale red. Then I diluted that red by adding a little *viride æris*, and a little more blue bice than *viride æris*, until it became of such a grey or pale white as verged to no one of the colours more than to another. For thus it became of a colour equal in whiteness to that of ashes, or of wood newly cut, or of a man's skin. The orpiment reflected more light than did any other of the powders, and therefore conduced more to the whiteness of the compounded colour than they. To assign the proportions accurately may be difficult, by reason of the different goodness of powders of the same kind. Accordingly, as the colour of any powder is more or less full and luminous, it ought to be used in a less or greater proportion.

Now, considering that these grey and dun colours may be also produced by mixing whites and blacks, and by consequence differ from perfect whites, not in species of colours but only in degree of luminousness, it is manifest that there is nothing more requisite to make them perfectly white than to increase their light sufficiently; and, on the contrary, if by increasing their light they can be brought to perfect whiteness, it will thence also follow that they are of the same species of colour with the best whites, and differ from them only in the quantity of light. And this I tried as follows: I took the third of the above-mentioned grey mixtures, (that which was compounded of orpiment, purple, bice, and *viride æris*) and rubbed it thickly upon the floor of my chamber where the Sun shone upon it through the opened casement; and by it, in the shadow, I laid a piece of white paper of the same bigness. Then, going from them to the distance of 12 or 18 feet, so that I could not discern the unevenness of the surface of the powder, nor the little shadows let fall from the gritty particles thereof, the powder appeared intensely white, so as to transcend even the paper itself in whiteness, especially if the paper were a little shaded from the light of the clouds, and then the paper compared with the powder appeared of such a grey colour as the powder had done before. But by laying the paper where the Sun shines through the glass of the window, or by shutting the window that the Sun might shine through the glass upon the powder, and by such other fit means of increasing or decreasing the lights wherewith the powder and paper were illuminated, the light wherewith the powder is illuminated may be made stronger in such a due proportion than the light wherewith the paper is illuminated that they shall both appear exactly alike in whiteness. For when I was trying this, a friend coming to visit me, I stopped him at the door, and before I told him what the colours were, or what I was doing, I asked him which of the two whites was the best, and wherein they differed. And after he had at that distance viewed them well, he answered that they were both good whites, and that he could not say which was best, nor wherein their colours differed. Now, if you consider that this white of the powder in the sunshine was compounded of the colours which the component powders (orpiment, purple, bice, and *viride œris*) have in the same sunshine, you must acknowledge by this experiment, as well as by the former, that perfect whiteness may be compounded of colours.

From what has been said it is also evident that the whiteness of the Sun's light is compounded of all the colours wherewith the several sorts of rays whereof that light consists, when by their several refrangibilities they are separated from one another, do tinge paper or any other white body whereon they fall. For those colours (by *Prop. II. Part 2.*) are unchangeable, and whenever all those rays with those their colours are mixed again, they reproduce the same white light as before.

Proposition 6. Problem 2

In a mixture of primary colours, the quantity and quality of each being given, to know the colour of the compound.

With the centre O [Fig. 11] and radius OD describe a circle ADF, and distinguish its circumference into seven parts DE, EF, FG, GA, AB, BC, CD, proportional to the seven musical tones or intervals of the eight sounds, *Sol, la, fa, sol, la, mi, fa, sol*, contained in an eight; that is, proportional to the number $\frac{1}{9}, \frac{1}{16}, \frac{1}{10}, \frac{1}{9}, \frac{1}{16}, \frac{1}{16}, \frac{1}{9}$. Let the first part DE represent a red colour, the second EF orange, the third FG yellow, the fourth CA green, the fifth AB blue, the sixth BC indigo, and the seventh CD violet. And conceive that these are all the colours of uncompounded light gradually passing into one another, as they do when made by prisms; the circumference DEFGABCD, representing the whole series of colours from one end of the Sun's coloured image to the other, so that from D to E be all degrees of red, at E the mean colour between red and orange, from E to F all degrees of orange, at F the mean between orange and yellow, from F to G all degrees of yellow, and so on. Let p be the centre of gravity of the arch DE, and $q, r, s, t, u, x,$ the centres of gravity of the arches EF, FG, GA, AB, BC, and CD, respectively, and about those centres of gravity let circles proportional to the number of rays of each colour in the given mixture be described: that is, the circle p proportional to the number of the red-making rays in the mixture, the circle q proportional to the number of the orange-making rays in the mixture, and so of the rest. Find the common centre of gravity of all those circles, p, q, r, s, t, u, x. Let that centre be Z; and from the centre of the circle ADF, through Z to the circumference, drawing the right line OY, the place of the point Y in the circumference shall shew the colour aris-

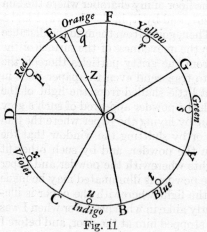

Fig. 11

ing from the composition of all the colours in the given mixture, and the line OZ shall be proportional to the fulness or intenseness of the colour; that is, to its distance from whiteness. As if Y fall in the middle between F and G, the compounded colour shall be the best yellow; if Y verge from the middle towards F or G, the compound colour shall accordingly be a yellow, verging towards orange or green. If Z fall upon the circumference, the colour shall be intense and florid in the highest degree; if it fall in the midway between the circumference and centre, it shall be but half so intense; that is, it shall be such a colour as would be made by diluting the intensest yellow with an equal quantity of whiteness; and if it fall upon the centre O, the colour shall have lost all its intenseness, and become a white. But it is to be noted that if the point Z fall in or near the line OD, the main ingredients being the red and violet, the colour compounded shall not be any of the prismatic colours, but a purple, inclining to red or violet, accordingly as the point Z lieth on the side of the line DO towards E or towards C, and in general the compounded violet is more bright and more fiery than the uncompounded. Also, if only two of the primary colours which in the circle are opposite to one another be mixed in an equal proportion, the point Z shall fall upon the centre O, and yet the colour compounded of those two shall not be perfectly white, but some faint anonymous colour. For I could never yet by mixing only two primary colours produce a perfect white. Whether it may be compounded of a mixture of three taken at equal distances in the circumference I do not know, but of four or five I do not much question but it may. But these are curiosities of little or no moment to the understanding the phenomena of Nature. For in all whites produced by Nature, there uses to be a mixture of all sorts of rays, and by consequence a composition of all colours.

To give an instance of this rule, suppose a colour is compounded of these homogeneal colours: of violet one part, of indigo one part, of blue two parts, of green three parts, of yellow five parts, of orange six parts, and of red ten parts. Proportional to these parts describe the circles x, v, t, s, r, q, p, respectively, that is, so that if the circle x be one, the circle v may be one, the circle t two, the circle s three, and the circles r, q and p, five, six and ten. Then I find Z the common centre of gravity of these circles, and through Z drawing the line OY, the point Y falls upon the circumference between E and F, something nearer to E than to F; and thence I conclude that the colour compounded of these ingredients will be an orange, verging a little more to red than to yellow. Also I find that OZ is a little less than one half of OY, and thence I conclude that this orange hath a little less than half the fulness or intenseness of an uncompounded orange; that is to say, that it is such an orange as may be made by mixing an homogeneal orange with a good white in the proportion of the Line OZ to the Line ZY, this proportion being not of the quantities of mixed orange and white powders, but of the quantities of the lights reflected from them.

This rule I conceive accurate enough for practice, though not mathematically accurate; and the truth of it may be sufficiently proved to sense by stopping any of the colours at the lens in the tenth experiment of this book. For the rest of the colours which are not stopped, but pass on to the focus of the lens, will there compound either accurately or very nearly such a colour as by this rule ought to result from their mixture.

PROPOSITION 7. THEOREM 5

All the colours in the universe which are made by light, and depend not on the power of imagination, are either the colours of homogeneal lights, or compounded of these, and that either accurately or very nearly, according to the rule of the foregoing problem.

For it has been proved (Prop. 1, Part 2) that the changes of colours made by refractions do not arise from any new modifications of the rays impressed by those refractions, and by the various terminations of light and shadow, as has been the constant and general opinion of philosophers. It has also been proved that the several colours of the homogeneal rays do constantly answer to their degrees of refrangibility (Prop. 1, Part 1 and Prop. 2, Part 2) and that their degrees of refrangibility cannot be changed by refractions and reflexions (Prop. 2, Part 1) and by consequence that those their colours are likewise immutable. It has also been proved directly by refracting and reflecting homogeneal lights apart, that their colours cannot be changed (Prop. 2, Part 2). It has been proved, also, that when the several sorts of rays are mixed, and in crossing pass through the same space, they do not act on one another so as to change each other's colorific qualities (Exper. 10, Part 2) but by mixing their actions in the sensorium beget a sensation differing from what either would do apart (that is, a sensation of a mean colour between their proper colours); and particularly when by the concourse and mixtures of all sorts of rays a white colour is produced, the white is a mixture of all the colours which the rays would have apart (Prop. 5, Part 2). The rays in that mixture do not lose or alter their several colorific qualities, but by all their various kinds of actions, mixed in the sensorium, beget a sensation of a middling colour between all their colours, which is whiteness. For whiteness is a mean between all colours, having itself indifferently to them all, so as with equal facility to be tinged with any of them. A red powder mixed with a little blue, or a blue with a little red, doth not presently lose its colour, but a white powder mixed with any colour is presently tinged with that colour, and is equally capable of being tinged with any colour whatever. It has been shewed, also, that as the Sun's light is mixed of all sorts of rays, so its whiteness is a mixture of the colours of all sorts of rays; those rays having from the beginning their several colorific qualities as well as their several refrangibilities, and retaining them perpetually unchanged notwithstanding any refractions or reflexions they may at any time suffer, and that whenever any sort of the Sun's rays is by any means (as by reflexion in Expers. 9 and 10, Part 1 or by refraction as happens in all refractions) separated from the rest, they then manifest their proper colours. These things have been proved, and the sum of all this amounts to the proposition here to be proved. For if the Sun's light is mixed of several sorts of rays, each of which have originally their several refrangibilities and colorific qualities, and notwithstanding their refractions and reflexions, and their various separations or mixtures, keep those their original properties perpetually the same without alteration; then all the colours in the world must be such as constantly ought to arise from the original colorific qualities of the rays whereof the lights consist by which those colours are seen. And, therefore, if the reason of any colour whatever be required, we have nothing else to do than to consider how the rays in the Sun's light have by reflexions or refractions, or other causes, been parted from one another, or mixed together; or otherwise to find out what sorts of rays are in the light by which that colour is made, and in what proportion; and then, by the last problem, to learn the colour which ought to arise by mixing those rays (or their colours) in that proportion. I speak here of colours so far as they arise from light. For they appear sometimes by other causes, as when by the power of phantasy we see colours in a dream, or a madman sees things before him which are not there; or when we see fire by striking the eye, or see colours like the eye of a peacock's feather by pressing our eyes in either corner whilst we look the other way. Where these and such like causes interpose not, the colour always answers to the sort or sorts of the rays whereof the light consists, as I have constantly found in whatever phenomena of colours I have hitherto been able to examine. I shall in the following Propositions give instances of this in the phenomena of chiefest note.

PROPOSITION 8. PROBLEM 3

By the discovered properties of light, to explain the colours made by prisms.

Let ABC [Fig. 12] represent a prism refracting the light of the Sun, which comes into a dark chamber through a hole Fϕ almost as broad as the prism, and let MN represent a white paper on which the refracted light is cast, and suppose the most refrangible or deepest violet-making rays fall upon the space Pπ, the least refrangible or deepest red-making rays upon the space Tτ, the middle sort between the indigo-making and blue-making rays upon the space Qχ, the middle sort of the green-making rays upon the space R, the middle sort between the yellow-making and orange-making rays upon the space Sσ, and

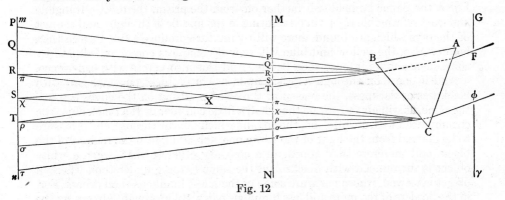

Fig. 12

other intermediate sorts upon intermediate spaces. For so the spaces upon which the several sorts adequately fall will, by reason of the different refrangibility of those sorts, be one lower than another. Now, if the paper MN be so near the prism that the spaces PT and $\pi\tau$ do not interfere with one another, the distance between them Tπ will be illuminated by all the sorts of rays in that proportion to one another which they have at their very first coming out of the prism, and consequently be white. But the spaces PT and $\pi\tau$ on either hand will not be illuminated by them all, and, therefore, will appear coloured. And particularly at P, where the outmost violet-making rays fall alone, the colour must be the deepest violet. At Q where the violet-making and indigo-making rays are mixed, it must be a violet inclining much to indigo. At R where the violet-making, indigo-making, blue-making, and one half of the green-making rays are mixed, their colours must (by the construction of the second problem) compound a middle colour between indigo and blue. At S where all the rays are mixed, except the red-making and orange-making, their colours ought by the same rule to compound a faint blue, verging more to green than indigo. And in the progress from S to T, this blue will grow more and more faint and dilute, till at T, where all the colours begin to be mixed, it ends in whiteness.

So again, on the other side of the white at τ, where the least refrangible or utmost red-making rays are alone, the colour must be the deepest red. At σ the mixture of red and orange will compound a red inclining to orange. At ρ the mixture of red, orange, yellow, and one half of the green must compound a middle colour between orange and yellow. At χ the mixture of all colours but violet and indigo will compound a faint yellow, verging more to green than to orange. And this yellow will grow more faint and dilute continually in its progress from χ to π, where by a mixture of all sorts of rays it will become white.

These colours ought to appear were the Sun's light perfectly white; but because it inclines to yellow, the excess of the yellow-making rays whereby 'tis tinged with that colour, being mixed with the faint blue between S and T, will draw it to a faint green. And so the colours in order from P to τ ought to be violet, indigo, blue, very faint green, white, faint yellow, orange, red. Thus it is by the computation; and they that please to view the colours made by a prism will find it so in Nature.

These are the colours on both sides the white when the paper is held between the prism and the point X where the colours meet, and the interjacent white vanishes. For if the paper be held still farther off from the prism, the most refrangible and least refrangible rays will be wanting in the middle of the light, and the rest of the rays which are found there will by mixture produce a fuller green than before. Also, the yellow and blue will now become less compounded, and by consequence more intense then before. And this also agrees with experience.

And if one look through a prism upon a white object encompassed with blackness or darkness, the reason of the colours arising on the edges is much the same, as will appear to one that shall a little consider it. If a black object be encompassed with a white one, the colours which appear through the prism are to be derived from the light of the white one, spreading into the regions of the black, and therefore they appear in a contrary order to that, when a white object is surrounded with black. And the same is to be understood when an object is viewed, whose parts are some of them less luminous than others. For, in the borders of the more and less luminous parts, colours ought always by the same principles to arise from the excess of the light of the more luminous, and to be of the same kind as if the darker parts were black, but yet to be more faint and dilute.

What is said of colours made by prisms may be easily applied to colours made by the glasses of telescopes or microscopes, or by the humours of the eye. For if the object-glass of a telescope be thicker on one side than on the other, or if one-half of the glass, or one-half of the pupil of the eye be covered with any opaque substance, the object-glass, or that part of it or of the eye which is not covered, may be considered as a wedge with crooked sides, and every wedge of glass or other pellucid substance has the effect of a prism in refracting the light which passes through it.

How the colours in the ninth and tenth experiments of the first part arise from the different reflexibility of light, is evident by what was there said. But it is observable in the ninth experiment that whilst the Sun's direct light is yellow, the excess of the blue-making rays in the reflected beam of light MN suffices only to bring that yellow to a pale white inclining to blue, and not to tinge it with a manifestly blue colour. To obtain, therefore, a better blue, I used instead of the yellow light of the Sun the white light of the clouds, by varying a little the experiment, as follows:

EXPER. 16. Let HFG [Fig. 13] represent a prism in the open air, and S the eye of the spectator viewing the clouds by their light coming into the prism at the plane side FIGK, and reflected in it by its base HEIG, and thence going out through its plane side HEFK to the eye. And when the prism and eye are conveniently placed, so that the angles of incidence and reflexion at the base may be about 40 degrees, the spectator will see a bow MN of a blue colour running from one end of the base to the other, with the concave side towards him, and the part of the base IMNG beyond this bow will be brighter than the other part EMNH on the other side of it. This blue colour MN, being made by nothing else than by reflexion of a specular superficies, seems so odd a phenomenon, and so difficult to be explained by the vulgar hypothesis of philosophers, that I could not but think it deserved to be taken notice of. Now, for understanding the reason of it, suppose the plane ABC to cut the plane sides and base of the prism perpendicularly. From the eye to the line BC, wherein that

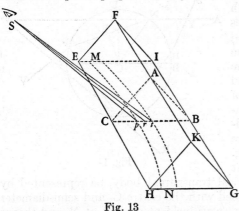

Fig. 13

plane cuts the base, draw the lines Sp and St, in the angles Spc 50 degrees $\frac{1}{9}$, and Stc 49 degrees $\frac{1}{28}$, and the point p will be the limit beyond which none of the most refrangible rays can pass through the base of the prism, and be refracted, whose incidence is such that they may be reflected to the eye; and the point t will be the like limit for the least refrangible rays (that is, beyond which none of them can pass through the base) whose incidence is such that by reflexion they may come to the eye. And the point r, taken in the middle way between p and t, will be the like limit for the meanly refrangible rays. And, therefore, all the least refrangible rays which fall upon the base beyond t, (that is, between t and B) and can come from thence to the eye, will be reflected thither; but on this side t (that is, between t and c) many of these rays will be transmitted through the base. And all the most refrangible rays which fall upon the base beyond p, (that is, between p and B) and can by reflexion come from thence to the eye will be reflected thither, but everywhere between p and c many of these rays will get through the base, and be refracted; and the same is to be understood of the meanly refrangible rays on either side of the point r. Whence it follows that the base of the prism must everywhere between t and B, by a total reflexion of all sorts of rays to the eye, look white and bright; and everywhere between p and C, by reason of the transmission of many rays of every sort, look more pale, obscure, and dark. But at *r*, and in other places between *p* and *t*, where all the more refrangible rays are reflected to the eye, and many of the less refrangible are transmitted, the excess of the most refrangible in the reflected light will tinge that light with their colour, which is violet and blue. And this happens by taking the line C *prt* B anywhere between the ends of the prism HG and EI.

PROPOSITION 9. PROBLEM 4

By the discovered properties of light, to explain the colours of the rainbow.

This bow never appears but where it rains in the sunshine, and may be made artificially by spouting up water which may break aloft, and scatter into drops, and fall down like rain. For the Sun shining upon these drops certainly causes the bow to appear to a spectator standing in a due position to the rain and Sun. And hence it is now agreed upon, that this bow is made by refraction of the Sun's light in drops of falling rain. This was understood by some of the ancients, and of late more fully discovered and explained by the famous Antonius de Dominis, Archbishop of Spalato in his book *De Radiis Visus & Lucis*, published by his friend Bartolus at Venice, in the year 1611, and written above 20 years before. For he teaches there how the interior bow is made in round drops of rain by two refractions of the Sun's light, and one reflexion between them, and the exterior by two refractions, and two sorts of reflexions between them in each drop of water, and proves his ex-

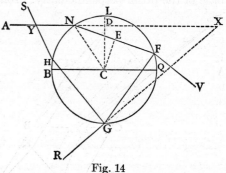

plications by experiments made with a phial full of water, and with globes of glass filled with water, and placed in the Sun to make the colours of the two bows appear in them. The same explication Descartes hath pursued in his *Meteors*, and mended that of the exterior bow. But whilst they understood not the true origin of colours, it's necessary to pursue it here a little farther. For understanding, therefore, how the bow is made, let

Fig. 14

a drop of rain, or any other spherical transparent body, be represented by the sphere BNFG, [Fig. 14] described with the centre C, and semi-diameter CN. And let AN be one of the Sun's rays incident upon it at N, and thence refracted to F, where let it either go out of the sphere by refraction towards V, or be reflected to G; and at G let it either go out by refraction to R, or be reflected to H; and at H let it go out by refraction towards S, cutting the incident ray in Y. Produce AN and RG, till they meet in X, and upon AX and NF, let fall the perpendiculars CD and CE, and produce CD till it fall upon the circumference at L. Parallel to the incident ray AN draw the diameter BQ, and let the sine of incidence out of air into water be to the sine of refraction as I to R. Now, if you suppose the point of incidence N to move from the point B continually till it come to L, the arch QF will first increase and then decrease, and so will the angle AXR which the rays AN and GR contain; and the arch QF and angle AXR will be biggest when ND is to CN as $\sqrt{\mathrm{II} - \mathrm{RR}}$ to $\sqrt{3\mathrm{RR}}$, in which case NE will be to ND as 2R to I. Also the angle AYS, which the rays

AN and HS contain, will first decrease and then increase and grow least when ND is to CN as $\sqrt{II-RR}$ to $\sqrt{8RR}$, in which case NE will be to ND as 3R to I. And so the angle which the next emergent ray (that is, the emergent ray after three reflexions) contains with the incident ray AN will come to its limit when ND is to CN as $\sqrt{II-RR}$ to $\sqrt{15RR}$, in which case NE will be to ND as 4R to I. And the angle which the ray next after that emergent (that is, the ray emergent after four reflexions) contains with the incident will come to its limit when ND is to CN as $\sqrt{II-RR}$ to $\sqrt{24RR}$, in which case NE will be to ND as 5R to I; and so on infinitely, the numbers 3, 8, 15, 24, &c. being gathered by continual addition of the terms of the arithmetical progression 3, 5, 7, 9, &c. The truth of all this mathematicians will easily examine.

Now, it is to be observed that, as when the sun comes to his tropics, days increase and decrease but a very little for a great while together; so when by increasing the distance CD, these angles come to their limits, they vary their quantity but very little for some time together; and, therefore, a far greater number of the rays which fall upon all the points N in the quadrant BL shall emerge in the limits of these angles than in any other inclinations. And further it is to be observed that the rays which differ in refrangibility will have different limits of their angles of emergence, and by consequence according to their different degrees of refrangibility emerge most copiously in different angles, and being separated from one another appear each in their proper colours. And what those angles are may be easily gathered from the foregoing theorem by computation.

For in the least refrangible rays the sines I and R (as was found above) are 108 and 81, and thence by computation the greatest angle AXR will be found 42 degrees and 2 minutes, and the least angle AYS, 50 degrees and 57 minutes. And in the most refrangible rays the sines I and R are 109 and 81, and thence by computation the greatest angle AXR will be found 40 degrees and 17 minutes, and the least angle AYS 54 degrees and 7 minutes.

Suppose, now, that O [Fig. 15] is the spectator's eye, and OP a line drawn parallel to the Sun's rays; and let POE, POF, POG, POH, be angles of 40 degrees 17 minutes, 42 degrees 2 minutes, 50 degrees 57 minutes, and 54 degrees 7 minutes, respectively, and these angles turned about their common side OP, shall with their other sides OE, OF, OG, OH, describe the verges of two rain-

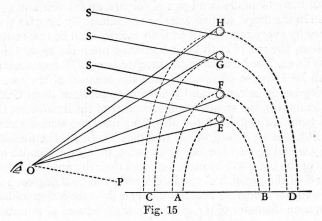

Fig. 15

bows AF, BE, and CHDG. For if E, F, G, H, be drops placed anywhere in the conical superficies described by OE, OF, OG, OH, and be illuminated by the Sun's rays SE, SF, SG, SH; the angle SEO being equal to the angle POE, or 40 degrees 17 minutes, shall be the greatest angle in which the most refrangible rays can after one reflexion be refracted to the eye; and, therefore, all the drops in the line OE shall send the most refrangible rays most copiously to the eye, and thereby strike the senses with the deepest violet colour in that region. And in like manner the angle SFO being equal to the angle POF, or 42 degrees 2 minutes, shall be the greatest in which the least refrangible rays after one reflexion can emerge out of the drops; and, therefore, those rays shall come most copiously to the eye from the drops in the line OF, and strike the senses with the deepest red colour in that region. And, by the same argument, the rays which have intermediate degrees of refrangibility shall come most copiously from drops between E and F, and strike the senses with the intermediate colours in the order which their degrees of refrangibility require; that is, in the progress from E to F, or from the inside of the bow to the outside, in this order: violet, indigo, blue, green, yellow, orange, red. But the violet, by the mixture of the white light of the clouds, will appear faint and incline to purple.

Again, the angle SGO being equal to the angle POG, or 50° 51′, shall be the least angle in which the least refrangible rays can after two reflexions emerge out of the drops; and, therefore, the least refrangible rays shall come most copiously to the eye from the drops in the line OG, and strike the sense with the deepest red in that region. And the angle SHO being equal to the angle POH, or 54 degrees 7 minutes, shall be the least angle in which the most refrangible rays after two reflexions can emerge out of the drops; and, therefore, those rays shall come most copiously to the eye from the drops in the line OH, and strike the senses with the deepest violet in that region. And by the same argument, the drops in the regions between G and H shall strike the sense with the intermediate colours in the order which their degrees of refrangibility require; that is, in the progress from G to H, or from the inside of the bow to the outside, in this order: red, orange, yellow, green, blue, indigo, violet. And since these four lines OE, OF, OG, OH, may be situated anywhere in the above-mentioned conical superficies, what is said of the drops and colours in these lines is to be understood of the drops and colours everywhere in those superficies.

Thus shall there be made two bows of colours, an interior and stronger, by one reflexion in the drops, and an exterior and fainter by two; for the light becomes fainter by every reflexion. And their colours shall lie in a contrary order to one another, the red of both bows bordering upon the space GF, which is between the bows. The breadth of the interior bow EOF measured across the colours shall be 1 degree 45 minutes, and the breadth of the exterior GOH shall be 3 degrees 10 minutes, and the distance between them GOF shall be 8 degrees 15 minutes, the greatest semi-diameter of the innermost; that is, the angle POF being 42 degrees 2 minutes, and the least semi-diameter of the outermost POG, being 50 degrees 57 minutes. These are the measures of the bows as they would be were the Sun but a point; for by the breadth of his body the breadth of the bows will be increased, and their distance decreased by half a degree, and so the breadth of the interior iris will be 2 degrees 15 minutes, that of the exterior 3 degrees 40 minutes, their distance 8 degrees 25 minutes, the greatest semi-diameter of the interior bow 42 degrees 17 minutes, and the least of the exterior 50 degrees 42 minutes. And such are the dimensions of the bows in the heavens found to be very nearly, when their colours appear strong and perfect. For once, by such means as I then had, I measured the greatest semi-diameter of the interior iris about 42 degrees, and the breadth of the red, yellow and green in that iris 63 or 64 minutes, besides the outmost faint red obscured by the brightness of the clouds, for which we may allow 3 or 4 minutes more. The breadth of the blue was about 40 minutes more besides the violet, which was so much obscured by the brightness of the clouds that I could not measure its breadth. But supposing the breadth of the blue and violet together to equal that of the red, yellow and green together, the whole breadth of this iris will be about $2\frac{1}{4}$ degrees, as above. The least distance between this iris and the exterior iris was about 8 degrees and 30 minutes. The exterior iris was broader than the interior, but so faint, especially on the blue side, that I could not measure its breadth distinctly. At another time when both bows appeared more distinct, I measured the breadth of the interior iris 2 degrees 10 minutes, and the breadth of the red, yellow and green in the exterior iris was to the breadth of the same colours in the interior as 3 to 2.

This explication of the rainbow is yet further confirmed by the known experiment (made by Antonius de Dominis and Descartes) of hanging up anywhere in the sunshine a glass globe filled with water, and viewing it in such a posture that the rays which come from the globe to the eye may contain with the Sun's rays an angle of either 42 or 50 degrees. For if the angle be about 42 or 43 degrees, the spectator (suppose at O) shall see a full red colour in that side of the globe opposed to the Sun as 'tis represented at F, and if that angle become less (suppose by depressing the globe to E) there will appear other colours, yellow, green and blue successive in the same side of the globe. But if the angle be made about 50 degrees (suppose by lifting up the globe to G) there will appear a red colour in that side of the globe towards the Sun, and if the angle be made greater (suppose by lifting up the globe to H) the red will turn successively to the other colours, yellow, green and blue. The same thing I have tried by letting a globe rest, and raising or depressing the eye, or otherwise moving it to make the angle of a just magnitude.

I have heard it represented that if the light of a candle be refracted by a prism to the eye, when the blue colour falls upon the eye the spectator shall see red in the prism, and when the red falls upon the eye he shall see blue; and if this were certain the colours of the globe and rainbow ought to appear in a contrary order to what we find. But the colours of the candle being very faint, the mistake seems to arise from the difficulty of discerning what colours fall on the eye. For, on the contrary, I have sometimes had occasion to observe, in the Sun's light refracted by a prism, that the spectator always sees that colour in the prism which falls upon his eye. And the same I have found true also in candle-light. For when the prism is moved slowly from the line which is drawn directly from the candle to the eye, the red appears first in the prism and then the blue; and, therefore, each of them is seen when it falls upon the eye. For the red passes over the eye first, and then the blue.

The light which comes through drops of rain by two refractions without any reflexion ought to appear strongest at the distance of about 26 degrees from the Sun, and to decay gradually both ways as the distance from him increases and decreases. And the same is to be understood of light transmitted through spherical hailstones. And if the hail be a little flatted, as it often is, the light transmitted may grow so strong at a little less distance than that of 26 degrees, as to form a halo about the Sun or Moon; which halo, as often as the hailstones are duly figured, may be coloured, and then it must be red within by the least refrangible rays, and blue without by the most refrangible ones, especially if the hailstones have opaque globules of snow in their centre to intercept the light within the halo (as Huygens has observed) and make the inside thereof more distinctly defined than it would otherwise be. For such hailstones, though spherical, by terminating the light by the snow, may make a halo red within and colourless without, and darker in the red than without, as halos used to be. For of those rays which pass close by the snow the rubriform will be least refracted, and so come to the eye in the directest lines.

The light which passes through a drop of rain after two refractions, and three or more reflexions, is scarce strong enough to cause a sensible bow; but in those cylinders of ice by which Huygens explains the parhelia, it may perhaps be sensible.

PROPOSITION 10. PROBLEM 5

By the discovered properties of light, to explain the permanent colours of natural bodies.

These colours arise from hence, that some natural bodies reflect some sorts of rays, others other sorts more copiously than the rest. Minium reflects the least refrangible or red-making rays most copiously, and thence appears red. Violets reflect the most refrangible most copiously, and thence have their colour, and so of other bodies. Every body reflects the rays of its own colour more copiously than the rest, and from their excess and predominance in the reflected light has its colour.

EXPER. 17. For if, in the homogeneal lights obtained by the solution of the problem proposed in the fourth Proposition of the first part of this book, you place bodies of several colours, you will find, as I have done, that every body looks most splendid and luminous in the light of its own colour. Cinnabar in the homogeneal red light is most resplendent, in the green light it is manifestly less resplendent, and in the blue light still less. Indigo in the violet blue light is most resplendent, and its splendour is gradually diminished as it is removed thence by degrees through the green and yellow light to the red. By a leek the green light, and next that the blue and yellow which compound green, are more strongly reflected than the other colours red and violet, and so of the rest. But to make these experiments the more manifest, such bodies ought to be chosen as have the fullest and most vivid colours, and two of those bodies are to be compared together. Thus, for instance, if cinnabar and ultra-marine blue, or some other full blue be held together in the red homogeneal light, they will both appear red, but the cinnabar will appear of a strongly luminous and resplendent red, and the ultra-marine blue of a faint obscure and dark red; and if they be held together in the blue homogeneal light, they will both appear blue, but the ultra-marine will appear of a strongly luminous and resplendent blue, and the cinnabar of a faint and dark blue. Which puts it out of dispute that the cinnabar reflects the red light much more copiously than the ultra-marine doth, and the ultra-marine reflects the blue light much more copiously than the cinnabar doth. The same experiment may be tried successfully with red lead and indigo or with any other two coloured bodies, if due allowance be made for the different strength or weakness of their colour and light.

And as the reason of the colours of natural bodies is evident by these experiments, so it is further confirmed and put past dispute by the two first experiments of the first part, whereby 'twas proved in such bodies that the reflected lights which differ in colours do differ also in degrees of refrangibility. For thence it's certain that some bodies reflect the more refrangible, others the less refrangible rays more copiously.

And that this is not only a true reason of these colours, but even the only reason, may appear further from this consideration that the colour of homogeneal light cannot be changed by the reflexion of natural bodies.

For if bodies by reflexion cannot in the least change the colour of any one sort of rays, they cannot appear coloured by any other means than by reflecting those which either are of their own colour, or which by mixture must produce it.

But in trying experiments of this kind, care must be had that the light be sufficiently homogeneal. For if bodies be illuminated by the ordinary prismatic colours, they will appear neither of their own daylight colours, nor of the colour of the light cast on them, but of some middle colour between both, as I have found by experience. Thus, red lead (for instance) illuminated with the ordinary prismatic green, will not appear either red or green, but orange or yellow, or between yellow and green, accordingly as the green light by which 'tis illuminated is more or less compounded. For because red lead appears red when illuminated with white light, wherein all sorts of rays are equally mixed, and in the green light all sorts of rays are not equally mixed, the excess of the yellow-making, green-making and blue-making rays in the incident green light will cause those rays to abound so much in the reflected light as to draw the colour from red towards their colour. And because the red lead reflects the red-making rays most copiously in proportion to their number, and next after them the orange-making and yellow-making rays, these rays in the reflected light will be more in proportion to the light than they were in the incident green light, and thereby will draw the reflected light from green towards their colour. And, therefore, the red lead will appear neither red nor green, but of a colour between both.

In transparently coloured liquors, 'tis observable that their colour uses to vary with their thickness. Thus, for instance, a red liquor in a conical glass, held between the light and the eye, looks of a pale and dilute yellow at the bottom where 'tis thin, and a little higher where 'tis thicker grows orange, and where 'tis still thicker becomes red, and where 'tis thickest the red is deepest and darkest. For it is to be conceived that such a liquor stops the indigo-making and violet-making rays most easily, the blue-making rays more difficultly, the green-making rays still more difficultly, and the red-making most difficultly; and that if the thickness of the liquor be only so much as suffices to stop a competent number of the violet-making and indigo-making rays, without diminishing much the number of the rest, the rest must (by Prop. 6, Part 2) compound a pale yellow. But if the liquor be so much thicker as to stop also a great number of the blue-making rays, and some of the green-making, the rest must compound an orange; and where it is so thick as to stop also a great number of the green-making and a considerable number of the yellow-making, the rest must begin to compound a red, and this red must grow deeper and darker as the yellow-making and orange-making rays are more and more stopped by increasing the thickness of the liquor, so that few rays besides the red-making can get through.

Of this kind is an experiment lately related to me by Mr. Halley, who, in diving deep into the sea in a diving vessel, found in a clear sunshine day that when he was sunk many fathoms deep into the water the upper part of his hand on which the Sun shone directly through the water and through a small glass window in the vessel appeared of a red colour, like that of a damask rose, and the water below and the under part of his hand illuminated by light reflected from the water below looked green. For thence it may be gathered, that the sea water reflects back the violet and blue-making rays most easily, and lets the red-making rays pass most freely and copiously to great depths. For thereby the Sun's direct light at all great depths, by reason of the predominating red-making rays, must appear red; and the greater the depth is, the fuller and intenser must that red be. And at such depths as the violet-making rays scarce penetrate unto, the blue-making, green-making, and yellow-making rays, being reflected from below more copiously than the red-making ones, must compound a green.

Now, if there be two liquors of full colours, (suppose a red and blue) and both of them so thick as suffices to make their colours sufficiently full, though either liquor be sufficiently transparent apart, yet will you not be able to see through both together. For, if only the red-making rays pass through one liquor, and only the blue-making through the other, no rays can pass through both. This Mr. Hook tried casually with glass wedges filled with red and blue liquors, and was surprised at the unexpected event, the reason of it being then unknown; which makes me trust the more to his experiment, though I have not tried it myself. But he that would repeat it must take care the liquors be of very good and full colours.

Now, whilst bodies become coloured by reflecting or transmitting this or that sort of rays more copiously than the rest, it is to be conceived that they stop and stifle in themselves the rays which they do not reflect or transmit. For, if gold be foliated and held between your eye and the light, the light looks of a greenish-blue, and therefore massy gold lets into its body the blue-making rays to be reflected to and fro within it till they be stopped and stifled, whilst it reflects the yellow-making outwards, and thereby looks yellow, and much after the same manner that leaf gold is yellow by reflected, and blue by transmitted light, and massy gold is yellow in all positions of the eye; there are some liquors, as the tincture of *lignum nephriticum*, and some sorts of glass, which transmit one sort of light most copiously, and reflect another sort, and thereby look of several colours, according to the position of the eye to the light. But, if these liquors or glasses were so thick and massy that no light could get through them, I question not but they would, like all other opaque bodies, appear of one and the same colour in all positions of the eye, though this I cannot yet affirm by experience. For all coloured bodies, so far as my observation reaches, may be seen through if made sufficiently thin, and, therefore, are in some measure transparent, and differ only in degrees of transparency from tinged transparent liquors, these liquors as well as those bodies by a sufficient thickness becoming opaque. A transparent body which looks of any colour by transmitted light may also look of the same colour by reflected light, the light of that colour being reflected by the farther surface of the body, or by the air beyond it. And then the reflected colour will be diminished, and perhaps cease, by making the body very thick, and pitching it on the backside to diminish the reflexion of its farther surface, so that the light reflected from the tinging particles may predominate. In such cases, the colour of the reflected light will be apt to vary from that of the light transmitted. But whence it is that tinged bodies and liquors reflect some sort of rays, and intromit or transmit other sorts, shall be said in the next book. In this Proposition I content myself to have put it past dispute that bodies have such properties, and thence appear coloured.

PROPOSITION 11. PROBLEM 6

By mixing coloured lights, to compound a beam of light of the same colour and nature with a beam of the Sun's direct light, and therein to experience the truth of the foregoing Propositions.

Let ABC *abc* [Fig. 16] represent a prism, by which the Sun's light let into a dark chamber through the hole F, may be refracted towards the lens MN, and paint upon it at *p*, *q*, *r*, *s*, and *t*, the usual colours (violet, blue, green, yellow, and red) and let the diverging rays by the refraction of this lens converge again towards X, and there, by the mixture of all those their colours, compound a white according to what was shewn above. Then let another prism DEG *deg*, parallel to the former, be placed at X, to refract that white light upwards towards Y. Let the refracting angles of the prisms and their distances from the lens be equal so that the rays, which converged from the lens towards X, and without refraction, would there have crossed and diverged again, may by the refraction of the second prism be reduced into parallelism and diverge no more. For then those rays will recompose a beam of white light XY. If the refracting angle of either prism be the bigger, that prism must be so much the nearer to the lens. You will know when the prisms and the lens are well set together, by observing if the beam of light XY, which comes out of the second prism, be perfectly white to the very edges of the light, and at all distances from the prism continue perfectly and totally white like a beam of the Sun's light. For till this happens, the position of the prisms and lens to one another must be corrected; and then if by the help of a long beam of wood, as is represented in the Figure, or by a tube, or some other such instrument, made for that purpose, they be made fast in that situation, you may try all the same experiments in this compounded beam of light XY which have been made in the Sun's direct light.

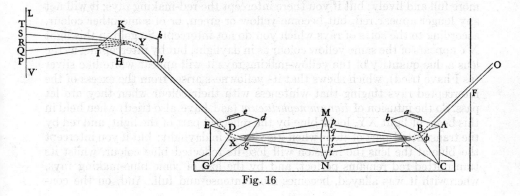

Fig. 16

For this compounded beam of light has the same appearance, and is endowed with all the same properties, with a direct beam of the Sun's light, so far as my observation reaches. And in trying experiments in this beam you may by stopping any of the colours, p, q, r, s, and t, at the lens, see how the colours produced in the experiments are no other than those which the rays had at the lens before they entered the composition of this beam; and, by consequence, that they arise not from any new modifications of the light by refractions and reflexions, but from the various separations and mixtures of the rays originally endowed with their colour-making qualities.

So, for instance, having with a lens $4\frac{1}{4}$ inches broad, and two prisms on either hand $6\frac{1}{4}$ feet distant from the lens, made such a beam of compounded light, to examine the reason of the colours made by prisms, I refracted this compounded beam of light XY with another prism HIK kh, and thereby cast the usual prismatic colours PQRST upon the paper LV placed behind. And then, by stopping any of the colours p, q, r, s, t, at the lens, I found that the same colour would vanish at the paper. So if the purple p was stopped at the lens, the purple P upon the paper would vanish, and the rest of the colours would remain unaltered, unless perhaps the blue, so far as some purple latent in it at the lens might be separated from it by the following refractions. And so by intercepting the green upon the lens, the green R upon the paper would vanish, and so of the rest; which plainly shews that as the white beam of light XY was compounded of several lights variously coloured at the lens, so the colours which afterwards emerge out of it by new refractions are no other than those of which its whiteness was compounded. The refraction of the prism HIK kh generates the colours PQRST upon the paper, not by changing the colorific qualities of the rays, but by separating the rays which had the very same colorific qualities before they entered the composition of the refracted beam of white light XY. For otherwise the rays which were of one colour at the lens might be of another upon the paper, contrary to what we find.

So again, to examine the reason of the colours of natural bodies, I placed such bodies in the beam of light XY, and found that they all appeared there of those their own colours which they have in daylight, and that those colours depend upon the rays which had the same colours at the lens before they entered the composition of that beam. Thus, for instance, cinnabar illuminated by this beam appears of the same red colour as in daylight; and if at the lens you intercept the green-making and blue-making rays, its redness will become more full and lively; but if you there intercept the red-making rays, it will not any longer appear red, but become yellow or green, or of some other colour, according to the sorts of rays which you do not intercept. So gold in this light XY appears of the same yellow colour as in daylight, but by intercepting at the lens a due quantity of the yellow-making rays it will appear white like silver (as I have tried), which shews that its yellowness arises from the excess of the intercepted rays tinging that whiteness with their colour when they are let pass. So the infusion of *lignum nephriticum* (as I have also tried) when held in this beam of light XY, looks blue by the reflected part of the light, and red by the transmitted part of it, as when 'tis viewed in daylight; but if you intercept the blue at the lens the infusion will lose its reflected blue colour, whilst its transmitted red remains perfect, and by the loss of some blue-making rays, wherewith it was allayed, becomes more intense and full. And, on the contrary, if the red and orange-making rays be intercepted at the lens, the infusion will lose its transmitted red, whilst its blue will remain and become more full and perfect. Which shews that the infusion does not tinge the rays with blue and red, but only transmits those most copiously which were red-making before, and reflects those most copiously which were blue-making before. And after the same manner may the reasons of other phenomena be examined, by trying them in this artificial beam of light XY.

BOOK TWO

Part I

Observations concerning the reflexions, refractions, and colours of thin transparent bodies.

It has been observed by others that transparent substances (as glass, water, air, &c.) when made very thin by being blown into bubbles, or otherwise formed into plates, do exhibit various colours according to their various thinness, altho' at a greater thickness they appear very clear and colourless. In the former book I forbore to treat of these colours, because they seemed of a more difficult consideration, and were not necessary for establishing the properties of light there discoursed of. But because they may conduce to further discoveries for completing the theory of light, especially as to the constitution of the parts of natural bodies, on which their colours or transparency depend, I have here set down an account of them. To render this discourse short and distinct, I have first described the principal of my Observations, and then considered and made use of them. The Observations are these:

OBSERVATION 1. Compressing two prisms hard together that their sides (which by chance were a very little convex) might somewhere touch one another, I found the place in which they touched to become absolutely transparent, as if they had there been one continued piece of glass. For when the light fell so obliquely on the air, which in other places was between them, as to be all reflected, it seemed in that place of contact to be wholly transmitted, insomuch that when looked upon it appeared like a black or dark spot, by reason that little or no sensible light was reflected from thence, as from other places; and when looked through it seemed (as it were) a hole in that air which was formed into a thin plate, by being compressed between the glasses. And through this hole objects that were beyond might be seen distinctly, which could not at all be seen through other parts of the glasses where the air was interjacent. Although the glasses were a little convex, yet this transparent spot was of a considerable breadth, which breadth seemed principally to proceed from the yielding inwards of the parts of the glasses, by reason of their mutual pressure. For by pressing them very hard together it would become much broader than otherwise.

OBS. 2. When the plate of air, by turning the prisms about their common axis, became so little inclined to the incident rays that some of them began to be transmitted, there arose in it many slender arcs of colours which at first were shaped almost like the conchoid, as you see them delineated in the first Figure. And by continuing the

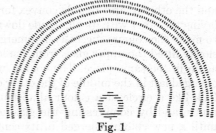

Fig. 1

457

motion of the prisms, these arcs increased and bended more and more about the said transparent spot, till they were completed into circles or rings encompassing it, and afterwards continually grew more and more contracted.

These arcs at their first appearance were of a violet and blue colour, and between them were white arcs of circles, which presently by continuing the motion of the prisms became a little tinged in their inward limbs with red and yellow, and to their outward limbs the blue was adjacent. So that the order of these colours from the central dark spot, was at that time white, blue, violet; black, red, orange, yellow, white, blue, violet, &c. But the yellow and red were much fainter than the blue and violet.

The motion of the prisms about their axis being continued, these colours contracted more and more, shrinking towards the whiteness on either side of it, until they totally vanished into it. And then the circles in those parts appeared black and white, without any other colours intermixed. But by further moving the prisms about, the colours again emerged out of the whiteness, the violet and blue at its inward limb, and at its outward limb the red and yellow. So that now their order from the central spot was white, yellow, red; black; violet, blue, white, yellow, red, &c., contrary to what it was before.

Obs. 3. When the rings or some parts of them appeared only black and white, they were very distinct and well-defined, and the blackness seemed as intense as that of the central spot. Also in the borders of the rings, where the colours began to emerge out of the whiteness, they were pretty distinct, which made them visible to a very great multitude. I have sometimes numbered above thirty successions (reckoning every black and white ring for one succession) and seen more of them, which by reason of their smallness I could not number. But in other positions of the prisms, at which the rings appeared of many colours, I could not distinguish above eight or nine of them, and the exterior of those were very confused and dilute.

In these two Observations to see the rings distinct, and without any other colour than black and white, I found it necessary to hold my eye at a good distance from them. For by approaching nearer, although in the same inclination of my eye to the plane of the rings, there emerged a bluish colour out of the white, which by dilating itself more and more into the black rendered the circles less distinct, and left the white a little tinged with red and yellow. I found also by looking through a slit or oblong hole, which was narrower than the pupil of my eye, and held close to it parallel to the prisms, I could see the circles much distincter and visible to a far greater number than otherwise.

Obs. 4. To observe more nicely the order of the colours which arose out of the white circles as the rays became less and less inclined to the plate of air, I took two object-glasses (the one a plano-convex for a fourteen-foot telescope, and the other a large double convex for one of about fifty-feet) and upon this, laying the other with its plane side downwards, I pressed them slowly together, to make the colours successively emerge in the middle of the circles, and then slowly lifted the upper glass from the lower to make them successively vanish again in the same place. The colour, which by pressing the glasses together, emerged last in the middle of the other colours, would upon its first appearance look like a circle of a colour almost uniform from the circumference to the centre and by compressing the glasses still more, grow continually broader until a new colour emerged in its centre, and thereby it became a ring encompassing that new colour. And by compressing the glasses still more, the diameter of this ring would increase, and the breadth of its orbit or perimeter decrease until another new colour emerged in the centre of the last. And so on until a third, a fourth, a fifth, and other following new colours successively emerged there, and became rings encompassing the innermost colour, the last of which was the black spot. And, on the contrary, by lifting up the upper glass from the lower, the diameter of the rings would decrease, and the breadth of their orbit increase, until their colours reached successively to the centre; and then, they being of a considerable breadth, I could more easily discern and distinguish their species than before. And by this means I observed their succession and quantity to be as followeth:

Next to the pellucid central spot made by the contact of the glasses succeeded blue, white, yellow, and red. The blue was so little in quantity that I could not discern it in the circles made by the prisms, nor could I well distinguish any violet in it, but the yellow and red were pretty copious, and seemed about as much in extent as the white, and four or five times more than the blue. The next circuit in order of colours immediately encompassing these were violet, blue, green, yellow, and red; and these were all of them copious and vivid, excepting the green, which was very little in quantity, and seemed much more faint and dilute than the other colours. Of the other four, the violet was the least in extent, and the blue less than the yellow or red. The third circuit or order was purple, blue, green, yellow, and red; in which the purple seemed more reddish than the violet in the former circuit, and the green was much more conspicuous, being as brisk and copious as any of the other colours, except the yellow, but the red began to be a little faded, inclining very much to purple. After this succeeded the fourth circuit of green and red. The green was very copious and lively, inclining on the one side to blue, and on the other side to yellow. But in this fourth circuit there was neither violet, blue, nor yellow, and the red was very imperfect and dirty. Also the succeeding colours became more and more imperfect and dilute, till after three or four revolutions they ended

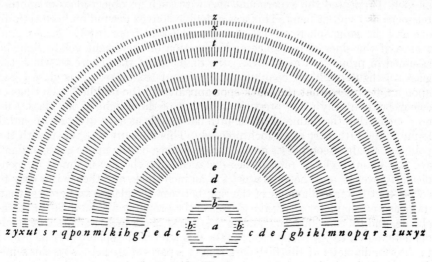

Fig. 2

in perfect whiteness. Their form, when the glasses were most compressed so as to make the black spot appear in the centre, is delineated in the second figure; where $a, b, c, d, e: f, g, h, i, k: l, m, n, o, p: q, r: s, t: v, x: y, z$, denote the colours reckoned in order from the center: black, blue, white, yellow, red; violet, blue, green, yellow, red; purple, blue, green, yellow, red; green, red; greenish blue, red; greenish blue, pale red; greenish blue, reddish white.

OBS. 5. To determine the interval of the glasses, or thickness of the interjacent air, by which each colour was produced, I measured the diameters of the first six rings at the most lucid part of their orbits, and, squaring them, I found their squares to be in the arithmetical progression of the odd numbers, 1, 3, 5, 7, 9, 11. And since one of these glasses was plane, and the other spherical, their intervals at those rings must be in the same progression. I measured also the diameters of the dark or faint rings between the more lucid colours, and found their squares to be in the arithmetical progression of the even numbers, 2, 4, 6, 8, 10, 12. And it being very nice and difficult to take these measures exactly, I repeated them divers times at divers parts of the glasses, that by their agreement I might be confirmed in them. And the same method I used in determining some others of the following observations.

OBS. 6. The diameter of the sixth ring at the most lucid part of its orbit was $\frac{58}{100}$ parts of an inch, and the diameter of the sphere on which the double convex object-glass was ground was about 102 feet, and hence I gathered the thickness of the air or aereal interval of the glasses at that ring. But some time after, suspecting that in making this observation I had not determined the diameter of the sphere with sufficient accurateness, and being uncertain whether the plano-convex glass was truly plane, and not something concave or convex on that side which I accounted plane; and whether I had not pressed the glasses together, as I often did, to make them touch (for by pressing such glasses together their parts easily yield inwards, and the rings thereby become sensibly broader than they would be, did the glasses keep their figures), I repeated the experiment, and found the diameter of the sixth lucid ring about $\frac{55}{100}$ parts of an inch. I repeated the experiment also with such an object-glass of another telescope as I had at hand. This was a double convex ground on both sides to one and the same sphere, and its focus was distant from it $83\frac{2}{5}$ inches. And thence, if the sines of incidence and refraction of the bright yellow light be assumed in proportion as 11 to 17, the diameter of the sphere to which the glass was figured will by computation be found 182 inches. This glass I laid upon a flat one, so that the black spot appeared in the middle of the rings of colours without any other pressure than that of the weight of the glass. And now, measuring the diameter of the fifth dark circle as accurately as I could, I found it the fifth part of an inch precisely. This measure was taken with the points of a pair of compasses on the upper surface on the upper glass, and my eye was about eight or nine inches distance from the glass, almost perpendicularly over it, and the glass was $\frac{1}{6}$ of an inch thick, and thence it is easy to collect that the true diameter of the ring between the glasses was greater than its measured diameter above the glasses in the proportion of 80 to 79, or thereabouts, and by consequence equal to $\frac{16}{79}$ parts of an inch, and its true semidiameter equal to $\frac{8}{79}$ parts. Now, as the diameter of the sphere (182 inches) is to the semidiameter of this fifth dark ring ($\frac{8}{79}$ parts of an inch), so is this semidiameter to the thickness of the air at this fifth dark ring; which is, therefore,

$\frac{32}{567.931}$ or $\frac{100}{1.774.784}$ parts of an inch; and the fifth part thereof (viz., the $\frac{1}{88.739}$th part of an inch) is the thickness of the air at the first of these dark rings.

The same experiment I repeated with another double convex object-glass ground on both sides to one and the same sphere. Its focus was distant from it $168\frac{1}{2}$ inches, and, therefore, the diameter of that sphere was 184 inches. This glass being laid upon the same plain glass, the diameter of the fifth of the dark rings, when the black spot in their centre appeared plainly without pressing the glasses, was by the measure of the compasses upon the upper glass $\frac{121}{600}$ parts of an inch, and by consequence between the glasses it was $\frac{1.222}{6.000}$; for the upper glass was $\frac{1}{6}$ of an inch thick, and my eye was distant from it 8 inches. And a third proportional to half this from the diameter of the sphere is $\frac{5}{88.850}$ parts of an inch. This is, therefore, the thickness of the air at this ring, and a fifth part thereof (viz., the $\frac{1}{88.850}$th part of an inch) is the thickness thereof at the first of the rings, as above.

I tried the same thing by laying these object-glasses upon flat pieces of a broken looking-glass, and found the same measures of the rings; which makes me rely upon them till they can be determined more accurately by glasses ground to larger spheres, though in such glasses greater care must be taken of a true plane.

These dimensions were taken when my eye was placed almost perpendicularly over the glasses, being about an inch, or an inch and a quarter, distant from the incident rays, and eight inches distant from the glass; so that the rays were inclined to the glass in an angle of about four degrees. Whence, by the following Observation, you will understand that had the rays been perpendicular to the glasses, the thickness of the air at these rings would have been less in the proportion of the radius to the secant of four degrees (that is, of 10,000 to 10,024). Let the thicknesses found be, therefore, diminished in this proportion, and they will become $\frac{1}{88.952}$ and $\frac{1}{89.063}$, or (to use the nearest round number) the $\frac{1}{89.000}$th part of an inch. This is the thickness of the air at the darkest part of the first dark ring made by perpendicular rays; and half this thickness multiplied by the progression, 1, 3, 5, 7, 9, 11, &c. gives the thicknesses of the air at the most luminous parts of all the brightest rings, viz., $\frac{1}{178.000}$, $\frac{3}{178.000}$, $\frac{5}{178.000}$, $\frac{7}{178.000}$, &c., their arithmetical means $\frac{2}{178.000}$, $\frac{4}{178.000}$, $\frac{6}{178.000}$, &c. being its thicknesses at the darkest parts of all the dark ones.

OBS. 7. The rings were least when my eye was placed perpendicularly over the glasses in the axis of the rings; and when I viewed them obliquely they became bigger, continually swelling as I removed my eye farther from the axis. And partly by measuring the diameter of the same circle at several obliquities of my eye, partly by other means, as also by making use of the two prisms for very great obliquities, I found its diameter, and consequently the thickness of the air, at its perimeter in all those obliquities to be very nearly in the proportions expressed in the following Table:

Angle of incidence on the air		Angle of refraction into the air		Diameter of the ring	Thickness of the air
Deg.	Min.				
00	00	00	00	10	10
06	26	10	00	$10\frac{1}{13}$	$10\frac{2}{13}$
12	45	20	00	$10\frac{1}{3}$	$10\frac{2}{3}$
18	49	30	00	$10\frac{3}{4}$	$11\frac{1}{2}$
24	30	40	00	$11\frac{2}{5}$	13
29	37	50	00	$12\frac{1}{2}$	$15\frac{1}{2}$
33	58	60	00	14	20
35	47	65	00	$15\frac{1}{4}$	$23\frac{1}{4}$
37	19	70	00	$16\frac{4}{5}$	$28\frac{1}{4}$
38	33	75	00	$19\frac{1}{4}$	37
39	27	80	00	$22\frac{6}{7}$	$52\frac{1}{4}$
40	00	85	00	29	$84\frac{1}{12}$
40	11	90	00	35	$122\frac{1}{2}$

In the two first columns are expressed the obliquities of the incident and emergent rays to the plate of the air; that is, their angles of incidence and refraction. In the third column the diameter of any coloured ring at those obliquities is expressed in parts, of which ten constitute that diameter when the rays are perpendicular. And in the fourth column the thickness of the air at the circumference of that ring is expressed in parts, of which also ten constitute its thickness when the rays are perpendicular.

And from these measures I seem to gather this rule: that the thickness of the air is proportional to the secant of an angle, whose sine is a certain mean proportional between the sines of incidence and refraction. And that mean proportional, so far as by these measures I can determine it, is the first of a hundred and six arithmetical mean proportionals between those sines counted from the bigger sine; that is, from the sine of refraction when the refraction is made out of the glass into the plate of air, or from the sine of incidence when the refraction is made out of the plate of air into the glass.

Obs. 8. The dark spot in the middle of the rings increased also by the obliquation of the eye, although almost insensibly. But, if instead of the object-glasses the prisms were made use of, its increase was more manifest when viewed so obliquely that no colours appeared about it. It was least when the rays were incident most obliquely on the interjacent air, and as the obliquity decreased it increased more and more until the coloured rings appeared, and then decreased again, but not so much as it increased before. And hence it is evident that the transparency was not only at the absolute contact of the glasses, but also where they had some little interval. I have sometimes observed the diameter of that spot to be between half and two fifth parts of the diameter of the exterior circumference of the red in the first circuit or revolution of colours when viewed almost perpendicularly; whereas when viewed obliquely it hath wholly vanished and become opaque and white like the other parts of the glass; whence it may be collected that the glasses did then scarcely, or not at all, touch one another, and that their interval at the perimeter of that spot when viewed perpendicularly was about a fifth or sixth part of their interval at the circumference of the said red.

Obs. 9. By looking through the two contiguous object-glasses, I found that the interjacent air exhibited rings of colours, as well by transmitting light as by reflecting it. The central spot was now white, and from it the order of the colours were yellowish red; black, violet, blue, white, yellow, red; violet, blue, green, yellow, red, &c. But these colours were very faint and dilute, unless when the light was trajected very obliquely through the glasses; for by that means they became pretty vivid. Only the first yellowish red, like the blue in the fourth Observation, was so little and faint as scarcely to be discerned. Comparing the coloured rings made by reflexion, with these made by transmission of the light, I found that white was opposite to black, red to blue, yellow to violet, and green to a compound of red and violet. That is, those parts of the glass were black when looked through, which when looked upon appeared white, and on the contrary. And so those which in one case exhibited blue, did in the other case exhibit red. And the like of the other colours. The manner you have represented in the third Figure, where AB, CD, are the surfaces of the glasses contiguous at E, and the black lines between them are their distances in arithmetical progression, and the colours written above are seen by reflected light, and those below by light transmitted.

OBS. 10. Wetting the object-glasses a little at their edges, the water crept in slowly between them, and the circles thereby became less and the colours more faint, insomuch that as the water crept along, one half of them at which it first arrived would appear broken off from the other half, and contracted into a less room. By measuring them I found the proportions of their diameters to the diameters of the like circles made by air to be about seven to eight, and consequently the intervals of the glasses at like circles, caused by those two mediums (water and air) are as about three to four. Perhaps it may be a general rule that, if any other medium more or less dense than water be compressed between the glasses, their intervals at the rings caused thereby will be to their intervals caused by interjacent air, as the sines are which measure the refraction made out of that medium into air.

OBS. 11. When the water was between the glasses, if I pressed the upper glass variously at its edges to make the rings move nimbly from one place to another, a little white spot would immediately follow the centre of them, which upon creeping in of the ambient water into that place would presently vanish. Its appearance was such as interjacent air would have caused, and it exhibited the same colours. But it was not air, for where any bubbles of air were in the water they would not vanish. The reflexion must have rather been caused by a subtler medium which could recede through the glasses at the creeping in of the water.

OBS. 12. These observations were made in the open air. But farther to examine the effects of coloured light falling on the glasses, I darkened the room, and viewed them by reflexion of the colours of a prism cast on a sheet of white paper, my eye being so placed that I could see the coloured paper by reflexion in the glasses, as in a looking-glass. And by this means the rings became distincter and visible to a far greater number than in the open air. I have sometimes seen more than twenty of them, whereas in the open air I could not discern above eight or nine.

OBS. 13. Appointing an assistant to move the prism to and fro about its axis, that all the colours might successively fall on that part of the paper which I saw by reflexion from that part of the glasses, where the circles appeared, so that all the colours might be successively reflected from the circles to my eye, whilst I held it immovable, I found the circles which the red light made to be manifestly bigger than those which were made by the blue and violet. And it was very pleasant to see them gradually swell or contract accordingly as the colour of the light was changed. The interval of the glasses at any of the rings, when they were made by the utmost red light, was to their interval at the same ring when made by the utmost violet, greater than as 3 to 2, and less than as 13 to 8. By the most of my Observations it was as 14 to 9. And this proportion seemed very nearly the same in all obliquities of my eye, unless when two prisms were made use of instead of the object-glasses. For then at a certain great obliquity of my eye, the rings made by the several colours seemed equal, and at a greater obliquity those made by the violet would be greater than the same rings made by the red, the refraction of the prism in this case causing the most refrangible rays to fall more obliquely on that plate of the air than the least refrangible ones. Thus the experiment succeeded in the coloured light, which was sufficiently strong and copious to make the rings sensible. And thence it may be gathered that, if the most refrangible and least refrangible rays had been copious enough to make the rings sensible without the mixture of other rays, the proportion which here was 14 to 9 would have been a little greater, suppose $14\frac{1}{4}$ or $14\frac{1}{3}$ to 9.

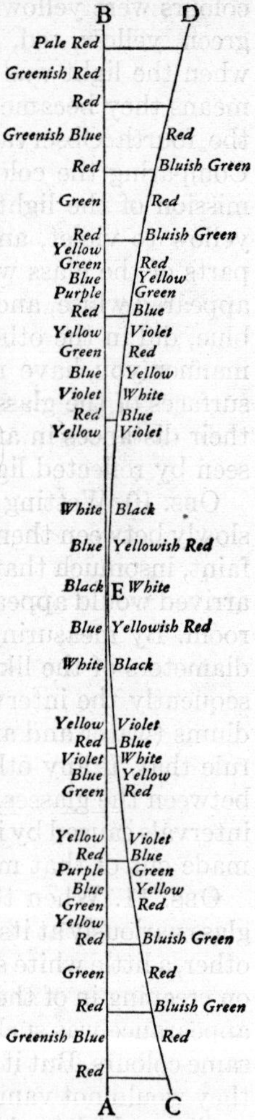

OBS. 14. Whilst the prism was turned about its axis with a uniform motion, to make all the several colours fall successively upon the object-glasses, and thereby to make the rings contract and dilate, the contraction or dilatation of each ring thus made by the variation of its colour was swiftest in the red, and slowest in the violet, and in the intermediate colours it had intermediate degrees of celerity. Comparing the quantity of contraction and dilatation made by all the degrees of each colour, I found that it was greatest in the red, less in the yellow, still less in the blue, and least in the violet. And to make as just an estimation as I could of the proportions of their contractions or dilatations, I observed that the whole contraction or dilatation of the diameter of any ring made by all the degrees of red was to that of the diameter of the same ring made by all the degrees of violet, as about four to three, or five to four, and that when the light was of the middle colour, between yellow and green, the diameter of the ring was very nearly an arithmetical mean between the greatest diameter of the same ring made by the outmost red, and the least diameter thereof made by the outmost violet—contrary to what happens in the colours of the oblong spectrum made by the refraction of a prism, where the red is most contracted, the violet most expanded, and in the midst of all the colours is the confine of green and blue. And hence I seem to collect that the thicknesses of the air between the glasses there, where the ring is successively made by the limits of the five

B	D
Pale Red	
Greenish Red	
Red	
Greenish Blue	Red
Red	Bluish Green
Green	Red
Red / Yellow	Bluish Green
Green	Red
Blue	Yellow
Purple	Green
Red	Blue
Yellow	Violet
Green	Red
Blue	Yellow
Violet	White
Red / Yellow	Blue / Violet
White	Black
Blue	Yellowish Red
Black E	White
Blue	Yellowish Red
White	Black
Yellow / Red	Violet / Blue
Violet / Blue	White / Yellow
Green	Red
Yellow / Red	Violet / Blue
Purple / Blue	Green / Yellow
Green / Yellow	Red
Red	Bluish Green
Green	Red
Red	Bluish Green
Greenish Blue	Red
Red	
A	C

Fig. 3

principal colours (red, yellow, green, blue, violet) in order (that is, by the extreme red, by the limit of red and yellow in the middle of the orange, by the limit of yellow and green, by the limit of green and blue, by the limit of blue and violet in the middle of the indigo, and by the extreme violet) are to one another very nearly as the sixth lengths of a chord which sound the notes in a sixth major, *sol, la, mi, fa, sol, la*. But it agrees something better with the Observation to say that the thicknesses of the air between the glasses there, where the rings are successively made by the limits of the seven colours (red, orange, yellow, green, blue, indigo, violet in order) are to one another as the cube roots of the squares of the eight lengths of a chord, which sound the notes in an eighth, *sol, la, fa, sol, la, mi, fa, sol;* that is, as the cube roots of the squares of the numbers, 1, $\frac{8}{9}$, $\frac{5}{6}$, $\frac{3}{4}$, $\frac{2}{3}$, $\frac{3}{5}$, $\frac{9}{16}$, $\frac{1}{2}$.

OBS. 15. These rings were not of various colours like those made in the open air, but appeared all over of that prismatic colour only with which they were illuminated. And by projecting the prismatic colours immediately upon the glasses, I found that the light which fell on the dark spaces which were between the coloured rings was transmitted through the glasses without any variation

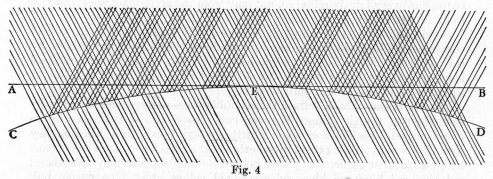

Fig. 4

of colour. For on a white paper placed behind, it would paint rings of the same colour with those which were reflected, and of the bigness of their immediate spaces. And from thence the origin of these rings is manifest; namely, that the air between the glasses, according to its various thickness, is disposed in some places to reflect, and in others to transmit, the light of any one colour (as you may see represented in the fourth Figure) and in the same place to reflect that of one colour where it transmits that of another.

OBS. 16. The squares of the diameters of these rings made by any prismatic colour were in arithmetical progression, as in the fifth Observation. And the diameter of the sixth circle, when made by the citrine yellow, and viewed almost perpendicularly, was about $\frac{58}{100}$ parts of an inch, or a little less, agreeable to the sixth Observation.

The precedent Observations were made with a rarer thin medium, terminated by a denser, such as was air or water compressed between two glasses. In those that follow are set down the appearances of a denser medium thinned within a rarer, such as are plates of Muscovy glass, bubbles of water, and some other thin substances terminated on all sides with air.

OBS. 17. If a bubble be blown with water first made tenacious by dissolving a little soap in it, 'tis a common observation that after a while it will appear tinged with a great variety of colours. To defend these bubbles from being agitated by the external air (whereby their colours are irregularly moved one among another, so that no accurate observation can be made of them), as soon as I had blown any of them I covered it with a clear glass, and by that means its colours emerged in a very regular order, like so many concentric rings encompassing the top of the bubble. And as the bubble grew thinner by the continual subsiding of the water, these rings dilated slowly and overspread the whole bubble, descending in order to the bottom of it, where they vanished successively. In the meanwhile, after all the colours were emerged at the top, there grew in the centre of the rings a small round black spot, like that in the first Observation, which continually dilated itself till it became sometimes more than $\frac{1}{2}$ or $\frac{3}{4}$ of an inch in breadth before the bubble broke. At first I thought there had been no light reflected from the water in that place, but, observing it more curiously, I saw within it several smaller round spots which appeared much blacker and darker than the rest, whereby I knew that there was some reflexion at the other places which were not so dark as those spots. And by further trial I found that I could see the images of some things (as of a candle or the Sun) very faintly reflected, not only from the great black spot, but also from the little darker spots which were within it.

Besides the aforesaid coloured rings there would often appear small spots of colours, ascending and descending up and down the sides of the bubble, by reason of some inequalities in the subsiding of the water. And sometimes small black spots generated at the sides would ascend up to the larger black spot at the top of the bubble, and unite with it.

Obs. 18. Because the colours of these bubbles were more extended and lively than those of the air thinned between two glasses, and so more easy to be distinguished, I shall here give you a further description of their order, as they were observed in viewing them by reflexion of the skies when of a white colour, whilst a black substance was placed behind the bubble. And they were these: red, blue; red, blue; red, blue; red, green; red, yellow, green, blue, purple; red, yellow, green, blue, violet; red, yellow, white, blue, black.

The three first successions of red and blue were very dilute and dirty, especially the first, where the red seemed in a manner to be white. Among these there was scarce any other colour sensible besides red and blue, only the blues (and principally the second blue) inclined a little to green.

The fourth red was also dilute and dirty, but not so much as the former three; after that succeeded little or no yellow, but a copious green, which at first inclined a little to yellow, and then became a pretty brisk and good willow green, and afterwards changed to a bluish colour; but there succeeded neither blue nor violet.

The fifth red at first inclined very much to purple, and afterwards became more bright and brisk, but yet not very pure. This was succeeded with a very bright and intense yellow, which was but little in quantity, and soon changed to green; but that green was copious and something more pure, deep and lively, than the former green. After that followed an excellent blue of a bright sky colour, and then a purple, which was less in quantity than the blue, and much inclined to red.

The sixth red was at first of a very fair and lively scarlet, and soon after of a brighter colour, being very pure and brisk, and the best of all the reds. Then after a lively orange followed an intense bright and copious yellow, which was also the best of all the yellows, and this changed first to a greenish yellow, and then to a greenish blue; but the green between the yellow and the blue was very little and dilute, seeming rather a greenish white than a green. The blue which succeeded became very good, and of a very bright sky colour, but yet something inferior to the former blue; and the violet was intense and deep with little or no redness in it, and less in quantity than the blue.

In the last red appeared a tincture of scarlet next to violet, which soon changed to a brighter colour, inclining to an orange; and the yellow which followed was at first pretty good and lively, but afterwards it grew more dilute until by degrees it ended in perfect whiteness. And this whiteness, if the water was very tenacious and well-tempered, would slowly spread and dilate itself over the greater part of the bubble; continually growing paler at the top, where at length it would crack in many places, and those cracks, as they dilated, would appear of a pretty good, but yet obscure and dark, sky colour; the white between the blue spots diminishing, until it resembled the threads of an irregular network, and soon after vanished, and left all the upper part of the bubble of the said dark blue colour. And this colour, after the aforesaid manner, dilated itself downwards, until sometimes it hath overspread the whole bubble. In the mean while at the top, which was of a darker blue than the bottom, and appeared also full of many round blue spots (something darker than the rest) there would emerge one or more very black spots, and within those, other spots of an intenser blackness, which I mentioned in the former Observation; and these continually dilated themselves until the bubble broke.

If the water was not very tenacious, the black spots would break forth in the white, without any sensible intervention of the blue. And sometimes they would break forth within the precedent yellow, or red, or perhaps within the blue of the second order, before the intermediate colours had time to display themselves.

By this description you may perceive how great an affinity these colours have with those of air described in the fourth Observation, although set down in a contrary order, by reason that they begin to appear when the bubble is thickest, and are most conveniently reckoned from the lowest and thickest part of the bubble upwards.

OBS. 19. Viewing in several oblique positions of my eye the rings of colours emerging on the top of the bubble, I found that they were sensibly dilated by increasing the obliquity, but yet not so much by far as those made by thinned air in the seventh Observation. For there they were dilated so much as, when viewed most obliquely, to arrive at a part of the plate more than twelve times thicker than that where they appeared when viewed perpendicularly; whereas, in this case, the thickness of the water at which they arrived when viewed most obliquely was, to that thickness which exhibited them by perpendicular rays, something less than as 8 to 5. By the best of my observations it was between 15 and 15½ to 10; an increase about 24 times less than in the other case.

Sometimes the bubble would become of an uniform thickness all over, except at the top of it near the black spot, as I knew, because it would exhibit the same appearance of colours in all positions of the eye. And then the colours which were seen at its apparent circumference by the obliquest rays would be different from those that were seen in other places, by rays less oblique to it.

And divers spectators might see the same part of it of differing colours, by viewing it at very differing obliquities. Now, observing how much the colours at the same places of the bubble, or at divers places of equal thickness, were varied by the several obliquities of the rays, by the assistance of the 4th, 14th, 16th, and 18th Observations, as they are hereafter explained, I collect the thickness of the water requisite to exhibit any one and the same colour, at several obliquities, to be very nearly in the proportion expressed in this Table.

Incidence on the water		Refraction into the water		Thickness of the water
Deg.	Min.	Deg.	Min.	
00	00	00	00	10
15	00	11	11	$10\frac{1}{4}$
30	00	22	1	$10\frac{4}{5}$
45	00	32	2	$11\frac{4}{5}$
60	00	40	30	13
75	00	46	25	$14\frac{1}{2}$
90	00	48	35	$15\frac{1}{5}$

In the two first columns are expressed the obliquities of the rays to the superficies of the water (that is, their angles of incidence and refraction), where I suppose that the sines which measure them are in round numbers, as 3 to 4, though probably the dissolution of soap in the water may a little alter its refractive virtue. In the third column, the thickness of the bubble, at which any one colour is exhibited in those several obliquities, is expressed in parts, of which ten constitute its thickness when the rays are perpendicular. And the rule found by the seventh Observation agrees well with these measures, if duly applied; namely, that the thickness of a plate of water requisite to exhibit one and the same colour at several obliquities of the eye is proportional to the secant of an angle, whose sine is the first of a hundred and six arithmetical mean proportionals between the sines of incidence and refraction counted from the lesser sine; that is, from the sine of refraction when the refraction is made out of air into water, otherwise from the sine of incidence.

I have sometimes observed that the colours which arise on polished steel by heating it, or on bell-metal, and some other metalline substances, when melted and poured on the ground, where they may cool in the open air, have, like the colours of water-bubbles, been a little changed by viewing them at divers obliquities, and particularly that a deep blue, or violet, when viewed very obliquely, hath been changed to a deep red. But the changes of these colours are not so great and sensible as of those made by water. For the scoria, or vitrified part of the metal, which most metals when heated or melted do continually protrude and send out to their surface, and which by covering the metals in form of a thin glassy skin, causes these colours, is much denser than water; and I find that the change made by the obliquation of the eye is least in colours of the densest thin substances.

OBS. 20. As in the ninth Observation, so here, the bubble, by transmitted light, appeared of a contrary colour to that which it exhibited by reflexion. Thus, when the bubble being looked on by the light of the clouds reflected from it, seemed red at its apparent circumference, if the clouds at the same time, or immediately after, were viewed through it, the colour at its circumference would be blue. And, on the contrary, when by reflected light it appeared blue, it would appear red by transmitted light.

OBS. 21. By wetting very thin plates of Muscovy glass, whose thinness made the like colours appear, the colours became more faint and languid, especially by wetting the plates on that side opposite to the eye; but I could not perceive any variation of their species. So, then, the thickness of a plate requisite to produce any colour depends only on the density of the plate, and not on that of the ambient medium. And hence, by the 10th and 16th Observations, may be known the thickness which bubbles of water, or plates of Muscovy glass, or other substances, have at any colour produced by them.

OBS. 22. A thin transparent body, which is denser than its ambient medium, exhibits more brisk and vivid colours than that which is so much rarer; as I have particularly observed in the air and glass. For blowing glass very thin at a lamp furnace, those plates encompassed with air did exhibit colours much more vivid than those of air made thin between two glasses.

OBS. 23. Comparing the quantity of light reflected from the several rings, I found that it was most copious from the first or inmost, and in the exterior rings became gradually less and less. Also the whiteness of the first ring was stronger than that reflected from those parts of the thin medium or plate which were without the rings; as I could manifestly perceive by viewing at a distance the rings made by the two object-glasses; or by comparing two bubbles of water blown at distant times, in the first of which the whiteness appeared, which succeeded all the colours, and, in the other, the whiteness which preceded them all.

OBS. 24. When the two object-glasses were laid upon one another, so as to make the rings of the colours appear, though with my naked eye I could not discern above eight or nine of those rings, yet by viewing them through a prism I have seen a far greater multitude, insomuch that I could number more than forty, besides many others, that were so very small and close together that I could not keep my eye steady on them severally so as to number them, but by their extent I have sometimes estimated them to be more than a hundred. And I believe the experiment may be improved to the discovery of far greater numbers. For they seem to be really unlimited, though visible only so far as they can be separated by the refraction of the prism, as I shall hereafter explain.

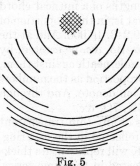

Fig. 5

But it was but one side of these rings (namely, that towards which the refraction was made) which by that refraction was rendered distinct, and the other side became more confused than when viewed by the naked eye, insomuch that there I could not discern above one or two, and sometimes none of those rings, of which I could discern eight or nine with my naked eye. And their segments or arcs, which on the other side appeared so numerous, for the most part exceeded not the third part of a circle. If the refraction was very great, or the prism very distant from the object-glasses, the middle part of those arcs became also confused, so as to disappear and constitute an even whiteness, whilst on either side their ends, as also the whole arcs farthest from the centre, became distincter than before, appearing in the form as you see them designed in the fifth Figure.

The arcs, where they seemed distinctest, were only white and black successively, without any other colours intermixed. But in other places there appeared colours whose order was inverted by the refraction in such manner that, if I first held the prism very near the object-glasses and then gradually removed it farther off towards my eye, the colours of the 2d, 3d, 4th and following rings, shrunk towards the white that emerged between them, until they wholly vanished into it at the middle of the arcs, and afterwards emerged again in a contrary order. But at the ends of the arcs they retained their order unchanged.

I have sometimes so laid one object-glass upon the other that, to the naked eye, they have all over seemed uniformly white, without the least appearance of any of the coloured rings; and yet, by viewing them through a prism, great multitudes of those rings have discovered themselves. And in like manner plates of Muscovy glass, and bubbles of glass blown at a lamp-furnace, which were not so thin as to exhibit any colours to the naked eye, have through the prism exhibited a great variety of them ranged irregularly up and down in the form of waves. And so bubbles of water, before they began to exhibit their colours to the naked eye of a bystander, have appeared through a prism, girded about with many parallel and horizontal rings; to produce which effect it was necessary to hold the prism parallel, or very nearly parallel, to the horizon, and to dispose it so that the rays might be refracted upwards.

Part II

Remarks upon the foregoing Observations.

HAVING given my Observations of these colours, before I make use of them to unfold the causes of the colours of natural bodies it is convenient that, by the simplest of them (such as are the 2d, 3d, 4th, 9th, 12th, 18th, 20th, and 24th) I first explain the more compounded. And first, to shew how the colours in the fourth and eighteenth Observations are produced, let there be taken in any right line from the point Y, [Fig. 6] the lengths YA, YB, YC, YD, YE, YF, YG, YH, in proportion to one another, as the cube roots of the squares of the numbers, $\frac{1}{2}$, $\frac{9}{16}$, $\frac{3}{5}$, $\frac{2}{3}$, $\frac{3}{4}$, $\frac{5}{6}$, $\frac{8}{9}$, 1, whereby the lengths of a musical chord to sound all the notes in an eighth are represented; that is, in the proportion of the numbers 6,300, 6,814, 7,114, 7,631, 8,255, 8,855, 9,243, 10,000. And at the points A, B, C, D, E, F, G, H, let perpendiculars Aa, Bβ, &c. be erected, by whose intervals the extent of the several colours, set underneath against them, is to be represented. Then divide the line Aa in such proportion as the numbers 1, 2, 3, 5, 6, 7, 9, 10, 11, &c. set at the points of division denote. And through those divisions from Y draw lines 1I, 2K, 3L, 5M, 6N, 7O, &c.

Now, if A2 be supposed to represent the thickness of any thin transparent body, at which the outmost violet is most copiously reflected in the first ring, or series of colours, then by the 13th Observation, HK will represent its thickness, at which the utmost red is most copiously reflected in the same series. Also, by the 5th and 16th Observations, A6 and HN will denote the thicknesses at which those extreme colours are most copiously reflected in the second series, and A10 and HQ the thicknesses at which they are most copiously reflected in the third series, and so on. And the thickness at which any of the intermediate colours are reflected most copiously, will, according to the 14th Observation, be defined by the distance of the line AH from the intermediate parts of the

Fig. 6

lines 2K, 6N, 10Q, &c. against which the names of .those colours are written below.

But farther, to define the latitude of these colours in each ring or series, let A1 design the least thickness, and A3 the greatest thickness, at which the extreme violet in the first series is reflected, and let HI and HL design the like limits for the extreme red, and let the intermediate colours be limited by the intermediate parts of the lines 1I and 3L, against which the names of those colours are written, and so on; but yet with this caution: that the reflexions be supposed strongest at the intermediate spaces, 2K, 6N, 10Q, &c. and from thence to decrease gradually towards these limits, 1I, 3L, 5M, 7O, &c. on either side; where you must not conceive them to be precisely limited, but to decay indefinitely. And whereas I have assigned the same latitude to every series, I did it because, although the colours in the first series seem to be a little broader than the rest, by reason of a stronger reflexion there, yet that inequality is so insensible as scarcely to be determined by observation.

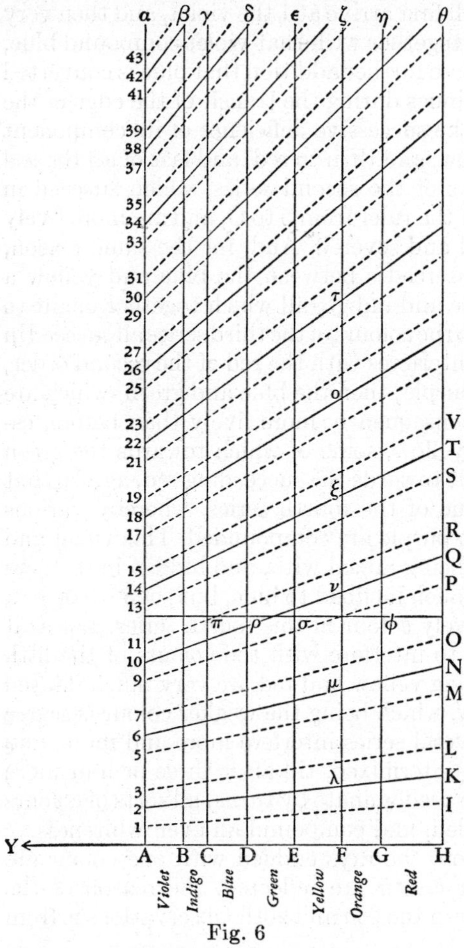

Now, according to this description, conceiving that the rays originally of several colours are by turns reflected at the spaces 1I, L3, 5M, O7, 9P, R11, &c. and transmitted at the spaces AHI1, 3LM5, 7OP9, &c. it is easy to know what colour must in the open air be exhibited at any thickness of a transparent thin body. For if a ruler be applied parallel to AH, at that distance from it by which the thickness of the body is represented, the alternate spaces 1IL3, 5MO7, &c. which it crosseth will denote the reflected original colours, of which the colour exhibited in the open air is compounded. Thus, if the constitution of the green in the third series of colours be desired, apply the ruler as you see at πρσφ, and by its passing through some of the blue at π and yellow at σ, as well as through the green at ρ, you may conclude that the green exhibited at that thickness of the body is principally constituted of original green, but not without a mixture of some blue and yellow.

By this means you may know how the colours from the centre of the rings outward ought to succeed in order as they were described in the 4th and 18th

Observations. For if you move the ruler gradually from AH through all distances, having passed over the first space which denotes little or no reflexion to be made by thinnest substances, it will first arrive at 1 the violet, and then very quickly at the blue and green, which together with that violet compound blue, and then at the yellow and red, by whose further addition that blue is converted into whiteness, which whiteness continues during the transit of the edge of the ruler from I to 3, and after that by the successive deficience of its component colours, turns first to compound yellow, and then to red, and last of all the red ceaseth at L. Then begin the colours of the second series, which succeed in order during the transit of the edge of the ruler from 5 to O, and are more lively than before, because more expanded and severed. And, for the same reason, instead of the former white there intercedes between the blue and yellow a mixture of orange, yellow, green, blue and indigo, all which together ought to exhibit a dilute and imperfect green. So the colours of the third series all succeed in order; first, the violet, which a little interferes with the red of the second order, and is thereby inclined to a reddish purple; then the blue and green, which are less mixed with other colours, and consequently more lively than before, especially the green; then follows the yellow, some of which towards the green is distinct and good, but that part of it towards the succeeding red, as also that red is mixed with the violet and blue of the fourth series, whereby various degrees of red very much inclining to purple are compounded. This violet and blue, which should succeed this red, being mixed with, and hidden in it, there succeeds a green. And this at first is much inclined to blue, but soon becomes a good green, the only unmixed and lively colour in this fourth series. For as it verges towards the yellow, it begins to interfere with the colours of the fifth series, by whose mixture the succeeding yellow and red are very much diluted and made dirty, especially the yellow, which being the weaker colour is scarce able to shew itself. After this the several series interfere more and more, and their colours become more and more intermixed, till after three or four more revolutions (in which the red and blue predominate by turns) all sorts of colours are in all places pretty equally blended, and compound an even whiteness.

And since, by the 15th Observation, the rays endued with one colour are transmitted, where those of another colour are reflected, the reason of the colours made by the transmitted light in the 9th and 20th Observations is from hence evident.

If not only the order and species of these colours, but also the precise thickness of the plate, or thin body at which they are exhibited, be desired in parts of an inch, that may be also obtained by assistance of the 6th or 16th Observations. For according to those Observations the thickness of the thinned air, which between two glasses exhibited the most luminous parts of the first six rings were $\frac{1}{178,000}, \frac{3}{178,000}, \frac{5}{178,000}, \frac{7}{178,000}, \frac{9}{178,000}, \frac{11}{178,000}$, parts of an inch. Suppose the light reflected most copiously at these thicknesses be the bright citrine yellow, or confine of yellow and orange, and these thicknesses will be $F\lambda$, $F\mu$, Fv, $F\xi$, Fo, $F\tau$. And this being known, it is easy to determine what thickness of air is represented by $G\varphi$, or by any other distance of the ruler from AH.

But further, since by the 10th Observation the thickness of air was to the thickness of water, which between the same glasses exhibited the same colour, as 4 to 3, and by the 21st Observation the colours of thin bodies are not varied by varying the ambient medium, the thickness of a bubble of water, exhibiting any colour will be ¾ of the thickness of air producing the same colour. And so, according to the same 10th and 21st Observations, the thickness of a plate of glass, whose refraction of the mean refrangible ray, is measured by the proportion of the sines 31 to 20, may be $\frac{20}{31}$ of the thickness of air producing the same colours; and the like of other mediums. I do not affirm that this proportion of 20 to 31 holds in all the rays; for the sines of other sorts of rays have other proportions. But the differences of those proportions are so little that I do not here consider them. On these grounds I have composed the following Table, wherein the thickness of air, water, and glass, at which each colour is most intense and specific, is expressed in parts of an inch divided into ten hundred thousand equal parts.

The thickness of coloured plates and particles

		of Air	Water	Glass
Their colours of the first order....	Very black	$\frac{1}{2}$	$\frac{3}{8}$	$\frac{10}{31}$
	Black	1	$\frac{3}{4}$	$\frac{20}{31}$
	Beginning of black	2	$1\frac{1}{2}$	$1\frac{2}{7}$
	Blue	$2\frac{2}{5}$	$1\frac{4}{5}$	$1\frac{11}{22}$
	White	$5\frac{1}{4}$	$3\frac{7}{8}$	$3\frac{2}{5}$
	Yellow	$7\frac{1}{9}$	$5\frac{1}{3}$	$4\frac{3}{5}$
	Orange	8	6	$5\frac{1}{6}$
	Red	9	$6\frac{3}{4}$	$5\frac{4}{5}$
Of the second order..............	Violet	$11\frac{1}{6}$	$8\frac{3}{8}$	$7\frac{1}{5}$
	Indigo	$12\frac{5}{6}$	$9\frac{5}{8}$	$8\frac{2}{11}$
	Blue	14	$10\frac{1}{2}$	9
	Green	$15\frac{1}{8}$	$11\frac{2}{3}$	$9\frac{5}{7}$
	Yellow	$16\frac{2}{7}$	$12\frac{1}{5}$	$10\frac{2}{5}$
	Orange	$17\frac{2}{9}$	13	$11\frac{1}{9}$
	Bright red	$18\frac{1}{3}$	$13\frac{3}{4}$	$11\frac{5}{6}$
	Scarlet	$19\frac{2}{3}$	$14\frac{3}{4}$	$12\frac{2}{3}$
Of the third order...............	Purple	21	$15\frac{3}{4}$	$13\frac{11}{20}$
	Indigo	$22\frac{1}{10}$	$16\frac{4}{7}$	$14\frac{1}{4}$
	Blue	$23\frac{2}{5}$	$17\frac{11}{20}$	$15\frac{1}{10}$
	Green	$25\frac{1}{5}$	$18\frac{9}{10}$	$16\frac{1}{4}$
	Yellow	$27\frac{1}{7}$	$20\frac{1}{3}$	$17\frac{1}{2}$
	Red	29	$21\frac{3}{4}$	$18\frac{5}{7}$
	Bluish-red	32	24	$20\frac{2}{3}$
Of the fourth order.............	Bluish-green	34	$25\frac{1}{2}$	22
	Green	$35\frac{2}{7}$	$26\frac{1}{2}$	$22\frac{3}{4}$
	Yellowish-green	36	27	$23\frac{2}{9}$
	Red	$40\frac{1}{3}$	$30\frac{1}{4}$	26
Of the fifth order...............	Greenish-blue	46	$34\frac{1}{2}$	$29\frac{2}{3}$
	Red	$52\frac{1}{2}$	$39\frac{3}{8}$	34
Of the sixth order...............	Greenish-blue	$58\frac{3}{4}$	44	38
	Red	65	$48\frac{3}{4}$	42
Of the seventh order.............	Greenish-blue	71	$53\frac{1}{4}$	$45\frac{4}{5}$
	Ruddy white	77	$57\frac{3}{4}$	$49\frac{2}{3}$

Now, if this Table be compared with the 6th scheme, you will there see the constitution of each colour, as to its ingredients, or the original colours of which it is compounded, and thence be enabled to judge of its intenseness or imperfection; which may suffice in explication of the 4th and 18th Observations, unless it be further desired to delineate the manner how the colours appear when the two object-glasses are laid upon one another. To do which, let there be described a large arc of a circle, and a straight line which may touch that arc, and parallel to that tangent several occult lines, at such distances from it as the numbers set against the several colours in the Table denote. For the arc and its tangent will represent the superficies of the glasses terminating the interjacent air; and the places where the occult lines cut the arc will show at what distances from the centre, or point of contact, each colour is reflected.

There are also other uses of this Table. For by its assistance the thickness of the bubble in the 19th Observation was determined by the colours which it exhibited. And so the bigness of the parts of natural bodies may be conjectured by their colours, as shall be hereafter shewn. Also, if two or more very thin plates be laid one upon another, so as to compose one plate equalling them all in thickness, the resulting colour may be hereby determined. For instance, Mr. Hook observed, as is mentioned in his *Micrographia*, that a faint yellow plate of Muscovy glass laid upon a blue one, constituted a very deep purple. The yellow of the first order is a faint one, and the thickness of the plate exhibiting it, according to the Table, is $4\frac{3}{5}$, to which add 9, the thickness exhibiting blue of the second order, and the sum will be $13\frac{3}{5}$, which is the thickness exhibiting the purple of the third order.

To explain, in the next place, the circumstances of the 2d and 3d Observations; that is, how the rings of the colours may (by turning the prisms about their common axis the contrary way to that expressed in those observations) be converted into white and black rings, and afterwards into rings of colours again, the colours of each ring lying now in an inverted order: it must be remembered that those rings of colours are dilated by the obliquation of the rays to the air which intercedes the glasses, and that according to the Table in the 7th Observation their dilatation or increase of their diameter is most manifest and speedy when they are obliquest. Now, the rays of yellow being more refracted by the first superficies of the said air than those of red, are thereby made more oblique to the second superficies, at which they are reflected to produce the coloured rings, and consequently the yellow circle in each ring will be more dilated than the red; and the excess of its dilatation will be so much the greater, by how much the greater is the obliquity of the rays, until at last it become of equal extent with the red of the same ring. And for the same reason the green, blue, and violet will be also so much dilated by the still greater obliquity of their rays, as to become all very nearly of equal extent with the red; that is, equally distant from the centre of the rings. And then all the colours of the same ring must be coincident, and by their mixture exhibit a white ring. And these white rings must have black and dark rings between them, because they do not spread and interfere with one another, as before. And for that reason also they must become distincter, and visible to far greater numbers. But yet the violet being obliquest will be something more dilated, in proportion to its extent, than the other colours, and so very apt to appear at the exterior verges of the white.

Afterwards, by a greater obliquity of the rays, the violet and blue become more sensibly dilated than the red and yellow, and so, being farther removed from the centre of the rings, the colours must emerge out of the white in an order contrary to that which they had before; the violet and blue at the exterior limbs of each ring, and the red and yellow at the interior. And the violet, by reason of the greatest obliquity of its rays, being in proportion most of all expanded, will soonest appear at the exterior limb of each white ring, and become more conspicuous than the rest. And the several series of colours belonging to the several rings, will, by their unfolding and spreading, begin again to interfere, and thereby render the rings less distinct, and not visible to so great numbers.

If instead of the prisms the object-glasses be made use of, the rings which they exhibit become not white and distinct by the obliquity of the eye, by reason that the rays in their passage through that air which intercedes the glasses are very nearly parallel to those lines in which they were first incident on the glasses, and consequently the rays endued with several colours are not inclined one more than another to that air, as it happens in the prisms.

There is yet another circumstance of these experiments to be considered, and that is why the black and white rings which, when viewed at a distance appear distinct, should not only become confused by viewing them near at hand, but also yield a violet colour at both the edges of every white ring. And the reason is that the rays which enter the eye at several parts of the pupil have several obliquities to the glasses, and those which are most oblique, if considered apart, would represent the rings bigger than those which are the least oblique. Whence the breadth of the perimeter of every white ring is expanded outwards by the obliquest rays, and inwards by the least oblique. And this expansion is so much the greater by how much the greater is the difference of the obliquity; that is, by how much the pupil is wider, or the eye nearer to the glasses. And the breadth of the violet must be most expanded, because the rays apt to excite a sensation of that colour are most oblique to a second or farther superficies of the thinned air at which they are reflected, and have also the greatest variation of obliquity, which makes that colour soonest emerge out of the edges of the white. And as the breadth of every ring is thus augmented, the dark intervals must be diminished, until the neighbouring rings become continuous, and are blended, the exterior first, and then those nearer the centre; so that they can no longer be distinguished apart, but seem to constitute an even and uniform whiteness.

Among all the Observations there is none accompanied with so odd circumstances as the twenty-fourth. Of those the principal are, that in thin plates, which to the naked eye seem of an even and uniform transparent whiteness, without any terminations of shadows, the refraction of a prism should make rings of colours appear, whereas it usually makes objects appear coloured only there where they are terminated with shadows, or have parts unequally luminous; and that it should make those rings exceedingly distinct and white, although it usually renders objects confused and coloured. The cause of these things you will understand by considering that all the rings of colours are really in the plate, when viewed with the naked eye, although by reason of the great breadth of their circumferences they so much interfere and are blended together that they seem to constitute an uniform whiteness. But when the rays pass through the prism to the eye, the orbits of the several colours in every ring are refracted, some more than others, according to their degrees of refrangibility; by which means the colours on one side of the ring (that is, in the circumference on one side of its centre) become more unfolded and dilated, and those on the other side more complicated and contracted. And where by a due refraction they are so much contracted that the several rings become narrower than to interfere with one another, they must appear distinct, and also white, if the constituent colours be so much contracted as to be wholly coincident. But on the other side, where the orbit of every ring is made broader by the farther unfolding of its colours, it must interfere more with other rings than before, and so become less distinct.

To explain this a little further, suppose the concentric circles AV, and BX, [Fig. 7] represent the red and violet of any order, which, together with the intermediate colours, constitute any one of these rings. Now, these being viewed through a prism, the violet circle BX, will, by a greater refraction, be farther translated from its place than the red AV, and so approach nearer to it on that side of the circles, towards which the refractions are made. For instance, if the red be translated to *av*, the violet may be translated to *bx*, so as to approach nearer to it at *x* than before; and if the red be farther translated to av, the violet may be so much farther translated to bx as to convene with it at x; and if the red be yet farther translated to *a*Υ, the violet may be still so much farther translated to *β*ξ as to pass beyond it at ξ, and convene with it at *e* and *f*. And this being understood not only of the red and violet, but of all the other intermediate colours, and also of every revolution of those colours, you will easily perceive how those of the same revolution or order, by their nearness at

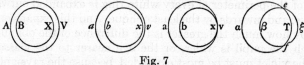

Fig. 7

xv and Υξ, and their coincidence at xv, *e* and *f*, ought to constitute pretty distinct arcs of circles, especially at xv, or at *e* and *f*; and that they will appear severally at *xv*, and at xv exhibit whiteness by their coincidence, and again appear severally at Υξ, but yet in a contrary order to that which they had before, and still retain beyond *e* and *f*. But on the other side, at *ab*, ab, or *aβ*, these colours must become much more confused by being dilated and spread so as to interfere with those of other orders. And the same confusion will happen at Υξ between *e* and *f*, if the refraction be very great, or the prism very distant from the object-glasses; in which case no parts of the rings will be seen, save only two little arcs at *e* and *f*, whose distance from one another will be augmented by removing the prism still farther from the object-glasses. And these little arcs must be distinctest and whitest at their middle, and at their ends, where they begin to grow confused, they must be coloured. And the colours at one end of every arc must be in a contrary order to those at the other end, by reason that they cross in the intermediate white; namely, their ends, which verge towards Υξ, will be red and yellow on that side next the centre, and blue and violet on the other side. But their other ends which verge from Υξ, will on the contrary be blue and violet on that side towards the centre, and on the other side red and yellow.

Now, as all these things follow from the properties of light by a mathematical way of reasoning, so the truth of them may be manifested by experiments. For in a dark room, by viewing these rings through a prism, by reflexion of the several prismatic colours, which an assistant causes to move to and fro upon a wall or paper from whence they are reflected, whilst the spectator's eye, the prism, and the object-glasses (as in the 13th Observation) are placed steady;

the position of the circles made successively by the several colours, will be found such, in respect of one another, as I have described in the Figures *abxv*, or abxv, or $\alpha\beta\xi\Upsilon$. And by the same method the truth of the explications of other Observations may be examined.

By what hath been said, the like phenomena of water and thin plates of glass may be understood. But in small fragments of those plates there is this further observable, that where they lie flat upon a table, and are turned about their centres whilst they are viewed through a prism, they will in some postures exhibit waves of various colours; and some of them exhibit these waves in one or two positions only, but the most of them do in all positions exhibit them, and make them for the most part appear almost all over the plates. The reason is that the superficies of such plates are not even, but have many cavities and swellings, which, how shallow soever, do a little vary the thickness of the plate. For at the several sides of those cavities, for the reasons newly described, there ought to be produced waves in several postures of the prism. Now, though it be but some very small and narrower parts of the glass by which these waves for the most part are caused, yet they may seem to extend themselves over the whole glass, because from the narrowest of those parts there are colours of several orders; that is, of several rings, confusedly reflected, which by refraction of the prism are unfolded, separated, and, according to their degrees of refraction, dispersed to several places, so as to constitute so many several waves, as there were divers orders of colours promiscuously reflected from that part of the glass.

These are the principal phenomena of thin plates or bubbles, whose explications depend on the properties of light, which I have heretofore delivered. And these you see do necessarily follow from them, and agree with them, even to their very least circumstances; and not only so, but do very much tend to their proof. Thus, by the 24th Observation it appears that the rays of several colours, made as well by thin plates or bubbles as by refractions of a prism, have several degrees of refrangibility; whereby those of each order, which at the reflexion from the plate or bubble are intermixed with those of other orders, are separated from them by refraction, and associated together so as to become visible by themselves like arcs of circles. For if the rays were all alike refrangible, 'tis impossible that the whiteness, which to the naked sense appears uniform, should by refraction have its parts transposed and ranged into those black and white arcs.

It appears also that the unequal refractions of difform rays proceed not from any contingent irregularities; such as are veins, an uneven polish, or fortuitous position of the pores of glass; unequal and casual motions in the air or ether, the spreading, breaking, or dividing the same ray into many diverging parts; or the like. For, admitting any such irregularities, it would be impossible for refractions to render those rings so very distinct and well defined as they do in the 24th Observation. It is necessary, therefore, that every ray have its proper and constant degree of refrangibility connate with it, according to which its refraction is ever justly and regularly performed; and that several rays have several of those degrees.

And what is said of their refrangibility may be also undersood of their reflexibility; that is, of their dispositions to be reflected, some at a greater and others at a less thickness of thin plates or bubbles; namely, that those dispositions are also connate with the rays, and immutable; as may appear by the

13th, 14th, and 15th Observations, compared with the fourth and eighteenth.

By the precedent Observations, it appears also that whiteness is a dissimilar mixture of all colours, and that light is a mixture of rays endued with all those colours. For, considering the multitude of the rings of colours in the 3d, 12th, and 24th Observations, it is manifest that although in the 4th and 18th Observations there appear no more than eight or nine of those rings, yet there are really a far greater number, which so much interfere and mingle with one another as, after those eight or nine revolutions, to dilute one another wholly, and constitute an even and sensibly uniform whiteness. And, consequently, that whiteness must be allowed a mixture of all colours, and the light which conveys it to the eye must be a mixture of rays endued with all those colours.

But further; by the 24th Observation it appears that there is a constant relation between colours and refrangibility; the most refrangible rays being violet, the least refrangible red, and those of intermediate colours having proportionably intermediate degrees of refrangibility. And by the 13th, 14th, and 15th Observations, compared with the 4th or 18th, there appears to be the same constant relation between colour and reflexibility; the violet being in like circumstances reflected at least thicknesses of any thin plate or bubble, the red at greatest thicknesses, and the intermediate colours at intermediate thicknesses. Whence it follows that the colorific dispositions of rays are also connate with them, and immutable; and, by consequence, that all the productions and appearances of colours in the world are derived, not from any physical change caused in light by refraction or reflexion, but only from the various mixtures or separations of rays, by virtue of their different refrangibility or reflexibility. And in this respect the science of colours becomes a speculation as truly mathematical as any other part of Optics. I mean, so far as they depend on the nature of light, and are not produced or altered by the power of imagination, or by striking or pressing the eye.

Part III

Of the permanent colours of natural bodies, and the analogy between them and the colours of thin transparent plates.

I AM now come to another part of this design, which is to consider how the phenomena of thin transparent plates stand related to those of all other natural bodies. Of these bodies I have already told you that they appear of divers colours, accordingly as they are disposed to reflect most copiously the rays originally endued with those colours. But their constitutions, whereby they reflect some rays more copiously than others, remain to be discovered; and these I shall endeavour to manifest in the following Propositions.

PROPOSITION 1

Those superficies of transparent bodies reflect the greatest quantity of light, which have the greatest refracting power; that is, which intercede mediums that differ most in their refractive densities. And in the confines of equally refracting mediums there is no reflexion.

The analogy between reflexion and refraction will appear by considering

that, when light passeth obliquely out of one medium into another which refracts from the perpendicular, the greater is the difference of their refractive
density, the less obliquity of incidence is requisite to cause a total reflexion.
For as the sines are which measure the refraction, so is the sine of incidence at
which the total reflexion begins, to the radius of the circle; and, consequently,
that angle of incidence is least where there is the greatest difference of the
sines. Thus, in the passing of light out of water into air, where the refraction
is measured by the ratio of the sines 3 to 4, the total reflexion begins when the
angle of incidence is about 48 degrees 35 minutes. In passing out of glass into
air, where the refraction is measured by the ratio of the sines 20 to 31, the total
reflexion begins when the angle of incidence is 40 degrees 10 minutes; and so in
passing out of crystal, or more strongly refracting mediums into air, there is
still a less obliquity requisite to cause a total reflexion. Superficies therefore
which refract most do soonest reflect all the light which is incident on them, and
so must be allowed most strongly reflexive.

But the truth of this Proposition will further appear by observing that, in
the superficies interceding two transparent mediums (such as are air, water, oil,
common glass, crystal, metalline glasses, island glasses, white transparent arsenic, diamonds, &c.), the reflexion is stronger or weaker accordingly as the
superficies hath a greater or less refracting power. For in the confine of air and
sal-gem 'tis stronger than in the confine of air and water, and still stronger in
the confine of air and common glass or crystal, and stronger in the confine of
air and a diamond. If any of these, and such like transparent solids, be immerged in water, its reflexion becomes much weaker than before; and still
weaker if they be immerged in the more strongly refracting liquors of well-
rectified oil of vitriol or spirit of turpentine. If water be distinguished into two
parts by any imaginary surface, the reflexion in the confine of those two parts
is none at all. In the confine of water and ice 'tis very little; in that of water and
oil 'tis something greater; in that of water and sal-gem still greater; and in
that of water and glass, or crystal or other denser substances still greater,
accordingly as those mediums differ more or less in their refracting powers.
Hence, in the confine of common glass and crystal, there ought to be a weak
reflexion, and a stronger reflexion in the confine of common and metalline
glass; though I have not yet tried this. But in the confine of two glasses of
equal density there is not any sensible reflexion, as was shewn in the first Observation. And the same may be understood of the superficies separating two
crystals, or two liquors, or any other substances in which no refraction is
caused. So, then, the reason why uniform pellucid mediums (such as water,
glass, or crystal) have no sensible reflexion but in their external superficies,
where they are adjacent to other mediums of a different density, is because all
their contiguous parts have one and the same degree of density.

PROPOSITION 2

*The least parts of almost all natural bodies are in some measure transparent: And
the opacity of those bodies ariseth from the multitude of reflexions caused in their
internal parts.*

That this is so has been observed by others, and will easily be granted by
them that have been conversant with microscopes. And it may be also tried
by applying any substance to a hole through which some light is immitted

into a dark room. For how opaque soever that substance may seem in the open
air, it will by that means appear very manifestly transparent if it be of a sufficient thinness. Only white metalline bodies must be excepted, which by reason
of their excessive density seem to reflect almost all the light incident on their
first superficies; unless by solution in menstruums they be reduced into very
small particles, and then they become transparent.

PROPOSITION 3

*Between the parts of opaque and coloured bodies are many spaces, either empty, or
replenished with mediums of other densities; as water between the tinging corpuscles
wherewith any liquor is impregnated, air between the aqueous globules that constitute clouds or mists; and for the most part spaces void of both air and water, but
yet perhaps not wholly void of all substance, between the parts of hard bodies.*

The truth of this is evinced by the two precedent Propositions. For, by the
second Proposition, there are many reflexions made by the internal parts of
bodies, which, by the first Proposition, would not happen if the parts of those
bodies were continued without any such interstices between them; because
reflexions are caused only in superficies, which separate mediums of a differing
density (Prop. 1).

But further, that this discontinuity of parts is the principal cause of the
opacity of bodies will appear by considering that opaque substances become
transparent by filling their pores with any substance of equal or almost equal
density with their parts. Thus, paper dipped in water or oil, the *Oculus mundi*
stone steeped in water, linen cloth oiled or varnished, and many other substances soaked in such liquors as will intimately pervade their little pores,
become by that means more transparent than otherwise; so, on the contrary,
the most transparent substances may, by evacuating their pores, or separating
their parts, be rendered sufficiently opaque; as salts or wet paper, or the *Oculus
mundi* stone by being dried, horn by being scraped, glass by being reduced to
powder, or otherwise flawed; turpentine by being stirred about with water till
they mix imperfectly, and water by being formed into many small bubbles,
either alone in the form of froth, or by shaking it together with oil of turpentine, or olive oil, or with some other convenient liquor with which it will not
perfectly incorporate. And to the increase of the opacity of these bodies, it
conduces something, that by the 23d Observation the reflexions of very thin
transparent substances are considerably stronger than those made by the same
substances of a greater thickness.

PROPOSITION 4

*The parts of bodies and their interstices must not be less than of some definite big-
ness, to render them opaque and coloured.*

For the opaquest bodies, if their parts be subtly divided (as metals, by
being dissolved in acid menstruums, &c.), become perfectly transparent. And
you may also remember that in the eighth Observation there was no sensible
reflexion at the superficies of the object-glasses, where they were very near one
another, though they did not absolutely touch. And in the 17th Observation
the reflexion of the water-bubble where it became thinnest was almost insensible, so as to cause very black spots to appear on the top of the bubble, by the
want of reflected light.

On these grounds I perceive it is that water, salt, glass, stones, and such like substances are transparent. For, upon divers considerations, they seem to be as full of pores or interstices between their parts as other bodies are, but yet their parts and interstices to be too small to cause reflexions in their common surfaces.

PROPOSITION 5

The transparent parts of bodies, according to their several sizes, reflect rays of one colour, and transmit those of another, on the same grounds that thin plates or bubbles do reflect or transmit those rays. And this I take to be the ground of all their colours.

For if a thinned or plated body, which being of an even thickness appears all over of one uniform colour, should be slit into threads, or broken into fragments, of the same thickness with the plate, I see no reason why every thread or fragment should not keep its colour, and by consequence why a heap of those threads or fragments should not constitute a mass or powder of the same colour, which the plate exhibited before it was broken. And the parts of all natural bodies, being like so many fragments of a plate, must on the same grounds exhibit the same colours.

Now, that they do so will appear by the affinity of their properties. The finely coloured feathers of some birds, and particularly those of peacocks' tails, do, in the very same part of the feather, appear of several colours in several positions of the eye, after the very same manner that thin plates were found to do in the 7th and 19th Observations; and, therefore, their colours arise from the thinness of the transparent parts of the feathers; that is, from the slenderness of the very fine hairs, or *capillamenta*, which grow out of the sides of the grosser lateral branches or fibres of those feathers. And to the same purpose it is that the webs of some spiders, by being spun very fine, have appeared coloured, as some have observed, and that the coloured fibres of some silks, by varying the position of the eye, do vary their colour. Also the colours of silks, cloths, and other substances, which water or oil can intimately penetrate, become more faint and obscure by being immerged in those liquors, and recover their vigour again by being dried; much after the manner declared of thin bodies in the 10th and 21st Observations. Leaf-gold, some sorts of painted glass, the infusion of *lignum nephriticum*, and some other substances, reflect one colour, and transmit another, like thin bodies in the 9th and 20th Observations. And some of those coloured powders which painters use may have their colours a little changed by being very elaborately and finely ground. Where I see not what can be justly pretended for those changes, besides the breaking of their parts into less parts by that contrition, after the same manner that the colour of a thin plate is changed by varying its thickness. For which reason also it is that the coloured flowers of plants and vegetables, by being bruised, usually become more transparent than before, or at least in some degree or other change their colours. Nor is it much less to my purpose that, by mixing divers liquors, very odd and remarkable productions and changes of colours may be effected, of which no cause can be more obvious and rational than that the saline corpuscles of one liquor do variously act upon or unite with the tinging corpuscles of another, so as to make them swell, or shrink (whereby not only their bulk but their density also may be changed) or to divide them into smaller corpuscles (whereby a coloured liquor may become transparent), or to make many of them associate into one cluster, whereby two transparent liquors may compose a coloured one. For we see how apt those saline menstruums are to penetrate and dissolve substances to which they are applied, and some of them to precipitate what others dissolve. In like manner, if we consider the various phenomena of the atmosphere, we may observe that when vapours are first raised they hinder not the transparency of the air, being divided into parts too small to cause any reflexion in their superficies. But when in order to compose drops of rain they begin to coalesce and constitute globules of all intermediate sizes, those globules, when they become of convenient size to reflect some colours and transmit others, may constitute clouds of various colours, according to their sizes. And I see not what can be rationally conceived in so transparent a substance as water for the production of these colours, besides the various sizes of its fluid and globular parcels.

PROPOSITION 6

The parts of bodies on which their colours depend, are denser than the medium which pervades their interstices.

This will appear by considering that the colour of a body depends not only on the rays which are incident perpendicularly on its parts, but on those also which are incident at all other angles. And that, according to the 7th Observation, a very little variation of obliquity will change the reflected colour, where the thin body or small particles is rarer than the ambient medium, insomuch that such a small particle will at diversely oblique incidences reflect all sorts of colours, in so great a variety that the colour resulting from them all, confusedly reflected from a heap of such particles, must rather be a white or grey than any other colour, or at best it must be but a very imperfect and dirty colour. Whereas if the thin body or small particle be much denser than the ambient medium, the colours, according to the 19th Observation, are so little changed by the variation of obliquity, that the rays which are reflected least obliquely may predominate over the rest, so much as to cause a heap of such particles to appear very intensely of their colour.

It conduces also something to the confirmation of this Proposition that, according to the 22d Observation, the colours exhibited by the denser thin body within the rarer are more brisk than those exhibited by the rarer within the denser.

PROPOSITION 7

The bigness of the component parts of natural bodies may be conjectured by their colours.

For since the parts of these bodies (by Prop. 5), do most probably exhibit the same colours with a plate of equal thickness, provided they have the same refractive density; and since their parts seem for the most part to have much the same density with water or glass, as by many circumstances is obvious to collect; to determine the sizes of those parts, you need only have recourse to the precedent Tables, in which the thickness of water or glass exhibiting any colour is expressed. Thus, if it be desired to know the diameter of a corpuscle, which being of equal density with glass shall reflect green of the third order, the number $16\frac{1}{4}$ shews it to be $\frac{16\frac{1}{4}}{10,000}$ parts of an inch.

The greatest difficulty is here to know of what order the colour of any body is. And for this end we must have recourse to the 4th and 18th Observations; from whence may be collected these particulars.

Scarlets, and other *reds*, *oranges*, and *yellows*, if they be pure and intense, are most probably of the second order. Those of the first and third order also may be pretty good; only the yellow of the first order is faint, and the orange and red of the third order have a great mixture of violet and blue.

There may be good *greens* of the fourth order, but the purest are of the third. And of this order the green of all vegetables seems to be, partly by reason of the intenseness of their colours, and partly because when they wither some of them turn to a greenish yellow, and others to a more perfect yellow or orange, or perhaps to red, passing first through all the aforesaid intermediate colours. Which changes seem to be effected by the exhaling of the moisture which may leave the tinging corpuscles more dense, and something augmented by the accretion of the oily and earthy part of that moisture. Now the green, without doubt, is of the same order with those colours into which it changeth, because the changes are gradual, and those colours, though usually not very full, yet are often too full and lively to be of the fourth order.

Blues and *purples* may be either of the second or third order, but the best are of the third. Thus the colour of violets seems to be of that order, because their syrup by acid liquors turns red, and by urinous and alkalizate turns green. For since it is of the nature of acids to dissolve or attenuate, and of alkalies to precipitate or incrassate, if the purple colour of the syrup was of the second order an acid liquor, by attenuating its tinging corpuscles, would change it to a red of the first order, and an alkali by incrassating them would change it to a green of the second order; which red and green, especially the green, seem too imperfect to be the colours produced by these changes. But if the said purple be supposed of the third order, its change to red of the second, and green of the third, may without any inconvenience be allowed.

If there be found any body of a deeper and less reddish purple than that of the violets, its colour most probably is of the second order. But yet there being no body commonly known whose colour is constantly more deep than theirs, I have made use of their name to denote the deepest and least reddish purples, such as manifestly transcend their colour in purity.

The *blue* of the first order, though very faint and little, may possibly be the colour of some substances; and particularly the azure colour of the skies seems to be of this order. For all vapours when they begin to condense and coalesce into small parcels become first of that bigness, whereby such an azure must be reflected before they can constitute clouds of other colours. And so, this being the first colour which vapours begin to reflect, it ought to be the colour of the finest and most transparent skies, in which vapours are not arrived to that grossness requisite to reflect other colours, as we find it is by experience.

Whiteness, if most intense and luminous, is that of the first order, if less strong and luminous, a mixture of the colours of several orders. Of this last kind is the whiteness of froth, paper, linen, and most white substances; of the former I reckon that of white metals to be. For whilst the densest of metals, gold, if foliated, is transparent, and all metals become transparent if dissolved in menstruums or vitrified, the opacity of white metals ariseth not from their density alone. They, being less dense than gold, would be more transparent than it, did not some other cause concur with their density to make them opaque. And this cause I take to be such a bigness of their particles as fits them to reflect the white of the first order. For, if they be of other thicknesses, they may reflect other colours, as is manifest by the colours which appear upon hot steel in tempering it, and sometimes upon the surface of melted metals in the skin or scoria which arises upon them in their cooling. And as the white of the first order is the strongest which can be made by plates of transparent substances, so it ought to be stronger in the denser substances of metals than in the rarer of air, water, and glass. Nor do I see but that metallic substances of such a thickness as may fit them to reflect the white of the first order, may, by reason of their great density (according to the tenor of the first of these Propositions) reflect all the light incident upon them, and so be as opaque and splendent as it's possible for any body to be. Gold or copper mixed with less than half their weight of silver, or tin, or regulus of antimony, in fusion, or amalgamed with a very little mercury, become white; which shews both that the particles of white metals have much more superficies, and so are smaller, than those of gold and copper, and also that they are so opaque as not to suffer the particles of gold or copper to shine through them. Now, it is scarce to be doubted but that the colours of gold and copper are of the second and third order; and, therefore, the particles of white metals cannot be much bigger than is requisite to make them reflect the white of the first order. The volatility of mercury argues that they are not much bigger, nor may they be much less, lest they lose their opacity, and become either transparent as they do when attenuated by vitrification, or by solution in menstruums, or black as they do when ground smaller, by rubbing silver, or tin, or lead upon other substances to draw black lines. The first and only colour which white metals take by grinding their particles smaller is black, and therefore their white ought to be that which borders upon the black spot in the centre of the rings of colours; that is, the white of the first order. But, if you would hence gather the bigness of metallic particles, you must allow for their density. For were mercury transparent, its density is such that the sine of incidence upon it (by my computation) would be to the sine of its refraction as 71 to 20, or 7 to 2. And, therefore, the thickness of its particles, that they may exhibit the same colours with those of bubbles of water, ought to be less than the thickness of the skin of those bubbles in the proportion of 2 to 7. Whence it's possible that the particles of mercury may be as little as the particles of some transparent and volatile fluids, and yet reflect the white of the first order.

Lastly, for the production of *black*, the corpuscles must be less than any of those which exhibit colours. For at all greater sizes there is too much light reflected to constitute this colour. But if they be supposed a little less than is requisite to reflect the white and very faint blue of the first order, they will, according to the 4th, 8th, 17th and 18th Observations, reflect so very little light as to appear intensely black, and yet may perhaps variously refract it to and fro within themselves so long, until it happen to be stifled and lost, by which means they will appear black in all positions of the eye without any transparency. And from hence may be understood why fire, and the more subtle dissolver putrefaction, by dividing the particles of substances, turn them to black; why small quantities of black substances impart their colour very freely and intensely to other substances to which they are applied, the minute particles of these, by reason of their very great number, easily over-spreading the gross particles of others; why glass ground very elaborately with sand on a copper plate, till it be well polished, makes the sand, together with what is worn off from the glass and copper, become very black: why black substances do soonest of all others become hot in the Sun's light and burn (which effect may proceed partly from the multitude of refractions in a little room, and partly from the easy commotion of so very small corpuscles;) and why blacks are usually a little inclined to a bluish colour. For that they are so may be seen by illuminating white paper by light reflected from black sub-stances. For the paper will usually appear of a bluish-white; and the reason is that black borders in the obscure blue of the order described in the 18th Obser-vation, and, therefore, reflects more rays of that colour than of any other.

In these descriptions I have been the more particular, because it is not im-possible but that miscroscopes may at length be improved to the discovery of the particles of bodies on which their colours depend, if they are not already in some measure arrived to that degree of perfection. For if those instruments are or can be so far improved as with sufficient distinctness to represent objects five or six hundred times bigger than at a foot distance they appear to our naked eyes, I should hope that we might be able to discover some of the great-est of those corpuscles. And by one that would magnify three or four thousand times perhaps they might all be discovered, but those which produce blackness. In the meanwhile I see nothing material in this discourse that may rationally be doubted of, excepting this position: That transparent corpuscles of the same thickness and density with a plate do exhibit the same colour. And this I would have understood not without some latitude, as well because those corpuscles may be of irregular figures, and many rays must be obliquely incident on them, and so have a shorter way through them than the length of their diameters, as because the straitness of the medium put in on all sides within such corpuscles may a little alter its motions or other qualities on which the reflexion depends. But yet I cannot much suspect the last, because I have observed of some small plates of Muscovy glass, which were of an even thickness, that through a micro-scope they have appeared of the same colour at their edges and corners where the included medium was terminated, which they appeared of in other places. However, it will add much to our satisfaction if those corpuscles can be dis-covered with microscopes; which, if we shall at length attain to, I fear it will be the utmost improvement of this sense. For it seems impossible to see the more secret and noble works of Nature within the corpuscles by reason of their transparency.

PROPOSITION 8

The cause of reflexion is not the impinging of light on the solid or impervious parts of bodies, as is commonly believed.

This will appear by the following considerations: First, that in the passage of light out of glass into air there is a reflexion as strong as in its passage out of air into glass, or rather a little stronger, and by many degrees stronger than in its passage out of glass into water. And it seems not probable that air should have more strongly reflecting parts than water or glass. But if that should possibly be supposed, yet it will avail nothing; for the reflexion is as strong or stronger when the air is drawn away from the glass (suppose by the air-pump invented by Otto Gueriet, and improved and made useful by Mr. Boyle) as when it is adjacent to it. Secondly, if light in its passage out of glass into air be incident more obliquely than at an angle of 40 or 41 degrees it is wholly reflected, if less obliquely it is in great measure transmitted. Now, it is not to be imagined that light at one degree of obliquity should meet with pores enough in the air to transmit the greater part of it, and at another degree of obliquity should meet with nothing but parts to reflect it wholly, especially considering that in its passage out of air into glass, how oblique soever be its incidence, it finds pores enough in the glass to transmit a great part of it. If any man suppose that it is not reflected by the air, but by the outmost superficial parts of the glass, there is still the same difficulty; besides that, such a supposition is unintelligible, and will also appear to be false by applying water behind some part of the glass instead of air. For so in a convenient obliquity of the rays, (suppose of 45 or 46 degrees) at which they are all reflected where the air is adjacent to the glass, they shall be in great measure transmitted where the water is adjacent to it; which argues that their reflexion or transmission depends on the constitution of the air and water behind the glass, and not on the striking of the rays upon the parts of the glass. Thirdly, if the colours made by a prism placed at the entrance of a beam of light into a darkened room be successively cast on a second prism placed at a greater distance from the former, in such manner that they are all alike incident upon it, the second prism may be so inclined to the incident rays that those which are of a blue colour shall be all reflected by it, and yet those of a red colour pretty copiously transmitted. Now, if the reflexion be caused by the parts of air or glass, I would ask why at the same obliquity of incidence the blue should wholly impinge on those parts, so as to be all reflected, and yet the red find pores enough to be in a great measure transmitted. Fourthly, where two glasses touch one another, there is no sensible reflexion, as was declared in the first Observation; and yet I see no reason why the rays should not impinge on the parts of glass, as much when contiguous to other glass as when contiguous to air. Fifthly, when the top of a water-bubble (in the 17th Observation) by the continual subsiding and exhaling of the water grew very thin, there was such a little and almost insensible quantity of light reflected from it that it appeared intensely black; whereas round about that black spot, where the water was thicker, the reflexion was so strong as to make the water seem very white. Nor is it only at the least thickness of thin plates or bubbles that there is no manifest reflexion, but at many other thicknesses continually greater and greater. For in the 15th Observation the rays of the same colour were by turns transmitted at one thickness, and reflected at another thickness, for an indeterminate number of successions. And yet in the superficies of the thinned body, where it is of any one thickness, there are as many parts for the rays to impinge on as where it is of any other thickness. Sixthly, if reflexion were caused by the parts of reflecting bodies, it would be impossible for thin plates or bubbles, at one and the same place, to reflect the rays of one colour, and transmit those of another, as they do according to the 13th and 15th Observations. For it is not to be imagined that at one place the rays which, for instance, exhibit a blue colour, should have the fortune to dash upon the parts, and those which exhibit a red to hit upon the pores of the body; and then at another place, where the body is either a little thicker or a little thinner, that on the contrary the blue should hit upon its pores, and the red upon its parts. Lastly, were the rays of light reflected by impinging on the solid parts of bodies, their reflexions from polished bodies could not be so regular as they are. For in polishing glass with sand, putty, or tripoli, it is not to be imagined that those substances can, by grating and fretting the glass, bring all its least particles to an accurate polish; so that all their surfaces shall be truly plane or truly spherical, and look all the same way, so as together to compose one even surface. The smaller the particles of those substances are, the smaller will be the scratches by which they continually fret and wear away the glass until it be polished; but be they never so small they can wear away the glass no otherwise than by grating and scratching it, and breaking the protuberances; and, therefore, polish it no otherwise than by bringing its roughness to a very fine grain, so that the scratches and frettings of the surface become too small to be visible. And, therefore, if light were reflected by impinging upon the solid parts of the glass, it would be scattered as much by the most polished glass as by the roughest. So, then, it remains a problem how glass polished by fretting substances can reflect light so regularly as it does. And this problem is scarce otherwise to be solved than by saying that the reflexion of a ray is effected, not by a single point of the reflecting body, but by some power of the body which is evenly diffused all over its surface, and by which it acts upon the ray without immediate contact. For that the parts of bodies do act upon light at a distance shall be shewn hereafter.

Now, if light be reflected, not by impinging on the solid parts of bodies but by some other principle, it's probable that as many of its rays as impinge on the solid parts of bodies are not reflected but stifled and lost in the bodies. For otherwise we must allow two sorts of reflexions. Should all the rays be reflected which impinge on the internal parts of clear water or crystal, those substances would rather have a cloudy colour than a clear transparency. To make bodies look black, it's necessary that many rays be stopped, retained, and lost in them; and it seems not probable that any rays can be stopped and stifled in them which do not impinge on their parts.

And hence we may understand that bodies are much more rare and porous than is commonly believed. Water is nineteen times lighter, and by consequence nineteen times rarer, than gold; and gold is so rare as very readily and without the least opposition to transmit the magnetic effluvia, and easily to admit quick-silver into its pores, and to let water pass through it. For a concave sphere of gold filled with water, and soldered up, has, upon pressing the sphere with great force, let the water squeeze through it, and stand all over its outside in multitudes of small drops, like dew, without bursting or cracking the body of the gold, as I have been informed by an eye-witness. From all which we may conclude that gold has more pores than solid parts, and by consequence that water has above forty times more pores than parts. And he that shall find out an hypothesis by which water may be so rare, and yet not be capable of compression by force, may doubtless by the same hypothesis make gold, and water, and all other bodies, as much rarer as he pleases; so that light may find a ready passage through transparent substances.

The magnet acts upon iron through all dense bodies not magnetic nor red hot, without any diminution of its virtue; as for instance, through gold, silver, lead, glass, water. The gravitating power of the Sun is transmitted through the vast bodies of the planets without any diminution, so as to act upon all their parts to their very centres with the same force and according to the same laws, as if the part upon which it acts were not surrounded with the body of the planet. The rays of light, whether they be very small bodies projected, or only motion or force propagated, are moved in right lines; and whenever a ray of light is by any obstacle turned out of its rectilinear way, it will never return into the same rectilinear way, unless perhaps by very great accident. And yet light is transmitted through pellucid solid bodies in right lines to very great distances. How bodies can have a sufficient quantity of pores for producing these effects is very difficult to conceive, but perhaps not altogether impossible. For the colours of bodies arise from the magnitudes of the particles which reflect them, as was explained above. Now, if we conceive these particles of bodies to be so disposed amongst themselves that the intervals or empty spaces between them may be equal in magnitude to them all; and that these particles may be composed of other particles much smaller, which have as much empty space between them as equals all the magnitudes of these smaller particles; and that in like manner these smaller particles are again composed of others much smaller, all which together are equal to all the pores or empty spaces between them; and so on perpetually till you come to solid particles, such as have no pores or empty spaces within them; and if in any gross body there be, for instance, three such degrees of particles, the least of which are solid, this body will have seven times more pores than solid parts. But if there be four such degrees of particles, the least of which are solid, the body will have fifteen times more pores than solid parts. If there be five degrees, the body will have one and thirty times more pores than solid parts. If six degrees, the body will have sixty and three times more pores than solid parts. And so on perpetually. And there are other ways of conceiving how bodies may be exceeding porous. But what is really their inward frame is not yet known to us.

PROPOSITION 9

Bodies reflect and refract light by one and the same power, variously exercised in various circumstances.

This appears by several considerations. First, because when light goes out of glass into air, as obliquely as it can possibly do, if its incidence be made still more oblique, it becomes totally reflected. For the power of the glass after it has refracted the light as obliquely as is possible, if the incidence be still made more oblique, becomes too strong to let any of its rays go through, and by consequence causes total reflexions. Secondly, because light is alternately reflected and transmitted by thin plates of glass for many successions, accordingly as the thickness of the plate increases in an arithmetical progression. For here the thickness of the glass determines whether that power by which glass acts upon light shall cause it to be reflected, or suffer it to be transmitted. And, thirdly, because those surfaces of transparent bodies which have the greatest refracting power reflect the greatest quantity of light, as was shewn in the first Proposition.

PROPOSITION 10

If light be swifter in bodies than in vacuo, in the proportion of the sines which measure the refraction of the bodies the forces of the bodies to reflect and refract light are very nearly proportional to the densities of the same bodies; excepting that unctuous and sulphureous bodies refract more than others of this same density.

Let AB represent the refracting plane surface of any body, and IC a ray incident very obliquely upon the body in C, so that the angle ACI may be infinitely little, and let CR be the refracted ray. From a given point B per-

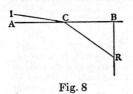

Fig. 8

pendicular to the refracting surface erect BR meeting with the refracting ray CR in R, and if CR represent the motion of the refracted ray, and this motion be distinguished into two motions CB and BR, whereof CB is parallel to the refracting plane, and BR per- pendicular to it: CB shall represent the motion of the incident ray, and BR the motion generated by the refraction, as opticians have of late explained.

Now, if any body or thing, in moving through any space of a given breadth terminated on both sides by two parallel planes, be urged forward in all parts of that space by forces tending directly forwards towards the last plane, and, before its incidence on the first plane, had no motion towards it, or but an infinitely little one; and if the forces in all parts of that space, between the planes, be at equal distances from the planes equal to one another, but at several distances be bigger or less in any given proportion, the motion gener- ated by the forces in the whole passage of the body or thing through that space shall be in a subduplicate proportion of the forces, as mathematicians will easily understand. And, therefore, if the space of activity of the refracting superficies of the body be considered as such a space, the motion of the ray generated by the refracting force of the body, during its passage through that space (that is, the motion BR) must be in subduplicate proportion of that refracting force. I say, therefore, that the square of the line BR, and by consequence the refract- ing force of the body, is very nearly as the density of the same body. For this will appear by the following Table, wherein the proportion of the sines which measure the refractions of several bodies, the square of BR, supposing CB an unit, the densities of the bodies estimated by their specific gravities, and their refractive power in respect of their densities are set down in several columns.

The refraction of the air in this Table is determined by that of the atmosphere observed by astronomers. For, if light pass through many refracting substances or mediums gradually denser and denser, and terminated with parallel surfaces, the sum of all the refractions will be equal to the single refraction which it would have suffered in passing immediately out of the first medium into the last. And this holds true, though the number of the refracting substances be increased to infinity, and the distances from one another as much decreased, so that the light may be refracted in every point of its passage, and by continual refractions bent into a curve-line. And, therefore, the whole refraction of light, in passing through the atmosphere from the highest and rarest part thereof down to the lowest and densest part, must be equal to the refraction which it would suffer in passing at like obliquity out of a vacuum immediately into air of equal density with that in the lowest part of the atmosphere.

Now, although a pseudo-topaz, a selenitis, rock crystal, island crystal, vulgar glass (that is, sand melted together) and glass of antimony, which are terres- trial stony alkalizate concretes, and air which probably arises from such sub- stances by fermentation, be substances very differing from one another in density, yet by this Table, they have their refractive powers almost in the same proportion to one another as their densities are, excepting that the refraction of that strange substance, island crystal, is a little bigger than the rest. And particularly air, which is 3,500 times rarer than the pseudo-topaz, and 4,400 times rarer than glass of antimony, and 2,000 times rarer than the selenitis, glass vulgar, or crystal of the rock, has notwithstanding its rarity the same refractive

The refracting bodies	The proportion of the sines of incidence and refraction of yellow light	The square of BR, to which the refracting force of the body is proportionate	The density and specific gravity of the body	The refractive power of the body in respect of its density
A pseudo-topazius, being a natural, pellucid, brittle, hairy stone, of a yellow colour....	23 to 14	1.699	4.27	3979
Air......................	3201 to 3200	0.000625	0.0012	5208
Glass of antimony.........	17 to 9	2.568	5.28	4864
A selenitis................	61 to 41	1.213	2.252	5386
Glass vulgar..............	31 to 20	1.4025	2.58	5436
Crystal of the rock........	25 to 16	1.445	2.65	5450
Island crystal.............	5 to 3	1.778	2.72	6536
Sal gemmæ.................	17 to 11	1.388	2.143	6477
Alum.....................	35 to 24	1.1267	1.714	6570
Borax....................	22 to 15	1.1511	1.714	6716
Nitre.....................	32 to 21	1.345	1.9	7079
Danzig vitriol.............	303 to 200	1.295	1.715	7551
Oil of vitriol..............	10 to 7	1.041	1.7	6124
Rain water...............	529 to 396	0.7845	1.	7845
Gum arabic...............	31 to 21	1.179	1.375	8574
Spirit of wine well rectified..	100 to 73	0.8765	0.866	10121
Camphor..................	3 to 2	1.25	0.996	12551
Olive oil..................	22 to 15	1.1511	0.913	12607
Linseed oil................	40 to 27	1.1948	0.932	12819
Spirit of turpentine........	25 to 17	1.1626	0.874	13222
Amber....................	14 to 9	1.42	1.04	13654
A diamond................	100 to 41	4.949	3.4	14556

power in respect of its density which those very dense substances have in respect of theirs, excepting so far as those differ from one another.

Again, the refraction of camphor, olive oil, linseed oil, spirit of turpentine and amber, which are fat sulphureous unctuous bodies, and a diamond, which probably is an unctuous substance coagulated, have their refractive powers in proportion to one another as their densities without any considerable variation. But the refractive powers of these unctuous substances are two or three times greater in respect of their densities than the refractive powers of the former substances in respect of theirs.

Water has a refractive power in a middle degree between those two sorts of substances, and probably is of a middle nature. For out of it grow all vegetable and animal substances, which consist as well of sulphureous fat and inflammable parts, as of earthy lean and alkalizate ones.

Salts and vitriols have refractive powers in a middle degree between those of earthy substances and water, and accordingly are composed of those two sorts of substances. For by distillation and rectification of their spirits a great part of them goes into water, and a great part remains behind in the form of a dry fixed earth capable of vitrification.

Spirit of wine has a refractive power in a middle degree between those of water and oily substances, and accordingly seems to be composed of both, united by fermentation; the water, by means of some saline spirits with which 'tis impregnated, dissolving the oil, and volatizing it by the action. For spirit of wine is inflammable by means of its oily parts, and being distilled often from salt of tartar, grows by every distillation more and more aqueous and phlegmatic. And chemists observe that vegetables (as lavender, rue, marjoram, &c.) distilled *per se*, before fermentation yield oils without any burning spirits, but after fermentation yield ardent spirits without oils; which shews that their oil is by fermentation converted into spirit. They find also that if oils be poured in a small quantity upon fermentating vegetables, they distil over after fermentation in the form of spirits.

So then, by the foregoing Table, all bodies seem to have their refractive powers proportional to their densities (or very nearly); excepting so far as they partake more or less of sulphureous oily particles, and thereby have their refractive power made greater or less. Whence it seems rational to attribute the refractive power of all bodies chiefly, if not wholly, to the sulphureous parts with which they abound. For it's probable that all bodies abound more or less with sulphurs. And as light congregated by a burning-glass acts most upon sulphureous bodies, to turn them into fire and flame, so, since all action is mutual, sulphurs ought to act most upon light. For that the action between light and bodies is mutual may appear from this consideration: that the densest bodies which refract and reflect light most strongly grow hottest in the summer Sun, by the action of the refracted or reflected light.

I have hitherto explained the power of bodies to reflect and refract, and shewed that thin transparent plates, fibres, and particles do, according to their several thicknesses and densities, reflect several sorts of rays, and thereby appear of several colours; and by consequence that nothing more is requisite for producing all the colours of natural bodies than the several sizes and densities of their transparent particles. But whence it is that these plates, fibres, and particles do, according to their several thicknesses and densities, reflect several sorts of rays, I have not yet explained. To give some insight into this matter, and make way for understanding the next part of this book, I shall conclude this part with a few more Propositions. Those which preceded respect the nature of bodies, these the nature of light; for both must be understood before the reason of their actions upon one another can be known. And because the last Proposition depended upon the velocity of light, I will begin with a Proposition of that kind.

PROPOSITION 11

Light is propagated from luminous bodies in time, and spends about seven or eight minutes of an hour in passing from the Sun to the Earth.

This was observed first by Römer, and then by others, by means of the eclipses of the satellites of Jupiter. For these eclipses, when the Earth is between the Sun and Jupiter, happen about seven or eight minutes sooner than they ought to do by the Tables, and when the Earth is beyond the Sun they happen about seven or eight minutes later than they ought to do; the reason being that the light of the satellites has farther to go in the latter case than in the former by the diameter of the Earth's orbit. Some inequalities of time may arise from the eccentricities of the orbs of the satellites; but those cannot answer in all the satellites, and at all times to the position and distance of the Earth from the Sun. The mean motions of Jupiter's satellites is also swifter in his descent from his aphelium to his perihelium, than in his ascent in the other half of his orb. But this inequality has no respect to the position of the Earth, and in the three interior satellites is insensible, as I find by computation from the theory of their gravity.

PROPOSITION 12

Every ray of light in its passage through any refracting surface is put into a certain transient constitution or state, which in the progress of the ray returns at equal intervals, and disposes the ray at every return to be easily transmitted through the next refracting surface, and between the returns to be easily reflected by it.

This is manifest by the 5th, 9th, 12th, and 15th Observations. For by those Observations it appears that one and the same sort of rays at equal angles of incidence on any thin transparent plate, is alternately reflected and transmitted for many successions accordingly as the thickness of the plate increases in arithmetical progression of the numbers, 0, 1, 2, 3, 4, 5, 6, 7, 8, &c. so that if the first reflexion (that which makes the first or innermost of the rings of colours there described) be made at the thickness 1, the rays shall be transmitted at the thicknesses 0, 2, 4, 6, 8, 10, 12, &c. and thereby make the central spot and rings of light, which appear by transmission, and be reflected at the thickness 1, 3, 5, 7, 9, 11, &c. and thereby make the rings which appear by reflexion. And this alternate reflexion and transmission, as I gather by the 24th Observation, continues for above a hundred vicissitudes, and by the Observations in the next part of this book, for many thousands, being propagated from one surface of a glass plate to the other, though the thickness of the plate be a quarter of an inch or above; so that this alternation seems to be propagated from every refracting surface to all distances without end or limitation.

This alternate reflexion and refraction depends on both the surfaces of every thin plate, because it depends on their distance. By the 21st Observation, if either surface of a thin plate of Muscovy glass be wetted, the colours caused by the alternate reflexion and refraction grow faint; and, therefore, it depends on them both.

It is therefore performed at the second surface; for if it were performed at the first, before the rays arrive at the second, it would not depend on the second.

It is also influenced by some action or disposition propagated from the first to the second, because otherwise at the second it would not depend on the first. And this action or disposition, in its propagation, intermits and returns by equal intervals, because in all its progress it inclines the ray at one distance from the first surface to be reflected by the second, at another to be transmitted by it, and that by equal intervals for innumerable vicissitudes. And because the ray is disposed to reflexion at the distances 1, 3, 5, 7, 9, &c. and to transmission at the distances 0, 2, 4, 6, 8, 10, &c. (for its transmission through the first surface is at the distance 0, and it is transmitted through both together, if their distance be infinitely little or much less than 1) the disposition to be transmitted at the distances 2, 4, 6, 8, 10, &c. is to be accounted a return of the same disposition which the ray first had at the distance 0; that is, at its transmission through the first refracting surface. All which is the thing I would prove.

What kind of action or disposition this is; whether it consists in a circulating or a vibrating motion of the ray, or of the medium, or something else, I do not here enquire. Those that are averse from assenting to any new discoveries, but such as they can explain by an hypothesis, may for the present suppose that as stones by falling upon water put the water into an undulating motion, and all bodies by percussion excite vibrations in the air, so the rays of light, by impinging on any refracting or reflecting surface, excite vibrations in the refracting or reflecting medium or substance, and by exciting them agitate the solid parts of the refracting or reflecting body, and by agitating them cause the body to grow warm or hot; that the vibrations thus excited are propagated in the refracting or reflecting medium or substance, much after the manner that vibrations are propagated in the air for causing sound, and move faster than the rays so as to overtake them; and that when any ray is in that part of the vibration which conspires with its motion, it easily breaks through a refracting surface, but when it is in the contrary part of the vibration which impedes its motion it is easily reflected; and, by consequence, that every ray is successively disposed to be easily reflected, or easily transmitted, by every vibration which overtakes it. But whether this hypothesis be true or false I do not here consider. I content myself with the bare discovery that the rays of light are, by some cause or other, alternately disposed to be reflected or refracted for many vicissitudes.

DEFINITION

The returns of the disposition of any ray to be reflected I will call its fits of easy reflexion, and those of its disposition to be transmitted its fits of easy transmisson, and the space it passes between every return and the next return, the interval of its fits.

PROPOSITION 13

The reason why the surfaces of all thick transparent bodies reflect part of the light incident on them, and refract the rest, is that some rays at their incidence are in fits of easy reflexion, and others in fits of easy transmission.

This may be gathered from the 24th Observation, where the light reflected by thin plates of air and glass, which to the naked eye appeared evenly white all over the plate, did through a prism appear waved with many successions of light and darkness made by alternate fits of easy reflexion and easy transmission, the prism severing and distinguishing the waves of which the white reflected light was composed, as was explained above.

And hence light is in fits of easy reflexion and easy transmission before its incidence on transparent bodies. And probably it is put into such fits at its first emission from luminous bodies, and continues in them during all its progress. For these fits are of a lasting nature, as will appear by the next part of this book.

In this Proposition I suppose the transparent bodies to be thick; because if the thickness of the body be much less than the interval of the fits of easy reflexion and transmission of the rays, the body loseth its reflecting power. For if the rays, which at their entering into the body are put into fits of easy transmission, arrive at the farthest surface of the body before they be out of those fits, they must be transmitted. And this is the reason why bubbles of water lose their reflecting power when they grow very thin; and why all opaque bodies, when reduced into very small parts, become transparent.

PROPOSITION 14

Those surfaces of transparent bodies, which if the ray be in a fit of refraction do refract it most strongly, if the ray be in a fit of reflexion do reflect it most easily.

For we shewed above, in Prop. 8, that the cause of reflexion is not the impinging of light on the solid impervious parts of bodies, but some other power by which those solid parts act on light at a distance. We shewed also, in Prop. 9, that bodies reflect and refract light by one and the same power, variously exercised in various circumstances; and in Prop. 1 that the most strongly refracting surfaces reflect the most light. All which compared together evince and rarify both this and the last Proposition.

PROPOSITION 15

In any one and the same sort of rays, emerging in any angle out of any refracting surface into one and the same medium, the interval of the following fits of easy reflexion and transmission are either accurately or very nearly as the rectangle of the secant of the angle of refraction, and of the secant of another angle, whose sine is the first of 106 arithmetical mean proportionals, between the sines of incidence and refraction, counted from the sine of refraction.

This is manifest by the 7th and 19th Observations.

PROPOSITION 16

In several sorts of rays emerging in equal angles out of any refracting surface into the same medium, the intervals of the following fits of easy reflexion and easy transmission are either accurately, or very nearly, as the cube roots of the squares of the lengths of a chord, which found the notes in an eight, sol, la, fa, sol, la, mi, fa, sol, with all their intermediate degrees answering to the colours of those rays, according to the analogy described in the seventh experiment of the second part of the first book.

This is manifest by the 13th and 14th Observations.

PROPOSITION 17

If rays of any sort pass perpendicularly into several mediums, the intervals of the fits of easy reflexion and transmission in any one medium are to those intervals in any other, as the sine of incidence to the sine of refraction, when the rays pass out of the first of those two mediums into the second.

This is manifest by the 10th Observation.

PROPOSITION 18

If the rays which paint the colour in the confine of yellow and orange pass perpendicularly out of any medium into air, the intervals of their fits of easy reflexion are the $\frac{1}{89,000}$th part of an inch. And of the same length are the intervals of their fits of easy transmission.

This is manifest by the 6th Observation.

From these Propositions it is easy to collect the intervals of the fits of easy reflexion and easy transmission of any sort of rays refracted in any angle into any medium; and thence to know whether the rays shall be reflected or transmitted at their subsequent incidence upon any other pellucid medium. Which thing, being useful for understanding the next part of this book, was here to be set down. And for the same reason I add the two following Propositions.

PROPOSITION 19

If any sort of rays falling on the polite surface of any pellucid medium be reflected back, the fits of easy reflexion, which they have at the point of reflexion, shall still continue to return; and the returns shall be at distances from the point of reflexion in the arithmetical progression of the numbers 2, 4, 6, 8, 10, 12, &c. and between these fits the rays shall be in fits of easy transmission.

For since the fits of easy reflexion and easy transmission are of a returning nature, there is no reason why these fits, which continued till the ray arrived at the reflecting medium and there inclined the ray to reflexion, should there cease. And if the ray at the point of reflexion was in a fit of easy reflexion, the progression of the distances of these fits from that point must begin from 0, and so be of the numbers 0, 2, 4, 6, 8, &c. And, therefore, the progression of the distances of the intermediate fits of easy transmission, reckoned from the same point, must be in the progression of the odd numbers 1, 3, 5, 7, 9, &c. contrary to what happens when the fits are propagated from points of refraction.

PROPOSITION 20

The intervals of the fits of easy reflexion and easy transmission, propagated from points of reflexion into any medium, are equal to the intervals of the like fits which the same rays would have if refracted into the same medium in angles of refraction equal to their angles of reflexion.

For when light is reflected by the second surface of thin plates, it goes out afterwards freely at the first surface to make the rings of colours which appear by reflexion; and, by the freedom of its egress, makes the colours of these rings more vivid and strong than those which appear on the other side of the plates by the transmitted light. The reflected rays are, therefore, in fits of easy transmission at their egress; which would not always happen if the intervals of the fits within the plate after reflexion were not equal, both in length and number, to their intervals before it. And this confirms also the proportions set down in the former Proposition. For if the rays both in going in and out at the first surface be in fits of easy transmission, and the intervals and numbers of those fits between the first and second surface, before and after reflexion, be equal, the distances of the fits of easy transmission from either surface must be in the same progression after reflexion as before; that is, from the first surface which transmitted them in the progression of the even numbers 0, 2, 4, 6, 8, &c. and from the second which reflected them, in that of the odd numbers 1, 3, 5, 7, &c. But these two Propositions will become much more evident by the Observations in the following part of this book.

Part IV

Observations concerning the reflexions and colours of thick transparent polished plates.

THERE is no glass or speculum how well soever polished but, besides the light which it refracts or reflects regularly, scatters every way irregularly a faint light, by means of which the polished surface, when illuminated in a dark room by a beam of the Sun's light, may be easily seen in all positions of the eye. There are certain phenomena of this scattered light, which when I first observed them, seemed very strange and surprising to me. My Observations were as follows.

OBS. 1. The Sun shining into my darkened chamber through a hole one-third of an inch wide, I let the intromitted beam of light fall perpendicularly upon a glass speculum ground concave on one side and convex on the other, to a sphere of five feet and eleven inches radius, and quick-silvered over on the convex side. And holding a white opaque chart or a quire of paper at the centre of the spheres to which the speculum was ground (that is, at the distance of about five feet and eleven inches from the speculum, in such manner that the beam of light might pass through a little hole made in the middle of the chart to the speculum, and thence be reflected back to the same hole) I observed upon the chart four or five concentric irises or rings of colours, like rainbows, encompassing the hole much after the manner that those, which in the fourth and following Observations of the first part of this book appeared between the object-glasses, encompassed the black spot, but yet larger and fainter than those. These rings as they grew larger and larger became diluter and fainter, so that the fifth was scarce visible. Yet sometimes, when the Sun shone very clear, there appeared faint lineaments of a sixth and seventh. If the distance of the chart from the speculum was much greater or much less than that of six feet, the rings became dilute and vanished. And if the distance of the speculum from the window was much greater than that of six feet, the reflected beam of light would be so broad, at the distance of six feet from the speculum where the rings appeared, as to obscure one or two of the innermost rings. And, therefore, I usually placed the speculum at about six feet from the window, so that its focus might there fall in with the centre of its concavity at the rings upon the chart. And this posture is always to be understood in the following Observations where no other is expressed.

OBS. 2. The colours of these rainbows succeeded one another from the centre outwards, in the same form and order with those which were made in the ninth Observation of the first part of this book, by light not reflected but transmitted through the two object-glasses. For, first, there was in their common centre a white round spot of faint light, something broader than the reflected beam of light, which beam sometimes fell upon the middle of the spot, and sometimes by a little inclination of the speculum receded from the middle, and left the spot white to the centre.

This white spot was immediately encompassed with a dark grey or russet, and that dark grey with the colours of the first iris; which colours on the inside next the dark grey were a little violet and indigo, and next to that a blue, which on the outside grew pale, and then succeeded a little greenish yellow, and after that a brighter yellow, and then on the outward edge of the iris a red which on the outside inclined to purple.

This iris was immediately encompassed with a second, whose colours were, in order from the inside outwards: purple, blue, green, yellow, light red, a red mixed with purple.

Then immediately followed the colours of the third iris, which were in order outwards a green inclining to purple, a good green, and a red more bright than that of the former iris.

The fourth and fifth iris seemed of a bluish-green within, and red without, but so faintly that it was difficult to discern the colours.

OBS. 3. Measuring the diameters of these rings upon the chart as accurately as I could, I found them also in the same proportion to one another with the rings made by light transmitted through the two object-glasses. For the diameters of the four first of the bright rings measured between the brightest parts of their orbits, at the distance of six feet from the speculum, were $1^{11}/_{16}$, $2^3/_8$, $2^{11}/_{12}$, $3^3/_8$ inches, whose squares are in arithmetical progression of the numbers 1, 2, 3, 4. If the white circular spot in the middle be reckoned amongst the rings, and its central light, where it seems to be most luminous, be put equipollent to an infinitely little ring, the squares of the diameters of the rings will be in the progression 0, 1, 2, 3, 4, &c. I measured also the diameters of the dark circles between these luminous ones, and found their squares in the progression of the numbers $\frac{1}{2}$, $1\frac{1}{2}$, $2\frac{1}{2}$, $3\frac{1}{2}$, &c. the diameters of the first four, at the distance of six feet from the speculum, being $1^3/_{16}$, $2^1/_{16}$, $2^2/_3$, $3^3/_{20}$ inches. If the distance of the chart from the speculum was increased or diminished, the diameters of the circles were increased or diminished proportionally.

OBS. 4. By the analogy between these rings and those described in the Observations of the first part of this book, I suspected that there were many more of them which spread into one another, and by interfering mixed their colours, and diluted one another so that they could not be seen apart. I viewed them, therefore, through a prism, as I did those in the 24th Observation of the first part of this book. And when the prism was so placed as by refracting the light of their mixed colours to separate them, and distinguish the rings from one another, as it did those in that Observation, I could then see them distincter than before, and easily number eight or nine of them, and sometimes twelve or thirteen. And had not their light been so very faint, I question not but that I might have seen many more.

OBS. 5. Placing a prism at the window to refract the intromitted beam of light, and cast the oblong spectrum of colours on the speculum, I covered the speculum with a black paper which had in the middle of it a hole to let any one of the colours pass through to the speculum, whilst the rest were intercepted by the paper. And now I found rings of that colour only which fell upon the speculum. If the speculum was illuminated with red, the rings were totally red with dark intervals; if with blue they were totally blue; and so of the other colours. And when they were illuminated with any one colour, the squares of their diameters, measured between their most luminous parts, were in the arithmetical progression of the numbers, 0, 1, 2, 3, 4 and the squares of the diameters of their dark intervals in the progression of the intermediate numbers

$\frac{1}{2}$, $1\frac{1}{2}$, $2\frac{1}{2}$, $3\frac{1}{2}$. But if the colour was varied, they varied their magnitude. In the red they were largest, in the indigo and violet least, and in the intermediate colours (yellow, green, and blue) they were of several intermediate bignesses answering to the colour; that is, greater in yellow than in green, and greater in green than in blue. And hence I knew that when the speculum was illuminated with white light, the red and yellow on the outside of the rings were produced by the least refrangible rays, and the blue and violet by the most refrangible, and that the colours of each ring spread into the colours of the neighbouring rings on either side, after the manner explained in the first and second parts of this book, and by mixing diluted one another so that they could not be distinguished, unless near the centre where they were least mixed. For in this Observation I could see the rings more distinctly, and to a greater number than before, being able in the yellow light to number eight or nine of them, besides a faint shadow of a tenth. To satisfy myself how much the colours of the several rings spread into one another, I measured the diameters of the second and third rings, and found them, when made by the confine of the red and orange, to be to the same diameters when made by the confine of blue and indigo, as 9 to 8, or thereabouts. For it was hard to determine this proportion accurately. Also the circles made successively by the red, yellow, and green differed more from one another than those made successively by the green, blue and indigo. For the circle made by the violet was too dark to be seen. To carry on the computation, let us therefore suppose that the differences of the diameters of circles made by the outmost red, the confine of red and orange, the confine of orange and yellow, the confine of yellow and green, the confine of green and blue, the confine of blue and indigo, the confine of indigo and violet, and outmost violet, are in proportion as the differences of the lengths of a monochord which sound the tones in an eight: *sol, la, fa, sol, la, mi, fa, sol;* that is, as the numbers $\frac{1}{9}, \frac{1}{18}, \frac{1}{12}, \frac{1}{12}, \frac{2}{27}, \frac{1}{27}, \frac{1}{18}$. And if the diameter of the circle made by the confine of red and orange be 9A, and that of the circle made by the confine of blue and indigo be 8A as above, their difference (9A$-$8A) will be to the difference of the diameters of the circles made by the outmost red, and by the confine of red and orange, as $\frac{1}{18}+\frac{1}{12}+\frac{1}{12}+\frac{2}{27}$ to $\frac{1}{9}$ (that is, as $\frac{8}{27}$ to $\frac{1}{9}$, or 8 to 3) and to the difference of the circles made by the outmost violet, and by the confine of blue and indigo, as $\frac{1}{18}+\frac{1}{12}+\frac{1}{12}+\frac{2}{27}$ to $\frac{1}{27}+\frac{1}{18}$ (that is, as $\frac{8}{27}$ to $\frac{5}{54}$, or as 16 to 5). And, therefore, these differences will be $\frac{3}{8}$A and $\frac{5}{16}$A. Add the first to 9A and subduct the last from 8A, and you will have the diameters of the circles made by the least and most refrangible rays $\frac{75}{8}$A and $\frac{61\frac{1}{2}}{8}$A. These diameters are, therefore, to one another as 75 to $61\frac{1}{2}$ or 50 to 41, and their squares as 2,500 to 1,681; that is, as 3 to 2 very nearly. Which proportion differs not much from the proportion of the diameters of the circles made by the outmost red and outmost violet, in the 13th Observation of the first part of this book.

OBS. 6. Placing my eye where these rings appeared plainest, I saw the speculum tinged all over with waves of colours (red, yellow, green, blue) like those which in the Observations of the first part of this book appeared between the object-glasses, and upon bubbles of water, but much larger. And after the manner of those, they were of various magnitudes in various positions of the eye, swelling and shrinking as I moved my eye this way and that way. They were formed like arcs of concentric circles, as those were; and when my eye was over against the centre of the concavity of the speculum, (that is, 5 feet and 10 inches distant from the speculum) their common centre was in a right line with that centre of concavity, and with the hole in the window. But in other postures of my eye their centre had other positions. They appeared by the light of the clouds propagated to the speculum through the hole in the window; and when the Sun shone through that hole upon the speculum, his light upon it was of the colour of the ring whereon it fell, but by its splendor obscured the rings made by the light of the clouds, unless when the speculum was removed to a great distance from the window so that his light upon it might be broad and faint. By varying the position of my eye, and moving it nearer to or farther from the direct beam of the Sun's light, the colour of the Sun's reflected light constantly varied upon the speculum, as it did upon my eye, the same colour always appearing to a bystander upon my eye which to me appeared upon the speculum. And thence I knew that the rings of colours upon the chart were made by these reflected colours, propagated thither from the speculum in several angles, and that their production depended not upon the termination of light and shadow.

Obs. 7. By the analogy of all these phenomena with those of the like rings of colours described in the first part of this book, it seemed to me that these colours were produced by this thick plate of glass, much after the manner that those were produced by very thin plates. For, upon trial, I found that if the quick-silver were rubbed off from the backside of the speculum, the glass alone would cause the same rings of colours, but much more faint than before; and, therefore, the phenomenon depends not upon the quick-silver, unless so far as the quick-silver, by increasing the reflexion of the backside of the glass, increases the light of the rings of colours. I found also that a speculum of metal without glass made some years since for optical uses, and very well wrought, produced none of those rings; and thence I understood that these rings arise not from one specular surface alone, but depend upon the two surfaces of the plate of glass whereof the speculum was made, and upon the thickness of the glass between them. For as in the 7th and 19th Observations of the first part of this book a thin plate of air, water, or glass of an even thickness appeared of one colour when the rays were perpendicular to it, of another when they were a little oblique, of another when more oblique, of another when still more oblique, and so on; so here, in the sixth Observation, the light which emerged out of the glass in several obliquities made the glass appear of several colours, and being propagated in those obliquities to the chart, there painted rings of those colours. And as the reason why a thin plate appeared of several colours in several obliquities of the rays was that the rays of one and the same sort are reflected by the thin plate at one obliquity and transmitted at another, and those of other sorts transmitted where these are reflected, and reflected where these are transmitted; so the reason why the thick plate of glass whereof the speculum was made did appear of various colours in various obliquities, and in those obliquities propagated those colours to the chart, was that the rays of one and the same sort did at one obliquity emerge out of the glass, at another did not emerge, but were reflected back towards the quick-silver by the hither surface of the glass, and accordingly as the obliquity became greater and greater, emerged and were reflected alternately for many successions; and that in one and the same obliquity the rays of one sort were reflected, and those of another transmitted. This is manifest by the fifth Observation of this part of this book. For in that Observation, when the speculum was illuminated by any one of the prismatic colours, that light made many rings of the same colour upon the chart with dark intervals, and, therefore, at its emergence out of the speculum was alternately transmitted and not transmitted from the speculum to the chart for many successions, according to the various obliquities of its emergence. And when the colour cast on the speculum by the prism was varied, the rings became of the colour cast on it, and varied their bigness with their colour; and, therefore, the light was now alternately transmitted and not transmitted from the speculum to the chart at other obliquities than before. It seemed to me, therefore, that these rings were of one and the same original with those of thin plates, but yet with this difference: that those of thin plates are made by the alternate reflexions and transmissions of the rays at the second surface of the plate, after one passage through it; but here the rays go twice through the plate before they are alternately reflected and transmitted. First, they go through it from the first surface to the quick-silver, and then return through it from the quick-silver to the first surface, and there are either transmitted to the chart or reflected back to the quick-silver, accordingly as they are in their fits of easy reflexion or transmission when they arrive at that surface. For the intervals of the fits of the rays which fall perpendicularly on the speculum, and are reflected back in the same perpendicular lines, by reason of the equality of these angles and lines, are of the same length and number within the glass after reflexion as before, by the 19th Proposition of the third part of this book. And, therefore, since all the rays that enter through the first surface are in their fits of easy transmission at their entrance, and as many of these as are reflected by the second are in their fits of easy reflexion there, all these must be again in their fits of easy transmission at their return to the first, and by consequence there go out of the glass to the chart, and form upon it the white spot of light in the centre of the rings. For the reason holds good in all sorts of rays, and, therefore, all sorts must go out promiscuously to that spot, and by their mixture cause it to be white. But the intervals of the fits of those rays which are reflected more obliquely than they enter, must be greater after reflexion than before, by the 15th and 20th Propositions. And thence it may happen that the rays at their return to the first surface may in certain obliquities be in fits of easy reflexion, and return back to the quick-silver, and in other intermediate obliquities be again in fits of easy transmission, and so go out to the chart, and paint on it the rings of colours about the white spot. And because the intervals of the fits at equal obliquities are greater and fewer in the less refrangible rays, and less and more numerous in the more refrangible, therefore the less refrangible at equal obliquities shall make fewer rings than the more refrangible, and the rings made by those shall be larger than the like number of rings made by these; that is, the red rings shall be larger than the yellow, the yellow than the green, the green than the blue, and the blue than the violet, as they were really found to be in the fifth Observation. And, therefore, the first ring of all colours encompassing the white spot of light shall be red without any violet within, and yellow, and green, and blue in the middle, as it was found in the second Observation; and these colours in the second ring, and those that follow, shall be more expanded, till they spread into one another, and blend one another by interfering.

These seem to be the reasons of these rings in general; and this put me upon observing the thickness of the glass, and considering whether the dimensions and proportions of the rings may be truly derived from it by computation.

Obs. 8. I measured, therefore, the thickness of this concavo-convex plate of glass, and found it everywhere one-quarter of an inch precisely. Now, by the sixth Observation of the first part of this book, a thin plate of air transmits the brightest light of the first ring (that is, the bright yellow) when its thickness is the $\frac{1}{89,000}$th part of an inch; and by the tenth Observation of the same part, a thin plate of glass transmits the same light of the same ring when its thickness is less in proportion of the sine of refraction to the sine of incidence (that is, when its thickness is the $\frac{11}{1,513,000}$th or $\frac{1}{137,545}$th part of an inch, supposing the sines are as 11 to 17). And if this thickness be doubled, it transmits the same bright light of the second ring; if tripled, it transmits that of the third, and so on; the bright yellow light in all these cases being in its fits of transmission. And, therefore, if its thickness be multiplied 34,386 times, so as to become one-quarter of an inch, it transmits the same bright light of the 34,386th ring. Suppose this be the bright yellow light transmitted perpendicularly from the reflecting convex side of the glass through the concave side to the white spot in the centre of the rings of colours on the chart; and by a rule in the 7th and 19th Observations in the first part of this book, and by the 15th and 20th Propositions of the third part of this book, if the rays be made oblique to the glass, the thickness of the glass requisite to transmit the same bright light of the same ring in any obliquity is to this thickness of one-quarter of an inch, as the secant of a certain angle to the radius, the sine of which angle is the first of a hundred and six arithmetical means between the sines of incidence and refraction, counted from the sine of incidence when the refraction is made out of any plated body into any medium encompassing it; that is, in this case, out of glass into air. Now, if the thickness of the glass be increased by degrees, so as to bear to its first thickness (viz., that of a quarter of an inch), the proportions which 34,386 (the number of fits of the perpendicular rays in going through the glass towards the white spot in the centre of the rings) hath to 34,385, 34,384, 34,383, and 34,382 (the numbers of the fits of the oblique rays in going through the glass towards the first, second, third, and fourth rings of colours); and if the first thickness be divided into 100,000,000 equal parts, the increased thicknesses will be 100,002,908, 100,005,816, 100,008,725, and 100,011,633, and the angles of which these thicknesses are secants will be 26′ 13″, 37′ 5″, 45′ 6″, and 52′ 26″, the radius being 100,000,000; and the sines of these angles are 762, 1,079, 1,321, and 1,525, and the proportional sines of refraction 1,172, 1,659, 2,031, and 2,345, the radius being 100,000. For since the sines of incidence out of glass into air are to the sines of refraction as 11 to 17, and to the above-mentioned secants as 11 to the first of 106 arithmetical means between 11 and 17 (that is, as 11 to 11 $\frac{6}{106}$), those secants will be to the sines of refraction as 11 $\frac{6}{106}$ to 17, and by this analogy will give these sines. So, then, if the obliquities of the rays to the concave surface of the glass be such that the sines of their refraction in passing out of the glass through that surface into the air be 1,172, 1,659, 2,031, 2,345, the bright light of the 34,386th ring shall emerge at the thicknesses of the glass, which are to one-quarter of an inch as 34,386 to 34,385, 34,384, 34,383, 34,382, respectively. And, therefore, if the thickness in all these cases be one-quarter of an inch (as it is in the glass of which the speculum was made) the bright light of the 34,385th ring shall emerge where the sine of refraction is 1,172, and that of the 34,384th, 34,383rd, and 34,382nd ring where the sine is 1,659, 2,031, and 2,345, respectively. And in these angles of refraction the light of these rings shall be propagated from the speculum to the chart, and there paint rings about the white central round spot of light which, we said, was the light of the 34,386th ring. And the semidiameters of these rings shall subtend the angles of refraction made at the concave surface of the speculum, and by consequence their diameters shall be to the distance of the chart from the speculum as those sines of refraction doubled are to the radius (that is, as 1,172, 1,659, 2,031, and 2,345, doubled, are to 100,000). And, therefore, if the distance of the chart from the concave surface of the speculum be six feet (as it was in the third of these Observations), the diameters of the rings of this bright yellow light upon the chart shall be 1.688, 2.389, 2.925, 3.375 inches; for these diameters are to six feet as the above-mentioned sines doubled are to the radius. Now, these diameters of the bright yellow rings, thus found by computation, are the very same with those found in the third of these Observations by measuring them, viz., with $1^{11}/_{16}$, $2^3/_8$, $2^{11}/_{12}$, and $3^3/_8$ inches; and, therefore, the theory of deriving these rings from the thickness of the plate of glass of which the speculum was made, and from the obliquity of the emerging rays, agrees with the Observation. In this computation I have equalled the diameters of the bright rings made by light of all colours, to the diameters of the rings made by the bright yellow. For this yellow makes the brightest part of the rings of all colours. If you desire the diameters of the rings made by the light of any other unmixed colour, you may find them readily by putting them to the diameters of the bright yellow ones in a subduplicate proportion of the intervals of the fits of the rays of those colours when equally inclined to the refracting or reflecting surface which caused those fits; that is, by putting the diameters of the rings made by the rays in the extremities and limits of the seven colours (red, orange, yellow, green, blue, indigo, violet) proportional to the cube roots of the numbers, 1, $8/_9$, $5/_6$, $3/_4$, $2/_3$, $3/_5$, $9/_{16}$, $1/_2$, which express the lengths of a monochord sounding the notes in an eighth. For by this means the diameters of the rings of these colours will be found pretty nearly in the same proportion to one another which they ought to have by the fifth of these Observations.

And thus I satisfied myself that these rings were of the same kind and original with those of thin plates, and by consequence that the fits or alternate dispositions of the rays to be reflected and transmitted are propagated to great distances from every reflecting and refracting surface. But yet to put the matter out of doubt, I added the following Observation.

OBS. 9. If these rings thus depend on the thickness of the plate of glass, their diameters at equal distances from several speculums made of such concavo-convex plates of glass as are ground on the same sphere ought to be reciprocally in a subduplicate proportion of the thicknesses of the plates of glass. And if this proportion be found true by experience it will amount to a demonstration that these rings (like those formed in thin plates) do depend on the thickness of the glass. I procured, therefore, another concavo-convex plate of glass ground on both sides to the same sphere with the former plate. Its thickness was $\frac{5}{62}$ parts of an inch; and the diameters of the three first bright rings measured between the brightest parts of their orbits at the distance of six feet from the glass were 3, $4^1/_6$, $5^1/_8$ inches. Now, the thickness of the other glass being one-quarter of an inch was to the thickness of this glass as $\frac{1}{4}$ to $\frac{5}{62}$; that is, as 31 to 10, or 310,000,000 to 100,000,000; and the roots of these numbers are 17,607 and 10,000, and in the proportion of the first of these roots to the second are the diameters of the bright rings made in this Observation by the thinner glass, 3, $4\frac{1}{6}$, $5\frac{1}{8}$, to the diameters of the same rings made in the third of these Observations by the thicker glass $1\frac{11}{16}$, $2\frac{3}{8}$, $2\frac{11}{12}$; that is, the diameters of the rings are reciprocally in a subduplicate proportion of the thicknesses of the plates of glass.

So, then, in plates of glass which are alike concave on one side, and alike convex on the other side, and alike quick-silvered on the convex sides, and differ in nothing but their thickness, the diameters of the rings are reciprocally in a subduplicate proportion of the thicknesses of the plates. And this shews sufficiently that the rings depend on both the surfaces of the glass. They depend on the convex surface because they are more luminous when that surface is quick-silvered over than when it is without quick-silver. They depend also upon the concave surface, because without that surface a speculum makes them not. They depend on both surfaces, and on the distances between them, because their bigness is varied by varying only that distance. And this dependence is of the same kind with that which the colours of thin plates have on the distance of the surfaces of those plates, because the bigness of the rings, and their proportion to one another, and the variation of their bigness arising from the variation of the thickness of the glass, and the orders of their colours, is such as ought to result from the Propositions in the end of the third part of this book, derived from the phenomena of the colours of thin plates set down in the first part.

There are yet other phenomena of these rings of colours, but such as follow from the same Propositions, and therefore confirm both the truth of those Propositions, and the analogy between these rings and the rings of colours made by very thin plates. I shall subjoin some of them.

OBS. 10. When the beam of the Sun's light was reflected back from the speculum, not directly to the hole in the window but to a place a little distant from it, the common centre of that spot, and of all the rings of colours, fell in the middle way between the beam of the incident light and the beam of the reflected light, and by consequence in the centre of the spherical concavity of the speculum, whenever the chart on which the rings of colours fell was placed at that centre. And as the beam of reflected light by inclining the speculum receded more and more from the beam of incident light and from the common centre of the coloured rings between them, those rings grew bigger and bigger, and so also did the white round spot, and new rings of colours emerged successively out of their common centre, and the white spot became a white ring encompassing them; and the incident and reflected beams of light always fell upon the opposite parts of this white ring, illuminating its perimeter like two mock Suns in the opposite parts of an iris. So, then, the diameter of this ring, measured from the middle of its light on one side to the middle of its light on the other side, was always equal to the distance between the middle of the incident beam of light, and the middle of the reflected beam measured at the chart on which the rings appeared. And the rays which formed this ring were reflected by the speculum in angles equal to their angles of incidence, and by consequence to their angles of refraction at their entrance into the glass, but yet their angles of reflexion were not in the same planes with their angles of incidence.

OBS. 11. The colours of the new rings were in a contrary order to those of the former, and arose after this manner: the white round spot of light in the middle of the rings continued white to the centre till the distance of the incident and reflected beams at the chart was about $\frac{1}{8}$ parts of an inch, and then it began to grow dark in the middle. And when that distance was about $1\frac{3}{16}$ of an inch, the white spot was become a ring encompassing a dark round spot which in the middle inclined to violet and indigo. And the luminous rings encompassing it were grown equal to those dark ones which in the four first Observations encompassed them; that is to say, the white spot was grown a white ring equal to the first of those dark rings, and the first of those luminous rings was now grown equal to the second of those dark ones, and the second of those luminous ones to the third of those dark ones, and so on. For the diameters of the luminous rings were now $1\frac{3}{16}$, $2\frac{1}{16}$, $2\frac{2}{3}$, $3\frac{3}{20}$, &c. inches.

When the distance between the incident and reflected beams of light became a little bigger, there emerged out of the middle of the dark spot after the indigo a blue, and then out of that blue a pale green, and soon after a yellow and red. And when the colour at the centre was brightest (being between yellow and red) the bright rings were grown equal to those rings which in the four first Observations next encompassed them; that is to say, the white spot in the middle of those rings was now become a white ring equal to the first of those bright rings, and the first of those bright ones was now become equal to the second of those, and so on. For the diameters of the white ring, and of the other luminous rings encompassing it, were now $1\frac{11}{16}$, $2\frac{3}{8}$, $2\frac{11}{12}$, $3\frac{3}{8}$, &c. or thereabouts.

When the distance of the two beams of light at the chart was a little more increased, there emerged out of the middle, in order, after the red: a purple, a blue, a green, a yellow, and a red inclining much to purple; and when the colour was brightest (being between yellow and red) the former indigo, blue, green, yellow, and red were become an iris or ring of colours equal to the first of those luminous rings which appeared in the four first Observations, and the white ring which was now become the second of the luminous rings was grown equal to the second of those, and the first of those which was now become the third ring was become equal to the third of those, and so on. For their diameters were $1\frac{11}{16}$, $2\frac{3}{8}$, $2\frac{11}{12}$, $3\frac{3}{8}$ inches, the distance of the two beams of light, and the diameter of the white ring being $2\frac{3}{8}$ inches.

When these two beams became more distant there emerged out of the middle of the purplish red, first a darker round spot, and then out of the middle of that spot a brighter. And now the former colours (purple, blue, green, yellow, and purplish red) were become a ring equal to the first of the bright rings mentioned in the four first Observations, and the rings about this ring were grown equal to the rings about that, respectively; the distance between the two beams of light and the diameter of the white ring (which was now become the third ring) being about 3 inches.

The colours of the rings in the middle began now to grow very dilute, and if the distance between the two beams was increased half an inch, or an inch more, they vanished whilst the white ring, with one or two of the rings next it on either side, continued still visible. But if the distance of the two beams of light was still more increased, these also vanished; for the light which coming from several parts of the hole in the window fell upon the speculum in several angles of incidence, made rings of several bignesses, which diluted and blotted out one another, as I knew by intercepting some part of that light. For if I intercepted that part which was nearest to the axis of the speculum, the rings would be less; if the other part which was remotest from it, they would be bigger.

Obs. 12. When the colours of the prism were cast successively on the speculum, that ring which in the two last Observations was white, was of the same bigness in all the colours, but the rings without it were greater in the green than in the blue, and still greater in the yellow, and greatest in the red. And, on the contrary, the rings within that white circle were less in the green than in the blue, and still less in the yellow, and least in the red. For the angles of reflexion of those rays which made this ring, being equal to their angles of incidence, the fits of every reflected ray within the glass after reflexion are equal in length and number to the fits of the same ray within the glass before its incidence on the reflecting surface. And, therefore, since all the rays of all sorts at their entrance into the glass were in a fit of transmission, they were also in a fit of transmission at their returning to the same surface after reflexion; and by consequence were transmitted, and went out to the white ring on the chart. This is the reason why that ring was of the same bigness in all the colours, and why in a mixture of all it appears white. But in rays which are reflected in other angles, the intervals of the fits of the least refrangible being greatest, make the rings of their colour in their progress from this white ring, either outwards or inwards, increase or decrease by the greatest steps; so that the rings of this colour without are greatest, and within least. And this is the reason why in the last Observation, when the speculum was illuminated with white light, the exterior rings made by all colours appeared red without and blue within, and the interior blue without and red within.

These are the phenomena of thick convexo-concave plates of glass, which are everywhere of the same thickness. There are yet other phenomena when these plates are a little thicker on one side than on the other, and others when the plates are more or less concave than convex, or plano-convex, or double-convex. For in all these cases the plates make rings of colours, but after various manners; all which, so far as I have yet observed, follow from the Propositions in the end of the third part of this book, and so conspire to confirm the truth of those Propositions. But the phenomena are too various, and the calculations whereby they follow from those Propositions too intricate, to be here prosecuted. I content myself with having prosecuted this kind of phenomena so far as to discover their cause, and by discovering it to ratify the Propositions in the third Part of this book.

Obs. 13. As light reflected by a lens quick-silvered on the backside makes the rings of colours above described, so it ought to make the like rings of colours in passing through a drop of water. At the first reflexion of the rays within the drop, some colours ought to be transmitted, as in the case of a lens, and others to be reflected back to the eye. For instance, if the diameter of a small drop or globule of water be about the 500th part of an inch, so that a red-making ray in passing through the middle of this globule has 250 fits of easy transmission within the globule, and that all the red-making rays which are at a certain distance from this middle ray round about it have 249 fits within the globule, and all the like rays at a certain farther distance round about it have 248 fits, and all those at a certain farther distance 247 fits, and so on; these concentric circles of rays after their transmission, falling on a white paper, will make concentric rings of red upon the paper, supposing the light which passes through one single globule strong enough to be sensible. And, in like manner, the rays of other colours will make rings of other colours. Suppose, now, that in a fair day the Sun shines through a thin cloud of such globules of water or hail, and that the globules are all of the same bigness; and the Sun seen through this cloud shall appear encompassed with the like concentric rings of colours, and the diameter of the first ring of red shall be $7\frac{1}{4}°$, that of the second $10\frac{1}{4}°$, that of the third $12° 33'$. And accordingly, as the globules of water are bigger or less, the rings shall be less or bigger. This is the theory, and experience answers it. For in June, 1692, I saw by reflexion in a vessel of stagnating water three halos, crowns, or rings of colours about the Sun, like three little rainbows, concentric to his body. The colours of the first or innermost crown were blue next the Sun, red without, and white in the middle between the blue and red. Those of the second crown were purple and blue within, and pale red without, and green in the middle. And those of the third were pale blue within, and pale red without; these crowns enclosed one another immediately, so that their colours proceeded in this continual order from the Sun outward: blue, white, red; purple, blue, green, pale yellow and red; pale blue, pale red. The diameter of the second crown measured from the middle of the yellow and red on one side of the Sun, to the middle of the same colour on the other side was $9\frac{1}{3}$ degrees, or thereabouts. The diameters of the first and third I had not time to measure, but that of the first seemed to be about five or six degrees, and that of the third about twelve. The like crowns appear sometimes about the Moon; for in the beginning of the year 1664, February 19th at night, I saw two such crowns about her. The diameter of the first or innermost was about three degrees, and that of the second about five degrees and a half. Next about the Moon was a circle of white, and next about that the inner crown, which was of a bluish-green within next the white, and of a yellow and red without, and next about these colours were blue and green on the inside of the outward crown, and red on the outside of it. At the same time there appeared a halo about 22 degrees 35' distant from the centre of the Moon. It was elliptical, and its long diameter was perpendicular to the horizon, verging below farthest from the Moon. I am told that the Moon has sometimes three or more concentric crowns of colours encompassing one another next about her body. The more equal the globules of water or ice are to one another, the more crowns of colours will appear, and the colours will be the more lively. The halo at the distance of $22\frac{1}{2}$ degrees from the Moon is of another sort. By its being oval and remoter from the Moon below than above, I conclude that it was made by refraction in some sort of hail or snow floating in the air in an horizontal posture, the refracting angle being about 58 or 60 degrees.

BOOK THREE

Part I

*Observations concerning the inflexions of the rays of light, and
the colours made thereby.*

GRIMALDI has informed us that if a beam of the Sun's light be let into a dark room through a very small hole, the shadows of things in this light will be larger than they ought to be if the rays went on by the bodies in straight lines, and that these shadows have three parallel fringes, bands or ranks of coloured light adjacent to them. But if the hole be enlarged the fringes grow broad and run into one another, so that they cannot be distinguished. These broad shadows and fringes have been reckoned by some to proceed from the ordinary refraction of the air, but without due examination of the matter. For the circumstances of the phenomenon, so far as I have observed them, are as follows:

OBS. 1. I made in a piece of lead a small hole with a pin, whose breadth was the 42d part of an inch, for 21 of those pins laid together took up the breadth of half an inch. Through this hole I let into my darkened chamber a beam of the Sun's light, and found that the shadows of hairs, thread, pins, straws, and such like slender substances placed in this beam of light, were considerably broader than they ought to be, if the rays of light passed on by these bodies in right lines. And particularly a hair of a man's head, whose breadth was but the 280th part of an inch, being held in this light, at the distance of about twelve feet from the hole, did cast a shadow which at the distance of four inches from the hair was the sixtieth part of an inch broad (that is, above four times broader than the hair), and at the distance of two feet from the hair was about the eight and twentieth part of an inch broad (that is, ten times broader than the hair), and at the distance of ten feet was the eighth part of an inch broad (that is, 35 times broader).

Nor is it material whether the hair be encompassed with air, or with any other pellucid substance. For I wetted a polished plate of glass, and laid the hair in the water upon the glass, and then laying another polished plate of glass upon it, so that the water might fill up the space between the glasses, I held them in the aforesaid beam of light, so that the light might pass through them perpendicularly, and the shadow of the hair was at the same distances as big as before. The shadows of scratches made in polished plates of glass were also much broader than they ought to be, and the veins in polished plates of glass did also cast the like broad shadows. And, therefore, the great breadth of these shadows proceeds from some other cause than the refraction of the air.

Let the circle X [Fig. 1] represent the middle of the hair; ADG, BEH, CFI, three rays passing by one side of the hair at several distances; KNQ, LOR, MPS, three other rays passing by the other side of the hair at the like distances; D, E, F, and N, O, P, the places where the rays are bent in their passage by the hair; G, H, I, and Q, R, S, the places where the rays fall on a paper GQ; IS the

507

breadth of the shadow of the hair cast on the paper, and TI, VS, two rays passing to the points I and S without bending when the hair is taken away. And it's manifest that all the light between these two rays TI and VS is bent in passing by the hair, and turned aside from the shadow IS, because if any part of this light were not bent it would fall on the paper within the shadow, and there

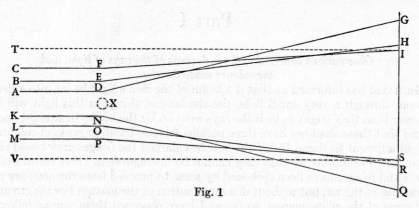

Fig. 1

illuminate the paper, contrary to experience. And because when the paper is at a great distance from the hair, the shadow is broad, and therefore the rays TI and VS are at a great distance from one another, it follows that the hair acts upon the rays of light at a good distance in their passing by it. But the action is strongest on the rays which pass by at least distances, and grows weaker and weaker accordingly as the rays pass by at distances greater and greater, as is represented in the scheme. For thence it comes to pass that the shadow of the hair is much broader in proportion to the distance of the paper from the hair, when the paper is nearer the hair, than when it is at a great distance from it.

OBS. 2. The shadows of all bodies (metals, stones, glass, wood, horn, ice, &c.) in this light were bordered with three parallel fringes or bands of coloured light, whereof that which was contiguous to the shadow was broadest and most luminous, and that which was remotest from it was narrowest, and so faint, as not easily to be visible. It was difficult to distinguish the colours, unless when the light fell very obliquely upon a smooth paper, or some other smooth white body, so as to make them appear much broader than they would otherwise do. And then the colours were plainly visible in this order: the first or innermost fringe was violet and deep blue next the shadow, and then light blue, green, and yellow in the middle, and red without. The second fringe was almost contiguous to the first, and the third to the second, and both were blue within, and yellow and red without, but their colours were very faint, especially those of the third. The colours, therefore, proceeded in this order from the shadow: violet, indigo, pale blue, green, yellow, red; blue, yellow, red; pale blue, pale yellow and red. The shadows made by scratches and bubbles in polished plates of glass were bordered with the like fringes of coloured light. And if plates of looking-glass, sloped off near the edges with a diamond-cut, be held in the same beam of light, the light which passes through the parallel planes of the glass will be bordered with the like fringes of colours where those planes meet with the diamond-cut, and by this means there will sometimes appear four or five fringes of colours. Let AB, CD [Fig. 2] represent the parallel planes of a looking-glass, and BD the plane of the diamond-cut, making at B a very obtuse angle with the plane AB. And let all the light between the rays ENI and FBM pass directly through the parallel planes of the glass, and fall upon the paper

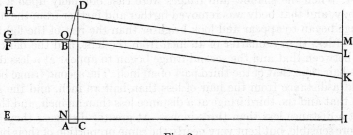

Fig. 2

between I and M, and all the light between the rays GO and HD be refracted by the oblique plane of the diamond-cut BD, and fall upon the paper between K and L; and the light which passes directly through the parallel planes of the glass, and falls upon the paper between I and M, will be bordered with three or more fringes at M.

So, by looking on the Sun through a feather or black ribband held close to the eye, several rainbows will appear; the shadows which the fibres or threads cast on the *tunica retina* being bordered with the like fringes of colours.

OBS. 3. When the hair was twelve feet distant from this hole, and its shadow fell obliquely upon a flat white scale of inches and parts of an inch placed half a foot beyond it, and also when the shadow fell perpendicularly upon the same scale placed nine feet beyond it, I measured the breadth of the shadow and fringes as accurately as I could, and found them in parts of an inch as follows:

At the distance of	Half a foot	Nine feet
The breadth of the shadow..............................	$\frac{1}{54}$	$\frac{1}{9}$
The breadth between the middles of the brightest light of the innermost fringes on either side the shadow..............	$\frac{1}{38}$ or $\frac{1}{39}$	$\frac{7}{50}$
The breadth between the middles of the brightest light of the middlemost fringes on either side the shadow............	$\frac{1}{23\frac{1}{2}}$	$\frac{4}{17}$
The breadth between the middles of the brightest light of the outmost fringes on either side the shadow..............	$\frac{1}{18}$ or $\frac{1}{18\frac{1}{2}}$	$\frac{3}{10}$
The distance between the middles of the brightest light of the first and second fringes................................	$\frac{1}{120}$	$\frac{1}{21}$
The distance between the middles of the brightest light of the second and third fringes................................	$\frac{1}{170}$	$\frac{1}{31}$
The breadth of the luminous part (green, white, yellow, and red) of the first fringe................................	$\frac{1}{170}$	$\frac{1}{32}$
The breadth of the darker space between the first and second fringes...	$\frac{1}{240}$	$\frac{1}{45}$
The breadth of the luminous part of the second fringe......	$\frac{1}{290}$	$\frac{1}{55}$
The breadth of the darker space between the second and third fringes...	$\frac{1}{340}$	$\frac{1}{63}$

These measures I took by letting the shadow of the hair, at half a foot distance, fall so obliquely on the scale as to appear twelve times broader than when it fell perpendicularly on it at the same distance, and setting down in this Table the twelfth part of the measures I then took.

Obs. 4. When the shadow and fringes were cast obliquely upon a smooth white body, and that body was removed farther and farther from the hair, the first fringe began to appear and look brighter than the rest of the light at the distance of less than a quarter of an inch from the hair, and the dark line or shadow between that and the second fringe began to appear at a less distance from the hair than that of the third part of an inch. The second fringe began to appear at a distance from the hair of less than half an inch, and the shadow between that and the third fringe at a distance less than an inch, and the third fringe at a distance less than three inches. At greater distances they became much more sensible, but kept very nearly the same proportion of their breadths and intervals which they had at their first appearing. For the distance between the middle of the first, and middle of the second fringe, was to the distance between the middle of the second and middle of the third fringe as three to two, or ten to seven. And the last of these two distances was equal to the breadth of the bright light or luminous part of the first fringe. And this breadth was to the breadth of the bright light of the second fringe as seven to four, and to the dark interval of the first and second fringe as three to two, and to the like dark interval between the second and third as two to one. For the breadths of the fringes seemed to be in the progression of the numbers 1, $\sqrt{\tfrac{1}{3}}$, $\sqrt{\tfrac{1}{5}}$, and their intervals to be in the same progression with them; that is, the fringes and their intervals together to be in the continual progression of the numbers 1, $\sqrt{\tfrac{1}{2}}$, $\sqrt{\tfrac{1}{3}}$, $\sqrt{\tfrac{1}{4}}$, $\sqrt{\tfrac{1}{5}}$, or thereabouts. And these proportions held the same very nearly at all distances from the hair; the dark intervals of the fringes being as broad in proportion to the breadth of the fringes at their first appearance as afterwards at great distances from the hair, though not so dark and distinct.

Obs. 5. The Sun shining into my darkened chamber through a hole a quarter of an inch broad, I placed at the distance of two or three feet from the hole a sheet of pasteboard, which was blacked all over on both sides, and in the middle of it had a hole about three-quarters of an inch square for the light to pass through. And behind the hole I fastened to the pasteboard with pitch the blade of a sharp knife, to intercept some part of the light which passed through the hole. The planes of the pasteboard and blade of the knife were parallel to one another, and perpendicular to the rays. And when they were so placed that none of the Sun's light fell on the pasteboard, but all of it passed through the hole to the knife, and there part of it fell upon the blade of the knife, and part of it passed by its edge, I let this part of the light which passed by, fall on a white paper two or three feet beyond the knife, and there saw two streams of faint light shoot out both ways from the beam of light into the shadow, like the tails of comets. But because the Sun's direct light by its brightness upon the paper obscured these faint streams, so that I could scarce see them, I made a little hole in the midst of the paper for that light to pass through and fall on a black cloth behind it; and then I saw the two streams plainly. They were like one another, and pretty nearly equal in length, and breadth, and quantity of light. Their light at that end next the Sun's direct light was pretty strong for the space of about a quarter of an inch, or half an inch, and in all its progress from that direct light decreased gradually till it became insensible. The whole length of either of these streams measured upon the paper at the distance of three feet from the knife was about six or eight inches; so that it subtended an angle at the edge of the knife of about 10 or 12, or at most 14 degrees. Yet sometimes I thought I saw it shoot three or four degrees farther, but with a light so very faint that I could scarce perceive it, and suspected it might (in some measure, at least) arise from some other cause than the two streams did. For, placing my eye in that light beyond the end of that stream which was behind the knife, and looking towards the knife, I could see a line of light upon its edge, and that not only when my eye was in the line of the streams, but also when it was without that line either towards the point of the knife, or towards the handle. This line of light appeared contiguous to the edge of the knife, and was narrower than the light of the innermost fringe, and narrowest when my eye was farthest from the direct light, and therefore seemed to pass between the light of that fringe and the edge of the knife, and that which passed nearest the edge to be most bent, though not all of it.

OBS. 6. I placed another knife by this, so that their edges might be parallel, and look towards one another, and that the beam of light might fall upon both the knives, and some part of it pass between their edges. And when the distance of their edges was about the 400th part of an inch, the stream parted in the middle, and left a shadow between the two parts. This shadow was so black and dark that all the light which passed between the knives seemed to be bent, and turned aside to the one hand or to the other. And as the knives still approached one another the shadow grew broader, and the streams shorter at their inward ends which were next the shadow, until upon the contact of the knives the whole light vanished, leaving its place to the shadow.

And hence I gather that the light which is least bent, and goes to the inward ends of the streams, passes by the edges of the knives at the greatest distance; and this distance, when the shadow begins to appear between the streams, is about the 800th part of an inch. And the light which passes by the edges of the knives at distances still less and less is more and more bent, and goes to those parts of the streams which are farther and farther from the direct light; because, when the knives approach one another till they touch, those parts of the streams vanish last which are farthest from the direct light.

OBS. 7. In the fifth Observation the fringes did not appear, but by reason of the breadth of the hole in the window became so broad as to run into one another, and, by joining, to make one continued light in the beginning of the streams. But in the sixth, as the knives approached one another a little before the shadow appeared between the two streams, the fringes began to appear on the inner ends of the streams on either side of the direct light; three on one side made by the edge of one knife, and three on the other side made by the edge of the other knife. They were distinctest when the knives were placed at the greatest distance from the hole in the window, and still became more distinct by making the hole less, insomuch that I could sometimes see a faint lineament of a fourth fringe beyond the three above mentioned. And as the knives continually approached one another, the fringes grew distincter and larger, until they vanished. The outmost fringe vanished first, and the middlemost next, and the innermost last. And after they were all vanished, and the line of light which was in the middle between them was grown very broad, enlarging itself on both sides into the streams of light described in the fifth Observation, the above-mentioned shadow began to appear in the middle of this line, and divide it along the middle into two lines of light, and increased until the whole light vanished. This enlargement of the fringes was so great that the rays which go to the innermost fringe seemed to be bent above twenty times more when this fringe was ready to vanish than when one of the knives was taken away.

And from this and the former Observation compared, I gather that the light of the first fringe passed by the edge of the knife at a distance greater than the 800th part of an inch, and the light of the second fringe passed by the edge of the knife at a greater distance than the light of the first fringe did, and that of the third at a greater distance than that of the second, and that of the streams of light described in the fifth and sixth Observations passed by the edges of the knives at less distances than that of any of the fringes.

Obs. 8. I caused the edges of two knives to be ground truly straight, and pricking their points into a board so that their edges might look towards one another, and meeting near their points contain a rectilinear angle, I fastened their handles together with pitch to make this angle invariable. The distance of the edges of the knives from one another at the distance of four inches from the angular point, where the edges of the knives met, was the eighth part of an inch; and, therefore, the angle contained by the edges was about 1 degree 54'. The knives thus fixed together I placed in a beam of the Sun's light, let into my darkened chamber through a hole the 42d part of an inch wide, at the distance of 10 or 15 feet from the hole, and let the light which passed between their edges fall very obliquely upon a smooth white ruler at the distance of half an inch, or an inch from the knives, and there saw the fringes by the two edges of the knives run along the edges of the shadows of the knives in lines parallel to those edges without growing sensibly broader, till they met in angles equal to the angle contained by the edges of the knives, and where they met and joined they ended without crossing one another. But if the ruler was held at a much greater distance from the knives, the fringes where they were farther from the place of their meeting were a little narrower, and became something broader and broader as they approached nearer and nearer to one another, and after they met they crossed one another, and then became much broader than before.

Whence I gather that the distances at which the fringes pass by the knives are not increased nor altered by the approach of the knives, but the angles in which the rays are there bent are much increased by that approach; and that the knife which is nearest any ray determines which way the ray shall be bent, and the other knife increases the bent.

Obs. 9. When the rays fell very obliquely upon the ruler at the distance of the third part of an inch from the knives, the dark line between the first and second fringe of the shadow of one knife, and the dark line between the first and second fringe of the shadow of the other knife met with one another, at the distance of the fifth part of an inch from the end of the light which passed between the knives at the concourse of their edges. And, therefore, the distance of the edges of the knives at the meeting of these dark lines was the 160th part of an inch. For as four inches to the eighth part of an inch, so is any length of the edges of the knives measured from the point of their concourse to the distance of the edges of the knives at the end of that length, and so is the fifth part of an inch to the 160th part. So, then, the dark lines above mentioned meet in the middle of the light which passes between the knives where they are distant the 160th part of an inch, and the one half of that light passes by the edge of one knife at a distance not greater than the 320th part of an inch, and falling upon the paper makes the fringes of the shadow of that knife, and the other half passes by the edge of the other knife, at a distance not greater than the 320th part of an inch, and falling upon the paper makes the fringes of the shadow of the other knife. But if the paper be held at a distance from the knives greater than the third part of an inch, the dark lines above mentioned meet at a greater distance than the fifth part of an inch from the end of the light which passed between the knives at the concourse of their edges; and, therefore, the light which falls upon the paper where those dark lines meet passes between the knives where the edges are distant above the 160th part of an inch.

For at another time, when the two knives were distant eight feet and five inches from the little hole in the window, made with a small pin as above, the light which fell upon the paper where the aforesaid dark lines met, passed between the knives, where the distance between their edges was as in the following Table, when the distance of the paper from the knives was also as follows:

Distances of the paper from the knives in inches	Distances between the edges of the knives in millesimal parts of an inch
$1\frac{1}{2}$	0.012
$3\frac{1}{3}$	0.020
$8\frac{3}{5}$	0.034
32	0.057
96	0.081
131	0.087

And hence I gather that the light which makes the fringes upon the paper is not the same light at all distances of the paper from the knives, but when the paper is held near the knives, the fringes are made by light which passes by the edges of the knives at a less distance, and is more bent than when the paper is held at a greater distance from the knives.

Obs. 10. When the fringes of the shadows of the knives fell perpendicularly upon a paper at a great distance from the knives, they were in the form of hyperbolas, and their dimensions were as follows: Let CA, CB [Fig. 3] represent lines drawn upon the paper parallel to the edges of the knives, and between which all the light would fall if it passed between the edges of the knives without inflexion; DE a right line drawn through C making the angles ACD, BCE, equal to one another, and terminating all the light which falls upon the paper from the point where the edges of the knives meet; *eis, fkt,* and *glv,* three hyperbolical lines representing the terminus of the shadow of one of the knives, the dark line between the first and second fringes of that shadow, and the dark line between the second and third fringes of the same shadow; *xip, ykq,* and *zlr,* three other hyperbolical lines representing the terminus of the shadow of the other knife, the dark line between the first and second fringes of that shadow, and the dark line between the second and third fringes of the same shadow.

And conceive that these three hyperbolas are like and equal to the former three, and cross them in the points i, k, and l, and that the shadows of the knives are terminated and distinguished from the first luminous fringes by the lines eis and xip, until the meeting and crossing of the fringes, and then those lines cross the fringes in the form of dark lines, terminating the first luminous fringes

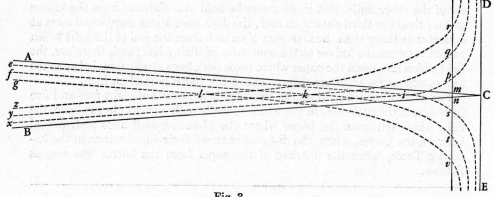

Fig. 3

within side, and distinguishing them from another light which begins to appear at i, and illuminates all the triangular space ipDEs comprehended by these dark lines, and the right line DE. Of these hyperbolas one asymptote is the line DE, and their other asymptotes are parallel to the lines CA and CB. Let rv represent a line drawn anywhere upon the paper parallel to the asymptote DE, and let this line cross the right lines AC in m, and BC in n, and the six dark hyperbolical lines in p, q, r; s, t, v; and by measuring the distances ps, qt, rv, and thence collecting the lengths of the ordinates np, nq, nr or ms, mt, mv, and doing this at several distances of the line rv from the asymptote DE, you may find as many points of these hyperbolas as you please, and thereby know that these curve lines are hyperbolas differing little from the conical hyperbola. And by measuring the lines Ci, Ck, Cl, you may find other points of these curves.

For instance, when the knives were distant from the hole in the window ten feet, and the paper from the knives nine feet, and the angle contained by the edges of the knives to which the angle ACB is equal was subtended by a chord which was to the radius as 1 to 32, and the distance of the line rv from the asymptote DE was half an inch, I measured the lines ps, qt, rv, and found them 0.35, 0.65, 0.98 inch, respectively; and by adding to their halves the line ½mn (which here was the 128th part of an inch, or 0.0078 inch), the sums np, nq, nr, were 0.1828, 0.3328, 0.4978 inch. I measured also the distances of the brightest parts of the fringes which run between pq and st, qr and tv, and next beyond r and v, and found them 0.5, 0.8, and 1.17 inches.

Obs. 11. The Sun shining into my darkened room through a small round hole made in a plate of lead with a slender pin, as above, I placed at the hole a prism to refract the light, and form on the opposite wall the spectrum of colours, described in the third experiment of the first book. And then I found that the shadows of all bodies held in the coloured light between the prism and the wall were bordered with fringes of the colour of that light in which they were held.

In the full red light they were totally red without any sensible blue or violet, and in the deep blue light they were totally blue without any sensible red or yellow; and so in the green light they were totally green, excepting a little yellow and blue, which were mixed in the green light of the prism. And comparing the fringes made in the several coloured lights, I found that those made in the red light were largest, those made in the violet were least, and those made in the green were of a middle bigness. For the fringes with which the shadow of a man's hair were bordered, being measured across the shadow at the distance of six inches from the hair, the distance between the middle and most luminous part of the first or innermost fringe on one side of the shadow, and that of the like fringe on the other side of the shadow, was in the full red light $\frac{1}{37\frac{1}{4}}$ of an inch, and in the full violet $\frac{7}{46}$. And the like distance between the middle and most luminous parts of the second fringes on either side the shadow was in the full red light $\frac{1}{22}$, and in the violet $\frac{1}{27}$ of an inch. And these distances of the fringes held the same proportion at all distances from the hair without any sensible variation.

So, then, the rays which made these fringes in the red light passed by the hair at a greater distance than those did which made the like fringes in the violet; and, therefore, the hair in causing these fringes acted alike upon the red light or least refrangible rays at a greater distance, and upon the violet or most refrangible rays at a less distance, and by those actions disposed the red light into larger fringes, and the violet into smaller, and the lights of intermediate colours into fringes of intermediate bignesses without changing the colour of any sort of light.

When, therefore, the hair in the first and second of these Observations was held in the white beam of the Sun's light, and cast a shadow which was bordered with three fringes of coloured light, those colours arose not from any new modifications impressed upon the rays of light by the hair, but only from the various inflexions whereby the several sorts of rays were separated from one another, which before separation, by the mixture of all their colours, composed the white beam of the Sun's light, but whenever separated compose lights of the several colours which they are originally disposed to exhibit. In this 11th Observation, where the colours are separated before the light passes by the hair, the least refrangible rays, which when separated from the rest make red, were inflected at a greater distance from the hair, so as to make three red fringes at a greater distance from the middle of the shadow of the hair; and the most refrangible rays which when separated make violet, were inflected at a less distance from the hair, so as to make three violet fringes at a less distance from the middle of the shadow of the hair. And other rays of intermediate degrees of refrangibility were inflected at intermediate distances from the hair, so as to make fringes of intermediate colours at intermediate distances from the middle of the shadow of the hair. And in the second Observation, where all the colours are mixed in the white light which passes by the hair, these colours are separated by the various inflexions of the rays, and the fringes which they make appear all together, and the innermost fringes being contiguous make one broad fringe composed of all the colours in due order, the violet lying on the inside of the fringe next the shadow, the red on the outside farthest from the shadow, and the blue, green, and yellow, in the middle. And, in like manner, the middlemost fringes of all the colours lying in order, and being contiguous, make another broad fringe composed of all the colours; and the outmost fringes of all the colours lying in order, and being contiguous, make a third broad fringe composed of all the colours. These are the three fringes of coloured light with which the shadows of all bodies are bordered in the second Observation.

When I made the foregoing Observations, I designed to repeat most of them with more care and exactness, and to make some new ones for determining the manner how the rays of light are bent in their passage by bodies, for making the fringes of colours with the dark lines between them. But I was then interrupted, and cannot now think of taking these things into further consideration. And since I have not finished this part of my design, I shall conclude with proposing only some queries, in order to a further search to be made by others.

QUERY 1. Do not bodies act upon light at a distance, and by their action bend its rays; and is not this action (*cœteris paribus*) strongest at the least distance?

QU. 2. Do not the rays which differ in refrangibility differ also in flexibility; and are they not by their different inflexions separated from one another, so as after separation to make the colours in the three fringes above described? And after what manner are they inflected to make those fringes?

QU. 3. Are not the rays of light, in passing by the edges and sides of bodies, bent several times backwards and forwards, with a motion like that of an eel? And do not the three fringes of coloured light above mentioned arise from three such bendings?

QU. 4. Do not the rays of light which fall upon bodies, and are reflected or refracted, begin to bend before they arrive at the bodies; and are they not reflected, refracted, and inflected, by one and the same principle, acting variously in various circumstances?

QU. 5. Do not bodies and light act mutually upon one another; that is to say, bodies upon light in emitting, reflecting, refracting and inflecting it, and light upon bodies for heating them, and putting their parts into a vibrating motion wherein heat consists?

QU. 6. Do not black bodies conceive heat more easily from light than those of other colours do, by reason that the light falling on them is not reflected outwards, but enters the bodies, and is often reflected and refracted within them, until it be stifled and lost?

QU. 7. Is not the strength and vigor of the action between light and sulphureous bodies observed above, one reason why sulphureous bodies take fire more readily, and burn more vehemently than other bodies do?

QU. 8. Do not all fixed bodies, when heated beyond a certain degree, emit light and shine; and is not this emission performed by the vibrating motions of their parts? And do not all bodies which abound with terrestrial parts, and especially with sulphureous ones, emit light as often as those parts are sufficiently agitated; whether that agitation be made by heat, or by friction, or percussion, or putrefaction, or by any vital motion, or any other cause? As for instance; sea-water in a raging storm; quick-silver agitated *in vacuo*; the back of a cat, or neck of a horse, obliquely struck or rubbed in a dark place; wood, flesh and fish while they putrefy; vapours arising from putrefied waters, usually called *ignes fatui;* stacks of moist hay or corn growing hot by fermentation; glow-worms and the eyes of some animals by vital motions; the vulgar phosphorus agitated by the attrition of any body, or by the acid particles of the air; amber and some diamonds by striking, pressing or rubbing them; scrapings of steel struck off with a flint; iron hammered very nimbly till it become so hot as to kindle sulphur thrown upon it; the axletrees of chariots taking fire by the rapid rotation of the wheels; and some liquors mixed with one another whose particles come together with an impetus, as oil of vitriol distilled from its weight of nitre, and then mixed with twice its weight of oil of anniseeds. So also a globe of glass about 8 or 10 inches in diameter, being put into a frame where it may be swiftly turned round its axis, will in turning shine where it rubs against the palm of one's hand applied to it. And if at the same time a piece of white paper or white cloth, or the end of one's finger be held at the distance of about a quarter of an inch or half an inch from that part of the glass where it is most in motion, the electric vapour which is excited by the friction of the glass against the hand will (by dashing against the white paper, cloth or finger) be put into such an agitation as to emit light, and make the white paper, cloth, or finger appear lucid like a glow-worm; and in rushing out of the glass will sometimes push against the finger so as to be felt. And the same things have been found by rubbing a long and large cylinder or glass or amber with a paper held in one's hand, and continuing the friction till the glass grew warm.

Qu. 9. Is not fire a body heated so hot as to emit light copiously? For what else is a red hot iron than fire? And what else is a burning coal than red hot wood?

Qu. 10. Is not flame a vapour, fume or exhalation heated red hot; that is, so hot as to shine? For bodies do not flame without emitting a copious fume, and this fume burns in the flame. The *ignis fatuus* is a vapour shining without heat, and is there not the same difference between this vapour and flame as between rotten wood shining without heat and burning coals of fire? In distilling hot spirits, if the head of the still be taken off, the vapour which ascends out of the still will take fire at the flame of a candle, and turn into flame, and the flame will run along the vapour from the candle to the still. Some bodies heated by motion, or fermentation, if the heat grow intense, fume copiously, and if the heat be great enough the fumes will shine and become flame. Metals in fusion do not flame for want of a copious fume, except spelter, which fumes copiously, and thereby flames. All flaming bodies, as oil, tallow, wax, wood, fossil coals, pitch, sulphur, by flaming waste and vanish into burning smoke, which smoke, if the flame be put out, is very thick and visible, and sometimes smells strongly, but in the flame loses its smell by burning, and according to the nature of the smoke the flame is of several colours, as that of sulphur blue, that of copper opened with sublimate green, that of tallow yellow, that of camphor white. Smoke passing through flame cannot but grow red-hot, and red-hot smoke can have no other appearance than that of flame. When gunpowder takes fire, it goes away into flaming smoke. For the charcoal and sulphur easily take fire, and set fire to the nitre, and the spirit of the nitre being thereby rarified into vapour, rushes out with explosion much after the manner that the vapour of water rushes out of an æolipile; the sulphur also being volatile is converted into vapour, and augments the explosion. And the acid vapour of the sulphur (namely, that which distils under a bell into oil of sulphur) entering violently into the fixed body of the nitre, sets loose the spirit of the nitre, and excites a great fermentation whereby the heat is further augmented, and the fixed body of the nitre is also rarified into fume, and the explosion is thereby made more vehement and quick. For if salt of tartar be mixed with gunpowder, and that mixture be warmed till it takes fire, the explosion will be more violent and quick than that of gunpowder alone; which cannot proceed from any other cause than the action of the vapour of the gunpowder upon the salt of tartar, whereby that salt is rarified. The explosion of gunpowder arises, therefore, from the violent action whereby all the mixture, being quickly and vehemently heated, is rarified and converted into fume and vapour: which vapour, by the violence of that action, becoming so hot as to shine, appears in the form of flame.

QU. 11. Do not great bodies conserve their heat the longest, their parts heating one another, and may not great dense and fixed bodies, when heated beyond a certain degree, emit light so copiously, as by the emission and reaction of its light, and the reflexions and refractions of its rays within its pores to grow still hotter, till it comes to a certain period of heat, such as is that of the Sun? And are not the Sun and fixed stars great earths vehemently hot, whose heat is conserved by the greatness of the bodies, and the mutual action and reaction between them, and the light which they emit, and whose parts are kept from fuming away, not only by their fixity, but also by the vast weight and density of the atmospheres incumbent upon them; and very strongly compressing them, and condensing the vapours and exhalations which arise from them? For if water be made warm in any pellucid vessel emptied of air, that water in the vacuum will bubble and boil as vehemently as it would in the open air in a vessel set upon the fire till it conceives a much greater heat. For the weight of the incumbent atmosphere keeps down the vapours, and hinders the water from boiling, until it grow much hotter than is requisite to make it boil *in vacuo*. Also a mixture of tin and lead being put upon a red-hot iron *in vacuo* emits a fume and flame, but the same mixture in the open air, by reason of the incumbent atmosphere, does not so much as emit any fume which can be perceived by sight. In like manner the great weight of the atmosphere which lies upon the globe of the Sun may hinder bodies there from rising up and going away from the Sun in the form of vapours and fumes, unless by means of a far greater heat than that which on the surface of our Earth would very easily turn them into vapours and fumes. And the same great weight may condense those vapours and exhalations as soon as they shall at any time begin to ascend from the Sun, and make them presently fall back again into him, and by that action increase his heat much after the manner that in our Earth the air increases the heat of a culinary fire. And the same weight may hinder the globe of the Sun from being diminished, unless by the emission of light, and a very small quantity of vapours and exhalations.

QU. 12. Do not the rays of light in falling upon the bottom of the eye excite vibrations in the *tunica retina?* Which vibrations, being propagated along the solid fibres of the optic nerves into the brain, cause the sense of seeing? For because dense bodies conserve their heat a long time, and the densest bodies conserve their heat the longest, the vibrations of their parts are of a lasting nature, and therefore may be propagated along solid fibres of uniform dense matter to a great distance, for conveying into the brain the impressions made upon all the organs of sense. For that motion which can continue long in one and the same part of a body, can be propagated a long way from one part to another, supposing the body homogeneal, so that the motion may not be reflected, refracted, interrupted or disordered by any unevenness of the body.

QU. 13. Do not several sorts of rays make vibrations of several bignesses, which according to their bignesses excite sensations of several colours, much after the manner that the vibrations of the air, according to their several bignesses excite sensations of several sounds? And particularly do not the most refrangible rays excite the shortest vibrations for making a sensation of deep violet, the least refrangible the largest for making a sensation of deep red, and the several intermediate sorts of rays, vibrations of several intermediate bignesses to make sensations of the several intermediate colours?

QU. 14. May not the harmony and discord of colours arise from the proportions of the vibrations propagated through the fibres of the optic nerves into the brain, as the harmony and discord of sounds arise from the proportions of the vibrations of the air? For some colours, if they be viewed together, are agreeable to one another, as those of gold and indigo, and others disagree.

QU. 15. Are not the species of objects seen with both eyes united where the optic nerves meet before they come into the brain, the fibres on the right side of both nerves uniting there, and after union going thence into the brain in the nerve which is on the right side of the head, and the fibres on the left side of both nerves uniting in the same place, and after union going into the brain in the nerve which is on the left side of the head, and these two nerves meeting in the brain in such a manner that their fibres make but one entire species or picture, half of which on the right side of the sensorium comes from the right side of both eyes through the right side of both optic nerves to the place where the nerves meet, and from thence on the right side of the head into the brain, and the other half on the left side of the sensorium comes in like manner from the left side of both eyes? For the optic nerves of such animals as look the same way with both eyes (as of men, dogs, sheep, oxen, &c.) meet before they come into the brain, but the optic nerves of such animals as do not look the same way with both eyes (as of fishes, and of the chameleon) do not meet, if I am rightly informed.

QU. 16. When a man in the dark presses either corner of his eye with his finger, and turns his eye away from his finger, he will see a circle of colours like those in the feather of a peacock's tail. If the eye and the finger remain quiet these colours vanish in a second minute of time, but if the finger be moved with a quavering motion they appear again. Do not these colours arise from such motions excited in the bottom of the eye by the pressure and motion of the finger as at other times are excited there by light for causing vision? And do not the motions once excited continue about a second of time before they cease? And when a man by a stroke upon his eye sees a flash of light, are not the like motions excited in the retina by the stroke? And when a coal of fire, moved nimbly in the circumference of a circle, makes the whole circumference appear like a circle of fire, is it not because the motions excited in the bottom of the eye by the rays of light are of a lasting nature, and continue till the coal of fire in going round returns to its former place? And considering the lastingness of the motions excited in the bottom of the eye by light, are they not of a vibrating nature?

QU. 17. If a stone be thrown into stagnating water, the waves excited thereby continue some time to arise in the place where the stone fell into the water, and are propagated from thence in concentric circles upon the surface of the water to great distances. And the vibrations or tremors excited in the air by percussion continue a little time to move from the place of percussion in concentric spheres to great distances. And in like manner, when a ray of light falls upon the surface of any pellucid body, and is there refracted or reflected, may not waves of vibrations, or tremors, be thereby excited in the refracting or reflecting medium at the point of incidence, and continue to arise there, and to be propagated from thence as long as they continue to arise and be propagated, when they are excited in the bottom of the eye by the pressure or motion of the finger or by the light which comes from the coal of fire in the experiments above mentioned? And are not these vibrations propagated from the point of incidence to great distances? And do they not overtake the rays of light, and, by overtaking them successively, do they not put them into the fits of easy reflexion and easy transmission described above? For if the rays endeavour to recede from the densest part of the vibration, they may be alternately accelerated and retarded by the vibrations overtaking them.

Qu. 18. If in two large tall cylindrical vessels of glass inverted, two little thermometers be suspended so as not to touch the vessels, and the air be drawn out of one of these vessels, and these vessels thus prepared be carried out of a cold place into a warm one, the thermometer *in vacuo* will grow warm as much, and almost as soon, as the thermometer which is not *in vacuo*. And when the vessels are carried back into the cold place, the thermometer *in vacuo* will grow cold almost as soon as the other thermometer. Is not the heat of the warm room conveyed through the vacuum by the vibrations of a much subtiler medium than air, which after the air was drawn out remained in the vacuum? And is not this medium the same with that medium by which light is refracted and reflected, and by whose vibrations light communicates heat to bodies, and is put into fits of easy reflexion and easy transmission? And do not the vibrations of this medium in hot bodies contribute to the intenseness and duration of their heat? And do not hot bodies communicate their heat to contiguous cold ones, by the vibrations of this medium propagated from them into the cold ones? And is not this medium exceedingly more rare and subtile than the air, and exceedingly more elastic and active? And doth it not readily pervade all bodies? And is it not (by its elastic force) expanded through all the heavens?

Qu. 19. Doth not the refraction of light proceed from the different density of this æthereal medium in different places, the light receding always from the denser parts of the medium? And is not the density thereof greater in free and open spaces void of air and other grosser bodies, than within the pores of water, glass, crystal, gems, and other compact bodies? For when light passes through glass or crystal, and falling very obliquely upon the farther surface thereof is totally reflected, the total reflexion ought to proceed rather from the density and vigour of the medium without and beyond the glass, than from the rarity and weakness thereof.

Qu. 20. Doth not this æthereal medium in passing out of water, glass, crystal, and other compact and dense bodies into empty spaces, grow denser and denser by degrees, and by that means refract the rays of light not in a point, but by bending them gradually in curved lines? And doth not the gradual condensation of this medium extend to some distance from the bodies, and thereby cause the inflexions of the rays of light, which pass by the edges of dense bodies, at some distance from the bodies?

Qu. 21. Is not this medium much rarer within the dense bodies of the Sun, stars, planets and comets, than in the empty celestial spaces between them? And in passing from them to great distances, doth it not grow denser and denser perpetually, and thereby cause the gravity of those great bodies towards one another, and of their parts towards the bodies; every body endeavouring to go from the denser parts of the medium towards the rarer? For if this medium be rarer within the Sun's body than at its surface, and rarer there than at the hundredth part of an inch from its body, and rarer there than at the fiftieth part of an inch from its body, and rarer there than at the orb of Saturn, I see no reason why the increase of density should stop anywhere, and not rather be continued through all distances from the Sun to Saturn, and beyond. And though this increase of density may at great distances be exceeding slow, yet if the elastic force of this medium be exceeding great, it may suffice to impel bodies from the denser parts of the medium towards the rarer, with all that power which we call gravity. And that the elastic force of this medium is exceeding great, may be gathered from the swiftness of its vibrations. Sounds move about 1,140 English feet in a second minute of time, and in seven or eight minutes of time they move about one hundred English miles. Light moves from the Sun to us in about seven or eight minutes of time, which distance is about 7,000,000 English miles, supposing the horizontal parallax of the Sun to be about 12″. And the vibrations or pulses of this medium, that they may cause the alternate fits of easy transmission and easy reflexion, must be swifter than light, and by consequence above 700,000 times swifter than sounds. And, therefore, the elastic force of this medium, in proportion to its density, must be above $700,000 \times 700,000$ (that is, above 490,000,000,000) times greater than the elastic force of the air is in proportion to its density. For the velocities of the pulses of elastic mediums are in a subduplicate ratio of the elasticities and the rarities of the mediums taken together.

As attraction is stronger in small magnets than in great ones in proportion to their bulk, and gravity is greater in the surfaces of small planets than in those of great ones in proportion to their bulk, and small bodies are agitated much more by electric attraction than great ones; so the smallness of the rays of light may contribute very much to the power of the agent by which they are refracted. And so if any one should suppose that æther (like our air) may contain particles which endeavour to recede from one another (for I do not know what this æther is) and that its particles are exceedingly smaller than those of air, or even than those of light: the exceeding smallness of its particles may contribute to the greatness of the force by which those particles may recede from one another, and thereby make that medium exceedingly more rare and elastic than air, and by consequence exceedingly less able to resist the motions of projectiles, and exceedingly more able to press upon gross bodies, by endeavouring to expand itself.

Qu. 22. May not planets and comets, and all gross bodies, perform their motions more freely, and with less resistance in this æthereal medium than in any fluid, which fills all space adequately without leaving any pores, and by consequence is much denser than quick-silver or gold? And may not its resistance be so small, as to be inconsiderable? For instance: if this æther (for so I will call it) should be supposed 700,000 times more elastic than our air, and above 700,000 times more rare, its resistance would be above 600,000,000 times less than that of water. And so small a resistance would scarce make any sensible alteration in the motions of the planets in ten thousand years. If any one would ask how a medium can be so rare, let him tell me how the air, in the upper parts of the atmosphere, can be above a hundred thousand thousand times rarer than gold. Let him also tell me how an electric body can by friction emit an exhalation so rare and subtile, and yet so potent, as by its emission to cause no sensible diminution of the weight of the electric body, and to be expanded through a sphere, whose diameter is above two feet, and yet to be able to agitate and carry up leaf copper, or leaf gold, at the distance of above a foot from the electric body? And how the effluvia of a magnet can be so rare and subtile as to pass through a plate of glass without any resistance or diminution of their force, and yet so potent as to turn a magnetic needle beyond the glass?

QU. 23. Is not vision performed chiefly by the vibrations of this medium, excited in the bottom of the eye by the rays of light, and propagated through the solid, pellucid and uniform capillamenta of the optic nerves into the place of sensation? And is not hearing performed by the vibrations either of this or some other medium, excited in the auditory nerves by the tremors of the air, and propagated through the solid, pellucid and uniform capillamenta of those nerves into the place of sensation? And so of the other senses.

QU. 24. Is not animal motion performed by the vibrations of this medium, excited in the brain by the power of the will, and propagated from thence through the solid, pellucid and uniform capillamenta of the nerves into the muscles, for contracting and dilating them? I suppose that the capillamenta of the nerves are each of them solid and uniform, that the vibrating motion of the æthereal medium may be propagated along them from one end to the other uniformly, and without interruption, for obstructions in the nerves create palsies. And that they may be sufficiently uniform, I suppose them to be pellucid when viewed singly, tho' the reflexions in their cylindrical surfaces may make the whole nerve (composed of many capillamenta) appear opaque and white. For opacity arises from reflecting surfaces, such as may disturb and interrupt the motions of this medium.

QU. 25. Are there not other original properties of the rays of light, besides those already described? An instance of another original property we have in the refraction of island crystal, described first by Erasmus Bartholinus, and afterwards more exactly by Huygens, in his book *De la Lumière.* This crystal is a pellucid, fissile stone, clear as water or crystal of the rock, and without colour; enduring a red heat without losing its transparency, and in a very strong heat calcining without fusion. Steeped a day or two in water, it loses its natural polish. Being rubbed on cloth, it attracts pieces of straws and other light things, like amber or glass; and with *aqua fortis* it makes an ebullition. It seems to be a sort of talc, and is found in form of an oblique parallelepiped, with six parallelogram sides and eight solid angles. The obtuse angles of the parallelograms are each of them 101 degrees and 52 minutes; the acute ones 78 degrees and 8 minutes. Two of the solid angles opposite to one another, as C and E, are compassed each of them with three of these obtuse angles, and each of the other six with one obtuse and two acute ones [Fig. 4]. It cleaves easily in planes parallel to any of its sides, and not in any other planes. It cleaves with a glossy polite surface not perfectly plane, but with some little

unevenness. It is easily scratched, and by reason of its softness it takes a polish
very difficultly. It polishes better upon polished looking-glass than upon metal,

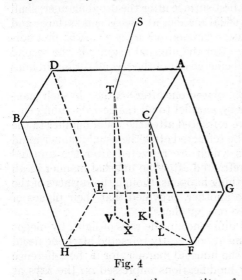

Fig. 4

and perhaps better upon pitch,
leather or parchment. Afterwards it
must be rubbed with a little oil or
white of an egg to fill up its scratches;
whereby it will become very transparent and polite. But for several
experiments it is not necessary to
polish it. If a piece of this crystalline
stone be laid upon a book, every
letter of the book seen through it
will appear double, by means of a
double refraction. And if any beam
of light falls either perpendicularly,
or in any oblique angle upon any
surface of this crystal, it becomes
divided into two beams by means of
the same double refraction. Which
beams are of the same colour with
the incident beam of light, and seem
equal to one another in the quantity of their light, or very nearly equal. One
of these refractions is performed by the usual rule of Optics, the sine of incidence out of air into this crystal being to the sine of refraction as five to
three. The other refraction, which may be called the unusual refraction, is
performed by the following rule:

Let ADBC represent the refracting surface of the crystal, C the biggest
solid angle at that surface, GEHF the opposite surface, and CK a perpendicular on that surface. This perpendicular makes with the edge of the crystal
CF, an angle of 19 degrees 3'. Join KF, and in it take KL, so that the angle
KCL be 6 degrees 40'. and the angle LCF 12 degrees 23'. And if ST represent
any beam of light incident at T in any angle upon the refracting surface ADBC,
let TV be the refracted beam determined by the given portion of the sines 5 to
3, according to the usual rule of Optics. Draw VX parallel and equal to KL.
Draw it the same way from V in which L lieth from K; and joining TX, this
line TX shall be the other refracted beam carried from T to X, by the unusual
refraction.

If, therefore, the incident beam ST be perpendicular to the refracting surface, the two beams TV and TX, into which it shall become divided, shall be
parallel to the lines CK and CL; one of those beams going through the crystal
perpendicularly, as it ought to do by the usual laws of Optics, and the other
TX by an unusual refraction diverging from the perpendicular, and making
with it an angle VTX of about 6⅔ degrees, as is found by experience. And
hence, the plane VTX, and such like planes which are parallel to the plane
CFK, may be called the planes of perpendicular refraction. And the coast towards which the lines KL and VX are drawn, may be called the coast of unusual refraction.

In like manner, crystal of the rock has a double refraction; but the difference
of the two refractions is not so great and manifest as in island crystal.

When the beam ST incident on island crystal is divided into two beams TV and TX, and these two beams arrive at the farther surface of the glass, the beam TV, which was refracted at the first surface after the usual manner, shall be again refracted entirely after the usual manner at the second surface; and the beam TX, which was refracted after the unusual manner in the first surface, shall be again refracted entirely after the unusual manner in the second surface; so that both these beams shall emerge out of the second surface in lines parallel to the first incident beam ST.

And if two pieces of island crystal be placed one after another, in such manner that all the surfaces of the latter be parallel to all the corresponding surfaces of the former, the rays which are refracted after the usual manner in the first surface of the first crystal, shall be refracted after the usual manner in all the following surfaces; and the rays which are refracted after the unusual manner in the first surface shall be refracted after the unusual manner in all the following surfaces. And the same thing happens, though the surfaces of the crystals be any ways inclined to one another, provided that their planes of perpendicular refraction be parallel to one another.

And, therefore, there is an original difference in the rays of light, by means of which some rays are in this experiment constantly refracted after the usual manner, and others constantly after the unusual manner; for if the difference be not original, but arises from new modifications impressed on the rays at their first refraction, it would be altered by new modifications in the three following refractions; whereas it suffers no alteration, but is constant, and has the same effect upon the rays in all the refractions. The unusual refraction is, therefore, performed by an original property of the rays. And it remains to be enquired whether the rays have not more original properties than are yet discovered.

Qu. 26. Have not the rays of light several sides, endued with several original properties? For if the planes of perpendicular refraction of the second crystal be at right angles with the planes of perpendicular refraction of the first crystal, the rays which are refracted after the usual manner in passing through the first crystal will be all of them refracted after the unusual manner in passing through the second crystal; and the rays which are refracted after the unusual manner in passing through the first crystal will be all of them refracted after the usual manner in passing through the second crystal. And, therefore, there are not two sorts of rays differing in their nature from one another, one of which is constantly and in all positions refracted after the usual manner, and the other constantly and in all positions after the unusual manner. The difference between the two sorts of rays, in the experiment mentioned in the 25th Question, was only in the positions of the sides of the rays to the planes of perpendicular refraction. For one and the same ray is here refracted, sometimes after the usual, and sometimes after the unusual manner, according to the position which its sides have to the crystals. If the sides of the ray are posited the same way to both crystals, it is refracted after the same manner in them both; but if that side of the ray which looks towards the coast of the unusual refraction of the first crystal be 90 degrees from that side of the same ray which looks toward the coast of the unusual refraction of the second crystal (which may be effected by varying the position of the second crystal to the first, and by consequence to the rays of light), the ray shall be refracted after several manners in the several crystals. There is nothing more required to determine whether the rays of light which fall upon the second crystal shall be refracted after the usual or after the unusual manner, but to turn about this crystal, so that the coast of this crystal's unusual refraction may be on this or on that side of the ray. And, therefore, every ray may be considered as having four sides or quarters, two of which opposite to one another incline the ray to be refracted after the unusual manner, as often as either of them are turned towards the coast of unusual refraction; and the other two, whenever either of them are turned towards the coast of unusual refraction, do not incline it to be otherwise refracted than after the usual manner. The two first may, therefore, be called the sides of unusual refraction. And since these dispositions were in the rays before their incidence on the second, third, and fourth surfaces of the two crystals, and suffered no alteration (so far as appears) by the refraction of the rays in their passage through those surfaces, and the rays were refracted by the same laws in all the four surfaces, it appears that those dispositions were in the rays originally, and suffered no alteration by the first refraction, and that by means of those dispositions the rays were refracted at their incidence on the first surface of the first crystal, some of them after the usual, and some of them after the unusual manner, accordingly as their sides of unusual refraction were then turned towards the coast of the unusual refraction of that crystal, or sideways from it.

Every ray of light has, therefore, two opposite sides, originally endued with a property on which the unusual refraction depends, and the other two opposite sides not endued with that property. And it remains to be enquired whether there are not more properties of light by which the sides of the rays differ, and are distinguished from one another.

In explaining the difference of the sides of the rays above mentioned, I have supposed that the rays fall perpendicularly on the first crystal. But if they fall obliquely on it, the success is the same. Those rays which are refracted after the usual manner in the first crystal will be refracted after the unusual manner in the second crystal, supposing the planes of perpendicular refraction to be at right angles with one another, as above; and on the contrary.

If the planes of the perpendicular refraction of the two crystals be neither parallel nor perpendicular to one another, but contain an acute angle, the two beams of light which emerge out of the first crystal will be each of them divided into two more at their incidence on the second crystal. For in this case the rays in each of the two beams will some of them have their sides of unusual refraction, and some of them their other sides turned towards the coast of the unusual refraction of the second crystal.

Qu. 27. Are not all hypotheses erroneous which have hitherto been invented for explaining the phenomena of light, by new modifications of the rays? For those phenomena depend not upon new modifications, as has been supposed, but upon the original and unchangeable properties of the rays.

Qu. 28. Are not all hypotheses erroneous in which light is supposed to consist in pression or motion, propagated through a fluid medium? For in all these hypotheses the phenomena of light have been hitherto explained by supposing that they arise from new modifications of the rays; which is an erroneous supposition.

If light consisted only in pression propagated without actual motion, it would not be able to agitate and heat the bodies which refract and reflect it. If it consisted in motion propagated to all distances in an instant, it would require an infinite force every moment, in every shining particle, to generate that motion. And if it consisted in pression or motion, propagated either in an instant or in time, it would bend into the shadow. For pression or motion cannot be propagated in a fluid in right lines, beyond an obstacle which stops part of the motion, but will bend and spread every way into the quiescent medium which lies beyond the obstacle. Gravity tends downwards, but the pressure of water arising from gravity tends every way with equal force, and is propagated as readily, and with as much force sideways as downwards, and through crooked passages as through straight ones. The waves on the surface of stagnating water, passing by the sides of a broad obstacle which stops part of them, bend afterwards and dilate themselves gradually into the quiet water behind the obstacle. The waves, pulses or vibrations of the air, wherein sounds consist, bend manifestly, though not so much as the waves of water. For a bell or a cannon may be heard beyond a hill which intercepts the sight of the sounding body, and sounds are propagated as readily through crooked pipes as through straight ones. But light is never known to follow crooked passages nor to bend into the shadow. For the fixed stars by the interposition of any of the planets cease to be seen. And so do the parts of the sun by the interposition of the Moon, Mercury or Venus. The rays which pass very near to the edges of any body are bent a little by the action of the body, as we shewed above; but this bending is not towards but from the shadow, and is performed only in the passage of the ray by the body, and at a very small distance from it. So soon as the ray is past the body, it goes right on.

To explain the unusual refraction of island crystal by pression or motion propagated, has not hitherto been attempted (to my knowledge) except by Huygens, who for that end supposed two several vibrating mediums within that crystal. But when he tried the refractions in two successive pieces of that crystal, and found them such as is mentioned above, he confessed himself at a loss for explaining them. For pressions or motions, propagated from a shining body through an uniform medium, must be on all sides alike; whereas by those experiments it appears that the rays of light have different properties in their different sides. He suspected that the pulses of æther in passing through the first crystal might receive certain new modifications, which might determine them to be propagated in this or that medium within the second crystal, according to the position of that crystal. But what modifications those might be he could not say, nor think of anything satisfactory in that point. And if he had known that the unusual refraction depends not on new modifications, but on the original and unchangeable dispositions of the rays, he would have found it as difficult to explain how those dispositions, which he supposed to be impressed on the rays by the first crystal, could be in them before their incidence on that crystal, and in general, how all rays emitted by shining bodies can have those dispositions in them from the beginning. To me, at least, this seems inexplicable, if light be nothing else than pression or motion propagated through æther.

And it is as difficult to explain by these hypotheses how rays can be alternately in fits of easy reflexion and easy transmission, unless perhaps one might suppose that there are in all space two æthereal vibrating mediums, and that the vibrations of one of them constitute light, and the vibrations of the other are swifter, and as often as they overtake the vibrations of the first, put them into those fits. But how two æthers can be diffused through all space, one of which acts upon the other, and by consequence is reacted upon, without retarding, shattering, dispersing and confounding one another's motions, is inconceivable. And against filling the heavens with fluid mediums, unless they be exceeding rare, a great objection arises from the regular and very lasting motions of the planets and comets in all manner of courses through the heavens. For thence it is manifest that the heavens are void of all sensible resistance, and by consequence of all sensible matter.

For the resisting power of fluid mediums arises partly from the attrition of the parts of the medium, and partly from the *vis inertiæ* of the matter. That part of the resistance of a spherical body which arises from the attrition of the parts of the medium is very nearly as the diameter, or, at the most, as the *factum* of the diameter, and the velocity of the spherical body together. And that part of the resistance which arises from the *vis inertiæ* of the matter is as the square of that *factum*. And by this difference the two sorts of resistance may be distinguished from one another in any medium; and these being distinguished, it will be found that almost all the resistance of bodies of a competent magnitude moving in air, water, quick-silver, and such like fluids with a competent velocity, arises from the *vis inertiæ* of the parts of the fluid.

Now, that part of the resisting power of any medium which arises from the tenacity, friction or attrition of the parts of the medium, may be diminished by dividing the matter into smaller parts, and making the parts more smooth and slippery; but that part of the resistance which arises from the *vis inertiæ* is proportional to the density of the matter, and cannot be diminished by dividing the matter into smaller parts, nor by any other means than by decreasing the density of the medium. And for these reasons the density of fluid mediums is very nearly proportional to their resistance. Liquors which differ not much in density as water, spirit of wine, spirit of turpentine, hot oil, differ not much in resistance. Water is thirteen or fourteen times lighter than quick-silver and by consequence thirteen or fourteen times rarer, and its resistance is less than that of quick-silver in the same proportion, or thereabouts, as I have found by experiments made with pendulums. The open air in which we breathe is eight or nine hundred times lighter than water, and by consequence eight or nine hundred times rarer, and accordingly its resistance is less than that of water in the same proportion, or thereabouts, as I have also found by experiments made with pendulums. And in thinner air the resistance is still less, and at length, by rarefying the air, becomes insensible. For small feathers falling in the open air meet with great resistance, but in a tall glass well emptied of air, they fall as fast as lead or gold, as I have seen tried several times. Whence the resistance seems still to decrease in proportion to the density of the fluid. For I do not find by any experiments that bodies moving in quick-silver, water, or air meet with any other sensible resistance than what arises from the density and tenacity of those sensible fluids, as they would do if the pores of those fluids, and all other spaces, were filled with a dense and subtile fluid. Now, if the resistance in a vessel well emptied of air was but a hundred times less than in the open air, it would be about a million of times less than in quick-silver. But it seems to be much less in such a vessel, and still much less in the heavens, at the height of three or four hundred miles from the Earth, or above. For Mr. Boyle has shewed that air may be rarified above ten thousand times in vessels of glass; and the heavens are much emptier of air than any vacuum we can make below. For since the air is compressed by the weight of the incumbent atmosphere, and the density of air is proportional to the force compressing it, it follows by computation that, at the height of about seven and a half English miles from the Earth, the air is four times rarer than at the surface of the Earth; and at the height of 15 miles it is sixteen times rarer than that at the surface of the Earth; and at the height of 22½, 30, or 38 miles, it is respectively 64, 256, or 1,024 times rarer, or thereabouts; and at the height of 76, 152, 228 miles, it is about 1,000,000, 1,000,000,000,000, or 1,000,000,000,000,000,000 times rarer; and so on.

Heat promotes fluidity very much by diminishing the tenacity of bodies. It makes many bodies fluid which are not fluid in cold, and increases the fluidity of tenacious liquids, as of oil, balsam, and honey, and thereby decreases their resistance. But it decreases not the resistance of water considerably, as it would do if any considerable part of the resistance of water arose from the attrition or tenacity of its parts. And, therefore, the resistance of water arises principally and almost entirely from the *vis inertiæ* of its matter; and by consequence, if the heavens were as dense as water, they would not have much less resistance than water; if as dense as quick-silver, they would not have much less resistance than quick-silver; if absolutely dense, or full of matter without any vacuum, let the matter be never so subtile and fluid, they would have a greater resistance than quick-silver. A solid globe in such a medium would lose above half its motion in moving three times the length of its diameter, and a globe not solid (such as are the planets), would be retarded sooner. And, therefore, to make way for the regular and lasting motions of the planets and comets, it's necessary to empty the heavens of all matter, except perhaps some very thin vapours, steams, or effluvia, arising from the atmospheres of the Earth, planets, and comets, and from such an exceedingly rare æthereal medium as we described above. A dense fluid can be of no use for explaining the phenomena of Nature, the motions of the planets and comets being better explained without it. It serves only to disturb and retard the motions of those great bodies, and make the frame of Nature languish; and in the pores of bodies it serves only to stop the vibrating motions of their parts, wherein their heat and activity consists. And as it is of no use, and hinders the operations of Nature, and makes her languish, so there is no evidence for its existence; and, therefore, it ought to be rejected. And if it be rejected, the hypotheses that light consists in pression or motion, propagated through such a medium, are rejected with it.

And, for rejecting such a medium, we have the authority of those the oldest and most celebrated philosophers of Greece and Phœnicia, who made a vacuum, and atoms, and the gravity of atoms, the first principles of their philosophy; tacitly attributing gravity to some other cause than dense matter. Later philosophers banish the consideration of such a cause out of natural philosophy, feigning hypotheses for explaining all things mechanically, and referring other causes to metaphysics; whereas the main business of natural philosophy is to argue from phenomena without feigning hypotheses, and to deduce causes from effects, till we come to the very first cause, which certainly is not mechanical; and not only to unfold the mechanism of the world, but chiefly to resolve these and such like questions. What is there in places almost empty of matter, and whence is it that the Sun and planets gravitate towards one another, without dense matter between them? Whence is it that Nature doth nothing in vain; and whence arises all that order and beauty which we see in the world? To what end are comets, and whence is it that planets move all one and the same way in orbs concentric, while comets move all manner of ways in orbs very eccentric; and what hinders the fixed stars from falling upon one another? How came the bodies of animals to be contrived with so much art, and for what ends were their several parts? Was the eye contrived without skill in Optics, and the ear without knowledge of sounds? How do the motions of the body follow from the will, and whence is the instinct in animals? Is not the sensory of animals that place to which the sensitive substance is present, and into which the sensible species of things are carried through the nerves and brain, that there they may be perceived by their immediate presence to that substance? And these things being rightly dispatched, does it not appear from phenomena that there is a Being incorporeal, living, intelligent, omnipresent, who in infinite space (as it were in his sensory) sees the things themselves intimately, and throughly perceives them, and comprehends them wholly by their immediate presence to himself? Of which things the images only carried through the organs of sense into our little sensoriums are there seen and beheld by that which in us perceives and thinks. And though every true step made in this philosophy brings us not immediately to the knowledge of the First Cause, yet it brings us nearer to it, and on that account is to be highly valued.

Qu. 29. Are not the rays of light very small bodies emitted from shining substances? For such bodies will pass through uniform mediums in right lines without bending into the shadow, which is the nature of the rays of light. They will also be capable of several properties, and be able to conserve their properties unchanged in passing through several mediums, which is another condition of the rays of light. Pellucid substances act upon the rays of light at a distance in refracting, reflecting, and inflecting them, and the rays mutually agitate the parts of those substances at a distance for heating them; and this action and reaction at a distance very much resembles an attractive force between bodies. If refraction be performed by attraction of the rays, the sines of incidence must be to the sines of refraction in a given proportion, as we shewed in our principles of philosophy. And this rule is true by experience. The rays of light in going out of glass into a vacuum, are bent towards the glass; and if they fall too obliquely on the vacuum, they are bent backwards into the glass, and totally reflected; and this reflexion cannot be ascribed to the resistance of an absolute vacuum, but must be caused by the power of the glass attracting the rays at their going out of it into the vacuum, and bringing them back. For if the farther surface of the glass be moistened with water or clear oil, or liquid and clear honey, the rays which would otherwise be reflected will go into the water, oil, or honey; and, therefore, are not reflected before they arrive at the farther surface of the glass, and begin to go out of it. If they go out of it into the water, oil, or honey, they go on, because the attraction of the glass is almost balanced and rendered ineffectual by the contrary attraction of the liquor. But if they go out of it into a vacuum which has no attraction to balance that of the glass, the attraction of the glass either bends and refracts them, or brings them back and reflects them.

And this is still more evident by laying together two prisms of glass, or two object-glasses of very long telescopes, the one plane, the other a little convex, and so compressing them that they do not fully touch, nor are too far asunder. For the light which falls upon the farther surface of the first glass where the interval between the glasses is not above the ten hundred thousandth part of an inch, will go through that surface, and through the air or vacuum between the glasses, and enter into the second glass, as was explained in the first, fourth, and eighth Observations of the first part of the second book. But, if the second glass be taken away, the light which goes out of the second surface of the first glass into the air or vacuum, will not go on forwards, but turns back into the first glass, and is reflected; and, therefore, it is drawn back by the power of the first glass, there being nothing else to turn it back. Nothing more is requisite for producing all the variety of colours, and degrees of refrangibility, than that the rays of light be bodies of different sizes, the least of which may take violet the weakest and darkest of the colours, and be more easily diverted by refracting surfaces from the right course; and the rest, as they are bigger and bigger, may make the stronger and more lucid colours (blue, green, yellow, and red) and be more and more difficultly diverted. Nothing more is requisite for putting the rays of light into fits of easy reflexion and easy transmission, than that they be small bodies which by their attractive powers, or some other force, stir up vibrations in what they act upon, which vibrations, being swifter than the rays, overtake them successively, and agitate them so as by turns to increase and decrease their velocities, and thereby put them into those fits. And, lastly, the unusual refraction of island crystal looks very much as if it were performed by some kind of attractive virtue lodged in certain sides both of the rays, and of the particles of the crystal. For were it not for some kind of disposition or virtue lodged in some sides of the particles of the crystal, and not in their other sides, and which inclines and bends the rays towards the coast of unusual refraction, the rays which fall perpendicularly on the crystal would not be refracted towards that coast rather than towards any other coast, both at their incidence and at their emergence, so as to emerge perpendicularly by a contrary situation of the coast of unusual refraction at the second surface; the crystal acting upon the rays after they have passed through it, and are emerging into the air; or, if you please, into a vacuum. And since the crystal by this disposition or virtue does not act upon the rays, unless when one of their sides of unusual refraction looks towards that coast, this argues a virtue or disposition in those sides of the rays which answers to, and sympathizes with, that virtue or disposition of the crystal as the poles of two magnets answer to one another. And as magnetism may be intended and remitted, and is found only in the magnet and in iron, so this virtue of refracting the perpendicular rays is greater in island crystal, less in crystal of the rock, and is not yet found in other bodies. I do not say that this virtue is magnetical: it seems to be of another kind. I only say that whatever it be, it's difficult to conceive how the rays of light, unless they be bodies, can have a permanent virtue in two of their sides which is not in their other sides, and this without any regard to their position to the space or medium through which they pass.

What I mean in this Question by a vacuum, and by the attractions of the rays of light towards glass or crystal, may be understood by what was said in the 18th, 19th, and 20th Questions.

Qu. 30. Are not gross bodies and light convertible into one another, and may not bodies receive much of their activity from the particles of light which enter their composition? For all fixed bodies being heated emit light so long as they continue sufficiently hot, and light mutually stops in bodies as often as its rays strike upon their parts, as we shewed above. I know no body less apt to shine than water; and yet water, by frequent distillations, changes into fixed earth, as Mr. Boyle has tried, and then this earth being enabled to endure a sufficient heat, shines by heat like other bodies.

The changing of bodies into light, and light into bodies, is very conformable to the course of Nature, which seems delighted with transmutations. Water, which is a very fluid, tasteless salt she changes by heat into vapour, which is a sort of air, and by cold into ice, which is a hard, pellucid, brittle, fusible stone; and this stone returns into water by heat, and vapour returns into water by cold. Earth by heat becomes fire, and by cold returns into earth. Dense bodies by fermentation rarefy into several sorts of air, and this air by fermentation, and sometimes without it, returns into dense bodies. Mercury appears sometimes in the form of a fluid metal, sometimes in the form of a hard brittle metal, sometimes in the form of a corrosive pellucid salt called sublimate, sometimes in the form of a tasteless, pellucid, volatile white earth called *Mercurius dulcis;* or in that of a red opaque volatile earth called Cinnabar; or in that of a red or white precipitate, or in that of a fluid salt; and in distillation it turns into vapour, and being agitated *in vacuo*, it shines like fire. And after all these changes it returns again into its first form of mercury. Eggs grow from insensible magnitudes, and change into animals; tadpoles into frogs; and worms into flies. All birds, beasts and fishes, insects, trees, and other vegetables, with their several parts, grow out of water and watery tinctures and salts, and by putrefaction return again into watery substances. And water standing a few days in the open air, yields a tincture, which (like that of malt) by standing longer yields a sediment and a spirit, but before putrefaction is fit nourishment for animals and vegetables. And among such various and strange transmutations, why may not Nature change bodies into light, and light into bodies?

Qu. 31. Have not the small particles of bodies certain powers, virtues, or forces, by which they act at a distance, not only upon the rays of light for reflecting, refracting, and inflecting them, but also upon one another for producing a great part of the phenomena of Nature? For it's well known that bodies act one upon another by the attractions of gravity, magnetism, and electricity; and these instances shew the tenor and course of Nature, and make it not improbable but that there may be more attractive powers than these. For Nature is very consonant and conformable to herself. How these attractions may be performed I do not here consider. What I call attraction may be performed by impulse, or by some other means unknown to me. I use that word here to signify only in general any force by which bodies tend towards one another, whatsoever be the cause. For we must learn from the phenomena of Nature what bodies attract one another, and what are the laws and properties of the attraction, before we enquire the cause by which the attraction is performed. The attractions of gravity, magnetism, and electricity reach to very sensible distances, and so have been observed by vulgar eyes, and there may be others which reach to so small distances as hitherto escape observation; and perhaps electrical attraction may reach to such small distances, even without being excited by friction.

For when salt of tartar runs *per deliquium,* is not this done by an attraction between the particles of the salt of tartar, and the particles of the water which float in the air in the form of vapours? And why does not common salt, or salt-petre, or vitriol, run *per deliquium,* but for want of such an attraction? Or why does not salt of tartar draw more water out of the air than in a certain propor-tion to its quantity, but for want of an attractive force after it is satiated with water? And whence is it but from this attractive power that water which alone distils with a gentle luke-warm heat, will not distil from salt of tartar without a great heat? And is it not from the like attractive power between the particles of oil of vitriol and the particles of water, that oil of vitriol draws to it a good quantity of water out of the air, and after it is satiated draws no more, and in distillation lets go the water very difficultly? And when water and oil of vitriol poured successively into the same vessel grow very hot in the mixing, does not this heat argue a great motion in the parts of the liquors? And does not this motion argue that the parts of the two liquors in mixing coalesce with violence, and by consequence rush towards one another with an accelerated motion? And when *aqua fortis,* or spirit of vitriol poured upon filings of iron dissolves the filings with a great heat and ebullition, is not this heat and ebullition ef-fected by a violent motion of the parts, and does not that motion argue that the acid parts of the liquor rush towards the parts of the metal with violence, and run forcibly into its pores till they get between its outmost particles, and the main mass of the metal, and surrounding those particles loosen them from the main mass, and set them at liberty to float off into the water? And when the acid particles, which alone would distil with an easy heat, will not separate from the particles of the metal without a very violent heat, does not this con-firm the attraction between them?

When spirit of vitriol poured upon common salt or saltpetre makes an ebulli-tion with the salt, and unites with it, and in distillation the spirit of the com-mon salt or saltpetre comes over much easier than it would do before, and the acid part of the spirit of vitriol stays behind, does not this argue that the fixed alkali of the salt attracts the acid spirit of the vitriol more strongly than its own spirit, and not being able to hold them both, lets go its own? And when oil of vitriol is drawn off from its weight of nitre, and from both the ingredients a compound spirit of nitre is distilled, and two parts of this spirit are poured on one part of oil of cloves or caraway seeds, or of any ponderous oil of vegetable or animal substances, or oil of turpentine thickened with a little balsam of sul-phur, and the liquors grow so very hot in mixing, as presently to send up a burning flame—does not this very great and sudden heat argue that the two liquors mix with violence, and that their parts in mixing run towards one an-other with an accelerated motion, and clash with the greatest force? And is it not for the same reason that well-rectified spirit of wine poured on the same compound spirit flashes; and that the *pulvis fulminans,* composed of sulphur, nitre, and salt of tartar, goes off with a more sudden and violent explosion than gunpowder, the acid spirits of the sulphur and nitre rushing towards one an-other, and towards the salt of tartar, with so great a violence as by the shock to turn the whole at once into vapour and flame? Where the dissolution is slow, it makes a slow ebullition and a gentle heat; and where it is quicker, it makes a greater ebullition with more heat; and where it is done at once, the ebullition is contracted into a sudden blast or violent explosion, with a heat equal to that of fire and flame. So when a drachm of the above-mentioned compound spirit of nitre was poured upon half a drachm of oil of caraway seeds *in vacuo*, the mixture immediately made a flash like gunpowder, and burst the exhausted receiver, which was a glass six inches wide and eight inches deep. And even the gross body of sulphur powdered, and with an equal weight of iron filings and a little water made into paste, acts upon the iron, and in five or six hours grows too hot to be touched, and emits a flame. And by these experiments compared with the great quantity of sulphur with which the Earth abounds, and the warmth of the interior parts of the Earth, and hot springs, and burning mountains, and with damps, mineral coruscations, earthquakes, hot suffocating exhalations, hurricanes, and spouts, we may learn that sulphureous steams abound in the bowels of the Earth and ferment with minerals, and sometimes take fire with a sudden coruscation and explosion; and, if pent up in subterraneous caverns, burst the caverns with a great shaking of the Earth, as in springing of a mine. And then the vapour generated by the explosion, expiring through the pores of the Earth, feels hot and suffocates, and makes tempests and hurricanes, and sometimes causes the land to slide, or the sea to boil, and carries up the water thereof in drops, which by their weight fall down again in spouts. Also some sulphureous steams, at all times when the Earth is dry, ascending into the air, ferment there with nitrous acids, and sometimes taking fire cause lightning and thunder, and fiery meteors. For the air abounds with acid vapours fit to promote fermentations, as appears by the rusting of iron and copper in it, the kindling of fire by blowing, and the beating of the heart by means of respiration. Now, the above-mentioned motions are so great and violent as to shew that in fermentations the particles of bodies which almost rest are put into new motions by a very potent principle, which acts upon them only when they approach one another, and causes them to meet and clash with great violence, and grow hot with the motion, and dash one another into pieces, and vanish into air and vapour and flame.

When salt of tartar *per deliquium*, being poured into the solution of any metal, precipitates the metal and makes it fall down to the bottom of the liquor in the form of mud, does not this argue that the acid particles are attracted more strongly by the salt of tartar than by the metal, and by the stronger attraction go from the metal to the salt of tartar? And so when a solution of iron in *aqua fortis* dissolves the *lapis calaminaris*, and lets go the iron, or a solution of copper dissolves iron immersed in it and lets go the copper, or a solution of silver dissolves copper and lets go the silver, or a solution of mercury in *aqua fortis* being poured upon iron, copper, tin, or lead, dissolves the metal and lets go the mercury—does not this argue that the acid particles of the *aqua fortis* are attracted more strongly by the *lapis calaminaris* than by iron, and more strongly by iron than by copper, and more strongly by copper than by silver, and more strongly by iron, copper, tin, and lead, than by mercury? And is it not for the same reason that iron requires more *aqua fortis* to dissolve it than copper, and copper more than the other metals; and that, of all metals, iron is dissolved most easily, and is most apt to rust; and, next after iron, copper?

When oil of vitriol is mixed with a little water, or is run *per deliquium*, and in distillation the water ascends difficultly, and brings over with it some part of the oil of vitriol in the form of spirit of vitriol, and this spirit (being poured upon iron, copper, or salt of tartar) unites with the body and lets go the water

—doth not this shew that the acid spirit is attracted by the water, and more attracted by the fixed body than by the water, and therefore lets go the water to close with the fixed body? And is it not for the same reason that the water and acid spirits which are mixed together in vinegar, *aqua fortis*, and spirit of salt, cohere and rise together in distillation; but if the menstruum be poured on salt of tartar, or on lead, or iron, or any fixed body which it can dissolve, the acid by a stronger attraction adheres to the body, and lets go the water? And is it not also from a mutual attraction that the spirits of soot and sea-salt unite and compose the particles of sal-ammoniac, which are less volatile than before, because grosser and freer from water; and that the particles of sal-ammoniac in sublimation carry up the particles of antimony, which will not sublime alone; and that the particles of mercury uniting with the acid particles of spirit of salt compose mercury sublimate and with the particles of sulphur, compose cinnabar; and that the particles of spirit of wine and spirit of urine well rectified unite and, letting go the water which dissolved them, compose a consistent body; and that in subliming cinnabar from salt of tartar, or from quicklime, the sulphur by a stronger attraction of the salt or lime lets go the mercury, and stays with the fixed body; and that when mercury sublimate is sublimed from antimony, or from regulus of antimony, the spirit of salt lets go the mercury, and unites with the antimonial metal which attracts it more strongly, and stays with it till the heat be great enough to make them both ascend together, and then carries up the metal with it in the form of a very fusible salt called butter of antimony, although the spirit of salt alone be almost as volatile as water, and the antimony alone as fixed as lead?

When *aqua fortis* dissolves silver and not gold, and *aqua regia* dissolves gold and not silver, may it not be said that *aqua fortis* is subtile enough to penetrate gold as well as silver, but wants the attractive force to give it entrance; and that *aqua regia* is subtile enough to penetrate silver as well as gold, but wants the attractive force to give it entrance? For *aqua regia* is nothing else than *aqua fortis* mixed with some spirit of salt, or with sal-ammoniac; and even common salt dissolved in *aqua fortis* enables the menstruum to dissolve gold, though the salt be a gross body. When, therefore, spirit of salt precipitates silver out of *aqua fortis*, is it not done by attracting and mixing with the *aqua fortis*, and not attracting, or perhaps repelling silver? And when water precipitates antimony out of the sublimate of antimony and sal-ammoniac, or out of butter of antimony, is it not done by its dissolving, mixing with, and weakening the sal-armoniac or spirit of salt, and its not attracting, or perhaps repelling, the antimony? And is it not for want of an attractive virtue between the parts of water and oil, of quick-silver and antimony, of lead and iron, that these substances do not mix; and by a weak attraction, that quick-silver and copper mix difficultly; and from a strong one, that quick-silver and tin, antimony and iron, water and salts, mix readily? And, in general, is it not from the same principle that heat congregates homogeneal bodies, and separates heterogeneal ones?

When arsenic with soap gives a regulus, and with mercury sublimate a volatile fusible salt, like butter of antimony, doth not this shew that arsenic, which is a substance totally volatile, is compounded of fixed and volatile parts, strongly cohering by a mutual attraction, so that the volatile will not ascend without carrying up the fixed? And so, when an equal weight of spirit of wine and oil of vitriol are digested together, and in distillation yield two fragrant and volatile spirits which will not mix with one another, and a fixed black earth remains behind—doth not this shew that oil of vitriol is composed of volatile and fixed parts strongly united by attraction, so as to ascend together in form of a volatile, acid, fluid salt, until the spirit of wine attracts and separates the volatile parts from the fixed? And, therefore, since oil of sulphur *per campanam* is of the same nature with oil of vitriol, may it not be inferred that sulphur is also a mixture of volatile and fixed parts so strongly cohering by attraction as to ascend together in sublimation? By dissolving flowers of sulphur in oil of turpentine, and distilling the solution, it is found that sulphur is composed of an inflammable thick oil or fat bitumen, an acid salt, a very fixed earth, and a little metal. The three first were found not much unequal to one another, the fourth in so small a quantity as scarce to be worth considering. The acid salt, dissolved in water, is the same with oil of sulphur *per campanam*, and abounding much in the bowels of the Earth, and particularly in marcasites—unites itself to the other ingredients of the marcasite, which are, bitumen, iron, copper, and earth, and with them compounds alum, vitriol, and sulphur. With the earth alone it compounds alum; with the metal alone, or metal and earth together, it compounds vitriol; and with the bitumen and earth it compounds sulphur. Whence it comes to pass that marcasites abound with those three minerals. And is it not from the mutual attraction of the ingredients that they stick together for compounding these minerals, and that the bitumen carries up the other ingredients of the sulphur, which without it would not sublime? And the same question may be put concerning all, or almost all, the gross bodies in Nature. For all the parts of animals and vegetables are composed of substances volatile and fixed, fluid and solid, as appears by their analysis; and so are salts and minerals, so far as chemists have been hitherto able to examine their composition.

When mercury sublimate is re-sublimed with fresh mercury, and becomes *mercurius dulcis*, which is a white, tasteless earth scarce dissolvable in water, and *mercurius dulcis* re-sublimed with spirit of salt returns into mercury sublimate; and when metals corroded with a little acid turn into rust, which is an earth tasteless and indissolvable in water, and this earth imbibed with more acid becomes a metallic salt; and when some stones, as spar of lead, dissolved in proper menstruums become salts—do not these things shew that salts are dry earth and watery acid united by attraction, and that the earth will not become a salt without so much acid as makes it dissolvable in water? Do not the sharp and pungent tastes of acids arise from the strong attraction whereby the acid particles rush upon and agitate the particles of the tongue? And when metals are dissolved in acid menstruums, and the acids in conjunction with the metal act after a different manner, so that the compound has a different taste much milder than before, and sometimes a sweet one—is it not because the acids adhere to the metallic particles, and thereby lose much of their activity? And if the acid be in too small a proportion to make the compound dissolvable in water, will it not by adhering strongly to the metal become unactive and lose its taste, and the compound be a tasteless earth? For such things as are not dissolvable by the moisture of the tongue, act not upon the taste.

As gravity makes the sea flow round the denser and weightier parts of the globe of the Earth, so the attraction may make the watery acid flow round the denser and compacter particles of earth for composing the particles of salt. For otherwise the acid would not do the office of a medium between the earth and common water, for making salts dissolvable in the water; nor would salt of tartar readily draw off the acid from dissolved metals, nor metals the acid from mercury. Now, as in the great globe of the Earth and sea, the densest bodies by their gravity sink down in water, and always endeavour to go towards the centre of the globe; so in particles of salt the densest matter may always endeavour to approach the centre of the particle: so that a particle of salt may be compared to a chaos, being dense, hard, dry, and earthy in the centre; and rare, soft, moist, and watery in the circumference. And hence it seems to be that salts are of a lasting nature, being scarce destroyed unless by drawing away their watery parts by violence, or by letting them soak into the pores of the central earth by a gentle heat in putrefaction, until the earth be dissolved by the water, and separated into smaller particles, which by reason of their smallness make the rotten compound appear of a black colour. Hence also it may be that the parts of animals and vegetables preserve their several forms, and assimilate their nourishment; the soft and moist nourishment easily changing its texture by a gentle heat and motion till it becomes like the dense, hard, dry, and durable earth in the centre of each particle. But when the nourishment grows unfit to be assimilated, or the central earth grows too feeble to assimilate it, the motion ends in confusion, putrefaction, and death.

If a very small quantity of any salt or vitriol be dissolved in a great quantity of water, the particles of the salt or vitriol will not sink to the bottom, though they be heavier in species than the water, but will evenly diffuse themselves into all the water, so as to make it as saline at the top as at the bottom. And does not this imply that the parts of the salt or vitriol recede from one another, and endeavour to expand themselves, and get as far asunder as the quantity of water, in which they float, will allow? And does not this endeavour imply that they have a repulsive force by which they fly from one another, or, at least, that they attract the water more strongly than they do one another? For as all things ascend in water which are less attracted than water, by the gravitating power of the Earth; so all the particles of salt which float in water, and are less attracted than water by any one particle of salt, must recede from that particle, and give way to the more attracted water.

When any saline liquor is evaporated to a cuticle and let cool, the salt concretes in regular figures; which argues that the particles of the salt, before they concreted, floated in the liquor at equal distances in rank and file, and by consequence that they acted upon one another by some power which at equal distances is equal, at unequal distances unequal. For by such a power they will range themselves uniformly, and without it they will float irregularly, and come together as irregularly. And since the particles of island crystal act all the same way upon the rays of light for causing the unusual refraction, may it not be supposed that, in the formation of this crystal, the particles not only ranged themselves in rank and file for concreting in regular figures, but also by some kind of polar virtue turned their homogeneal sides the same way.

The parts of all homogeneal hard bodies which fully touch one another stick together very strongly. And for explaining how this may be, some have invented hooked atoms, which is begging the question; and others tell us that bodies are glued together by rest (that is, by an occult quality, or rather by nothing); and others, that they stick together by conspiring motions (that is, by relative rest amongst themselves). I had rather infer from their cohesion that their particles attract one another by some force, which in immediate contact is exceeding strong, at small distances performs the chemical operations above mentioned, and reaches not far from the particles with any sensible effect.

All bodies seem to be composed of hard particles, for otherwise fluids would not congeal; as water, oils, vinegar, and spirit or oil of vitriol do by freezing; mercury by fumes of lead; spirit of nitre and mercury by dissolving the mercury and evaporating the phlegm; spirit of wine and spirit of urine by dephlegming and mixing them; and spirit of urine and spirit of salt by subliming them together to make sal-ammoniac. Even the rays of light seem to be hard bodies; for otherwise they would not retain different properties in their different sides. And, therefore, hardness may be reckoned the property of all uncompounded matter. At least, this seems to be as evident as the universal impenetrability of matter. For all bodies, so far as experience reaches, are either hard, or may be hardened; and we have no other evidence of universal impenetrability, besides a large experience without an experimental exception. Now, if compound bodies are so very hard as we find some of them to be, and yet are very porous, and consist of parts which are only laid together, the simple particles which are void of pores, and were never yet divided, must be much harder. For such hard particles, being heaped up together, can scarce touch one another in more than a few points, and therefore must be separable by much less force than is requisite to break a solid particle whose parts touch in all the space between them, without any pores or interstices to weaken their cohesion. And how such very hard particles, which are only laid together and touch only in a few points, can stick together, and that so firmly as they do, without the assistance of something which causes them to be attracted or pressed towards one another, is very difficult to conceive.

The same thing I infer also from the cohering of two polished marbles *in vacuo*, and from the standing of quick-silver in the barometer at the height of 50, 60 or 70 inches, or above, whenever it is well-purged of air and carefully poured in, so that its parts be everywhere contiguous both to one another and to the glass. The atmosphere by its weight presses the quick-silver into the glass, to the height of 29 or 30 inches. And some other agent raises it higher, not by pressing it into the glass, but by making its parts stick to the glass, and to one another. For upon any discontinuation of parts, made either by bubbles or by shaking the glass, the whole mercury falls down to the height of 29 or 30 inches.

And of the same kind with these experiments are those that follow: If two plane polished plates of glass (suppose two pieces of a polished looking-glass) be laid together, so that their sides be parallel and at a very small distance from one another, and then their lower edges be dipped into water, the water will rise up between them. And the less the distance of the glasses is, the greater will be the height to which the water will rise. If the distance be about the hundredth part of an inch, the water will rise to the height of about an inch; and if the distance be greater or less in any proportion, the height will be reciprocally proportional to the distance very nearly. For the attractive force of the glasses is the same, whether the distance between them be greater or less; and the weight of the water drawn up is the same, if the height of it be reciprocally proportional to the distance of the glasses. And in like manner, water ascends between two marbles polished plane, when their polished sides are parallel, and at

a very little distance from one another. And if slender pipes of glass be dipped
at one end into stagnating water, the water will rise up within the pipe, and the
height to which it rises will be reciprocally proportional to the diameter of the
cavity of the pipe, and will equal the height to which it rises between two planes
of glass, if the semi-diameter of the cavity of the pipe be equal to the distance
between the planes, or thereabouts. And these experiments succeed after the
same manner *in vacuo* as in the open air (as hath been tried before the Royal
Society) and therefore are not influenced by the weight or pressure of the atmosphere.

And if a large pipe of glass be filled with sifted ashes well pressed together in
the glass, and one end of the pipe be dipped into stagnating water, the water
will rise up slowly in the ashes, so as in the space of a week or fortnight to reach
up within the glass to the height of 30 or 40 inches above the stagnating water.
And the water rises up to this height by the action only of those particles of the
ashes which are upon the surface of the elevated water; the particles which are
within the water attracting or repelling it as much downwards as upwards.
And, therefore, the action of the particles is very strong. But the particles of
the ashes being not so dense and close together as those of glass, their action is
not so strong as that of glass, which keeps quick-silver suspended to the height
of 60 or 70 inches, and, therefore, acts with a force which would keep water suspended to the height of above 60 feet.

By the same principle, a sponge sucks in water, and the glands in the bodies
of animals, according to their several natures and dispositions, suck in various
juices from the blood.

If two plane polished plates of glass three or four inches broad, and twenty or
twenty-five long, be laid one of them parallel to the horizon, the other upon the
first, so as at one of their ends to touch one another, and contain an angle of
about 10 or 15 minutes, and the same be first moistened on their inward sides
with a clean cloth dipped into oil of oranges or spirit of turpentine, and a drop
or two of the oil or spirit be let fall upon the lower glass at the other; so soon as
the upper glass is laid down upon the lower, so as to touch it at one end as
above, and to touch the drop at the other end, making with the lower glass an
angle of about 10 or 15 minutes, the drop will begin to move towards the concourse of the glasses, and will continue to move with an accelerated motion till
it arrives at that concourse of the glasses. For the two glasses attract the drop,
and make it run that way towards which the attractions incline. And if when
the drop is in motion you lift up that end of the glasses where they meet, and
towards which the drop moves, the drop will ascend between the glasses, and
therefore is attracted. And as you lift up the glasses more and more, the drop
will ascend slower and slower, and at length rest, being then carried downward
by its weight, as much as upwards by the attraction. And by this means you
may know the force by which the drop is attracted at all distances from the
concourse of the glasses.

Now, by some experiments of this kind (made by Mr. Hauksbee), it has been
found that the attraction is almost reciprocally in a duplicate proportion of the
distance of the middle of the drop from the concourse of the glasses, viz., reciprocally in a simple proportion, by reason of the spreading of the drop, and
its touching each glass in a larger surface; and again reciprocally in a simple
proportion, by reason of the attractions growing stronger within the same quan-

tity of attracting surface. The attraction, therefore, within the same quantity of attracting surface, is reciprocally as the distance between the glasses. And, therefore, where the distance is exceeding small, the attraction must be exceeding great. By the Table in the second part of the second book, wherein the thicknesses of coloured plates of water between two glasses are set down, the thickness of the plate where it appears very black is three-eighths of the ten hundred thousandth part of an inch. And where the oil of oranges between the glasses is of this thickness, the attraction collected by the foregoing rule seems to be so strong as, within a circle of an inch in diameter, to suffice to hold up a weight equal to that of a cylinder of water of an inch in diameter, and two or three furlongs in length. And where it is of a less thickness, the attraction may be proportionally greater, and continue to increase, until the thickness do not exceed that of a single particle of the oil. There are, therefore, agents in nature able to make the particles of bodies stick together by very strong attractions. And it is the business of experimental philosophy to find them out.

Now, the smallest particles of matter may cohere by the strongest attractions, and compose bigger particles of weaker virtue; and many of these may cohere and compose bigger particles whose virtue is still weaker, and so on for divers successions, until the progression end in the biggest particles on which the operations in chemistry, and the colours of natural bodies depend, and which by cohering compose bodies of a sensible magnitude. If the body is compact, and bends or yields inward to pression—without any sliding of its parts, it is hard and elastic, returning to its figure with a force rising from the mutual attraction of its parts. If the parts slide upon one another, the body is malleable or soft. If they slip easily, and are of a fit size to be agitated by heat, and the heat is big enough to keep them in agitation, the body is fluid; and if it be apt to stick to things, it is humid; and the drops of every fluid affect a round figure by the mutual attraction of their parts, as the globe of the Earth and sea affects a round figure by the mutual attraction of its parts by gravity.

Since metals dissolved in acids attract but a small quantity of the acid, their attractive force can reach but to a small distance from them. And as in algebra, where affirmative quantities vanish and cease, there negative ones begin; so in mechanics, where attraction ceases, there a repulsive virtue ought to succeed. And that there is such a virtue seems to follow from the reflexions and inflexions of the rays of light. For the rays are repelled by bodies in both these cases, without the immediate contact of the reflecting or inflecting body. It seems also to follow from the emission of light, the ray so soon as it is shaken off from a shining body by the vibrating motion of the parts of the body, and gets beyond the reach of attraction, being driven away with exceeding great velocity. For that force which is sufficient to turn it back in reflexion may be sufficient to emit it. It seems also to follow from the production of air and vapour. The particles when they are shaken off from bodies by heat or fermentation, so soon as they are beyond the reach of the attraction of the body, receding from it, and also from one another with great strength, and keeping at a distance, so as sometimes to take up above a million of times more space than they did before in the form of a dense body. Which vast contraction and expansion seems unintelligible, by feigning the particles of air to be springy and ramous, or rolled up like hoops, or by any other means than a repulsive power. The particles of fluids which do not cohere too strongly, and are of such a smallness as renders them most susceptible to those agitations which keep liquors in a Fluor, are most easily separated and rarefied into vapour, and in the language of the chemists they are volatile, rarefying with an easy heat, and condensing with cold. But those which are grosser, and so less susceptible of agitation, or cohere by a stronger attraction, are not separated without a stronger heat, or perhaps not without fermentation. And these last are the bodies which chemists call fixed, and being rarefied by fermentation become true, permanent air; those particles receding from one another with the greatest force, and being most difficultly brought together, which upon contact cohere most strongly. And because the particles of permanent air are grosser, and arise from denser substances than those of vapours, thence it is that true air is more ponderous than vapour, and that a moist atmosphere is lighter than a dry one, quantity for quantity. From the same repelling power it seems to be that flies walk upon the water without wetting their feet; and that the object-glasses of long telescopes lie upon one another without touching; and that dry powders are difficultly made to touch one another so as to stick together, unless by melting them, or wetting them with water, which by exhaling may bring them together; and that two polished marbles, which by immediate contact stick together, are difficultly brought so close together as to stick.

And thus Nature will be very conformable to herself and very simple, performing all the great motions of the heavenly bodies by the attraction of gravity which intercedes those bodies, and almost all the small ones of their particles by some other attractive and repelling powers which intercede the particles. The *vis inertiæ* is a passive principle by which bodies persist in their motion or rest, receive motion in proportion to the force impressing it, and resist as much as they are resisted. By this principle alone there never could have been any motion in the world. Some other principle was necessary for putting bodies into motion; and now they are in motion, some other principle is necessary for conserving the motion. For from the various composition of two motions, 'tis very certain that there is not always the same quantity of motion in the world. For if two globes, joined by a slender rod, revolve about their common centre of gravity with a uniform motion, while that centre moves on uniformly in a right line drawn in the plane of their circular motion, the sum of the motions of the two globes, as often as the globes are in the right line described by their common centre of gravity, will be bigger than the sum of their motions when they are in a line perpendicular to that right line. By this instance it appears that motion may be got or lost. But by reason of the tenacity of fluids, and attrition of their parts, and the weakness of elasticity in solids, motion is much more apt to be lost than got, and is always upon the decay. For bodies which are either absolutely hard, or so soft as to be void of elasticity, will not rebound from one another. Impenetrability makes them only stop. If two equal bodies meet directly *in vacuo*, they will by the laws of motion stop where they meet, and lose all their motion, and remain in rest, unless they be elastic, and receive new motion from their spring. If they have so much elasticity as suffices to make them re-bound with a quarter, or half, or three-quarters of the force with which they come together, they will lose three-quarters, or half, or a quarter of their motion. And this may be tried by letting two equal pendulums fall against one another from equal heights. If the pendulums be of lead or soft clay, they will lose all or almost all their motions; if of elastic bodies they will lose all but what they recover from their elasticity. If it be said that they can lose no motion but what they communicate to other bodies, the consequence is, that *in vacuo* they can lose no motion, but when they meet they must go on and penetrate one another's dimensions. If three equal round vessels be filled (the one with water, the other with oil, the third with molten pitch), and the liquors be stirred about alike to give them a vortical motion, the pitch by its tenacity will lose its motion quickly, the oil being less tenacious will keep it longer, and the water being less tenacious will keep it longest, but yet will lose it in a short time. Whence it is easy to understand that if many contiguous vortices of molten pitch were each of them as large as those which some suppose to revolve about the Sun and fixed stars, yet these and all their parts would, by their tenacity and stiffness, communicate their motion to one another till they all rested among themselves. Vortices of oil or water, or some fluider matter, might continue longer in motion; but unless the matter were void of all tenacity and attrition of parts, and communication of motion (which is not to be supposed), the motion would constantly decay. Seeing, therefore, the variety of motion which we find in the world is always decreasing, there is a necessity of conserving and recruiting it by active principles, such as are the cause of gravity, by which planets and comets keep their motions in their orbs, and bodies acquire great motion in falling; and the cause of fermentation, by which the heart and blood of animals are kept in perpetual motion and heat; the inward parts of the earth are constantly warmed, and in some places grow very hot; bodies burn and shine, mountains take fire, the caverns of the earth are blown up, and the Sun continues violently hot and lucid, and warms all things by his light. For we meet with very little motion in the world, besides what is owing to these active principles. And if it were not for these principles, the bodies of the earth, planets, comets, Sun, and all things in them, would grow cold and freeze, and become inactive masses; and all putrefaction, generation, vegetation and life would cease, and the planets and comets would not remain in their orbs.

All these things being considered, it seems probable to me that God in the beginning formed matter in solid, massy, hard, impenetrable, moveable particles, of such sizes and figures, and with such other properties, and in such proportion to space, as most conduced to the end for which he formed them; and that these primitive particles being solids, are incomparably harder than any porous bodies compounded of them; even so very hard as never to wear or break in pieces; no ordinary power being able to divide what God himself made one in the first creation. While the particles continue entire, they may compose bodies of one and the same nature and texture in all ages; but should they wear away, or break in pieces, the nature of things depending on them would be changed. Water and earth, composed of old worn particles and fragments of particles, would not be of the same nature and texture now, with water and earth composed of entire particles in the beginning. And, therefore, that Nature may be lasting, the changes of corporeal things are to be placed only in the various separations and new associations and motions of these permanent particles; compound bodies being apt to break, not in the midst of solid particles, but where those particles are laid together, and only touch in a few points.

It seems to me, further, that these particles have not only a *vis inertiæ*, accompanied with such passive laws of motion as naturally result from that force, but also that they are moved by certain active principles, such as is that of gravity, and that which causes fermentation, and the cohesion of bodies. These principles I consider, not as occult qualities, supposed to result from the specific forms of things, but as general laws of nature, by which the things themselves are formed; their truth appearing to us by phenomena, though their causes be not yet discovered. For these are manifest qualities, and their causes only are occult. And the Aristotelians gave the name of occult qualities, not to manifest qualities, but to such qualities only as they supposed to lie hid in bodies, and to be the unknown causes of manifest effects. Such as would be the causes of gravity, and of magnetic and electric attractions, and of fermentations, if we should suppose that these forces or actions arose from qualities unknown to us, and incapable of being discovered and made manifest. Such occult qualities put a stop to the improvement of natural philosophy, and therefore of late years have been rejected. To tell us that every species of things is endowed with an occult specific quality by which it acts and produces manifest effects, is to tell us nothing; but to derive two or three general principles of motion from phenomena, and afterwards to tell us how the properties and actions of all corporeal things follow from those manifest principles, would be a very great step in philosophy, though the causes of those principles were not yet discovered. And, therefore, I scruple not to propose the principles of motion above mentioned, they being of very general extent, and leave their causes to be found out.

Now, by the help of these principles, all material things seem to have been composed of the hard and solid particles above mentioned, variously associated in the first creation by the counsel of an intelligent agent. For it became Him who created them to set them in order. And if He did so, it's unphilosophical to seek for any other origin of the world, or to pretend that it might arise out of a chaos by the mere laws of Nature; though, being once formed, it may continue by those laws for many ages. For while comets move in very eccentric orbs in all manner of positions, blind fate could never make all the planets move one and the same way in orbs concentric, some inconsiderable irregularities excepted, which may have risen from the mutual actions of comets and planets upon one another, and which will be apt to increase, till this system wants a reformation. Such a wonderful uniformity in the planetary system must be allowed the effect of choice. And so must the uniformity in the bodies of animals, they having generally a right and a left side shaped alike, and on either side of their bodies two legs behind, and either two arms, or two legs, or two wings before upon their shoulders, and between their shoulders a neck running down into a backbone, and a head upon it; and in the head two ears, two eyes, a nose, a mouth, and a tongue, alike situated. Also the first contrivance of those very artificial parts of animals, the eyes, ears, brain, muscles, heart, lungs, midriff, glands, larynx, hands, wings, swimming bladders, natural spectacles, and other organs of sense and motion; and the instinct of brutes and insects can be the effect of nothing else than the wisdom and skill of a powerful, ever-living agent, who being in all places, is more able by His will to move the bodies within His boundless uniform sensorium, and thereby to form and reform the parts of the Universe, than we are by our will to move the parts of our own bodies. And yet we are not to consider the world as the body of God, or the several parts thereof as the parts of God. He is a uniform Being, void of organs, members or parts, and they are his creatures subordinate to him, and subservient to His will; and

He is no more the soul of them than the soul of man is the soul of the species of things carried through the organs of sense into the place of its sensation, where it perceives them by means of its immediate presence, without the intervention of any third thing. The organs of sense are not for enabling the soul to perceive the species of things in its sensorium, but only for conveying them thither; and God has no need of such organs, He being everywhere present to the things themselves. And since space is divisible *in infinitum*, and matter is not necessarily in all places, it may be also allowed that God is able to create particles of matter of several sizes and figures, and in several proportions to space, and perhaps of different densities and forces, and thereby to vary the laws of Nature, and make worlds of several sorts in several parts of the Universe. At least, I see nothing of contradiction in all this.

As in mathematics, so in natural philosophy, the investigation of difficult things by the method of analysis, ought ever to precede the method of composition. This analysis consists in making experiments and observations, and in drawing general conclusions from them by induction, and admitting of no objections against the conclusions but such as are taken from experiments, or other certain truths. For hypotheses are not to be regarded in experimental philosophy. And although the arguing from experiments and observations by induction be no demonstration of general conclusions, yet it is the best way of arguing which the nature of things admits of, and may be looked upon as so much the stronger, by how much the induction is more general. And if no exception occur from phenomena, the conclusion may be pronounced generally. But if at any time afterwards any exception shall occur from experiments, it may then begin to be pronounced with such exceptions as occur. By this way of analysis we may proceed from compounds to ingredients, and from motions to the forces producing them; and, in general, from effects to their causes, and from particular causes to more general ones, till the argument end in the most general. This is the method of analysis; and the synthesis consists in assuming the causes discovered, and established as principles, and by them explaining the phenomena proceeding from them, and proving the explanations.

In the two first books of these Optics, I proceeded by this analysis to discover and prove the original differences of the rays of light in respect of refrangibility, reflexibility, and colour, and their alternate fits of easy reflexion and easy transmission, and the properties of bodies, both opaque and pellucid, on which their reflexions and colours depend. And these discoveries, being proved, may be assumed in the method of composition for explaining the phenomena arising from them, an instance of which method I gave in the end of the first book. In this third book I have only begun the analysis of what remains to be discovered about light and its effects upon the frame of Nature, hinting several things about it, and leaving the hints to be examined and improved by the further experiments and observations of such as are inquisitive. And if natural philosophy in all its parts, by pursuing this method, shall at length be perfected, the bounds of moral philosophy will be also enlarged. For so far as we can know by natural philosophy what is the First Cause, what power He has over us, and what benefits we recieve from Him, so far our duty towards Him, as well as that towards one another, will appear to us by the light of Nature. And no doubt, if the worship of false gods had not blinded the heathen, their moral philosophy would have gone farther than to the four cardinal virtues;

and instead of teaching the transmigration of souls, and to worship the Sun and Moon, and dead heroes, they would have taught us to worship our true Author and Benefactor, as their ancestors did under the government of Noah and his sons before they corrupted themselves.

TREATISE ON LIGHT

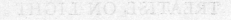

BIOGRAPHICAL NOTE

CHRISTIAAN HUYGENS, 1629–1695

THE family into which Christiaan Huygens was born, April 14, 1629, at The Hague, was one of the most eminent in both the political and literary development of the Dutch Renaissance. The father of the scientist, Constantijn Huygens, Lord of Zuylichem, was secretary of state for three successive Princes of Orange; he carried out many diplomatic missions, particularly to England where he was knighted in 1621. While there he became the friend of Donne, whose poetry he began translating into Dutch. As one of the leaders of the Amsterdam school, he was the intimate friend of Vondel, the Dutch national poet, and was himself Holland's foremost classical poet.

Sir Constantijn, who was a distinguished Latinist, a musician, and a mathematician, took upon himself the preliminary instruction of his sons. Christiaan, the second son, was trained as a boy in languages, drawing, and music. At thirteen he began the study of mechanics, which together with mathematics soon became his chief interest. But before devoting his entire attention to these subjects he was sent to Leyden to study law with Vinnius, who later dedicated his famous commentary on the *Institutes* to him. In 1646 Huygens transferred to Breda, where his father directed the new university, and two years later he took his degree in law. In both places he continued his pursuit of mathematics, particularly with Van Schooten, who included some of Huygens' notes in his edition of Descartes' *Geometry*.

At seventeen Huygens communicated his first mathematical discovery to Mersenne, who introduced him to the learned world as "the Dutch Archimedes," and soon after, he was in correspondence with the leading scientists of Europe. Descartes, on being shown a mathematical paper of Huygens, declared his confidence that "he will excel in this science wherein I see hardly anyone who knows anything." Although Descartes frequented Sir Constantijn's house, it does not appear that he ever met his son. They exchanged letters, Descartes called Huygens "a son of his own blood," and when Huygens was traveling in Denmark in 1649 with the Count of Nassau, he regretted that time and weather did not permit his crossing over to Sweden to visit Descartes, who was then living there at the invitation of Queen Christina.

At the age of twenty-one Huygens published his first works on mathematics, dealing with the quadrature of conic sections, and in 1654, he made the closest approximation so far obtained of the area of the circle. Two years later he sent to Van Schooten his work on probability, which while recognizing the priority of Pascal's and Fermat's treatment, constituted the first treatise on the subject when published in a volume of Van Schooten's mathematical writings. At the same time Huygens was working with his elder brother on astronomy. They found a new method of grinding and polishing lenses which overcame the defects of spherical and chromatic aberration and enabled them to construct an improved telescope. Huygens' first observations yielded the discovery of the Orion nebula and of a new satellite to Saturn as well as a truer description of the rings about that planet. The need for an exact measure of time in observing the heavens led Huygens to the invention of the pendulum-clock, which was presented to the states-general in 1657 and was followed a year later by a description of the requisite mechanism.

Huygens' reputation now became international. As early as 1655 the University of Angers had distinguished him with an honorary degree of doctor of laws. In 1663, on the occasion of a visit to England, he was elected a fellow of the Royal Society. Two years later, on the establishment of the French Royal Academy of Sciences, Colbert invited him to be its first foreign resident, and for the next fifteen years Huygens made his home in France. He received a handsome pension from Louis XIV and lived at Paris in the Bibliothèque du Roi. Although Huygens disliked the world of rank, wealth, and fashion, he did not live the life of a recluse in Paris; he even wrote some verses to the celebrated Ninon de Lenclos. Yet the greater part of his efforts, despite delicate health, were spent in intense scientific research. His treatises on "Dioptrics" and the concussion of elastic bodies were hailed not only for their discoveries, but also for the style in which they were presented, and Newton claimed that among modern writers he had most closely approximated the style of the ancients. His greatest work, the *Horologium oscillatorium* (1673), dealt with the problems raised by the pendulum-clock, and contained original discoveries sufficient for several important treatises.

Twice during his residence in Paris, Huygens returned to Holland in the hope that his native air would restore his health, and in 1681, perhaps because of the revocation of the Edict of Nantes, he severed his connections and left France. Upon his return to Holland, Huygens took up again the study of optics, physics, and astronomy. He had always been interested in useful inventions and, in addition to the pendulum-clock, had already improved the air pump and the barometer, provided the first idea of the micrometer, and introduced the use of a spiral band for a watch-spring. In

Holland he turned again to the construction of telescopes. Using lenses of long focal distance mounted on poles, he produced what were called "aerial telescopes." He also succeeded in constructing an almost perfectly achromatic eye-piece, still known by his name. His researches in optics finally led him to publish in 1690 his *Treatise on Light*, which had been written in French in 1678 while at Paris. In response to the need for some means of representing the solar system, Huygens constructed a "planetary machine" capable of showing the motions of the planets. It was apparently also at this time that he wrote the imaginative work found among his posthumous papers called *Cosmotheoros*, and translated into English under the title, *"The celestial worlds discovered, or conjectures concerning the inhabitants, plants, and productions of the worlds in the planets."*

Worn out by his great and varied activity and the burden of an enormous correspondence, Huygens died at The Hague, June 8, 1695, at the age of sixty-six.

CONTENTS

PREFACE

I WROTE this treatise during my sojourn in France twelve years ago, and I communicated it in the year 1678 to the learned persons who then composed the Royal Academy of Science, to the membership of which the King had done me the honour of calling me. Several of that body who are still alive will remember having been present when I read it, and above the rest those amongst them who applied themselves particularly to the study of mathematics; of whom I cannot cite more than the celebrated gentlemen, Cassini, Römer, and de la Hire. And, although I have since corrected and changed some parts, the copies which I had made of it at that time may serve for proof that I have yet added nothing to it save some conjectures touching the formation of Iceland crystal, and a novel observation on the refraction of rock crystal. I have desired to relate these particulars to make known how long I have meditated the things which now I publish, and not for the purpose of detracting from the merit of those who, without having seen anything that I have written, may be found to have treated of like matters: as has, in fact, occurred to two eminent geometricians, Messieurs Newton and Leibnitz, with respect to the problem of the figure of glasses for collecting rays when one of the surfaces is given.

One may ask why I have so long delayed to bring this work to the light. The reason is that I wrote it rather carelessly in the language in which it appears, with the intention of translating it into Latin, so doing in order to obtain greater attention to the thing. After which I proposed to myself to give it out along with another treatise on dioptrics, in which I explain the effects of telescopes and those things which belong more to that science. But the pleasure of novelty being past, I have put off from time to time the execution of this design, and I know not when I shall ever come to an end of it, being often turned aside either by business or by some new study. Considering which I have finally judged that it was better worth while to publish this writing, such as it is, than to let it run the risk, by waiting longer, of remaining lost.

There will be seen in it demonstrations of those kinds which do not produce as great a certitude as those of geometry, and which even differ much therefrom, since, whereas the geometers prove their propositions by fixed and incontestable principles, here the principles are verified by the conclusions to be drawn from them; the nature of these things not allowing of this being done otherwise. It is always possible to attain thereby to a degree of probability which very often is scarcely less than complete proof. To wit, when things which have been demonstrated by the principles that have been assumed correspond perfectly to the phenomena which experiment has brought under observation; especially when there are a great number of them, and further, principally, when one can imagine and foresee new phenomena which ought to follow from the hypotheses which one employs, and when one finds that therein the fact corresponds to our prevision. But if all these proofs of probability are met with in that which I propose to discuss, as it seems to me they are, this ought to be a very strong confirmation of the success of my inquiry; and it must be ill if the facts are not pretty much as I represent them. I would believe then that those who love to know the causes of things and who are able to admire the marvels of light, will find some satisfaction in these various speculations regarding it, and in the new explanation of its famous property which is the main foundation of the construction of our eyes, and of those great inventions which extend so vastly the use of them. I hope also that there will be some who, by following these beginnings, will penetrate much further into this question than I have been able to do, since the subject must be far from being exhausted. This appears from the passages which I have indicated where I leave certain difficulties without having resolved them, and still more from matters which I have not touched at all, such as luminous bodies of several sorts, and all that concerns colours; in which no one until now can boast of having succeeded. Finally, there remains much more to be investigated touching the nature of light which I do not pretend to have disclosed, and I shall owe much in return to him who shall be able to supplement that which is here lacking to me in knowledge.

The Hague, *January 8*, 1690

CHAPTER ONE

On Rays Propagated in Straight Lines

As happens in all the sciences in which geometry is applied to matter, the demonstrations concerning Optics are founded on truths drawn from experience. Such are: that the rays of light are propagated in straight lines; that the angles of reflexion and of incidence are equal; and that in refraction the ray is bent according to the law of sines, now so well-known, and which is no less certain than the preceding laws.

The majority of those who have written touching the various parts of Optics have contented themselves with presuming these truths. But some, more inquiring, have desired to investigate the origin and the causes, considering these to be in themselves wonderful effects of nature. In which they advanced some ingenious things, but not, however, such that the most intelligent folk do not wish for better and more satisfactory explanations. Wherefore I here desire to propound what I have meditated on the subject, so as to contribute as much as I can to the explanation of this department of natural science, which, not without reason, is reputed to be one of its most difficult parts. I recognize myself to be much indebted to those who were the first to begin to dissipate the strange obscurity in which these things were enveloped, and to give us hope that they might be explained by intelligible reasoning. But, on the other hand, I am astonished also that even here these have often been willing to offer, as assured and demonstrative, reasonings which were far from conclusive. For I do not find that any one has yet given a probable explanation of the first and most notable phenomena of light, namely, why it is not propagated except in straight lines, and how visible rays, coming from an infinitude of diverse places, cross one another without hindering one another in any way.

I shall therefore essay in this book, to give, in accordance with the principles accepted in the philosophy of the present day, some clearer and more probable reasons, firstly, of these properties of light propagated rectilinearly; secondly, of light which is reflected on meeting other bodies. Then I shall explain the phenomena of those rays which are said to suffer refraction on passing through transparent bodies of different sorts; and in this part I shall also explain the effects of the refraction of the air by the different densities of the atmosphere.

Thereafter, I shall examine the causes of the strange refraction of a certain kind of crystal which is brought from Iceland. And, finally, I shall treat of the various shapes of transparent and reflecting bodies by which rays are collected at a point or are turned aside in various ways. From this it will be seen with what facility, following our new theory, we find not only the ellipses, hyperbolas, and other curves which M. Descartes has ingeniously invented for this purpose; but also those which the surface of a glass lens ought to possess when its other surface is given as spherical or plane, or of any other figure that may be.

It is inconceivable to doubt that light consists in the motion of some sort of matter. For whether one considers its production, one sees that here upon the earth it is chiefly engendered by fire and flame which contain without doubt bodies that are in rapid motion, since they dissolve and melt many other bodies, even the most solid; or whether one considers its effects, one sees that when light is collected, as by concave mirrors, it has the property of burning as a fire does, that is to say, it disunites the particles of bodies. This is assuredly the mark of motion, at least in the true philosophy, in which one conceives the causes of all natural effects in terms of mechanical motions. This, in my opinion, we must necessarily do, or else renounce all hopes of ever comprehending anything in physics.

And as, according to this philosophy, one holds as certain that the sensation of sight is excited only by the impression of some movement of a kind of matter which acts on the nerves at the back of our eyes, there is here yet one reason more for believing that light consists in a movement of the matter which exists between us and the luminous body.

Further, when one considers the extreme speed with which light spreads on every side, and how, when it comes from different regions, even from those directly opposite, the rays traverse one another without hindrance, one may well understand that when we see a luminous object, it cannot be by any transport of matter coming to us from this object, in the way in which a shot or an arrow traverses the air; for assuredly that would too greatly impugn these two properties of light, especially the second of them. It is then in some other way that light spreads; and that which can lead us to comprehend it is the knowledge which we have of the spreading of sound in the air.

We know that by means of the air, which is an invisible and impalpable body, sound spreads around the spot where it has been produced by a movement which is passed on successively from one part of the air to another; and that the spreading of this movement, taking place equally rapidly on all sides, ought to form spherical surfaces ever enlarging and which strike our ears. Now there is no doubt at all that light also comes from the luminous body to our eyes by some movement impressed on the matter which is between the two; since, as we have already seen, it cannot be by the transport of a body which passes from one to the other. If, in addition, light takes time for its passage— which we are now going to examine—it will follow that this movement, impressed on the intervening matter, is successive; and consequently it spreads, as sound does, by spherical surfaces and waves: for I call them waves from their resemblance to those which are seen to be formed in water when a stone is thrown into it, and which present a successive spreading as circles, though these arise from another cause, and are only in a flat surface.

To see then whether the spreading of light takes time, let us consider first whether there are any facts of experience which can convince us to the contrary. As to those which can be made here on the earth, by striking lights at great distances, although they prove that light takes no sensible time to pass over these distances, one may say with good reason that they are too small, and that the only conclusion to be drawn from them is that the passage of light is extremely rapid. M. Descartes, who was of opinion that it is instantaneous, founded his views, not without reason, upon a better basis of experience, drawn from the eclipses of the moon; which, nevertheless, as I shall show, is not at all convincing. I will set it forth, in a way a little different from his, in order to make the conclusion more comprehensible.

Let A be the place of the sun, BD a part of the orbit or annual path of the

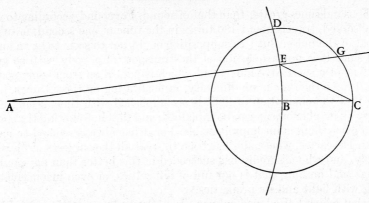

earth: ABC a straight line which I suppose to meet the orbit of the moon, which is represented by the circle CD, at C.

Now if light requires time, for example one hour, to traverse the space which is between the earth and the moon, it will follow that the earth having arrived at B, the shadow which it casts, or the interruption of the light, will not yet have arrived at the point C, but will only arrive there an hour after. It will then be one hour after, reckoning from the moment when the earth was at B, that the moon, arriving at C, will be obscured: but this obscuration or interruption of the light will not reach the earth till after another hour. Let us suppose that the earth in these two hours will have arrived at E. The earth then, being at E, will see the eclipsed moon at C, which it left an hour before, and at the same time will see the sun at A. For it being immovable, as I suppose with Copernicus, and the light moving always in straight lines, it must always appear where it is. But one has always observed, we are told, that the eclipsed moon appears at the point of the ecliptic opposite to the sun; and yet here it would appear in arrear of that point by an amount equal to the angle GEC, the supplement of AEC. This, however, is contrary to experience, since the angle GEC would be very sensible, and about 33 degrees. Now according to our computation, which is given in the treatise on the causes of the phenomena of Saturn, the distance BA between the earth and the sun is about twelve thousand diameters of the earth, and hence four hundred times greater than BC the distance of the moon, which is 30 diameters. Then the angle ECB will be nearly four hundred times greater than BAE, which is five minutes; namely, the path which the earth travels in two hours along its orbit; and thus the angle BCE will be nearly 33 degrees; and likewise the angle CEG, which is greater by five minutes.

But it must be noted that the speed of light in this argument has been assumed such that it takes a time of one hour to make the passage from here to the moon. If one supposes that for this it requires only one minute of time, then it is manifest that the angle CEG will only be 33 minutes; and if it requires only ten seconds of time, the angle will be less than six minutes. And then it will not be easy to perceive anything of it in observations of the eclipse; nor, consequently, will it be permissible to deduce from it that the movement of light is instantaneous.

It is true that we are here supposing a strange velocity that would be a hun-

dred thousand times greater than that of sound. For sound, according to what I
have observed, travels about 180 toises in the time of one second, or in about
one beat of the pulse. But this supposition ought not to seem to be an impossi-
bility; since it is not a question of the transport of a body with so great a
speed, but of a successive movement which is passed on from some bodies to
others. I have then made no difficulty, in meditating on these things, in supposing that the emanation of light is accomplished with time, seeing that in
this way all its phenomena can be explained, and that in following the contrary
opinion everything is incomprehensible. For it has always seemed to me that
even M. Descartes, whose aim has been to treat all the subjects of physics in-
telligibly, and who assuredly has succeeded in this better than anyone before
him, has said nothing that is not full of difficulties, or even inconceivable, in
dealing with light and its properties.

But that which I employed only as a hypothesis, has recently received great
seemingness as an established truth by the ingenious proof of Mr. Römer
which I am going here to relate, expecting him himself to give all that is needed
for its confirmation. It is founded, as is the preceding argument, upon celestial
observations, and proves not only that light takes time for its passage, but also
demonstrates how much time it takes, and that its velocity is even at least six
times greater than that which I have just stated.

For this he makes use of the eclipses suffered by the little planets which
revolve around Jupiter, and which often enter his shadow: and see what is his
reasoning. Let A be the sun, BCDE the annual
orbit of the earth, F Jupiter, GN the orbit of the
nearest of his satellites, for it is this one which is
more apt for this investigation than any of the
other three because of the quickness of its revolution. Let G be this satellite entering into the
shadow of Jupiter, H the same satellite emerging
from the shadow.

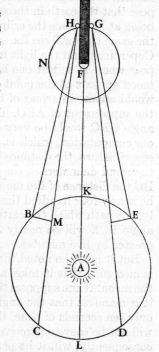

Let it be then supposed, the earth being at B
some time before the last quadrature, that one
has seen the said satellite emerge from the shadow;
it must needs be, if the earth remains at the same
place, that, after 42½ hours, one would again see
a similar emergence, because that is the time in
which it makes the round of its orbit, and when it
would come again into opposition to the sun. And
if the earth, for instance, were to remain always
at B during 30 revolutions of this satellite, one
would see it again emerge from the shadow after
30 times 42½ hours. But the earth having been
carried along during this time to C, increasing
thus its distance from Jupiter, it follows that if
light requires time for its passage the illumination
of the little planet will be perceived later at C
than it would have been at B, and that there must
be added to this time of 30 times 42½ hours that which the light has required
to traverse the space MC, the difference of the spaces CH, BH. Similarly, at

the other quadrature when the earth has come to E from D while approaching toward Jupiter, the immersions of the satellite ought to be observed at E earlier than they would have been seen if the earth had remained at D.

Now in quantities of observations of these eclipses, made during ten consecutive years, these differences have been found to be very considerable, such as ten minutes and more; and from them it has been concluded that in order to traverse the whole diameter of the annual orbit KL, which is double the distance from here to the sun, light requires about 22 minutes of time.

The movement of Jupiter in his orbit while the earth passed from B to C, or from D to E, is included in this calculation; and this makes it evident that one cannot attribute the retardation of these illuminations or the anticipation of the eclipses, either to any irregularity occurring in the movement of the little planet or to its eccentricity.

If one considers the vast size of the diameter KL, which according to me is some 24 thousand diameters of the earth, one will acknowledge the extreme velocity of light. For, supposing that KL is no more than 22 thousand of these diameters, it appears that being traversed in 22 minutes this makes the speed a thousand diameters in one minute, that is $16\frac{2}{3}$ diameters in one second or in one beat of the pulse, which makes more than 11 hundred times a hundred thousand toises; since the diameter of the earth contains 2,865 leagues, reckoned at 25 to the degree, and each league is 2,282 toises, according to the exact measurement which Mr. Picard made by order of the King in 1669. But sound, as I have said above, only travels 180 toises in the same time of one second: hence the velocity of light is more than six hundred thousand times greater than that of sound. This, however, is quite another thing from being instantaneous, since there is all the difference between a finite thing and an infinite. Now the successive movement of light being confirmed in this way, it follows, as I have said, that it spreads by spherical waves, like the movement of sound.

But if the one resembles the other in this respect, they differ in many other things; to wit, in the first production of the movement which causes them; in the matter in which the movement spreads; and in the manner in which it is propagated. As to that which occurs in the production of sound, one knows that it is occasioned by the agitation undergone by an entire body, or by a considerable part of one, which shakes all the contiguous air. But the movement of the light must originate as from each point of the luminous object, else we should not be able to perceive all the different parts of that object, as will be more evident in that which follows. And I do not believe that this movement can be better explained than by supposing that all those of the luminous bodies which are liquid, such as flames, and apparently the sun and the stars, are composed of particles which float in a much more subtle medium which agitates them with great rapidity, and makes them strike against the particles of the ether which surrounds them, and which are much smaller than they. But I hold also that in luminous solids such as charcoal or metal made red-hot in the fire, this same movement is caused by the violent agitation of the particles of the metal or of the wood; those of them which are on the surface striking similarly against the ethereal matter. The agitation, moreover, of the particles which engender the light ought to be much more prompt and more rapid than is that of the bodies which cause sound, since we do not see that the tremors of a body which is giving out a sound are capable of giving rise to light, even as the movement of the hand in the air is not capable of producing sound.

Now if one examines what this matter may be in which the movement coming from the luminous body is propagated, which I call ethereal matter, one will see that it is not the same that serves for the propagation of sound. For one finds that the latter is really that which we feel and which we breathe, and which being removed from any place still leaves there the other kind of matter that serves to convey light. This may be proved by shutting up a sounding body in a glass vessel from which the air is withdrawn by the machine which Mr. Boyle has given us, and with which he has performed so many beautiful experiments. But in doing this of which I speak, care must be taken to place the sounding body on cotton or on feathers, in such a way that it cannot communicate its tremors either to the glass vessel which encloses it, or to the machine; a precaution which has hitherto been neglected. For then after having exhausted all the air one hears no sound from the metal, though it is struck.

One sees here not only that our air, which does not penetrate through glass, is the matter by which sound spreads; but also that it is not the same air but another kind of matter in which light spreads; since if the air is removed from the vessel the light does not cease to traverse it as before.

And this last point is demonstrated even more clearly by the celebrated experiment of Torricelli, in which the tube of glass from which the quicksilver has withdrawn itself, remaining void of air, transmits light just the same as when air is in it. For this proves that a matter different from air exists in this tube, and that this matter must have penetrated the glass or the quicksilver, either one or the other, though they are both impenetrable to the air. And when, in the same experiment, one makes the vacuum after putting a little water above the quicksilver, one concludes equally that the said matter passes through glass or water, or through both.

As regards the different modes in which I have said the movements of sound and of light are communicated, one may sufficiently comprehend how this occurs in the case of sound if one considers that the air is of such a nature that it can be compressed and reduced to a much smaller space than that which it ordinarily occupies. And in proportion as it is compressed the more does it exert an effort to regain its volume; for this property along with its penetrability, which remains notwithstanding its compression, seems to prove that it is made up of small bodies which float about and which are agitated very rapidly in the ethereal matter composed of much smaller parts. So that the cause of the spreading of sound is the effort which these little bodies make in collisions with one another, to regain freedom when they are a little more squeezed together in the circuit of these waves than elsewhere.

But the extreme velocity of light, and other properties which it has, cannot admit of such a propagation of motion, and I am about to show here the way in which I conceive it must occur. For this, it is needful to explain the property which hard bodies must possess to transmit movement from one to another.

When one takes a number of spheres of equal size, made of some very hard substance, and arranges them in a straight line, so that they touch one another, one finds, on striking with a similar sphere against the first of these spheres, that the motion passes as in an instant to the last of them, which separates itself from the row, without one's being able to perceive that the others have been stirred. And even that one which was used to strike remains motionless with them. Whence one sees that the movement passes with an extreme velocity which is the greater, the greater the hardness of the substance of the spheres.

But it is still certain that this progression of motion is not instantaneous, but successive, and therefore must take time. For if the movement, or the disposition to movement, if you will have it so, did not pass successively through all these spheres, they would all acquire the movement at the same time, and hence would all advance together; which does not happen. For the last one leaves the whole row and acquires the speed of the one which was pushed. Moreover there are experiments which demonstrate that all the bodies which we reckon of the hardest kind, such as quenched steel, glass, and agate, act as springs and bend somehow, not only when extended as rods but also when they are in the form of spheres or of other shapes. That is to say, they yield a little in themselves at the place where they are struck, and immediately regain their former figure. For I have found that on striking with a ball of glass or of agate against a large and quite thick piece of the same substance which had a flat surface, slightly soiled with breath or in some other way, there remained round marks, of smaller or larger size according as the blow had been weak or strong. This makes it evident that these substances yield where they meet, and spring back: and for this time must be required.

Now in applying this kind of movement to that which produces light there is nothing to hinder us from estimating the particles of the ether to be of a substance as nearly approaching to perfect hardness and possessing a springiness as prompt as we choose. It is not necessary to examine here the causes of this hardness, or of that springiness, the consideration of which would lead us too far from our subject. I will say, however, in passing that we may conceive that the particles of the ether, notwithstanding their smallness, are in turn composed of other parts and that their springiness consists in the very rapid movement of a subtle matter which penetrates them from every side and constrains their structure to assume such a disposition as to give to this fluid matter the most overt and easy passage possible. This accords with the explanation which M. Descartes gives for the spring, though I do not, like him, suppose the pores to be in the form of round hollow canals. And it must not be thought that in this there is anything absurd or impossible, it being on the contrary quite credible that it is this infinite series of different sizes of corpuscles, having different degrees of velocity, of which Nature makes use to produce so many marvellous effects.

But though we shall ignore the true cause of springiness we still see that there are many bodies which possess this property; and thus there is nothing strange in supposing that it exists also in little invisible bodies like the particles of the ether. Also, if one wishes to seek for any other way in which the movement of light is successively communicated, one will find none which agrees better, with uniform progression, as seems to be necessary, than the property of springiness; because if this movement should grow slower in proportion as it is shared over a greater quantity of matter, in moving away from the source of the light, it could not conserve this great velocity over great distances. But by supposing springiness in the ethereal matter, its particles will have the property of equally rapid restitution whether they are pushed strongly or feebly; and thus the propagation of light will always go on with an equal velocity.

And it must be known that, although the particles of the ether are not ranged thus in straight lines, as in our row of spheres, but confusedly, so that one of them touches several others, this does not hinder them from transmitting their movement and from spreading it always forward. As to this, it is to

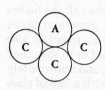

be remarked that there is a law of motion serving for this propagation, and verifiable by experiment. It is that when a sphere, such as A here, touches several other similar spheres CCC, if it is struck by another sphere B in such a way as to exert an impulse against all the spheres CCC which touch it, it transmits to them the whole of its movement, and remains after that motionless like the sphere B. And without supposing that the ethereal particles are of spherical form (for I see indeed no need to suppose them so) one may well understand that this property of communicating an impulse does not fail to contribute to the aforesaid propagation of movement.

Equality of size seems to be more necessary, because otherwise there ought to be some reflexion of movement backwards when it passes from a smaller particle to a larger one, according to the *Laws of Percussion* which I published some years ago.

However, one will see hereafter that we have to suppose such an equality not so much as a necessity for the propagation of light as for rendering that propagation easier and more powerful; for it is not beyond the limits of probability that the particles of the ether have been made equal for a purpose so important as that of light, at least in that vast space which is beyond the region of atmosphere and which seems to serve only to transmit the light of the sun and the stars.

I have then shown in what manner one may conceive light to spread successively, by spherical waves, and how it is possible that this spreading is accomplished with as great a velocity as that which experiments and celestial observations demand. Whence it may be further remarked that, although the particles are supposed to be in continual movement (for there are many reasons for this), the successive propagation of the waves cannot be hindered by this; because the propagation consists nowise in the transport of those particles but merely in a small agitation which they cannot help communicating to those surrounding, notwithstanding any movement which may act on them causing them to be changing positions amongst themselves.

But we must consider still more particularly the origin of these waves, and the manner in which they spread. And, first, it follows from what has been said on the production of light, that each little region of a luminous body, such as the sun, a candle, or a burning coal, generates its own waves of which that region is the centre. Thus, in the flame of a candle, having distinguished the points A, B, C, concentric circles described about each of these points represent the waves which come from them. And one must imagine the same about every point of the surface and of the part within the flame.

But as the percussions at the centres of these waves possess no regular succession, it must not be supposed that the waves themselves follow one another at equal distances: and if the distances marked in the figure appear to be such, it is rather to mark the progression of one and the same wave at equal intervals of time than to represent several of them issuing from one and the same centre.

After all, this prodigious quantity of waves which traverse one another without confusion and without effacing one another must not be deemed inconceivable; it being certain that one and the same particle of matter can serve for many waves coming from different sides or even from contrary directions, not only if it is struck by blows which follow one another closely but even for those which act on it at the same instant. It can do so because the spreading of the movement is successive. This may be proved by the row of equal spheres

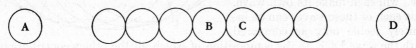

of hard matter, spoken of above. If against this row there are pushed from two opposite sides at the same time two similar spheres A and D, one will see each of them rebound with the same velocity which it had in striking, yet the whole row will remain in its place, although the movement has passed along its whole length twice over. And if these contrary movements happen to meet one another at the middle sphere, B, or at some other such as C, that sphere will yield and act as a spring at both sides, and so will serve at the same instant to transmit these two movements.

But what may at first appear full strange and even incredible is that the undulations produced by such small movements and corpuscles should spread to such immense distances; as for example, from the sun or from the stars to us. For the force of these waves must grow feeble in proportion as they move away from their origin, so that the action of each one in particular will without doubt become incapable of making itself felt to our sight. But one will cease to be astonished by considering how at a great distance from the luminous body an infinitude of waves, though they have issued from different points of this body, unite together in such a way that they sensibly compose one single wave only, which, consequently, ought to have enough force to make itself felt. Thus, this infinite number of waves which originate at the same instant from all points of a fixed star, big it may be as the sun, make practically only one single wave which may well have force enough to produce an impression on our eyes. Moreover, from each luminous point there may come many thousands of waves in the smallest imaginable time, by the frequent percussion of the corpuscles which strike the ether at these points: which further contributes to rendering their action more sensible.

There is the further consideration in the emanation of these waves, that each particle of matter, in which a wave spreads, ought not to communicate its motion only to the next particle which is in the straight line drawn from the luminous point, but that it also imparts some of it necessarily to all the others which touch it and which oppose themselves to its movement. So it arises that around each particle there is made a wave of which that particle is the centre. Thus, if DCF is a wave emanating from the luminous point A, which is its centre, the particle B, one of those comprised within the sphere DCF, will have made its particular or partial wave KCL, which will touch the wave DCF at C at the same moment that the principal wave emanating from the point A has arrived at DCF; and it is clear that it will be only the region C of the wave KCL which will touch the wave DCF, to wit, that which is in the straight line drawn through AB. Similarly the other particles of the sphere DCF, such as *bb*, *dd*, etc., will each make its own wave. But each of these waves can be in-finitely feeble only as compared

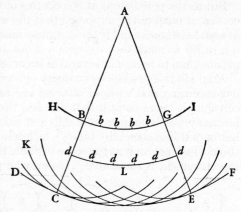

with the wave DCF, to the composition of which all the others contribute by the part of their surface which is most distant from the centre A.

One sees, in addition, that the wave DCF is determined by the distance attained in a certain space of time by the movement which started from the point A; there being no movement beyond this wave, though there will be in the space which it encloses, namely, in parts of the particular waves, those parts which do not touch the sphere DCF. And all this ought not to seem fraught with too much minuteness or subtlety, since we shall see in the sequel that all the properties of light, and everything pertaining to its reflexion and its refraction, can be explained in principle by this means. This is a matter which has been quite unknown to those who hitherto have begun to consider the waves of light, amongst whom are Mr. Hooke in his *Micrographia*, and Father Pardies, who, in a treatise of which he let me see a portion, and which he was unable to complete as he died shortly afterward, had undertaken to prove by these waves the effects of reflexion and refraction. But the chief foun-dation, which consists in the remark I have just made, was lacking in his dem-onstrations; and for the rest he had opinions very different from mine, as may be will appear some day if his writing has been preserved.

To come to the properties of light. We remark first that each portion of a wave ought to spread in such a way that its extremities lie always between the same straight lines drawn from the luminous point. Thus, the portion BG of the wave, having the luminous point A as its centre, will spread into the arc CE bounded by the straight lines ABC, AGE. For although the particular waves produced by the particles comprised within the space CAE spread also outside this space, they yet do not concur at the same instant to compose a wave which terminates the movement, as they do precisely at the circumfer-ence CE, which is their common tangent.

And hence one sees the reason why light, at least if its rays are not reflected or broken, spreads only by straight lines, so that it illuminates no object ex-cept when the path from its source to that object is open along such lines. For if, for example, there were an opening BG, limited by opaque bodies BH, GI, the wave of light which issues from the point A will always be terminated by the straight lines AC, AE, as has just been shown; the parts of the partial waves which spread outside the space ACE being too feeble to produce light there.

Now, however small we make the opening BG, there is always the same reason causing the light there to pass between straight lines; since this opening is always large enough to contain a great number of particles of the ethereal matter, which are of an inconceivable smallness; so that it appears that each little portion of the wave necessarily advances following the straight line which comes from the luminous point. Thus, then, we may take the rays of light as if they were straight lines.

It appears, moreover, by what has been remarked touching the feebleness of the particular waves, that it is not needful that all the particles of the ether should be equal amongst themselves, though equality is more apt for the propagation of the movement. For it is true that inequality will cause a particle, by pushing against another larger one, to strive to recoil with a part of its movement; but it will thereby merely generate backwards towards the luminous point some partial waves incapable of causing light, and not a wave compounded of many as CE was.

Another property of waves of light, and one of the most marvellous, is that when some of them come from different or even from opposing sides, they produce their effect across one another without any hindrance. Whence also it comes about that a number of spectators may view different objects at the same time through the same opening, and that two persons can at the same time see one another's eyes. Now, according to the explanation which has been given of the action of light, how the waves do not destroy nor interrupt one another when they cross one another, these effects which I have just mentioned are easily conceived. But in my judgement they are not at all easy to explain according to the views of M. Descartes, who makes light to consist in a continuous pressure merely tending to movement. For this pressure not being able to act from two opposite sides at the same time against bodies which have no inclination to approach one another, it is impossible so to understand what I have been saying about two persons mutually seeing one another's eyes, or how two torches can illuminate one another.

CHAPTER TWO

On Reflexion

HAVING explained the effects of waves of light which spread in a homogeneous matter, we will examine next that which happens to them on encountering other bodies. We will first make evident how the reflexion of light is explained by these same waves, and why it preserves equality of angles.

Let there be a surface AB; plane and polished, of some metal, glass, or other body, which at first I will consider as perfectly uniform (reserving to myself to deal at the end of this demonstration with the inequalities from which it cannot be exempt), and let a line AC, inclined to AB, represent a portion of a wave of light, the centre of which is so distant that this portion AC may be considered as a straight line; for I consider all this as in one plane, imagining to myself that the plane in which this figure is cuts the sphere of the wave through its centre and intersects the plane AB at right angles. This explanation will suffice once for all.

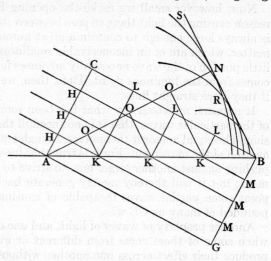

The piece C of the wave AC, will in a certain space of time advance as far as the plane AB at B, following the straight line CB, which may be supposed to come from the luminous centre, and which in consequence is perpendicular to AC. Now in this same space of time the portion A of the same wave, which has been hindered from communicating its movement beyond the plane AB, or at least partly so, ought to have continued its movement in the matter which is above this plane, and this along a distance equal to CB, making its own partial spherical wave, according to what has been said above. Which wave is here represented by the circumference SNR, the centre of which is A, and its semi-diameter AN equal to CB.

If one considers further the other pieces H of the wave AC, it appears that they will not only have reached the surface AB by straight lines HK parallel to CB, but that in addition they will have generated in the transparent air, from the centres K, K, K, particular spherical waves, represented here by circumferences the semi-diameters of which are equal to KM, that is to say, to the continuations of HK as far as the line BG parallel to AC. But all these circumferences have as a common tangent the straight line BN, namely, the same which is drawn from B as a tangent to the first of the circles, of which A is the centre, and AN the semi-diameter equal to BC, as is easy to see.

It is then the line BN (comprised between B and the point N where the perpendicular from the point A falls) which is, as it were, formed by all these circumferences, and which terminates the movement which is made by the reflexion of the wave AC; and it is also the place where the movement occurs in much greater quantity than anywhere else. Wherefore, according to that which has been explained, BN is the propagation of the wave AC at the moment when the piece C of it has arrived at B. For there is no other line which like BN is a common tangent to all the aforesaid circles, except BG below the plane AB; which line BG would be the propagation of the wave if the movement could have spread in a medium homogeneous with that which is above the plane. And if one wishes to see how the wave AC has come successively to BN, one has only to draw in the same figure the straight lines KO parallel to BN, and the straight lines KL parallel to AC. Thus one will see that the straight wave AC has become broken up into all the OKL parts successively, and that it has become straight again at NB.

Now it is apparent here that the angle of reflexion is made equal to the angle of incidence. For the triangles ACB, BNA, being rectangular and having the side AB common, and the side CB equal to NA, it follows that the angles opposite to these sides will be equal, and therefore also the angles CBA, NAB. But as CB, perpendicular to CA, marks the direction of the incident ray, so AN, perpendicular to the wave BN, marks the direction of the reflected ray; hence these rays are equally inclined to the plane AB.

But in considering the preceding demonstration, one might aver that it is indeed true that BN is the common tangent of the circular waves in the plane of this figure, but that these waves, being in truth spherical, have still an in-finitude of similar tangents, namely, all the straight lines which are drawn from the point B in the surface generated by the straight line BN about the axis BA. It remains, therefore, to demonstrate that there is no difficulty herein: and by the same argument one will see why the incident ray and the reflected ray are always in one and the same plane perpendicular to the reflecting plane. I say then that the wave AC, being regarded only as a line, produces no light. For a visible ray of light, however narrow it may be, has always some width, and consequently it is necessary, in representing the wave whose progression constitutes the ray, to put instead of a line AC some plane figure such as the circle HC in the following figure, by supposing, as we have done, the luminous point to be infinitely distant. Now it is easy to see, following the preceding demonstration, that each small piece of this wave HC having arrived at the plane AB, and there generating each one its particular wave, these will all have, when C arrives at B, a common plane which will touch them, namely, a circle BN similar to CH; and this will be intersected at its middle and at right

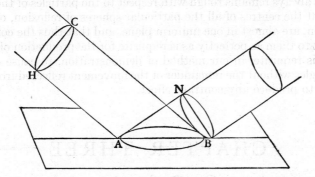

angles by the same plane which likewise intersects the circle CH and the ellipse AB.

One sees also that the said spheres of the partial waves cannot have any common tangent plane other than the circle BN; so that it will be this plane where there will be more reflected movement than anywhere else, and which will therefore carry on the light in continuance from the wave CH.

I have also stated in the preceding demonstration that the movement of the piece A of the incident wave is not able to communicate itself beyond the plane AB, or at least not wholly. Whence it is to be remarked that though the movement of the ethereal matter might communicate itself partly to that of the reflecting body, this could in nothing alter the velocity of progression of the waves on which the angle of reflexion depends. For a slight percussion ought to generate waves as rapid as strong percussion in the same matter. This comes about from the property of bodies which act as springs, of which we have spoken above; namely, that whether compressed little or much they recoil in equal times. Equally so in every reflexion of the light, against whatever body it may be, the angles of reflexion and incidence ought to be equal notwithstanding that the body might be of such a nature that it takes away a portion of the movement made by the incident light. And experiment shows that in fact there is no polished body the reflexion of which does not follow this rule.

But the thing to be above all remarked in our demonstration is that it does not require that the reflecting surface should be considered as a uniform plane, as has been supposed by all those who have tried to explain the effects of reflexion; but only an evenness such as may be attained by the particles of the matter of the reflecting body being set near to one another; which particles are larger than those of the ethereal matter, as will appear by what we shall say in treating of the transparency and opacity of bodies. For the surface consisting thus of particles put together, and the ethereal particles being above, and smaller, it is evident that one could not demonstrate the equality of the angles of incidence and reflexion by similitude to that which happens to a ball thrown against a wall, of which writers have always made use. In our way, on the other hand, the thing is explained without difficulty. For the smallness of the particles of quicksilver, for example, being such that one must conceive millions of them, in the smallest visible surface proposed, arranged like a heap of grains of sand which has been flattened as much as it is capable of being, this surface then becomes for our purpose as even as a polished glass is: and, although it always remains rough with respect to the particles of the ether it is evident that the centres of all the particular spheres of reflexion, of which we have spoken, are almost in one uniform plane, and that thus the common tangent can fit to them as perfectly as is requisite for the production of light. And this alone is requisite, in our method of demonstration, to cause equality of the said angles without the remainder of the movement reflected from all parts being able to produce any contrary effect.

CHAPTER THREE
On Refraction

In the same way as the effects of reflexion have been explained by waves of light reflected at the surface of polished bodies, we will explain transparency and the phenomena of refraction by waves which spread within and across diaphanous bodies, both solids, such as glass, and liquids, such as water, oils, etc. But in order that it may not seem strange to suppose this passage of waves in the interior of these bodies, I will first show that one may conceive it possible in more than one mode.

First, then, if the ethereal matter cannot penetrate transparent bodies at all, their own particles would be able to communicate successively the movement of the waves, the same as do those of the ether, supposing that, like those, they are of a nature to act as a spring. And this is easy to conceive as regards water and other transparent liquids, they being composed of detached particles. But it may seem more difficult as regards glass and other transparent and hard bodies, because their solidity does not seem to permit them to receive movement except in their whole mass at the same time. This, however, is not necessary because this solidity is not such as it appears to us, it being probable rather that these bodies are composed of particles merely placed close to one another and held together by some pressure from without of some other matter, and by the irregularity of their shapes. For primarily their rarity is shown by the facility with which there passes through them the matter of the vortices of the magnet, and that which causes gravity. Further, one cannot say that these bodies are of a texture similar to that of a sponge or of light bread, because the heat of the fire makes them flow and thereby changes the situation of the particles amongst themselves. It remains then that they are, as has been said, assemblages of particles which touch one another without constituting a continuous solid. This being so, the movement which these particles receive to carry on the waves of light, being merely communicated from some of them to others, without their going for that purpose out of their places or without derangement, it may very well produce its effect without prejudicing in any way the apparent solidity of the compound.

By pressure from without, of which I have spoken, must not be understood that of the air, which would not be sufficient, but that of some other more subtle matter, a pressure which I chanced upon by experiment long ago, namely, in the case of water freed from air, which remains suspended in a tube open at its lower end, notwithstanding that the air has been removed from the vessel in which this tube is enclosed.

One can then in this way conceive of transparency in a solid without any necessity that the ethereal matter which serves for light should pass through it, or that it should find pores in which to insinuate itself. But the truth is that this matter not only passes through solids, but does so even with great facility; of which the experiment of Torricelli, above cited, is already a proof. Because on the quicksilver and the water quitting the upper part of the glass tube, it appears that it is immediately filled with ethereal matter, since light passes across it. But here is another argument which proves this ready penetrability, not only in transparent bodies but also in all others.

When light passes across a hollow sphere of glass, closed on all sides, it is certain that it is full of ethereal matter, as much as the spaces outside the sphere. And this ethereal matter, as has been shown above, consists of particles which just touch one another. If, then, it were enclosed in the sphere in such a way that it could not get out through the pores of the glass, it would be obliged to follow the movement of the sphere when one changes its place: and it would require, consequently, almost the same force to impress a certain velocity on this sphere, when placed on a horizontal plane, as if it were full of water or perhaps of quicksilver: because every body resists the velocity of the motion which one would give to it, in proportion to the quantity of matter which it contains, and which is obliged to follow this motion. But, on the contrary, one finds that the sphere resists the impress of movement only in proportion to the quantity of matter of the glass of which it is made. Then it must be that the ethereal matter which is inside is not shut up, but flows through it with very great freedom. We shall demonstrate hereafter that by this process the same penetrability may be inferred also as relating to opaque bodies.

The second mode, then, of explaining transparency, and one which appears more probably true, is by saying that the waves of light are carried on in the ethereal matter, which continuously occupies the interstices or pores of transparent bodies. For since it passes through them continuously and freely, it follows that they are always full of it. And one may even show that these interstices occupy much more space than the coherent particles which constitute the bodies. For if what we have just said is true: that force is required to impress a certain horizontal velocity on bodies in proportion as they contain coherent matter; and if the proportion of this force follows the law of weights, as is confirmed by experiment, then the quantity of the constituent matter of bodies also follows the proportion of their weights. Now we see that water weighs only one-fourteenth part as much as an equal portion of quicksilver: therefore, the matter of the water does not occupy the fourteenth part of the space which its mass obtains. It must even occupy much less of it, since quicksilver is less heavy than gold, and the matter of gold is by no means dense, as follows from the fact that the matter of the vortices of the magnet and of that which is the cause of gravity pass very freely through it.

But it may be objected here that if water is a body of so great rarity, and if its particles occupy so small a portion of the space of its apparent bulk, it is very strange how it yet resists compression so strongly without permitting itself to be condensed by any force which one has hitherto essayed to employ, preserving even its entire liquidity while subjected to this pressure.

This is no small difficulty. It may, however, be resolved by saying that the very violent and rapid motion of the subtle matter which renders water liquid, by agitating the particles of which it is composed, maintains this liquidity in spite of the pressure which hitherto any one has been minded to apply to it.

The rarity of transparent bodies being then such as we have said, one easily conceives that the waves might be carried on in the ethereal matter which fills the interstices of the particles. And, moreover, one may believe that the progression of these waves ought to be a little slower in the interior of bodies, by reason of the small detours which the same particles cause. In which different velocity of light I shall show the cause of refraction to consist.

Before doing so, I will indicate the third and last mode in which transparency may be conceived; which is by supposing that the movement of the waves of light is transmitted indifferently both in the particles of the ethereal matter which occupy the interstices of bodies, and in the particles which compose them, so that the movement passes from one to the other. And it will be seen hereafter that this hypothesis serves excellently to explain the double refraction of certain transparent bodies.

Should it be objected that if the particles of the ether are smaller than those of transparent bodies (since they pass through their intervals), it would follow that they can communicate to them but little of their movement, it may be replied that the particles of these bodies are in turn composed of still smaller particles, and so it will be these secondary particles which will receive the movement from those of the ether.

Furthermore, if the particles of transparent bodies have a recoil a little less prompt than that of the ethereal particles, which nothing hinders us from supposing, it will again follow that the progression of the waves of light will be slower in the interior of such bodies than it is outside in the ethereal matter.

All this I have found as most probable for the mode in which the waves of light pass across transparent bodies. To which it must further be added in what respect these bodies differ from those which are opaque; and the more so since it might seem because of the easy penetration of bodies by the ethereal matter, of which mention has been made, that there would not be any body that was not transparent. For by the same reasoning about the hollow sphere which I have employed to prove the smallness of the density of glass and its easy penetrability by the ethereal matter, one might also prove that the same penetrability obtains for metals and for every other sort of body. For this sphere being, for example, of silver, it is certain that it contains some of the ethereal matter which serves for light, since this was there as well as in the air when the opening of the sphere was closed. Yet, being closed and placed upon a horizontal plane, it resists the movement which one wishes to give to it, merely according to the quantity of silver of which it is made; so that one must conclude, as above, that the ethereal matter which is enclosed does not follow the movement of the sphere; and that, therefore, silver, as well as glass, is very easily penetrated by this matter. Some of it is therefore present continuously and in quantities between the particles of silver and of all other opaque bodies: and since it serves for the propagation of light it would seem that these bodies ought also to be transparent, which, however, is not the case.

Whence then, one will say, does their opacity come? Is it because the particles which compose them are soft; that is to say, these particles being composed of others that are smaller, are they capable of changing their figure on receiving the pressure of the ethereal particles, the motion of which they thereby damp, and so hinder the continuance of the waves of light? That cannot be: for if the particles of the metals are soft, how is it that polished silver and mercury reflect light so strongly? What I find to be most probable herein is to say that metallic bodies, which are almost the only really opaque ones, have mixed amongst their hard particles some soft ones; so that some serve to cause reflexion and the others to hinder transparency; while, on the other hand, transparent bodies contain only hard particles which have the faculty of recoil, and serve together with those of the ethereal matter for the propagation of the waves of light, as has been said.

Let us pass now to the explanation of the effects of refraction, assuming, as we have done, the passage of waves of light through transparent bodies, and the diminution of velocity which these same waves suffer in them.

The chief property of refraction is that a ray of light, such as AB, being in the air, and falling obliquely upon the polished surface of a transparent body, such as FG, is broken at the point of incidence B in such a way that, with the straight line DBE which cuts the surface perpendicularly, it makes an angle CBE less than ABD which it made with the same perpendicular when in the air. And the measure of these angles is found by describing, about the point B, a circle which cuts the radii AB, BC. For the perpendiculars AD, CE, let fall from the points of intersection upon the straight line DE, which are called the sines of the angles ABD, CBE, have a certain ratio between themselves; which

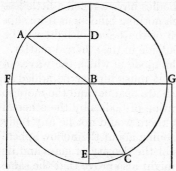

ratio is always the same for all inclinations of the incident ray, at least for a given transparent body. This ratio is, in glass, very nearly as 3 to 2; and in water very nearly as 4 to 3; and is likewise different in other diaphanous bodies.

Another property, similar to this, is that the refractions are reciprocal between the rays entering into a transparent body and those which are leaving it. That is to say, that if the ray AB in entering the transparent body is refracted into BC, then likewise CB being taken as a ray in the interior of this body will be refracted, on passing out, into BA.

To explain then the reasons of these phenomena according to our principles, let AB be the straight line which represents a plane surface bounding the transparent substances which lie towards C and towards N. When I say plane, that

does not signify a perfect evenness, but such as has been understood in treating of reflexion, and for the same reason. Let the line AC represent a portion of a wave of light, the centre of which is supposed so distant that this portion may be considered as a straight line. The piece C, then, of the wave AC, will in a certain space of time have advanced as far as the plane AB following the straight line CB, which may be imagined as coming from the luminous centre, and which

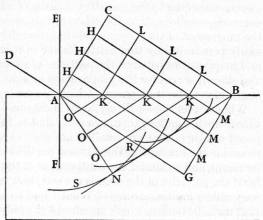

consequently will cut AC at right angles. Now in the same time the piece A would have come to G along the straight line AG, equal and parallel to CB; and all the portion of wave AC would be at GB if the matter of the transparent body transmitted the movement of the wave as quickly as the matter of the ether. But let us suppose that it transmits this movement less quickly, by one-third, for instance. Movement will then be spread from the point A, in the matter of the transparent body through a distance equal to two-thirds of CB, making its own particular spherical wave according to what has been said before. This wave is then represented by the circumference SNR, the centre of which is A, and its semi-diameter equal to two-thirds of CB. Then if one considers in order the other pieces H of the wave AC, it appears that in the same time that the piece C reaches B they will not only have arrived at the surface AB along the straight lines HK parallel to CB, but that, in addition, they will have generated in the diaphanous substance from the centres K, partial waves, represented here by circumferences the semi-diameters of which are equal to two-thirds of the lines KM, that is to say, to two-thirds of the prolongations of HK down to the straight line BG; for these semi-diameters would have been equal to entire lengths of KM if the two transparent substances had been of the same penetrability.

Now all these circumferences have for a common tangent the straight line BN; namely, the same line which is drawn as a tangent from the point B to the circumference SNR, which we considered first. For it is easy to see that all the other circumferences will touch the same BN, from B up to the point of contact N, which is the same point where AN falls perpendicularly on BN.

It is then BN, which is formed by small arcs of these circumferences, which terminates the movement that the wave AC has communicated within the transparent body, and where this movement occurs in much greater amount than anywhere else. And for that reason this line, in accordance with what has been said more than once, is the propagation of the wave AC at the moment when its piece C has reached B. For there is no other line below the plane AB which is, like BN, a common tangent to all these partial waves. And if one would know how the wave AC has come progressively to BN, it is necessary only to draw in the same figure the straight lines KO parallel to BN, and all the lines KL parallel to AC. Thus, one will see that the wave CA, from being a straight line, has become broken in all the positions LKO successively, and that it has again become a straight line at BN. This being evident by what has already been demonstrated, there is no need to explain it further.

Now, in the same figure, if one draws EAF, which cuts the plane AB at right angles at the point A, since AD is perpendicular to the wave AC, it will be DA which will mark the ray of incident light, and AN which was perpendicular to BN, the refracted ray: since the rays are nothing else than the straight lines along which the portions of the waves advance.

Whence it is easy to recognize this chief property of refraction, namely that the sine of the angle DAE has always the same ratio to the sine of the angle NAF, whatever be the inclination of the ray DA: and that this ratio is the same as that of the velocity of the waves in the transparent substance which is towards AE to their velocity in the transparent substance towards AF. For, considering AB as the radius of a circle, the sine of the angle BAC is BC, and the sine of the angle ABN is AN. But the angle BAC is equal to DAE, since each of them added to CAE makes a right angle. And the angle ABN is equal to NAF, since each of them with BAN makes a right angle. Then, also, the sine of the angle DAE is to the sine of NAF as BC is to AN. But the ratio of BC to AN was the same as that of the velocities of light in the substance which is towards AE and in that which is towards AF; therefore, also, the sine of the angle DAE will be to the sine of the angle NAF the same as the said velocities of light.

To see, consequently, what the refraction will be when the waves of light pass into a substance in which the movement travels more quickly than in that from which they emerge (let us again assume the ratio of 3 to 2), it is only necessary to repeat all the same construction and demonstration which we have just used, merely substituting everywhere $\frac{3}{2}$ instead of $\frac{2}{3}$. And it will be found by the same reasoning, in this other figure, that when the piece C of the wave AC shall have reached the surface AB at B, all the portions of the wave

AC will have advanced as far as BN, so that BC, the perpendicular on AC, is
to AN, the perpendicular on BN, as 2 to 3. And there will finally be this same
ratio of 2 to 3 between the sine of the angle EAD and the sine of the angle FAN.

Hence, one sees the reciprocal relation of the refractions of the ray on entering and on leaving one and the same transparent body: namely, that if NA

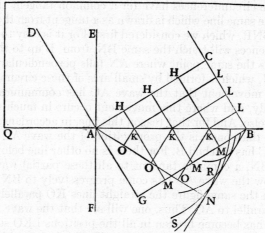

falling on the external surface AB is refracted into the direction AD, so the ray
AD will be refracted on leaving the transparent body into the direction AN.

One sees also the reason for a noteworthy accident which happens in this
refraction: which is this, that after a certain obliquity of the incident ray DA,
it begins to be quite unable to penetrate into the other transparent substance.
For if the angle DAQ or CBA is such that in the triangle ACB, CB is equal to
⅔ of AB, or is greater, then AN cannot form one side of the triangle ANB,
since it becomes equal to or greater than AB: so that the portion of wave BN
cannot be found anywhere, neither consequently can AN, which ought to be
perpendicular to it. And thus the incident ray DA does not then pierce the
surface AB.

When the ratio of the velocities of the waves is as 2 to 3, as in our example,
which is that which obtains for glass and air, the angle DAQ must be more than
48 degrees 11 minutes in order that the ray DA may be able to pass by refraction. And when the ratio of the velocities is as 3 to 4, as it is very nearly in
water and air, this angle DAQ must exceed 41 degrees 24 minutes. And this
accords perfectly with experiment.

But it might here be asked: since the meeting of the wave AC against the
surface AB ought to produce movement in the matter which is on the other
side, why does no light pass there? To which the reply is easy if one remembers
what has been said before. For although it generates an infinitude of partial
waves in the matter which is at the other side of AB, these waves never have
a common tangent line (either straight or curved) at the same moment; and
so there is no line terminating the propagation of the wave AC beyond the
plane AB, nor any place where the movement is gathered together in sufficiently great quantity to produce light. And one will easily see the truth of
this, namely, that CB being larger than ⅔ of AB, the waves excited beyond the
plane AB will have no common tangent if about the centres K one then draws

circles having radii equal to $\frac{3}{2}$ of the lengths LB to which they correspond. For all these circles will be enclosed in one another and will all pass beyond the point B.

Now it is to be remarked that from the moment when the angle DAQ is smaller than is requisite to permit the refracted ray DA to pass into the other transparent substance, one finds that the interior reflexion which occurs at the surface AB is much augmented in brightness, as is easy to realize by experiment with a triangular prism; and for this our theory can afford this reason. When the angle DAQ is still large enough to enable the ray DA to pass, it is evident that the light from the portion AC of the wave is collected in a minimum space when it reaches BN. It appears also that the wave BN becomes so much the smaller as the angle CBA or DAQ is made less, until when the latter is diminished to the limit indicated a little previously, this wave BN is collected together always at one point. That is to say, that when the piece C of the wave AC has then arrived at B, the wave BN which is the propagation of AC is entirely reduced to the same point B. Similarly, when the piece H has reached K, the part AH is entirely reduced to the same point K. This makes it evident that in proportion as the wave CA comes to meet the surface AB, there occurs a great quantity of movement along that surface; which movement ought also to spread within the transparent body and ought to have much re-enforced the partial waves which produce the interior reflexion against the surface AB, according to the laws of reflexion previously explained.

And because a slight diminution of the angle of incidence DAQ causes the wave BN, however great it was, to be reduced to zero, (for this angle being 49 degrees 11 minutes in the glass, the angle BAN is still 11 degrees 21 minutes, and the same angle being reduced by one degree only the angle BAN is reduced to zero, and so the wave BN reduced to a point) thence it comes about that the interior reflexion from being obscure becomes suddenly bright, so soon as the angle of incidence is such that it no longer gives passage to the refraction.

Now as concerns ordinary external reflexion, that is to say which occurs when the angle of incidence DAQ is still large enough to enable the refracted ray to penetrate beyond the surface AB, this reflexion should occur against the particles of the substance which touches the transparent body on its outside. And it apparently occurs against the particles of the air or others mingled with the ethereal particles and larger than they. So, on the other hand, the external reflexion of these bodies occurs against the particles which compose them, and which are also larger than those of the ethereal matter, since the latter flows in their interstices. It is true that there remains here some difficulty in those experiments in which this interior reflexion occurs without the particles of air being able to contribute to it, as in vessels or tubes from which the air has been extracted.

Experience, moreover, teaches us that these two reflexions are of nearly equal force, and that in different transparent bodies they are so much the stronger as the refraction of these bodies is the greater. Thus, one sees manifestly that the reflexion of glass is stronger than that of water, and that of diamond stronger than that of glass.

I will finish this theory of refraction by demonstrating a remarkable proposition which depends on it; namely, that a ray of light in order to go from one point to another, when these points are in different media, is refracted in such

wise at the plane surface which joins these two media that it employs the least
possible time: and exactly the same happens in the case of reflexion against a
plane surface. M. Fermat was the first to propound this property of refraction,
holding with us, and directly counter to the opinion of M. Descartes, that light
passes more slowly through glass and water than through air. But he assumed
besides this a constant ratio of sines, which we have just proved by these different degrees of velocity alone: or rather, what is equivalent, he assumed not
only that the velocities were different but that the light took the least time
possible for its passage, and thence deduced the constant ratio of the sines.
His demonstration, which may be seen in his printed works, and in the volume
of letters of M. Descartes, is very long; wherefore I give here another which is
simpler and easier.

Let KF be the plane surface; A the point in the medium which the light
traverses more easily, as the air; C the point in the other which is more difficult

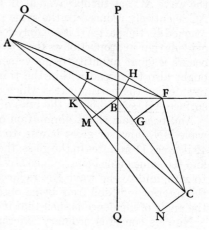

to penetrate, as water. And suppose
that a ray has come from A, by B, to C,
having been refracted at B according to
the law demonstrated a little before;
that is to say that, having drawn PBQ,
which cuts the plane at right angles,
let the sine of the angle ABP have to
the sine of the angle CBQ the same
ratio as the velocity of light in the medium where A is to the velocity of light
in the medium where C is. It is to be
shown that the time of passage of light
along AB and BC taken together is the
shortest that can be. Let us assume
that it may have come by other lines,
and, in the first place, along AF, FC,
so that the point of refraction F may be farther from B than the point A; and
let AO be a line perpendicular to AB, and FO parallel to AB; BH perpendicular to FO, and FG to BC.

Since then the angle HBF is equal to PBA, and the angle BFG equal to
QBC, it follows that the sine of the angle HBF will also have the same ratio to
the sine of BFG, as the velocity of light in the medium A is to its velocity in
the medium C. But these sines are the straight lines HF, BG, if we take BF as
the semi-diameter of a circle. Then these lines HF, BG, will bear to one another
the said ratio of the velocities. And, therefore, the time of the light along HF,
supposing that the ray had been OF, would be equal to the time along BG in
the interior of the medium C. But the time along AB is equal to the time along
OH; therefore, the time along OF is equal to the time along AB, BG. Again
the time along FC is greater than that along GC; then the time along OFC
will be longer than that along ABC. But AF is longer than OF, then the time
along AFC will by just so much more exceed the time along ABC.

Now let us assume that the ray has come from A to C along AK, KC; the
point of refraction K being nearer to A than the point B is; and let CN be the
perpendicular upon BC, KN parallel to BC: BM perpendicular upon KN, and
KL upon BA.

Here BL and KM are the sines of angles BKL, KBM; that is to say, of the angles PBA, QBC; and, therefore, they are to one another as the velocity of light in the medium A is to the velocity in the medium C. Then the time along LB is equal to the time along KM; and since the time along BC is equal to the time along MN, the time along LBC will be equal to the time along KMN. But the time along AK is longer than that along AL: hence, the time along AKN is longer than that along ABC. And KC being longer than KN, the time along AKC will exceed, by as much more, the time along ABC. Hence, it appears that the time along ABC is the shortest possible; which was to be proven.

CHAPTER FOUR
On the Refraction of the Air

WE have shown how the movement which constitutes light spreads by spherical waves in any homogeneous matter. And it is evident that when the matter is not homogeneous, but of such a constitution that the movement is communicated in it more rapidly toward one side than toward another, these waves cannot be spherical: but that they must acquire their figure according to the different distances over which the successive movement passes in equal times.

It is thus that we shall in the first place explain the refractions which occur in the air, which extends from here to the clouds and beyond. The effects of which refractions are very remarkable; for by them we often see objects which the rotundity of the earth ought otherwise to hide; such as islands, and the tops of mountains when one is at sea. Because also of them the sun and the moon appear as risen before in fact they have, and appear to set later: so that at times the moon has been seen eclipsed while the sun appeared still above the horizon. And so also the heights of the sun and of the moon, and those of all the stars, always appear a little greater than they are in reality, because of these same refractions, as astronomers know. But there is one experiment which renders this refraction very evident; which is that of fixing a telescope on some spot so that it views an object, such as a steeple or a house, at a distance of half a league or more. If then you look through it at different hours of the day, leaving it always fixed in the same way, you will see that the same spots of the object will not always appear at the middle of the aperture of the telescope, but that generally in the morning and in the evening, when there are more vapours near the earth, these objects seem to rise higher, so that the half or more of them will no longer be visible; and so that they seem lower toward mid-day when these vapours are dissipated.

Those who consider refraction to occur only in the surfaces which separate transparent bodies of different nature, would find it difficult to give a reason for all that I have just related; but according to our theory the thing is quite easy. It is known that the air which surrounds us, besides the particles which are proper to it and which float in the ethereal matter as has been explained, is full also of particles of water which are raised by the action of heat; and it has been ascertained further by some very definite experiments that as one mounts up higher the density of air diminishes in proportion. Now, whether the particles of water and those of air take part, by means of the particles of ethereal matter, in the movement which constitutes light, but have a less prompt recoil than these, or whether the encounter and hindrance which these particles of air and water offer to the propagation of movement of the ethereal progress retard the progression, it follows that both kinds of particles flying amidst the ethereal particles must render the air, from a great height down to the earth, gradually less easy for the spreading of the waves of light.

Whence the configuration of the waves ought to become nearly such as this

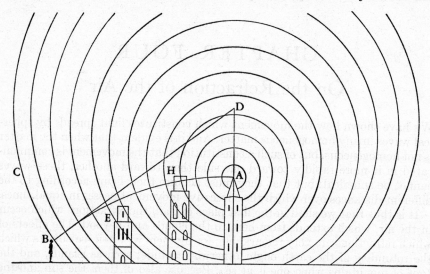

figure represents: namely, if A is a light, or the visible point of a steeple, the waves which start from it ought to spread more widely upwards and less widely downwards, but in other directions more or less as they approximate to these two extremes. This being so, it necessarily follows that every line intersecting one of these waves at right angles will pass above the point A, always excepting the one line which is perpendicular to the horizon.

Let BC be the wave which brings the light to the spectator who is at B, and let BD be the straight line which intersects this wave at right angles. Now because the ray or straight line by which we judge the spot where the object appears to us is nothing else than the perpendicular to the wave that reaches our eye, as will be understood by what was said above, it is manifest that the point A will be perceived as being in the line BD, and therefore higher than in fact it is.

Similarly if the earth be AB, and the top of the atmosphere CD, which probably is not a well defined spherical surface (since we know that the air becomes rare in proportion as one ascends, for above there is so much less of it to press down upon it), the waves of light from the sun coming, for instance, in such a way that so long as they have not reached the atmosphere CD the straight line AE intersects them perpendicularly, they ought, when they enter the atmosphere, to advance more quickly in elevated regions than in regions nearer to the earth. So that if CA is the wave which brings the light to the

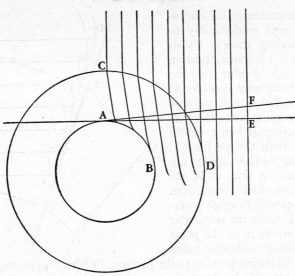

spectator at A, its region C will be the farthest advanced; and the straight line AF, which intersects this wave at right angles, and which determines the apparent place of the sun, will pass above the real sun, which will be seen along the line AE. And so it may occur that when it ought not to be visible in the absence of vapours, because the line AE encounters the rotundity of the earth, it will be perceived in the line AF by refraction. But this angle EAF is scarcely ever more than half a degree because the attenuation of the vapours alters the waves of light but little. Furthermore, these refractions are not altogether constant in all weathers, particularly at small elevations of 2 or 3 degrees; which results from the different quantity of aqueous vapours rising above the earth.

And this same thing is the cause why at certain times a distant object will be hidden behind another less distant one, and yet may at another time be able to be seen, although the spot from which it is viewed is always the same. But the reason for this effect will be still more evident from what we are going to remark touching the curvature of rays. It appears from the things explained above that the progression or propagation of a small part of a wave of light is properly what one calls a ray. Now these rays, instead of being straight as they are in homogeneous media, ought to be curved in an atmosphere of unequal penetrability. For they necessarily follow from the object to the eye the line which intersects at right angles all the progressions of the waves, as in the first figure [p. 576] the line AEB does, as will be shown hereafter; and it is this line which determines what interposed bodies would or would not hinder us from seeing the object. For although the point of the steeple A appears raised to D, it would yet not appear to the eye B if the tower H was between the two, because it crosses the curve AEB. But the tower E, which is beneath this curve, does not hinder the point A from being seen. Now according as the air near the earth exceeds in density that which is higher, the curvature of the ray AEB becomes greater: so that at certain times it passes above the summit E, which allows the point A to be perceived by the eye at B; and at other times it is intercepted by the same tower E which hides A from this same eye.

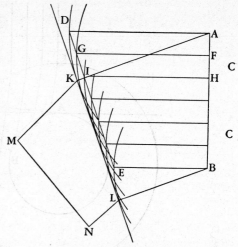

But to demonstrate this curvature of the rays conformably to all our preceding theory, let us imagine that AB is a small portion of a wave of light coming from the side C, which we may consider as a straight line. Let us also suppose that it is perpendicular to the horizon, the portion B being nearer to the earth than the portion A; and that, because the vapours are less hindering at A than at B, the particular wave which comes from the point A spreads through a certain space AD while the particular wave which starts from the point B spreads through a shorter space BE; AD and BE being parallel to the horizon. Further, supposing the straight lines FG, HI, etc., to be drawn from an infinitude of points in the straight line AB and to terminate on the line DE (which is straight or may be considered as such), let the different penetrabilities at the different heights in the air between A and B be represented by all these lines; so that the particular wave, originating from the point F, will spread across the space FG, and that from the point H across the space HI, while that from the point A spreads across the space AD.

Now if about the centres A, B, one describes the circles DK, EL, which represent the spreading of the waves which originate from these two points, and if one draws the straight line KL which touches these two circles, it is easy to see that this same line will be the common tangent to all the other circles drawn about the centres F, H, etc.; and that all the points of contact will fall within that part of this line which is comprised between the perpendiculars AK, BL. Then it will be the line KL which will terminate the movement of the particular waves originating from the points of the wave AB; and this movement will be stronger between the points KL, than anywhere else at the same instant, since an infinitude of circumferences concur to form this straight line; and consequently KL will be the propagation of the portion of wave AB, as has been said in explaining reflexion and ordinary refraction. Now it appears that AK and BL dip down toward the side where the air is less easy to penetrate: for AK being longer than BL, and parallel to it, it follows that the lines AB and KL, being prolonged, would meet at the side L. But the angle K is a right angle: hence KAB is necessarily acute, and consequently less than DAB. If one investigates in the same way the progression of the portion of the wave KL, one will find that after a further time it has arrived at MN in such a manner that the perpendiculars KM, LN dip down even more than do AK, BL. And this suffices to show that the ray will continue along the curved line which intersects all the waves at right angles, as has been said.

CHAPTER FIVE

On the Strange Refractions of Iceland Crystal

1. There is brought from Iceland, which is an island in the North Sea, in the latitude of 66 degrees, a kind of crystal or transparent stone, very remarkable for its figure and other qualities, but above all for its strange refractions. The causes of this have seemed to me to be worthy of being carefully investigated, the more so because amongst transparent bodies this one alone does not follow the ordinary rules with respect to rays of light. I have even been under some necessity to make this research, because the refractions of this crystal seemed to overturn our preceding explanation of regular refraction; which explanation, on the contrary, they strongly confirm, as will be seen after they have been brought under the same principle. In Iceland are found great lumps of this crystal, some of which I have seen of 4 or 5 pounds. But it occurs also in other countries, for I have had some of the same sort which had been found in France near the town of Troyes in Champagne, and some others which came from the island of Corsica, though both were less clear and only in little bits, scarcely capable of letting any effect of refraction be observed.

2. The first knowledge which the public has had about it is due to Mr. Erasmus Bartholinus, who has given a description of Iceland crystal and of its chief phenomena. But here I shall not desist from giving my own, both for the instruction of those who may not have seen his book, and because as respects some of these phenomena there is a slight difference between his observations and those which I have made: for I have applied myself with great exactitude to examine these properties of refraction, in order to be quite sure before undertaking to explain the causes of them.

3. As regards the hardness of this stone and the property which it has of being easily split, it must be considered rather as a species of talc than of crystal. For an iron spike effects an entrance into it as easily as into any other talc or alabaster, to which it is equal in gravity.

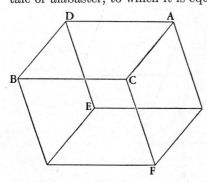

4. The pieces of it which are found have the figure of an oblique parallelepiped; each of the six faces being a parallelogram; and it admits of being split in three directions parallel to two of these opposed faces. Even in such wise, if you will, that all the six faces are equal and similar rhombuses. The figure here added represents a piece of this crystal. The obtuse angles of all the parallelograms, as C, D, here, are angles of 101 degrees 52 minutes, and consequently the acute angles, such as A and B, are of 78 degrees 8 minutes.

5. Of the solid angles, there are two opposite to one another, such as C and E, which are each composed of three equal obtuse plane angles. The other six are composed of two acute angles and one obtuse. All that I have just said has been likewise remarked by Mr. Bartholinus in the aforesaid treatise; if we differ it is only slightly about the values of the angles. He recounts, moreover, some other properties of this crystal; to wit, that when rubbed against cloth it attracts straws and other light things as do amber, diamond, glass, and Spanish wax. Let a piece be covered with water for a day or more, the surface loses its natural polish. When aquafortis is poured on it, it produces ebullition, especially, as I have found, if the crystal has been pulverized. I have also found by experiment that it may be heated to redness in the fire without being in anywise altered or rendered less transparent; but a very violent fire calcines it, nevertheless. Its transparency is scarcely less than that of water or of rock crystal, and devoid of colour. But rays of light pass through it in another fashion and produce those marvellous refractions the causes of which I am now going to try to explain; reserving for the end of this treatise the statement of my conjectures touching the formation and extraordinary configuration of this crystal.

6. In all other transparent bodies that we know there is but one sole and simple refraction; but in this substance there are two different ones. The effect is that objects seen through it, especially such as are placed right against it, appear double; and that a ray of sunlight, falling on one of its surfaces, parts itself into two rays and traverses the crystal thus.

7. It is again a general law in all other transparent bodies that the ray which falls perpendicularly on their surface passes straight on without suffering refraction, and that an oblique ray is always refracted. But in this crystal the perpendicular ray suffers refraction, and there are oblique rays which pass through it quite straight.

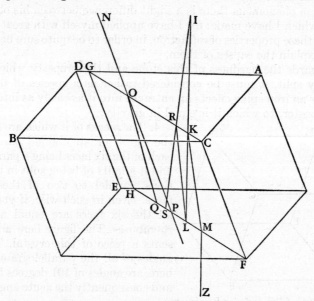

8. But in order to explain these phenomena more particularly, let there be, in the first place, a piece ABFE of the same crystal, and let the obtuse angle ACB, one of the three which constitute the equilateral solid angle C, be di-

vided into two equal parts by the straight line CG, and let it be conceived that the crystal is intersected by a plane which passes through this line and through the side CF, which plane will necessarily be perpendicular to the surface AB; and its section in the crystal will form a parallelogram GCFH. We will call this section the principal section of the crystal.

9. Now, if one covers the surface AB, leaving there only a small aperture at the point K, situated in the straight line CG, and if one exposes it to the sun, so that his rays face it perpendicularly above, then the ray IK will divide itself at the point K into two, one of which will continue to go on straight by KL, and the other will separate itself along the straight line KM, which is in the plane GCFH, and which makes with KL an angle of about 6 degrees 40 minutes, tending from the side of the solid angle C; and on emerging from the other side of the crystal it will turn again parallel to IK, along MZ. And as, in this extraordinary refraction, the point M is seen by the refracted ray MKI, which I consider as going to the eye at I, it necessarily follows that the point L, by virtue of the same refraction, will be seen by the refracted ray LRI, so that LR will be parallel to MK if the distance from the eye KI is supposed very great. The point L appears then as being in the straight line IRS; but the same point appears also, by ordinary refraction, to be in the straight line IK, hence, it is necessarily judged to be double. And, similarly, if L be a small hole in a sheet of paper or other substance which is laid against the crystal, it will appear when turned towards daylight as if there were two holes, which will seem the wider apart from one another the greater the thickness of the crystal.

10. Again, if one turns the crystal in such wise that an incident ray NO, of sunlight, which I suppose to be in the plane continued from GCFH, makes with GC an angle of 73 degrees and 20 minutes, and is consequently nearly parallel to the edge CF, which makes with FH an angle of 70 degrees 57 minutes, according to the calculation which I shall put at the end, it will divide itself at the point O into two rays, one of which will continue along OP in a straight line with NO, and will similarly pass out of the other side of the crystal without any refraction; but the other will be refracted and will go along OQ. And it must be noted that it is special to the plane through GCF and to those which are parallel to it, that all incident rays which are in one of these planes continue to be in it after they have entered the crystal and have become double; for it is quite otherwise for rays in all other planes which intersect the crystal, as we shall see afterwards.

11. I recognized at first by these experiments and by some others that of the two refractions which the ray suffers in this crystal, there is one which follows the ordinary rules; and it is this to which the rays KL and OQ belong. This is why I have distinguished this ordinary refraction from the other; and having measured it by exact observation, I found that its proportion, considered as to the sines of the angles which the incident and refracted rays make with the perpendicular, was very precisely that of 5 to 3, as was found also by Mr. Bartholinus, and consequently much greater than that of rock crystal, or of glass, which is nearly 3 to 2.

12. The mode of making these observations exactly is as follows. Upon a leaf of paper fixed on a thoroughly flat table there is traced a black line AB, and two others, CED and KML, which cut it at right angles and are more or less distant from one another according as it is desired to examine a ray that is

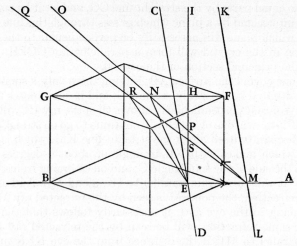

more or less oblique. Then place the crystal upon the intersection E so that the line AB concurs with that which bisects the obtuse angle of the lower surface, or with some line parallel to it. Then by placing the eye directly above the line AB it will appear single only; and one will see that the portion viewed through the crystal and the portions which appear outside it, meet together in a straight line: but the line CD will appear double, and one can distinguish the image which is due to regular refraction by the circumstance that when one views it with both eyes it seems raised up more than the other, or again by the circumstance that, when the crystal is turned around on the paper, this image remains stationary, whereas the other image shifts and moves entirely around. Afterwards let the eye be placed at I (remaining always in the plane perpendicular through AB) so that it views the image which is formed by regular refraction of the line CD making a straight line with the remainder of that line which is outside the crystal. And then, marking on the surface of the crystal the point H where the intersection E appears, this point will be directly above E. Then draw back the eye towards O, keeping always in the plane perpendicular through AB, so that the image of the line CD, which is formed by ordinary refraction, may appear in a straight line with the line KL viewed without refraction; and then mark on the crystal the point N where the point of intersection E appears.

13. Then one will know the length and position of the lines NH, EM, and of HE, which is the thickness of the crystal: which lines being traced separately upon a plan, and then joining NE and NM which cuts HE at P, the proportion of the refraction will be that of EN to NP, because these lines are to one another as the sines of the angles NPH, NEP, which are equal to those which the incident ray ON and its refraction NE make with the perpendicular to the surface. This proportion, as I have said, is sufficiently precisely as 5 to 3, and is always the same for all inclinations of the incident ray.

14. The same mode of observation has also served me for examining the extraordinary or irregular refraction of this crystal. For, the point H having been found and marked, as aforesaid, directly above the point E, I observed the appearance of the line CD, which is made by the extraordinary refraction;

and having placed the eye at Q, so that this appearance made a straight line with the line KL viewed without refraction, I ascertained the triangles REH, RES, and consequently the angles RSH, RES, which the incident and the refracted ray make with the perpendicular.

15. But I found in this refraction that the ratio of FR to RS was not constant, like the ordinary refraction, but that it varied with the varying obliquity of the incident ray.

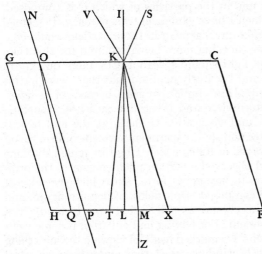

16. I found also that when QRE made a straight line, that is, when the incident ray entered the crystal without being refracted (as I ascertained by the circumstance that then the point E viewed by the extraordinary refraction appeared in the line CD, as seen without refraction) I found, I say, then that the angle QRG was 73 degrees 20 minutes, as has been already remarked; and so it is not the ray parallel to the edge of the crystal which crosses it in a straight line without being refracted, as Mr. Bartholinus believed, since that inclination is only 70 degrees 57 minutes, as was stated above. And this is to be noted, in order that no one may search in vain for the cause of the singular property of this ray in its parallelism to the edges mentioned.

17. Finally, continuing my observations to discover the nature of this refraction, I learned that it obeyed the following remarkable rule. Let the parallelogram GCFH, made by the principal section of the crystal, as previously determined, be traced separately. I found then that always, when the inclinations of two rays which come from opposite sides, as VK, SK here, are equal, their refractions KX and KT meet the bottom line HF in such wise that points X and T are equally distant from the point M, where the refraction of the perpendicular ray IK falls; and this occurs also for refractions in other sections of this crystal. But before speaking of those, which have also other particular properties, we will investigate the causes of the phenomena which I have already reported.

It was after having explained the refraction of ordinary transparent bodies by means of the spherical emanations of light, as above, that I resumed my examination of the nature of this crystal, wherein I had previously been unable to discover anything.

18. As there were two different refractions, I conceived that there were also two different emanations of waves of light, and that one could occur in the ethereal matter extending through the body of the crystal. Which matter, being present in much larger quantity than is that of the particles which compose it, was alone capable of causing transparency, according to what has been explained heretofore. I attributed to this emanation of waves the regular re-

fraction which is observed in this stone, by supposing these waves to be ordinarily of spherical form, and having a slower progression within the crystal than they have outside it; whence proceeds refraction as I have demonstrated.

19. As to the other emanation which should produce the irregular refraction, I wished to try what elliptical waves, or rather spheroidal waves, would do; and these I supposed would spread indifferently both in the ethereal matter diffused throughout the crystal and in the particles of which it is composed, according to the last mode in which I have explained transparency. It seemed to me that the disposition or regular arrangement of these particles could contribute to form spheroidal waves (nothing more being required for this than that the successive movement of light should spread a little more quickly in one direction than in the other) and I scarcely doubted that there were in this crystal such an arrangement of equal and similar particles, because of its figure and of its angles with their determinate and invariable measure. Touching which particles, and their form and disposition, I shall, at the end of this treatise, propound my conjectures and some experiments which confirm them.

20. The double emission of waves of light, which I had imagined, became more probable to me after I had observed a certain phenomenon in the ordinary [rock] crystal, which occurs in hexagonal form, and which, because of this regularity, seems also to be composed of particles, of definite figure, and ranged in order. This was, that this crystal, as well as that from Iceland, has a double refraction, though less evident. For having had cut from it some well-polished prisms of different sections, I remarked in all, in viewing through them the flame of a candle or the lead of window panes, that everything appeared double, though with images not very distant from one another. Whence I understood the reason why this substance, though so transparent, is useless for telescopes, when they have ever so little length.

21. Now this double refraction, according to my theory hereinbefore established, seemed to demand a double emission of waves of light, both of them spherical (for both the refractions are regular) and those of one series a little slower only than the others. For thus the phenomenon is quite naturally explained, by postulating substances which serve as vehicle for these waves, as I have done in the case of Iceland crystal. I had then less trouble after that in admitting two emissions of waves in one and the same body. And since it might have been objected that in composing these two kinds of crystal of equal particles of a certain figure, regularly piled, the interstices which these particles leave and which contain the ethereal matter would scarcely suffice to transmit the waves of light which I have localized there, I removed this difficulty by regarding these particles as being of a very rare texture, or rather as composed of other much smaller particles, between which the ethereal matter passes quite freely. This, moreover, necessarily follows from that which has been already demonstrated touching the small quantity of matter of which the bodies are built up.

22. Supposing, then, these spheroidal waves besides the spherical ones, I began to examine whether they could serve to explain the phenomena of the irregular refraction, and how by these same phenomena I could determine the figure and position of the spheroids: as to which I obtained at last the desired success, by proceeding as follows.

23. I considered first the effect of waves so formed, as respects the ray which

falls perpendicularly on the flat surface of a transparent body in which they should spread in this manner. I took AB for the exposed region of the surface. And, since a ray perpendicular to a plane, and coming from a very distant

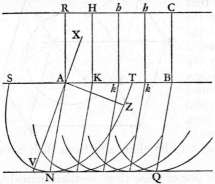

source of light, is nothing else, according to the precedent theory, than the incidence of a portion of the wave parallel to that plane, I supposed the straight line RC, parallel and equal to AB, to be a portion of a wave of light, in which an infinitude of points such as RH*h*C come to meet the surface AB at the points AK*k*B. Then instead of the hemispherical partial waves which in a body of ordinary refraction would spread from each of these last points, as we have above explained in treating of refraction, these must here be hemi-spheroids. The axes (or rather the major diameters) of these I supposed to be oblique to the plane AB, as is AV the semi-axis or semi-major diameter of the spheroid SVT, which represents the partial wave coming from the point A, after the wave RC has reached AB. I say axis or major diameter, because the same ellipse SVT may be considered as the section of a spheroid of which the axis is AZ perpendicular to AV. But, for the present, without yet deciding one or other, we will consider these spheroids only in those sections of them which make ellipses in the plane of this figure. Now taking a certain space of time during which the wave SVT has spread from A, it would needs be that from all the other points K*k*B there should proceed, in the same time, waves similar to SVT and similarly situated. And the common tangent NQ of all'these semi-ellipses would be the propagation of the wave RC which fell on AB, and would be the place where this movement occurs in much greater amount than anywhere else, being made up of arcs of an infinity of ellipses, the centres of which are along the line AB.

24. Now it appeared that this common tangent NQ was parallel to AB, and of the same length, but that it was not directly opposite to it, since it was comprised between the lines AN, BQ, which are diameters of ellipses having A and B for centres, conjugate with respect to diameters which are not in the straight line AB. And in this way I comprehended, a matter which had seemed to me very difficult, how a ray perpendicular to a surface could suffer refraction on entering a transparent body; seeing that the wave RC, having come to the aperture AB, went on forward thence, spreading between the parallel lines AN, BQ, yet itself remaining always parallel to AB, so that here the light does not spread along lines perpendicular to its waves, as in ordinary refraction, but along lines cutting the waves obliquely.

25. Inquiring subsequently what might be the position and form of these spheroids in the crystal, I considered that all the six faces produced precisely the same refractions. Taking, then, the parallelepiped AFB, of which the obtuse solid angle C is contained between the three equal plane angles, and imagining in it the three principal sections, one of which is perpendicular to the face DC and passes through the edge CF, another perpendicular to the face BF passing through the edge CA, and the third perpendicular to the face AF

passing through the edge BC; I knew that the refractions of the incident rays belonging to these three planes were all similar. But there could be no position of the spheroid which would have the same relation to these three sections except that in which the axis was also the axis of the solid angle C. Consequently I saw that the axis of this angle, that is to say, the straight line which traversed the crystal from the point C with equal inclination to the edges CF, CA, CB was the line which determined the position of the axis of all the spheroidal waves which one imagined to originate from some point, taken within or on the surface of the crystal, since all these spheroids ought to be alike, and have their axes parallel to one another.

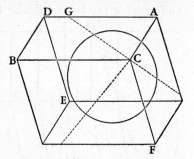

26. Considering after this the plane of one of these three sections, namely, that through GCF, the angle of which is 109 degrees 3 minutes, since the angle F was shown above to be 70 degrees 57 minutes; and, imagining a spheroidal wave about the centre C, I knew, because I have just explained it, that its axis must be in the same plane, the half of which axis I have marked CS in the next figure: and seeking by calculation (which will be given with others at the end of this discourse) the value of the angle CGS, I found it 45 degrees 20 minutes.

27. To know from this the form of this spheroid, that is to say, the proportion of the semi-diameters CS, CP, of its elliptical section, which are perpendicular to one another, I considered that the point M where the ellipse is touched by the straight line FH, parallel to CG, ought to be so situated that CM makes with the perpendicular CL an angle of 6 degrees 40 minutes; since, this being so, this ellipse satisfies what has been said about the refraction of the ray perpendicular to the surface CG, which is inclined to the perpendicular CL

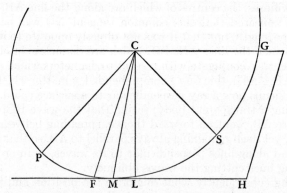

by the same angle. This, then, being thus disposed, and taking CM at 100,000 parts, I found by the calculation which will be given at the end, the semi-major diameter CP to be 105,032, and the semi-axis CS to be 93,410, the ratio of which numbers is very nearly 9 to 8; so that the spheroid was of the kind which resembles a compressed sphere, being generated by the revolution of an ellipse about its smaller diameter. I found also the value of CG the semi-diameter parallel to the tangent ML to be 98,779.

28. Now passing to the investigation of the refractions which obliquely incident rays must undergo, according to our hypothesis of spheroidal waves, I saw that these refractions depended on the ratio between the velocity of movement of the light outside the crystal in the ether, and that within the crystal. For supposing, for example, this proportion to be such that while the light in the crystal forms the spheroid GSP, as I have just said, it forms outside a sphere the semi-diameter of which is equal to the line N which will be determined hereafter, the following is the way of finding the refraction of the incident rays. Let there be such a ray RC falling upon the surface CK. Make CO perpendicular to RC, and across the angle KCO adjust OK, equal to N and perpendicular to CO; then draw KI, which touches the ellipse GSP, and from the point of contact I join IC, which will be the required refraction of the ray RC. The demonstration of this is, it will be seen, entirely similar to that of which we made use in explaining ordinary refraction. For the refraction of the ray RC is nothing else than the progression of the portion C of the wave CO, continued in the crystal. Now the portions H of this wave, during the time that O came to K, will have arrived at the surface CK along the straight lines Hx, and will, moreover, have produced in the crystal around the centres x some hemi-spheroidal partial waves similar to the hemi-spheroidal GSPg, and similarly disposed, and of which the major and minor diameters will bear the same

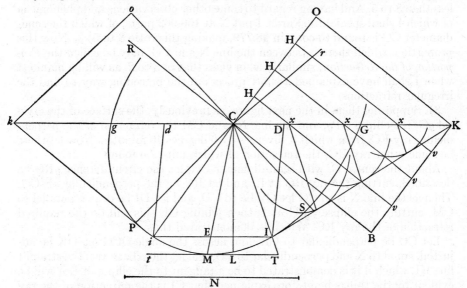

proportions to the lines xv (the continuations of the lines Hx up to KB parallel to CO) that the diameters of the spheroid GSPg bear to the line CB, or N. And it is quite easy to see that the common tangent of all these spheroids, which are here represented by ellipses, will be the straight line IK, which, consequently, will be the propagation of the wave CO; and the point I will be that of the point C, conformably with that which has been demonstrated in ordinary refraction.

Now as to finding the point of contact I, it is known that one must find CD a third proportional to the lines CK, CG, and draw DI parallel to CM, previously determined, which is the conjugate diameter to CG; for then, by drawing KI it touches the ellipse at I.

29. Now, as we have found CI the refraction of the ray RC, similarly, one will find C*i* the refraction of the ray *r*C, which comes from the opposite side, by making C*o* perpendicular to *r*C and following out the rest of the construction as before. Whence one sees that if the ray *r*C is inclined equally with RC, the line C*d* will necessarily be equal to CD, because C*k* is equal to CK, and C*g* to CG. And, in consequence, I*i* will be cut at E into equal parts by the line CM, to which DI and *di* are parallel. And because CM is the conjugate diameter to CG, it follows that *i*I will be parallel to *g*G. Therefore, if one prolongs the refracted rays CI, C*i*, until they meet the tangent ML at T and *t*, the distances MT, M*t*, will also be equal. And so, by our hypothesis, we explain perfectly the phenomenon mentioned above; to wit, that when there are two rays equally inclined, but coming from opposite sides, as here the rays RC, *rc*, their refractions diverge equally from the line followed by the refraction of the ray perpendicular to the surface, by considering these divergences in the direction parallel to the surface of the crystal.

30. To find the length of the line N, in proportion to CP, CS, CG, it must be determined by observations of the irregular refraction which occurs in this section of the crystal; and I find thus that the ratio of N to GC is just a little less than 8 to 5. And having regard to some other observations and phenomena of which I shall speak afterwards, I put N at 156,962 parts, of which the semi-diameter CG is found to contain 98,779, making this ratio 8 to $5\frac{1}{29}$. Now this proportion, which there is between the line N and CG, may be called the *Proportion of the Refraction;* similarly as in glass that of 3 to 2, as will be manifest when I shall have explained a short process in the preceding way to find the irregular refractions.

31. Supposing then, in the next figure, as previously, the surface of the crystal *g*G, the ellipse GP*g*, and the line N; and CM the refraction of the perpendicular ray FC, from which it diverges by 6 degrees 40 minutes. Now let there be some other ray RC, the refraction of which must be found.

About the centre C, with semi-diameter CG, let the circumference *g*RG be described, cutting the ray RC at R; and let RV be the perpendicular on CG. Then as the line N is to CG let CV be to CD, and let DI be drawn parallel to CM, cutting the ellipse *g*MG at I; then joining CI, this will be the required refraction of the ray RC. Which is demonstrated thus.

Let CO be perpendicular to CR, and across the angle OCG let OK be adjusted, equal to N and perpendicular to CO, and let there be drawn the straight line KI, which if it is demonstrated to be a tangent to the ellipse at I, it will be evident by the things heretofore explained that CI is the refraction of the ray RC. Now, since the angle RCO is a right angle, it is easy to see that the right-angled triangles RCV, KCO are similar. As then, CK is to KO, so also is RC to CV. But KO is equal to N, and RC to CG: then as CK is to N so will CG be to CV. But as N is to CG, so, by construction, is CV to CD. Then as CK is to CG so is CG to CD. And because DI is parallel to CM, the conjugate diameter to CG, it follows that KI touches the ellipse at I; which remained to be shown.

32. One sees, then, that as there is in the refraction of ordinary media a

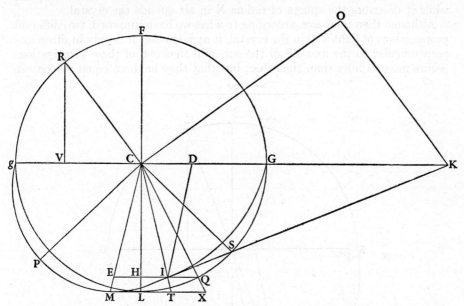

certain constant proportion between the sines of the angles which the incident ray and the refracted ray make with the perpendicular, so here there is such a proportion between CV and CD or IE; that is to say, between the sine of the angle which the incident ray makes with the perpendicular and the horizontal intercept, in the ellipse, between the refraction of this ray and the diameter CM. For the ratio of CV to CD is, as has been said, the same as that of N to the semi-diameter CG.

33. I will add here, before passing away, that in comparing together the regular and irregular refraction of this crystal, there is this remarkable fact, that if ABPS be the spheroid by which light spreads in the crystal in a certain space of time (which spreading, as has been said, serves for the irregular refraction), then the inscribed sphere BVST is the extension in the same space of time of the light which serves for the regular refraction.

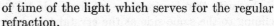

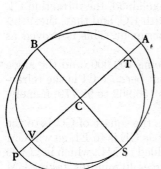

For we have stated before this that the line N being the radius of a spherical wave of light in air, while in the crystal it spread through the spheroid ABPS, the ratio of N to CS will be 156,962 to 93,410. But it has also been stated that the proportion of the regular refraction was 5 to 3; that is to say, that N being the radius of a spherical wave of light in air, its extension in the crystal would, in the same space of time, form a sphere the radius of which would be to N as 3 to 5. Now 156,962 is to 93,410 as 5 to 3 less $\frac{1}{41}$. So that it is sufficiently nearly, and may be exactly, the sphere BVST, which the light describes for the regular refraction in the crystal, while it describes the spheroid BPSA for the irregular refraction, and while it describes the sphere of radius N in air outside the crystal.

Although then there are, according to what we have supposed, two different propagations of light within the crystal, it appears that it is only in directions perpendicular to the axis BS of the spheroid that one of these propagations occurs more rapidly than the other; but that they have an equal velocity in

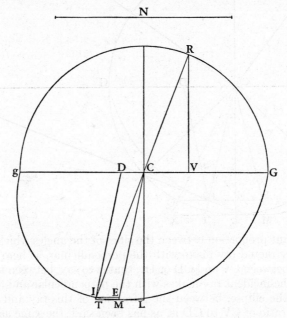

the other direction, namely, in that parallel to the same axis BS, which is also the axis of the obtuse angle of the crystal.

34. The proportion of the refraction being what we have just seen, I will now show that there necessarily follows thence that notable property of the ray which falling obliquely on the surface of the crystal enters it without suffering refraction. For supposing the same things as before, and that the ray RC makes with the same surface gG the angle RCG of 73 degrees 20 minutes, inclining to the same side as the crystal (of which ray mention has been made above); if one investigates, by the process above explained, the refraction CI, one will find that it makes exactly a straight line with RC, and that, thus, this ray is not deviated at all, conformably with experiment. This is proved as follows by calculation.

CG or CR being, as precedently, 98,779; CM being 100,000; and the angle RCV 73 degrees 20 minutes, CV will be 28,330. But because CI is the refraction of the ray RC, the proportion of CV to CD is 156,962 to 98,779, namely, that of N to CG; then CD is 17,828.

Now the rectangle gDC is to the square of DI as the square of CG is to the square of CM; hence DI or CE will be 98,353. But as CE is to EI, so will CM be to MT, which will then be 18,127. And being added to ML, which is 11,609 (namely the sine of the angle LCM, which is 6 degrees 40 minutes, taking CM

100,000 as radius) we get LT 27,936; and this is to LC 99,324 as CV to VR, that is to say, as 29,938, the tangent of the complement of the angle RCV, which is 73 degrees 20 minutes, is to the radius of the tables. Whence it appears that RCIT is a straight line; which was to be proved.

35. Further, it will be seen that the ray CI, in emerging through the opposite surface of the crystal, ought to pass out quite straight, according to the following demonstration, which proves that the reciprocal relation of refraction obtains in this crystal the same as in other transparent bodies; that is to say, that if a ray RC in meeting the surface of the crystal CG is refracted as CI, the ray CI emerging through the opposite parallel surface of the crystal which I suppose to be IB, will have its refraction IA parallel to the ray RC.

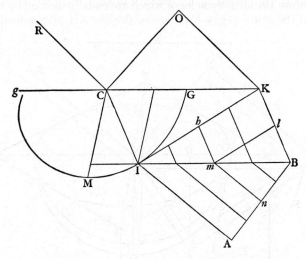

Let the same things be supposed as before; that is to say, let CO, perpendicular to CR, represent a portion of a wave, the continuation of which in the crystal is IK, so that the piece C will be continued on along the straight line CI, while O comes to K. Now, if one takes a second period of time equal to the first, the piece K of the wave IK will, in this second period, have advanced along the straight line KB, equal and parallel to CI, because every piece of the wave CO, on arriving at the surface CK, ought to go on in the crystal the same as the piece C; and in this same time there will be formed in the air from the point I a partial spherical wave having a semi-diameter IA equal to KO, since KO has been traversed in an equal time. Similarly, if one considers some other point of the wave IK, such as h, it will go along hm, parallel to CI, to meet the surface IB, while the point K traverses Kl equal to hm; and while this accomplishes the remainder lB, there will start from the point m a partial wave the semi-diameter of which, mn, will have the same ratio to lB as IA to KB. Whence it is evident that this wave of semi-diameter mn, and the other of semi-diameter IA will have the same tangent BA. And similarly for all the partial spherical waves which will be formed outside the crystal by the impact of all the points of the wave IK against the surface of the ether IB. It is then precisely the tangent BA which will be the continuation of the wave IK, outside the crystal, when the piece K has reached B. And in consequence IA,

which is perpendicular to BA, will be the refraction of the ray CI on emerging
from the crystal. Now it is clear that IA is parallel to the incident ray RC,
since IB is equal to CK, and IA equal to KO, and the angles A and O are right
angles.

It is seen then that, according to our hypothesis, the reciprocal relation of
refraction holds good in this crystal as well as in ordinary transparent bodies;
as is thus in fact found by observation.

36. I pass now to the consideration of other sections of the crystal, and of
the refractions there produced, on which, as will be seen, some other very remarkable phenomena depend.

Let ABH be a parallelepiped of crystal, and let the top surface AEHF be a
perfect rhombus, the obtuse angles of which are equally divided by the straight
line EF, and the acute angles by the straight line AH perpendicular to FE.

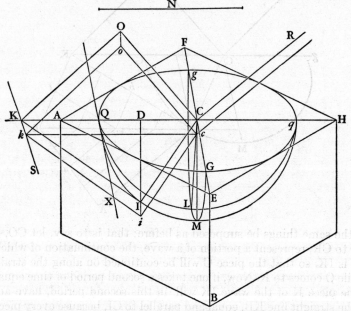

The section which we have hitherto considered is that which passes through
the lines EF, EB, and which at the same time cuts the plane AEHF at right
angles. Refractions in this section have this in common with the refractions in
ordinary media: that the plane which is drawn through the incident ray and
which also intersects the surface of the crystal at right angles is that in which
the refracted ray also is found. But the refractions which appertain to every
other section of this crystal have this strange property: that the refracted ray
always quits the plane of the incident ray perpendicular to the surface, and
turns away towards the side of the slope of the crystal. For which fact we shall
show the reason, in the first place, for the section through AH; and we shall
show at the same time how one can determine the refraction, according to our
hypothesis. Let there be, then, in the plane which passes through AH, and
which is perpendicular to the plane AFHE, the incident ray RC; it is required
to find its refraction in the crystal.

37. About the centre C, which I suppose to be in the intersection of AH and FE, let there be imagined a hemi-spheroid QGqgM, such as the light would form in spreading in the crystal, and let its section by the plane AEHF form the ellipse QGqg, the major diameter of which Qq, which is in the line AH, will necessarily be one of the major diameters of the spheroid; because the axis of the spheroid being in the plane through FEB, to which QC is perpendicular, it follows that QC is also perpendicular to the axis of the spheroid, and, consequently, QCq one of its major diameters. But the minor diameter of this ellipse, Gg, will bear to Qq the proportion which has been defined previously, Article 27, between CG and the major semi-diameter of the spheroid, CP, namely, that of 98,779 to 105,032.

Let the line N be the length of the travel of light in air during the time in which, within the crystal, it makes, from the centre C, the spheroid QGqgM. Then, having drawn CO perpendicular to the ray CR and situated in the plane through CR and AH, let there be adjusted, across the angle ACO, the straight line OK equal to N and perpendicular to CO, and let it meet the straight line AH at K. Supposing, consequently, that CL is perpendicular to the surface of the crystal AEHF, and that CM is the refraction of the ray which falls perpendicularly on this same surface, let there be drawn a plane through the line CM and through KCH, making in the spheroid the semi-ellipse QMq, which will be given, since the angle MCL is given of value 6 degrees 40 minutes. And it is certain, according to what has been explained above, Article 27, that a plane which would touch the spheroid at the point M, where I suppose the straight line CM to meet the surface, would be parallel to the plane QGq. If, then, through the point K one now draws KS parallel to Gg, which will be parallel also to QX, the tangent to the ellipse QGq at Q; and if one conceives a plane passing through KS and touching the spheroid, the point of contact will necessarily be in the ellipse QMq, because this plane through KS, as well as the plane which touches the spheroid at the point M, are parallel to QX, the tangent of the spheroid: for this consequence will be demonstrated at the end of this treatise. Let this point of contact be at I, then making KC, QC, DC proportionals, draw DI parallel to CM; also join CI. I say that CI will be the required refraction of the ray RC. This will be manifest if, in considering CO, which is perpendicular to the ray RC, as a portion of the wave of light, we can demonstrate that the continuation of its piece C will be found in the crystal at I, when O has arrived at K.

38. Now as in the chapter on reflexion, in demonstrating that the incident and reflected rays are always in the same plane perpendicular to the reflecting surface, we considered the breadth of the wave of light, so, similarly, we must here consider the breadth of the wave CO in the diameter Gg. Taking, then, the breadth Cc on the side toward the angle E, let the parallelogram COoc be taken as a portion of a wave, and let us complete the parallelograms CKkc, CIic, KIik, OKko. In the time, then, that the line Oo arrives at the surface of the crystal at Kk, all the points of the wave COoc will have arrived at the rectangle Kc along lines parallel to OK; and from the points of their incidences there will originate, beyond that, in the crystal partial hemi-spheroids, similar to the hemi-spheroid QMq, and similarly disposed. These hemispheroids will necessarily all touch the plane of the parallelogram KIik at the same instant that Oo has reached Kk. Which is easy to comprehend, since, of these hemi-

spheroids, all those which have their centres along the line CK, touch this plane in the line KI (for this is to be shown in the same way as we have demonstrated the refraction of the oblique ray in the principal section through EF) and all those which have their centres in the line Cc will touch the same plane KI in the line Ii; all these being similar to the hemi-spheroid QMq. Since, then, the parallelogram Ki is that which touches all these spheroids, this same parallelogram will be precisely the continuation of the wave COoc in the crystal, when Oo has arrived at Kk, because it forms the termination of the movement and because of the quantity of movement which occurs more there than anywhere else: and thus it appears that the piece C of the wave COoc has its continuation at I; that is to say, that the ray RC is refracted as CI.

From this it is to be noted that the proportion of the refraction for this section of the crystal is that of the line N to the semi-diameter CQ; by which one will easily find the refractions of all incident rays, in the same way as we have shown previously for the case of the section through FE; and the demonstration will be the same. But it appears that the said proportion of the refraction is less here than in the section through FEB; for it was there the same as the ratio of N to CG, that is to say, as 156,962 to 98,779, very nearly as 8 to 5; and here it is the ratio of N to CQ the major semi-diameter of the spheroid, that is to say, as 156,962 to 105,032, very nearly as 3 to 2, but just a little less. Which still agrees perfectly with what one finds by observation.

39. For the rest, this diversity of proportion of refraction produces a very singular effect in this crystal; which is that when it is placed upon a sheet of paper on which there are letters or anything else marked, if one views it from above with the two eyes situated in the plane of the section through EF, one sees the letters raised up by this irregular refraction more than when one puts one's eyes in the plane of section through AH: and the difference of these elevations appears by comparison with the other ordinary refraction of the crystal, the proportion of which is as 5 to 3, and which always raises the letters equally, and higher than the irregular refraction does. For one sees the letters and the paper on which they are written, as on two different stages at the same time; and in the first position of the eyes, namely, when they are in the plane through AH these two stages are four times more distant from one another than when the eyes are in the plane through EF.

We will show that this effect follows from the refractions; and it will enable us at the same time to ascertain the apparent place of a point of an object placed immediately under the crystal, according to the different situation of the eyes.

40. Let us see first by how much the irregular refraction of the plane through AH ought to lift the bottom of the crystal. Let the plane of this figure represent separately the section through Qq and CL, in which section there is also the ray RC, and let the semi-elliptic plane through Qq and CM be inclined to the former, as previously, by an angle of 6 degrees 40 minutes; and in this plane CI is then the refraction of the ray RC.

If now one considers the point I as at the bottom of the crystal, and that it is viewed by the rays ICR, Icr, refracted equally at the points Cc, which should be equally distant from D, and that these rays meet the two eyes at Rr; it is certain that the point I will appear raised to S where the straight lines RC, rc, meet; which point S is in DP, perpendicular to Qq. And if upon DP there is

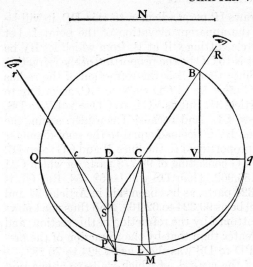

drawn the perpendicular IP, which will lie at the bottom of the crystal, the length SP will be the apparent elevation of the point I above the bottom.

Let there be described on Qq a semicircle cutting the ray CR at B, from which BV is drawn perpendicular to Qq; and let the proportion of the refraction for this section be, as before, that of the line N to the semi-diameter CQ.

Then as N is to CQ so is VC to CD, as appears by the method of finding the refraction which we have shown above, Article 31; but as VC is to CD, so is VB to DS. Then as N is to CQ, so is VB to DS. Let ML be perpendicular to CL. And because I suppose the eyes Rr to be distant about a foot or so from the crystal, and consequently the angle RSr very small, VB may be considered as equal to the semi-diameter CQ, and DP as equal to CL; then as N is to CQ so is CQ to DS. But N is valued at 156,962 parts, of which CM contains 100,000 and CQ 105,032. Then DS will have 70,283. But CL is 99,324, being the sine of the complement of the angle MCL which is 6 degrees 40 minutes; CM being supposed as radius. Then DP, considered as equal to CL, will be to DS as 99,324 to 70,283. And so the elevation of the point I by the refraction of this section is known.

41. Now let there be represented the other section through EF in the figure before the preceding one; and let CMg be the semi-ellipse, considered in Articles 27 and 28, which is made by cutting a spheroidal wave having centre C.

Let the point I, taken in this ellipse, be imagined again at the bottom of the crystal; and let it be viewed by the refracted rays ICR, Icr, which go to the two eyes; CR and cr being equally inclined to the surface of the crystal Gg. This being so, if one draws ID parallel to CM, which I suppose to be the refraction of the perpendicular ray incident at the point C, the distances DC, Dc, will be equal, as is easy to see by that which has been demonstrated in Article 28. Now it is certain that the point I should appear at S where the straight lines RC, rc meet when prolonged; and that this point will fall in the line

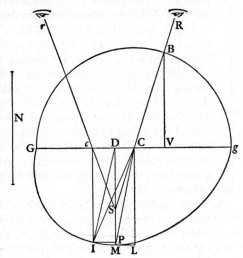

DP perpendicular to Gg. If one draws IP perpendicular to this DP, it will be the distance PS which will mark the apparent elevation of the point I. Let there be described on Gg a semicircle cutting CR at B, from which let BV be drawn perpendicular to Gg; and let N to GC be the proportion of the refraction in this section, as in Article 28. Since then CI is the refraction of the radius BC, and DI is parallel to CM, VC must be to CD as N to GC, according to what has been demonstrated in Article 31. But as VC is to CD so is BV to DS. Let ML be drawn perpendicular to CL. And because I consider, again, the eyes to be distant above the crystal, BV is deemed equal to the semi-diameter CG; and hence DS will be a third proportional to the lines N and CG: also DP will be deemed equal to CL. Now CG consisting of 98,778 parts, of which CM contains 100,000, N is taken as 156,962. Then DS will be 62,163. But CL is also determined, and contains 99,324 parts, as has been said in Articles 34 and 40. Then the ratio of PD to DS will be as 99,324 to 62,163. And thus one knows the elevation of the point at the bottom I by the refraction of this section; and it appears that this elevation is greater than that by the refraction of the preceding section, since the ratio of PD to DS was there as 99,324 to 70,283.

But by the regular refraction of the crystal, of which we have above said that the proportion is 5 to 3, the elevation of the point I, or P, from the bottom, will be $\frac{2}{5}$ of the height DP; as appears by this figure, where the point P being viewed by the rays PCR, Pcr, refracted equally at the surface Cc, this point must needs appear to be at S, in the perpendicular PD where the lines RC, rc meet when prolonged: and one knows that the line PC is to CS as 5 to 3, since they are to one another as the sine of the angle CSP or DSC is to the sine of the angle SPC. And because the ratio of PD to DS is deemed the same as that of PC to CS, the two eyes Rr being supposed very far above the crystal, the elevation PS will thus be $\frac{2}{5}$ of PD.

42. If one takes a straight line AB for the thickness of the crystal, its point B being at the bottom, and if one divides it at the points C, D, E, according to the proportions of the elevations found, making AE $\frac{3}{5}$ of AB, AB to AC as 99,324 to 70,283, and AB to AD as 99,324 to 62,163, these points will divide AB as in this figure. And it will be found that this agrees perfectly with experiment; that is to say, by placing the eyes above in the plane which cuts the crystal according to the shorter diameter of the rhombus, the regular refraction will lift up the letters to E; and one will see the bottom, and the letters over which it is placed, lifted up to D by the irregular refraction. But by placing the eyes above in the plane which cuts the crystal according to the longer diameter of the rhombus, the regular refraction will lift the letters to E as before; but the irregular refraction will make them, at the same time, appear lifted up only to C; and in such a way that the interval CE will be quadruple the interval ED, which one previously saw.

43. I have only to make the remark here that in both the positions of the eyes the images caused by the irregular refraction do not appear directly below those which proceed from the regular refraction, but they are separated from them by being more distant from the equilateral solid angle of the crystal.

That follows, indeed, from all that has been hitherto demonstrated about the irregular refraction; and it is particularly shown by these last demonstrations, from which one sees that the point I appears by irregular refraction at S in the perpendicular line DP, in which line also the image of the point P ought to appear by regular refraction, but not the image of the point I, which will be almost directly above the same point, and higher than S.

But as to the apparent elevation of the point I in other positions of the eyes above the crystal, besides the two positions which we have just examined, the image of that point by the irregular refraction will always appear between the two heights of D and C, passing from one to the other as one turns one's self around about the immovable crystal, while looking down from above. And all this is still found conformable to our hypothesis, as any one can assure himself after I shall have shown here the way of finding the irregular refractions which appear in all other sections of the crystal, besides the two which we have considered. Let us suppose one of the faces of the crystal, in which let there be the ellipse HDE, the centre C of which is also the centre of the spheroid HME in which the light spreads, and of which the said ellipse is the section. And let the incident ray be RC, the refraction of which it is required to find.

Let there be taken a plane passing through the ray RC and which is perpendicular to the plane of the ellipse HDE, cutting it along the straight line

BCK; and having in the same plane through RC made CO perpendicular to CR, let OK be adjusted across the angle OCK, so as to be perpendicular to OC and equal to the line N, which I suppose to measure the travel of the light in air during the time that it spreads in the crystal through the spheroid HDEM. Then in the plane of the ellipse HDE let KT be drawn, through the point K, perpendicular to BCK. Now if one conceives a plane

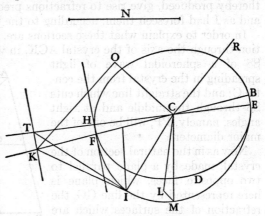

drawn through the straight line KT and touching the spheroid HME at I, the straight line CI will be the refraction of the ray RC, as is easy to deduce from that which has been demonstrated in Article 36.

But it must be shown how one can determine the point of contact I. Let there be drawn parallel to the line KT a line HF which touches the ellipse HDE, and let this point of contact be at H. And having drawn a straight line along CH to meet KT at T, let there be imagined a plane passing through the same CH and through CM (which I suppose to be the refraction of the perpendicular ray), which makes in the spheroid the elliptical section HME. It is certain that the plane which will pass through the straight line KT, and which will touch the spheroid, will touch it at a point in the ellipse HME, according to the Lemma which will be demonstrated at the end of the chapter. Now this point is necessarily the point I which is sought, since the plane drawn through TK can touch the spheroid at one point only. And this point I is easy to determine, since it is needful only to draw from the point T, which is in the plane of this ellipse, the tangent TI, in the way shown previously. For the ellipse HME is given, and its conjugate semi-diameters are CH and CM; because a straight line drawn through M, parallel to HE, touches the ellipse HME, as follows from the fact that a plane taken through M, and parallel to the plane HDE, touches the spheroid at that point M, as is seen from Articles 27 and 23. For the rest, the position of this ellipse, with respect to the plane through the ray RC and through CK, is also given; from which it will be easy to find the position of CI, the refraction corresponding to the ray RC.

Now it must be noted that the same ellipse HME serves to find the refractions of any other ray which may be in the plane through RC and CK. Because every plane, parallel to the straight line HF, or TK, which will touch the spheroid, will touch it in this ellipse, according to the Lemma quoted a little before.

I have investigated thus, in minute detail, the properties of the irregular refraction of this crystal, in order to see whether each phenomenon that is deduced from our hypothesis accords with that which is observed in fact. And this being so, it affords no slight proof of the truth of our suppositions and principles. But what I am going to add here confirms them again marvellously. It is this: that there are different sections of this crystal, the surfaces of which, thereby produced, give rise to refractions precisely such as they ought to be, and as I had foreseen them, according to the preceding theory.

In order to explain what these sections are, let ABKF be the principal section through the axis of the crystal ACK, in which there will also be the axis SS of a spheroidal wave of light spreading in the crystal from the centre C; and the straight line which cuts SS through the middle and at right angles, namely, PP, will be one of the major diameters.

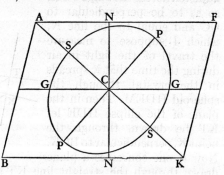

Now as in the natural section of the crystal, made by a plane parallel to two opposite faces, which plane is here represented by the line GG, the refraction of the surfaces which are produced by it will be governed by the hemi-spheroids GNG, according to what has been explained in the preceding theory. Similarly, cutting the crystal through NN, by a plane perpendicular to the parallelogram ABKF, the refraction of the surfaces will be governed by the hemi-spheroids NGN. And if one cuts it through PP, perpendicularly to the said parallelogram, the refraction of the surfaces ought to be governed by the hemi-spheroids PSP, and so for others. But I saw that if the plane NN was almost perpendicular to the plane GG, making the angle NCG, which is on the side A, an angle of 90 degrees 40 minutes, the hemi-spheroids NGN would become similar to the hemi-spheroids GNG, since the planes NN and GG were equally inclined by an angle of 45 degrees 20 minutes to the axis SS. In consequence it must needs be, if our theory is true, that the surfaces which the section through NN produces should effect the same refractions as the surfaces of the section through GG. And not only the surfaces of the section NN but all other sections produced by planes which might be inclined to the axis at an angle equal to 45 degrees 20 minutes. So that there are an infinitude of planes which ought to produce precisely the same refractions as the natural surfaces of the crystal, or as the section parallel to any one of those surfaces which are made by cleavage.

I saw also that by cutting it by a plane taken through PP, and perpendicular to the axis SS, the refraction of the surfaces ought to be such that the perpendicular ray should suffer thereby no deviation; and that for oblique rays there would always be an irregular refraction, differing from the regular, and by which objects placed beneath the crystal would be less elevated than by that other refraction.

That, similarly, by cutting the crystal by any plane through the axis SS, such as the plane of the figure is, the perpendicular ray ought to suffer no refraction; and that for oblique rays there were different measures for the irregular refraction according to the situation of the plane in which the incident ray was.

Now these things were found in fact so; and, after that, I could not doubt that a similar success could be met with everywhere. Whence I concluded that one might form from this crystal solids similar to those which are its natural forms, which should produce, at all their surfaces, the same regular and irregular refractions as the natural surfaces, and which, nevertheless, would cleave in quite other ways, and not in directions parallel to any of their faces. That out of it one would be able to fashion pyramids, having their base square, pentagonal, hexagonal, or with as many sides as one desired, all the surfaces of which should have the same refractions as the natural surfaces of the crystal, except the base, which will not refract the perpendicular ray. These surfaces will each make an angle of 45 degrees 20 minutes with the axis of the crystal, and the base will be the section perpendicular to the axis.

That, finally, one could also fashion out of it triangular prisms, or prisms with as many sides as one would, of which neither the sides nor the bases would refract the perpendicular ray, although they would yet all cause double refraction for oblique rays. The cube is included amongst these prisms, the bases of which are sections perpendicular to the axis of the crystal, and the sides are sections parallel to the same axis.

From all this it further appears that it is not at all in the disposition of the layers of which this crystal seems to be composed, and according to which it splits in three different senses, that the cause resides of its irregular refraction; and that it would be in vain to wish to seek it there.

But in order that any one who has some of this stone may be able to find, by his own experience, the truth of what I have just advanced, I will state here the process of which I have made use to cut it and to polish it. Cutting is easy by the slicing wheels of lapidaries, or in the way in which marble is sawn: but polishing is very difficult, and by employing the ordinary means one more often depolishes the surfaces than makes them lucent.

After many trials, I have at last found that for this service no plate of metal must be used, but a piece of mirror glass made matt and depolished. Upon this, with fine sand and water, one smooths the crystal little by little, in the same way as spectacle glasses, and polishes it simply by continuing the work, but ever reducing the material. I have not, however, been able to give it perfect clarity and transparency; but the evenness which the surfaces acquire enables one to observe in them the effects of refraction better than in those made by cleaving the stone, which always have some inequality.

Even when the surface is only moderately smoothed, if one rubs it over with a little oil or white of egg, it becomes quite transparent, so that the refraction is discerned in it quite distinctly. And this aid is specially necessary when it is wished to polish the natural surfaces to remove the inequalities; because one cannot render them lucent equally with the surfaces of other sections, which take a polish so much the better the less nearly they approximate to these natural planes.

Before finishing the treatise on this crystal, I will add one more marvellous phenomenon which I discovered after having written all the foregoing. For though I have not been able till now to find its cause, I do not for that reason wish to desist from describing it, in order to give opportunity to others to investigate it. It seems that it will be necessary to make still further suppositions besides those which I have made; but these will not, for all that, cease to keep their probability after having been confirmed by so many tests.

The phenomenon is, that by taking two pieces of this crystal and applying them one over the other, or rather holding them with a space between the two, if all the sides of one are parallel to those of the other, then a ray of light, such as AB, is divided into two in the first piece, namely into BD and BC, following

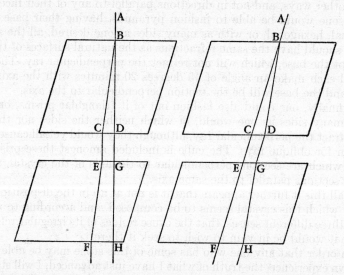

the two refractions, regular and irregular. On penetrating thence into the other piece each ray will pass there without further dividing itself in two; but that one which underwent the regular refraction, as here DG, will undergo again only a regular refraction at GH; and the other, CE, an irregular refraction at EF. And the same thing occurs not only in this disposition, but also in all those cases in which the principal section of each of the pieces is situated in one and the same plane, without it being needful for the two neighbouring surfaces to be parallel. Now it is marvellous why the rays CE and DG, incident from the air on the lower crystal, do not divide themselves the same as the first ray AB.

One would say that it must be that the ray DG in passing through the upper piece has lost something which is necessary to move the matter which serves for the irregular refraction; and that likewise CE has lost that which was necessary to move the matter which serves for regular refraction: but there is yet another thing which upsets this reasoning. It is that when one disposes the two crystals in such a way that the planes which constitute the principal sections intersect one another at right angles, whether the neighbouring surfaces are parallel or not, then the ray which has come by the regular refraction, as DG, undergoes only an irregular refraction in the lower piece; and on the contrary the ray which has come by the irregular refraction, as CE, undergoes only a regular refraction.

But in all the infinite other positions, besides those which I have just stated, the rays DG, CE, divide themselves anew each one into two, by refraction in the lower crystal, so that from the single ray AB there are four, sometimes of equal brightness, sometimes some much less bright than others, according to the varying agreement in the positions of the crystals: but they do not appear to have all together more light than the single ray AB.

When one considers here how, while the rays CE, DG remain the same, it depends on the position that one gives to the lower piece whether it divides them both in two, or whether it does not divide them, and yet how the ray AB above is always divided; it seems that one is obliged to conclude that the waves of light, after having passed through the first crystal, acquire a certain form or disposition in virtue of which, when meeting the texture of the second crystal, in certain positions, they can move the two different kinds of matter which serve for the two species of refraction; and when meeting the second crystal in another position are able to move only one of these kinds of matter. But to tell how this occurs, I have hitherto found nothing which satisfies me.

Leaving, then, to others this research, I pass to what I have to say touching the cause of the extraordinary figure of this crystal, and why it cleaves easily in three different senses, parallel to any one of its surfaces.

There are many bodies, vegetable, mineral, and congealed salts, which are formed with certain regular angles and figures. Thus, among flowers there are many which have their leaves disposed in ordered polygons, to the number of 3, 4, 5, or 6 sides, but not more. This well deserves to be investigated, both as to the polygonal figure, and as to why it does not exceed the number 6.

Rock crystal grows ordinarily in hexagonal bars, and diamonds are found which occur with a square point and polished surfaces. There is a species of small flat stones, piled up directly upon one another, which are all of pentagonal figure with rounded angles, and the sides a little folded inwards. The grains of gray salt which are formed from sea water affect the figure, or at least the angle, of the cube; and in the congelations of other salts, and in that of sugar, there are found other solid angles with perfectly flat faces. Small snowflakes almost always fall in little stars with 6 points, and sometimes in hexagons with straight sides. And I have often observed, in water which is beginning to freeze, a kind of flat and thin foliage of ice, the middle ray of which throws out branches inclined at an angle of 60 degrees. All these things are worthy of being carefully investigated to ascertain how and by what artifice Nature there operates. But it is not now my intention to treat fully of this matter. It seems that in general the regularity which occurs in these productions comes from the arrangement of the small invisible equal particles of which they are composed. And, coming to our Iceland crystal, I say that if there were a pyramid such as ABCD, composed of small rounded corpuscles, not spherical but flattened spheroids, such as would be made by the rotation of the ellipse GH around its lesser diameter EF (of which the ratio to the greater diameter is very nearly that of 1 to the square root of 8)—I say that then the solid angle of the point D would be equal to the obtuse and equilateral angle of this crystal. I say, further, that if these corpuscles were lightly stuck together, on breaking this pyramid it would break along faces parallel to those that make its point: and by this means, as it is easy to see, it would produce prisms similar to those of the same crystal as this other figure represents. The reason is that when broken in this fashion a whole layer separates easily from its neighbouring layer, since each spheroid has to be detached only from the three spheroids of the next layer; of which three there is but one which touches it on its flattened surface, and the other two at the edges. And

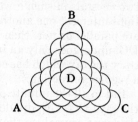

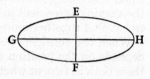

the reason that the surfaces separate sharp and polished is that if any spheroid of the neighbouring surface would come out by attaching itself to the surface which is being separated, it would be needful for it to detach itself from six other spheroids which hold it locked, and four of which press it by these flattened surfaces. Since, then, not only the angles of our crystal but also the manner in which it splits agree precisely with what is observed in the assemblage composed of such spheroids, there is great reason to believe that the particles are shaped and ranged in the same way.

There is even probability enough that the prisms of this crystal are produced by the breaking up of pyramids, since Mr. Bartholinus relates that he occasionally found some pieces of triangularly pyramidal figure. But when a mass is composed interiorly only of these little spheroids thus piled up, whatever form it may have exteriorly, it is certain, by the same reasoning which I have just explained, that if broken it would produce similar prisms. It remains to be seen whether there are other reasons which confirm our conjecture, and whether there are none which are repugnant to it.

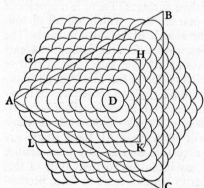

It may be objected that this crystal, being so composed, might be capable of cleavage in yet two more fashions; one of which would be along planes parallel to the base of the pyramid, that is to say to the triangle ABC; the other would be parallel to a plane the trace of which is marked by the lines GH, HK, KL. To which I say that both the one and the other, though practicable, are more difficult than those which were parallel to any one of the three planes of the pyramid; and that, therefore, when striking on the crystal in order to break it, it ought always to split rather along these three planes than along the two others. When one has a number of spheroids of the form above described, and ranges them in a pyramid, one sees why the two methods of division are more difficult. For in the case of that division which would be parallel to the base, each spheroid would be obliged to detach itself from three others which it touches upon their flattened surfaces, which hold more strongly than the contacts at the edges. And besides that, this division will not occur along entire layers, because each of the spheroids of a layer is scarcely held at all by the 6 of the same layer that surround it, since they only touch it at the edges; so that it adheres readily to the neighbouring layer, and the others to it, for the same reason; and this causes uneven surfaces. Also one sees by experiment that when grinding down the crystal on a rather rough stone, directly on the equilateral solid angle, one verily finds much facility in reducing it in this direction, but much difficulty afterwards in polishing the surface which has been flattened in this manner.

As for the other method of division along the plane GHKL, it will be seen that each spheroid would have to detach itself from four of the neighbouring layer, two of which touch it on the flattened surfaces, and two at the edges. So that this division is likewise more difficult than that which is made parallel to one of the surfaces of the crystal; where, as we have said, each spheroid is detached from only three of the neighbouring layer: of which three there is one only which touches it on the flattened surface, and the other two at the edges only.

However, that which has made me know that in the crystal there are layers in this last fashion is that in a piece weighing half a pound which I possess, one sees that it is split along its length, as is the above-mentioned prism by the plane GHKL; as appears by colours of the iris extending throughout this whole plane, although the two pieces still hold together. All this proves, then, that the composition of the crystal is such as we have stated. To which I again add this experiment; that if one passes a knife scraping along any one of the natural surfaces, and downwards as it were from the equilateral obtuse angle, that is to say, from the apex of the pyramid, one finds it quite hard; but by scraping in the opposite sense an incision is easily made. This follows manifestly from the situation of the small spheroids; over which, in the first manner, the knife glides; but in the other manner it seizes them from beneath almost as if they were the scales of a fish.

I will not undertake to say anything touching the way in which so many corpuscles all equal and similar are generated, nor how they are set in such beautiful order; whether they are formed first and then assembled, or whether they arrange themselves thus in coming into being and as fast as they are produced, which seems to me more probable. To develop truths so recondite there would be needed a knowledge of nature much greater than that which we have. I will add only that these little spheroids could well contribute to form the spheroids of the waves of light, here above supposed, these as well as those being similarly situated, and with their axes parallel.

Calculations which have been supposed in this chapter

Mr. Bartholinus, in his treatise of this crystal, puts at 101 degrees the obtuse angles of the faces, which I have stated to be 101 degrees 52 minutes. He states that he measured these angles directly on the crystal, which is difficult to do with ultimate exactitude, because the edges such as CA, CB, in this figure, are generally worn, and not quite straight. For more certainty, therefore, I preferred to measure actually the obtuse angle by which the faces CBDA, CBVF are inclined to one another, namely, the angle

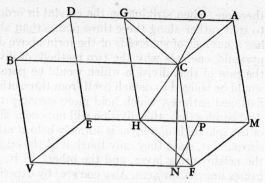

OCN formed by drawing CN perpendicular to FV, and CO perpendicular to DA. This angle OCN I found to be 105 degrees; and its supplement CNP to be 75 degrees, as it should be.

To find from this the obtuse angle BCA, I imagined a sphere having its centre at C, and on its surface a spherical triangle, formed by the intersection of three planes which enclose the solid angle C. In this equilateral triangle, which is ABF in this other figure, I see that each of the angles should be 105 degrees, namely, equal to the angle OCN; and that each of the sides should be of as many degrees as the angle ACB, or ACF, or BCF. Having then drawn the arc FQ perpendicular to the side AB, which it divides equally at Q, the triangle FQA has a right angle at Q, the angle A 105 degrees, and F half as much, namely 52 degrees 30 minutes; whence the hypotenuse AF is found to be 101 degrees 52 minutes. And this arc AF is the measure of the angle ACF in the figure of the crystal.

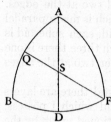

In the same figure, if the plane CGHF cuts the crystal so that it divides the obtuse angles ACB, MHV in the middle, it is stated, in Article 10, that the angle CFH is 70 degrees 57 minutes. This again is easily shown in the same spherical triangle ABF, in which it appears that the arc FQ is as many degrees as the angle GCF in the crystal, the supplement of which is the angle CFH. Now the arc FQ is found to be 109 degrees 3 minutes. Then its supplement, 70 degrees 57 minutes, is the angle CFH.

It was stated, in Article 26, that the straight line CS, which in the preceding figure is CH, being the axis of the crystal, that is to say, being equally inclined to the three sides CA, CB, CF, the angle GCH is 45 degrees 20 minutes. This is also easily calculated by the same spherical triangle. For by drawing the other arc AD which cuts BF equally, and intersects FQ at S, this point will be the centre of the triangle. And it is easy to see that the arc SQ is the measure of the angle GCH in the figure which represents the crystal. Now in the triangle QAS, which is right-angled, one knows also the angle A, which is 52 degrees 30 minutes, and the side AQ 50 degrees 56 minutes; whence the side SQ is found to be 45 degrees 20 minutes.

In Article 27 it was required to show that PMS, being an ellipse the centre of which is C, and which touches the straight line MD at M so that the angle MCL which CM makes with CL, perpendicular on DM, is 6 degrees 40 minutes, and its semi-minor axis CS making with CG (which is parallel to MD)

an angle GCS of 45 degrees 20 minutes,—it was required to show, I say, that, CM being 100,000 parts, PC the semi-major diameter of this ellipse is 105,032 parts, and CS, the semi-minor diameter, 93,410.

Let CP and CS be prolonged and meet the tangent DM at D and Z; and from the point of contact M let MN and MO be drawn as perpendiculars to

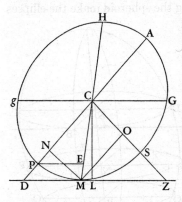

CP and CS. Now because the angles SCP, GCL, are right angles, the angle PCL will be equal to GCS which was 45 degrees 20 minutes. And deducting the angle LCM, which is 6 degrees 40 minutes, from LCP, which is 45 degrees 20 minutes, there remains MCP, 38 degrees 40 minutes. Considering, then, CM as a radius of 100,000 parts, MN, the sine of 38 degrees 40 minutes, will be 62,479. And in the right-angled triangle MND, MN will be to ND as the radius of the tables is to the tangent of 45 degrees 20 minutes (because the angle NMD is equal to DCL, or GCS); that is to say, as 100,000 to 101,170: whence results ND, 63,210. But NC is 78,079 of the same parts, CM being 100,000, because NC is the sine of the complement of the angle MCP, which was 38 degrees 40 minutes. Then the whole line DC is 141,289; and CP, which is a mean proportional between DC and CN, since MD touches the ellipse, will be 105,032.

Similarly, because the angle OMZ is equal to CDZ, or LCZ, which is 44 degrees 40 minutes, being the complement of GCS, it follows that, as the radius of the tables is to the tangent of 44 degrees 40 minutes, so will OM 78,079 be to OZ 77,176. But OC is 62,479 of these same parts of which CM is 100,000, because it is equal to MN, the sine of the angle MCP, which is 38 degrees 40 minutes. Then the whole line CZ is 139,655; and CS, which is a mean proportional between CZ and CO will be 93,410.

At the same place it was stated that GC was found to be 98,779 parts. To prove this, let PE be drawn in the same figure parallel to DM, and meeting CM at E. In the right-angled triangle CLD the side CL is 99,324 (CM being 100,000), because CL is the sine of the complement of the angle LCM, which is 6 degrees 40 minutes. And since the angle LCD is 45 degrees 20 minutes, being equal to GCS, the side LD is found to be 100,486: whence, deducting ML 11,609 there will remain MD 88,877. Now as CD (which was 141,289) is to DM 88,877, so will CP 105,032 be to PE 66,070. But as the rectangle MEH (or rather the difference of the squares on CM and CE) is to the square on MC, so is the square on PE to the square on Cg; then also as the difference of the squares on DC and CP to the square on CD, so also is the square on PE to the square on gC. But DP, CP, and PE are known; hence, also one knows GC, which is 98,779.

Lemma which has been supposed

If a spheroid is touched by a straight line, and also by two or more planes which are parallel to this line, though not parallel to one another, all the points of contact of the line, as well as of the planes, will be in one and the same ellipse made by a plane which passes through the centre of the spheroid.

Let LED be the spheroid touched by the line BM at the point B, and also
by the planes parallel to this line at the points O and A. It is required to demonstrate that the points B, O, and A are in one and the same ellipse made in
the spheroid by a plane which passes through its centre.

Through the line BM, and through the points O and A, let there be drawn
planes parallel to one another, which, in cutting the spheroid make the ellipses
LBD, POP, QAQ; which will all be similar
and similarly disposed, and will have their
centres K, N, R, in one and the same diameter of the spheroid, which will also be
the diameter of the ellipse made by the section of the plane that passes through the
centre of the spheroid, and which cuts the
planes of the three said ellipses at right
angles: for all this is manifest by Proposition 15 of the book of *Conoids and Spheroids*
of Archimedes. Further, the two latter
planes, which are drawn through the points
O and A, will also, by cutting the planes
which touch the spheroid in these same
points, generate straight lines, as OH and
AS, which will, as is easy to see, be parallel
to BM; and all three, BM, OH, AS, will

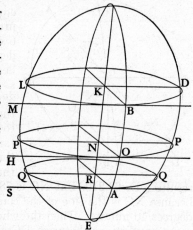

touch the ellipses LBD, POP, QAQ in these points, B, O, A; since they are in
the planes of these ellipses, and at the same time in the planes which touch the
spheroid. If now from these points B, O, A, there are drawn the straight lines
BK, ON, AR, through the centres of the same ellipses, and if through these
centres there are drawn also the diameters LD, PP, QQ, parallel to the tangents BM, OH, AS; these will be conjugate to the aforesaid BK, ON, AR. And
because the three ellipses are similar and similarly disposed, and have their diameters LD, PP, QQ parallel, it is certain that their conjugate diameters BK,
ON, AR, will also be parallel. And the centres K, N, R being, as has been
stated, in one and the same diameter of the spheroid, these parallels BK, ON,
AR will necessarily be in one and the same plane, which passes through this
diameter of the spheroid, and, in consequence, the points R, O, A are in one
and the same ellipse made by the intersection of this plane. Which was to be
proved. And it is manifest that the demonstration would be the same if,
besides the points O, A, there had been others in which the spheroid had been
touched by planes parallel to the straight line BM.

CHAPTER SIX

On the Figures of the Transparent Bodies

Which serve for refraction and for reflexion

AFTER having explained how the properties of reflexion and refraction follow from what we have supposed concerning the nature of light and of opaque bodies and of transparent media, I will here set forth a very easy and natural way of deducing, from the same principles, the true figures which serve, either by reflexion or by refraction, to collect or disperse the rays of light, as may be desired. For though I do not see yet that there are means of making use of these figures, so far as relates to refraction, not only because of the difficulty of shaping the glasses of telescopes with the requisite exactitude according to these figures, but also because there exists in refraction itself a property which hinders the perfect concurrence of the rays, as Mr. Newton has very well proved by experiment, I will yet not desist from relating the invention, since it offers itself, so to speak, of itself, and because it further confirms our theory of refraction, by the agreement which here is found between the refracted ray and the reflected ray. Besides, it may occur that some one in the future will discover in it utilities which at present are not seen.

To proceed, then, to these figures, let us suppose first that it is desired to find a surface CDE which shall reassemble at a point B rays coming from another point A; and that the summit of the surface shall be the given point D in the straight line AB. I say that, whether by reflexion or by refraction, it is

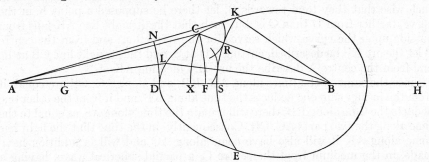

only necessary to make this surface such that the path of the light from the point A to all points of the curved line CDE, and from these to the point of concurrence (as here the path along the straight lines AC, CB, along AL, LB, and along AD, DB), shall be everywhere traversed in equal times: by which principle the finding of these curves becomes very easy.

So far as relates to the reflecting surface, since the sum of the lines AC, CB ought to be equal to that of AD, DB, it appears that DCE ought to be an ellipse; and for refraction, the ratio of the velocities of waves of light in the media A and B being supposed to be known, for example that of 3 to 2 (which is the same, as we have shown, as the ratio of the sines in the refraction), it is

only necessary to make DH equal to $\frac{3}{2}$
of DB; and having after that described
from the centre A some arc FC, cutting
DB at F, then describe another from
centre B with its semi-diameter BX
equal to $\frac{2}{3}$ of FH; and the point of intersection of the two arcs will be one
of the points required, through which
the curve should pass. For this point,
having been found in this fashion, it is
easy forthwith to demonstrate that the
time along AC, CB will be equal to the
time along AD, DB.

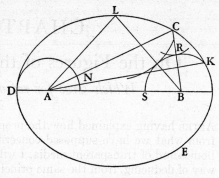

For, assuming that the line AD represents the time which the light takes to
traverse this same distance AD in air, it is evident that DH, equal to $\frac{3}{2}$ of DB,
will represent the time of the light along DB in the medium, because it needs
here more time in proportion as its speed is slower. Therefore, the whole line
AH will represent the time along AD, DB. Similarly, the line AC or AF will
represent the time along AC; and FH, being by construction equal to $\frac{3}{2}$ of CB,
it will represent the time along CB in the medium; and, in consequence, the
whole line AH will represent also the time along AC, CB. Whence it appears
that the time along AC, CB is equal to the time along AD, DB. And, similarly,
it can be shown, if L and K are other points in the curve CDE, that the times
along AL, LB, and along AK, KB, are always represented by the line AH, and,
therefore, equal to the said time along AD, DB.

In order to show further that the surfaces which these curves will generate
by revolution will direct all the rays which reach them from the point A in
such wise that they tend towards B, let there be supposed a point K in the
curve, farther from D than C is, but such that the straight line AK falls from
outside upon the curve which serves for the refraction; and from the centre
B let the arc KS be described, cutting BD at S, and the straight line CB at R;
and from the centre A describe the arc DN meeting AK at N.

Since the sums of the times along AK, KB, and along AC, CB are equal, if
from the former sum one deducts the time along KB, and if from the other one
deducts the time along RB, there will remain the time along AK as equal to the
time along the two parts AC, CR. Consequently, in the time that the light has
come along AK it will also have come along AC and will in addition have
made, in the medium from the centre C, a partial spherical wave, having a
semi-diameter equal to CR. And this wave will necessarily touch the circumference KS at R, since CB cuts this circumference at right angles. Similarly,
having taken any other point L in the curve, one can show that in the same
time as the light passes along AL it will also have come along AL and in addition will have made a partial wave, from the centre L, which will touch the
same circumference KS. And so with all other points of the curve CDE. Then,
at the moment that the light reaches K the arc KRS will be the termination
of the movement, which has spread from A through DCK. And thus this same
arc will constitute in the medium the propagation of the wave emanating from
A; which wave may be represented by the arc DN, or by any other nearer the
centre A. But all the pieces of the arc KRS are propagated successively along

straight lines which are perpendicular to them, that is to say, which tend to
the centre B (for that can be demonstrated in the same way as we have proved
above that the pieces of spherical waves are propagated along the straight lines
coming from their centre), and these progressions of the pieces of the waves
constitute the rays themselves of light. It appears, then, that all these rays
tend here towards the point B.

One might also determine the point C, and all the others, in this curve which
serves for the refraction, by dividing DA at G in such a way that DG is $\frac{2}{3}$ of
DA, and describing from the centre B any arc CX which cuts BD at X, and
another from the centre A with its semi-diameter AF equal to $\frac{3}{2}$ of GX; or
rather, having described, as before, the arc CX, it is only necessary to make
DF equal to $\frac{3}{2}$ of DX, and from the centre A to strike the arc FC; for these two

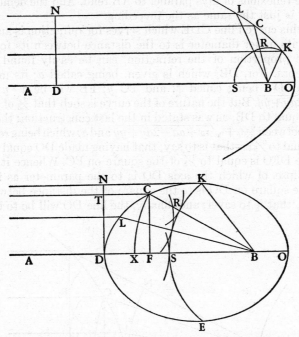

constructions, as may be easily known, come back to the first one which was
shown before. And it is manifest by the last method that this curve is the same
that M. Descartes has given in his *Geometry*, and which he calls the first of his
Ovals.

It is only a part of this oval which serves for the refraction, namely, the part
DK, ending at K, if AK is the tangent. As to the other part, Descartes has
remarked that it could serve for reflexions, if there were some material of a
mirror of such a nature that, by its means, the force of the rays (or, as we
should say, the velocity of the light, which he could not say, since he held that
the movement of light was instantaneous) could be augmented in the proportion of 3 to 2. But we have shown that in our way of explaining reflexion, such
a thing could not arise from the matter of the mirror, and it is entirely impossible.

From what has been demonstrated about this oval, it will be easy to find the figure which serves to collect to a point incident parallel rays. For by supposing just the same construction, but the point A infinitely distant, giving parallel rays, our oval becomes a true ellipse, the construction of which differs in no way from that of the oval, except that FC, which previously was an arc of a circle, is here a straight line, perpendicular to DB. For the wave of light DN, being likewise represented by a straight line, it will be seen that all the points of this wave, travelling as far as the surface KD along lines parallel to DB, will advance subsequently towards the point B, and will arrive there at the same time. As for the ellipse which served for reflexion, it is evident that it will here become a parabola, since its focus A may be regarded as infinitely distant from the other, B, which is here the focus of the parabola, towards which all the reflexions of rays parallel to AB tend. And the demonstration of these effects is just the same as the preceding.

But that this curved line CDE which serves for refraction is an ellipse, and is such that its major diameter is to the distance between its foci as 3 to 2, which is the proportion of the refraction, can be easily found by the calculus of algebra. For, DB, which is given, being called a; its undetermined perpendicular DT being called x; and TC y; FB will be $a-y$; CB will be $\sqrt{xx+aa-2ay+yy}$. But the nature of the curve is such that $\frac{2}{3}$ of TC together with CB is equal to DB, as was stated in the last construction: then the equation will be between $\frac{2}{3}y+\sqrt{xx+aa-2ay+yy}$ and a; which being reduced, gives $\frac{6}{5}ay-yy$ equal to $\frac{9}{5}xx$; that is to say, that having made DO equal to $\frac{6}{5}$ of DB, the rectangle DFO is equal to $\frac{9}{5}$ of the square on FC. Whence it is seen that DC is an ellipse, of which the axis DO is to the parameter as 9 to 5; and, therefore, the square on DO is to the square of the distance between the foci as 9 to $9-5$, that is to say 4; and, finally, the line DO will be to this distance as 3 to 2.

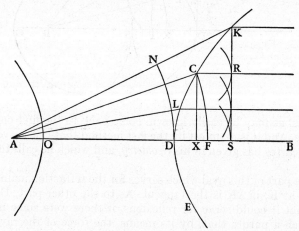

Again, if one supposes the point B to be infinitely distant, in lieu of our first oval we shall find that CDE is a true hyperbola; which will make those rays become parallel which come from the point A. And, in consequence also, those which are parallel within the transparent body will be collected outside at the point A. Now it must be remarked that CX and KS become straight lines per-

pendicular to BA, because they represent arcs of circles the centre of which is
infinitely distant. And the intersection of the perpendicular CX with the arc
FC will give the point C, one of those through which the curve ought to pass.
And this operates so that all the parts of the wave of light DN, coming to meet
the surface KDE, will advance thence along parallels to KS and will arrive at
this straight line at the same time; of which the proof is again the same as that
which served for the first oval. Besides, one finds by a calculation as easy as
the preceding one, that CDE is here a hyperbola of which the axis DO is $\frac{4}{5}$ of
AD, and the parameter equal to AD. Whence, it is easily proved that DO is to
the distance between the foci as 3 to 2.

These are the two cases in which conic sections serve for refraction, and are
the same which are explained, in his *Dioptrique*, by Descartes, who first found
out the use of these lines in relation to refraction, as also that of the ovals the

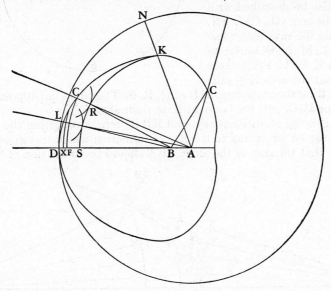

first of which we have already set forth. The second oval is that which serves
for rays that tend to a given point; in which oval, if the apex of the surface
which receives the rays is D, it will happen that the other apex will be situated
between B and A, or beyond A, according as the ratio of AD to DB is given of
greater or lesser value. And in this latter case it is the same as that which
Descartes calls his third oval.

Now the finding and construction of this second oval is the same as that of
the first, and the demonstration of its effect likewise. But it is worthy of remark
that in one case this oval becomes a perfect circle, namely when the ratio of
AD to DB is the same as the ratio of the refractions, here as 3 to 2, as I observed a long time ago. The fourth oval, serving only for impossible reflexions,
there is no need to set it forth.

As for the manner in which M. Descartes discovered these lines, since he has
given no explanation of it, nor anyone else since that I know of, I will say here,
in passing, what it seems to me it must have been. Let it be proposed to find
the surface generated by the revolution of the curve KDE, which, receiving

the incident rays coming to it from the point A, shall deviate them toward the point B. Then considering this other curve as already known, and that its apex D is in the straight line AB, let us divide it up into an infinitude of small pieces by the points G, C, F; and having drawn from each of these points, straight lines towards A to represent the incident rays, and other straight lines towards B, let there also be described with centre A the arcs GL, CM, FN, DO, cutting the rays that come from A at L, M, N, O; and from the points K, G, C, F, let there be described the arcs KQ, GR,

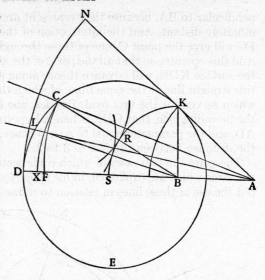

CS, FT cutting the rays towards B at Q, R, S, T; and let us suppose that the straight line HKZ cuts the curve at K at right angles.

Then AK being an incident ray, and KB its refraction within the medium, it needs must be, according to the law of refraction which was known to M. Descartes, that the sine of the angle ZKA should be to the sine of the angle

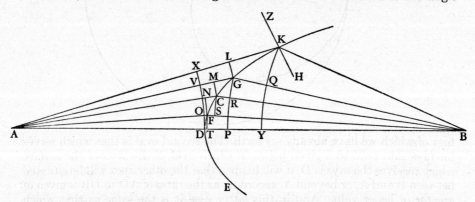

HKB as 3 to 2, supposing that this is the proportion of the refraction of glass; or rather, that the sine of the angle KGL should have this same ratio to the sine of the angle GKQ, considering KG, GL, KQ as straight lines because of their smallness. But these sines are the lines KL and GQ, if GK is taken as the radius of the circle. Then LK ought to be to GQ as 3 to 2; and in the same ratio MG to CR, NC to FS, OF to DT. Then also the sum of all the antecedents to all the consequents would be as 3 to 2. Now, by prolonging the arc DO until it meets AK at X, KX is the sum of the antecedents. And by prolonging the arc KQ till it meets AD at Y, the sum of the consequents is DY. Then KX ought to be to DY as 3 to 2. Whence, it would appear that the curve KDE was of such a nature that having drawn from some point which had been assumed,

such as K, the straight lines KA, KB, the excess by which AK surpasses AD
should be to the excess of DB over KB, as 3 to 2. For it can similarly be demonstrated, by taking any other point in the curve, such as G, that the excess of
AG over AD, namely VG, is to the excess of BD over DG, namely DP, in
this same ratio of 3 to 2. And, following this principle, M. Descartes constructed

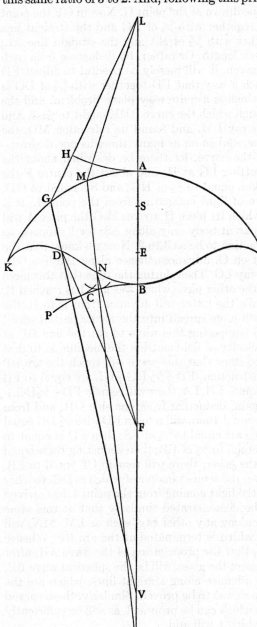

these curves in his *Geometry;*
and he easily recognized that
in the case of parallel rays,
these curves became hyperbolas and ellipses.

Let us now return to our
method and let us see how it
leads without difficulty to the
finding of the curves which
one side of the glass requires
when the other side is of a
given figure; a figure not only
plane or spherical, or made
by one of the conic sections
(which is the restriction with
which Descartes proposed this
problem, leaving the solution
to those who should come
after him) but generally any
figure whatever: that is to
say, one made by the revolution of any given curved line
to which one must merely
know how to draw straight
lines as tangents.

Let the given figure be that
made by the revolution of
some curve such as AK about
the axis AV, and that this
side of the glass receives rays
coming from the point L.
Furthermore, let the thickness AB of the middle of the
glass be given, and the point
F at which one desires the
rays to be all perfectly re-
united, whatever be the first
refraction occurring at the
surface AK.

I say that for this the sole
requirement is that the out-
line BDK which constitutes
the other surface shall be
such that the path of the

light from the point L to the surface AK, and from thence to the surface BDK, and from thence to the point F, shall be traversed everywhere in equal times, and in each case in a time equal to that which the light employs to pass along the straight line LF of which the part AB is within the glass.

Let LG be a ray falling on the arc AK. Its refraction GV will be given by means of the tangent which will be drawn at the point G. Now in GV the point D must be found such that FD together with $\frac{3}{2}$ of DG and the straight line GL, may be equal to FB together with $\frac{3}{2}$ of BA and the straight line AL; which, as is clear, make up a given length. Or rather, by deducting from each the length of LG, which is also given, it will merely be needful to adjust FD up to the straight line VG in such a way that FD together with $\frac{3}{2}$ of DG is equal to a given straight line, which is a quite easy plane problem: and the point D will be one of those through which the curve BDK ought to pass. And similarly, having drawn another ray LM, and found its refraction MO, the point N will be found in this line, and so on as many times as one desires.

To demonstrate the effect of the curve, let there be described about the centre L the circular arc AH, cutting LG at H; and about the centre F the arc BP; and in AB let AS be taken equal to $\frac{2}{3}$ of HG; and SE equal to GD. Then, considering AH as a wave of light emanating from the point L, it is certain that during the time in which its piece H arrives at G the piece A will have advanced within the transparent body only along AS; for I suppose, as above, the proportion of the refraction to be as 3 to 2. Now we know that the piece of wave, which is incident on G, advances thence along the line GD, since GV is the refraction of the ray LG. Then during the time that this piece of wave has taken from G to D, the other piece which was at S has reached E, since GD, SE are equal. But while the latter will advance from E to B, the piece of wave which was at D will have spread into the air its partial wave, the semi-diameter of which, DC (supposing this wave to cut the line DF at C), will be $\frac{3}{2}$ of EB, since the velocity of light outside the medium is to that inside as 3 to 2. Now it is easy to show that this wave will touch the arc BP at this point C. For since, by construction, FD$+\frac{3}{2}$DG$+$GL are equal to FB $+\frac{3}{2}$BA$+$AL; on deducting the equals LH, LA, there will remain FD$+\frac{3}{2}$DG$+$ GH equal to FB$+\frac{3}{2}$BA. And, again, deducting from one side GH, and from the other side $\frac{3}{2}$ of AS, which are equal, there will remain FD with $\frac{3}{2}$ DG equal to FB with $\frac{3}{2}$ of BS. But $\frac{3}{2}$ of DG are equal to $\frac{3}{2}$ of ES; then FD is equal to FB with $\frac{3}{2}$ of BE. But DC was equal to $\frac{3}{2}$ of EB; then deducting these equal lengths from one side and from the other, there will remain CF equal to FB. And thus it appears that the wave, the semi-diameter of which is DC, touches the arc BP at the moment when the light coming from the point L has arrived at B along the line LB. It can be demonstrated similarly that at this same moment the light that has come along any other ray, such as LM, MN, will have propagated the movement which is terminated at the arc BP. Whence it follows, as has been often said, that the propagation of the wave AH, after it has passed through the thickness of the glass, will be the spherical wave BP, all the pieces of which ought to advance along straight lines, which are the rays of light, to the centre F. Which was to be proved. Similarly, these curved lines can be found in all the cases which can be proposed, as will be sufficiently shown by one or two examples which I will add.

Let there be given the surface of the glass AK, made by the revolution about the axis BA of the line AK, which may be straight or curved. Let there be also given in the axis the point L and the thickness BA of the glass; and let it be required to find the other surface KDB, which receiving rays that are parallel to AB will direct them in such wise that after being again refracted at the given surface AK they will all be reassembled at the point L.

From the point L let there be drawn to some point of the given line AK the straight line LG, which, being considered as a ray of light, its refraction GD will then be found. And this line being then prolonged at one side or the other will meet the straight line BL, as here at V. Let there then be erected on AB the perpendicular BC, which will represent a wave of light coming from the infinitely distant point F, since we have supposed the rays to be parallel. Then all the parts of this wave BC must arrive at the same time at the point L; or

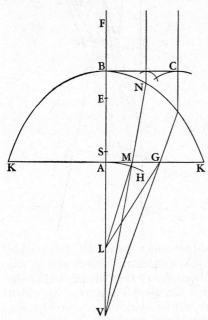

rather all the parts of a wave emanating from the point L must arrive at the same time at the straight line BC. And for that it is necessary to find in the line VGD the point D, such that having drawn DC parallel to AB, the sum of CD plus $\frac{3}{2}$ of DG, plus GL may be equal to $\frac{3}{2}$ of AB plus AL: or rather, on deducting from both sides GL, which is given, CD plus $\frac{3}{2}$ of DG must be equal to a given length; which is a still easier problem than the preceding construction. The point D thus found will be one of those through which the curve ought to pass; and the proof will be the same as before. And by this it will be proved that the waves which come from the point L, after having passed through the glass KAKB, will take the form of straight lines, as BC; which is the same thing as saying that the rays will become parallel. Whence it follows reciprocally that parallel rays falling on the surface KDB will be reassembled at the point L.

Again, let there be given the surface AK, of any desired form, generated by revolution about the axis AB, and let the thickness of the glass at the middle be AB. Also, let the point L be given in the axis behind the glass; and let it be supposed that the rays which fall on the surface AK tend to this point, and that it is required to find the surface BD, which on their emergence from the glass turns them as if they came from the point F in front of the glass.

Having taken any point G in the line AK, and drawing the straight line IGL, its part GI will represent one of the incident rays, the refraction of which, GV, will then be found: and it is in this line that we must find the point D, one of those through which the curve DG ought to pass. Let us suppose that it has been found: and about L as centre let there be described GT, the arc of a circle cutting the straight line AB at T, in case the distance LG is greater than LA; for otherwise the arc AH must be described about the same centre, cutting the straight line LG at H. This arc GT (or AH, in the other case) will represent an incident wave of light, the rays of which tend towards L. Similarly, about the centre F let there be described the circular arc DQ, which will represent a wave emanating from the point F.

Then the wave TG, after having passed through the glass, must form the wave QD; and for this I observe that the time taken by the light along GD in the glass must be equal to that taken along the three, TA, AB, and BQ, of which AB alone is within the glass. Or, rather, having taken AS equal to $\frac{2}{3}$ of AT, I observe that $\frac{3}{2}$ of GD ought to be equal to $\frac{3}{2}$ of SB, plus BQ; and, deducting both of them from FD or FQ, that FD less $\frac{3}{2}$ of GD ought to be equal to FB less $\frac{3}{2}$ of SB. And this last difference is a given length: and all that is required is to draw the straight line FD from the given point F to meet VG so that it may be thus. Which is a problem quite similar to that which served for the first of these constructions, where FD plus $\frac{3}{2}$ of GD had to be equal to a given length.

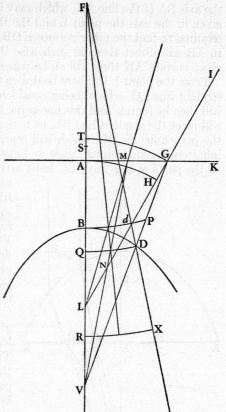

In the demonstration it is to be observed that, since the arc BC falls within the glass, there must be conceived an arc RX, concentric with it and on the other side of QD. Then, after it shall have been shown that the piece G of the wave GT arrives at D at the same time that the piece T arrives at Q, which is easily deduced from the construction, it will be evident as a consequence that the partial wave generated at the point D will touch the arc RX at the moment when the piece Q shall have come to R, and that thus this arc will at the same moment be the termination of the movement that comes from the wave TG; whence all the rest may be concluded.

Having shown the method of finding these curved lines which serve for the perfect concurrence of the rays, there remains to be explained a notable thing touching the uncoordinated refraction of spherical, plane, and other surfaces: an effect which if ignored might cause some doubt concerning what we have several times said, that rays of light are straight lines which intersect at right angles the waves which travel along them.

For in the case of rays which, for example, fall parallel upon a spherical surface AFE, intersecting one another, after refraction, at different points, as the figure [P. 617] represents; what can the waves of light be, in this transparent body, which are cut at right angles by the converging rays? For they can not be spherical. And what will these waves become after the said rays begin to inter-

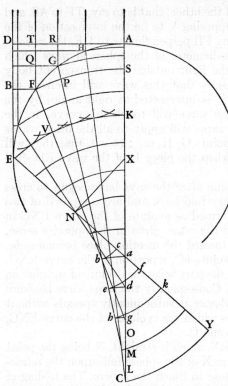

sect one another? It will be seen in the solution of this difficulty that something very remarkable comes to pass herein, and that the waves do not cease to persist though they do not continue entire, as when they cross the glasses designed according to the construction we have seen.

According to what has been shown above, the straight line AD, which has been drawn at the summit of the sphere, at right angles to the axis parallel to which the rays come, represents the wave of light; and in the time taken by its piece D to reach the spherical surface AGE at E, its other parts will have met the same surface at F, G, H, etc., and will have also formed spherical partial waves of which these points are the centres. And the surface EK which all those waves will touch, will be the continuation of the wave AD in the sphere at the moment when the piece D has reached E. Now the line EK is not an arc of a circle, but is a curved line formed as the evolute of another curve ENC, which touches all the rays HL, GM, FO, etc., that are the refractions of the parallel rays, if we imagine laid over the convexity ENC a thread which in unwinding describes at its end E the said curve EK. For, supposing that this curve has been thus described, we will show that the said waves formed from the centres F, G, H, etc., will all touch it.

It is certain that the curve EK and all the others described by the evolution of the curve ENC, with different lengths of thread, will cut all the rays HL, GM, FO, etc., at right angles, and in such wise that the parts of them intercepted between two such curves will all be equal; for this follows from what has been demonstrated in our treatise *de Motu Pendulorum*. Now imagining the incident rays as being infinitely near to one another, if we consider two of them, as RG, TF, and draw GQ perpendicular to RG, and if we suppose the curve FS which intersects GM at P to have been described by evolution from the curve NC, beginning at F, as far as which the thread is supposed to extend, we may assume the small piece FP as a straight line perpendicular to the ray GM, and similarly the arc GF as a straight line. But GM being the refraction of the ray RG, and FP being perpendicular to it, QF must be to GP as 3 to 2, that is to say in the proportion of the refraction; as was shown above in explaining the discovery of Descartes. And the same thing occurs in all the small arcs GH, HA, etc., namely that in the quadrilaterals which enclose them the side parallel to the axis is to the opposite side as 3 to 2. Then also as 3 to 2 will the sum of the one set be to the sum of the other; that is to say, TF to AS, and DE to AK, and BE to SK or DV, supposing V to be the intersection of the curve EK and the ray FO. But, making FB perpendicular to DE, the ratio of 3 to 2 is also that of BE to the semi-diameter of the spherical wave which emanated from the point F while the light outside the transparent body traversed the space BE. Then it appears that this wave will intersect the ray FM at the same point V where it is intersected at right angles by the curve EK, and consequently that the wave will touch this curve. In the same way it can be proved that the same will apply to all the other waves above mentioned, originating at the points G, H, etc.; to wit, that they will touch the curve EK at the moment when the piece D of the wave ED shall have reached E.

Now to say what these waves become after the rays have begun to cross one another: it is that from thence they fold back and are composed of two contiguous parts, one being a curve formed as evolute of the curve ENC in one sense, and the other as evolute of the same curve in the opposite sense. Thus the wave KE, while advancing toward the meeting place becomes *abc*, whereof the part *ab* is made by the evolute *b*C, a portion of the curve ENC, while the end C remains attached; and the part *bc* by the evolute of the portion *b*E while the end E remains attached. Consequently the same wave becomes *def*, then *ghk*, and finally CY, from whence it subsequently spreads without any fold, but always along curved lines which are evolutes of the curve ENC, increased by some straight line at the end C.

There is even, in this curve, a part EN which is straight, N being the point where the perpendicular from the centre X of the sphere falls upon the refraction of the ray DE, which I now suppose to touch the sphere. The folding of the waves of light begins from the point N up to the end of the curve C, which point is formed by taking AC to CX in the proportion of the refraction, as here 3 to 2.

As many other points as may be desired in the curve NC are found by a Theorem which Mr. Barrow has demonstrated in section 12 of his *Lectiones Opticæ*, though for another purpose. And it is to be noted that a straight line equal in length to this curve can be given. For since it together with the line NE is equal to the line CK, which is known, since DE is to AK in the proportion of the refraction, it appears that by deducting EN from CK the remainder will be equal to the curve NC.

Similarly the waves that are folded back in reflexion by a concave spherical mirror can be found. Let ABC be the section, through the axis, of a hollow hemisphere, the centre of which is D, its axis being DB, parallel to which I suppose the rays of light to come. All the reflexions of those rays which fall upon the quarter-circle AB will touch a curved line AFE, of which line the end E is at the focus of the hemisphere,

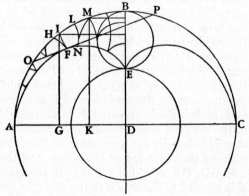

that is to say, at the point which divides the semi-diameter BD into two equal parts. The points through which this curve ought to pass are found by taking, beyond A, some arc AO, and making the arc OP double the length of it; then dividing the chord OP at F in such wise that the part FP is three times the part FO; for then F is one of the required points.

And as the parallel rays are merely perpendiculars to the waves which fall on the concave surface, which waves are parallel to AD, it will be found that as they come successively to encounter the surface AB, they form on reflexion folded waves composed of two curves which originate from two opposite evolutions of the parts of the curve AFE. So, taking AD as an incident wave, when the part AG shall have met the surface AI, that is to say when the piece G shall have reached I, it will be the curves HF, FI, generated as evolutes of the curves FA, FE, both beginning at F, which together constitute the propagation of the part AG. And a little afterwards, when the part AK has met the surface AM, the piece K having come to M, then the curves LN, NM, will together constitute the propagation of that part. And thus this folded wave will continue to advance until the point N has reached the focus E. The curve AFE can be seen in smoke, or in flying dust, when a concave mirror is held opposite the sun. And it should be known that it is none other than that curve which is described by the point E on the circumference of the circle EB, when that circle is made to roll within another whose semi-diameter is ED and whose centre is D. So that it is a kind of cycloid, of which, however, the points can be found geometrically.

Its length is exactly equal to $\frac{3}{4}$ of the diameter of the sphere, as can be found and demonstrated by means of these waves, nearly in the same way as the mensuration of the preceding curve; though it may also be demonstrated in other ways, which I omit as outside the subject. The area AOBEFA, comprised between the arc of the quarter-circle, the straight line BE, and the curve EFA, is equal to the fourth part of the quadrant DAB.

THE GREAT IDEAS, Volumes 2 and 3

••••••••••••••••••••••••••••••	FAMILY
ANGEL	FATE
ANIMAL	FORM
ARISTOCRACY	GOD
ART	GOOD AND EVIL
ASTRONOMY	GOVERNMENT
BEAUTY	HABIT
BEING	HAPPINESS
CAUSE	HISTORY
CHANCE	HONOR
CHANGE	HYPOTHESIS
CITIZEN	IDEA
CONSTITUTION	IMMORTALITY
COURAGE	INDUCTION
CUSTOM AND	INFINITY
CONVENTION	JUDGMENT
DEFINITION	JUSTICE
DEMOCRACY	KNOWLEDGE
DESIRE	LABOR
DIALECTIC	LANGUAGE
DUTY	LAW
EDUCATION	LIBERTY
ELEMENT	LIFE AND DEATH
EMOTION	LOGIC
ETERNITY	LOVE
EVOLUTION	MAN
EXPERIENCE	MATHEMATICS